1970

C. S.

University of St. Francis

S0-BMV-448

3 0301 00020394 9

ADVANCED CALCULUS

To Edith

ADVANCED CALCULUS

robert c. james
harvey mudd college

wadsworth publishing company, inc.
belmont, california

Second printing: August 1967

© *1966 by Wadsworth Publishing Company, Inc., Belmont, California. All rights reserved. No part of this book may be reproduced in any form, by mimeograph or any other means, without permission in writing from the publisher.*

L.C. Cat. Card No.: 66–14725

Printed in the United States of America

517
J 282

PREFACE

g.

Publisher

7-21-70

This book is designed to serve as an introduction to analysis for mathematicians and for serious engineers and scientists. Depending on the emphasis of the instructor, it can be used either for a rigorous course or for a semi-rigorous course. The usual formal skills in algebra, trigonometry, and elementary calculus are assumed. Some parts of elementary calculus are reviewed after appropriate foundations are laid, but previous knowledge is neither ignored nor expected to be discarded. The book gives a systematic and modern approach to differential and integral calculus. A modern point of view is used in developing theories and explanations, but considerable attention is given to developing mathematical techniques for use in applications of mathematics.

Many illustrations are included to demonstrate applications of theory and techniques. Historical remarks on the struggles that took place in the development of mathematics are designed to encourage the struggling student and to emphasize the importance of understanding the foundations and theory of the subject. The numerous problems vary from the very easy to the very challenging. Problem numbers are in boldface italic type when answers are given in the appendix. An asterisk on a problem number indicates that information furnished by that problem will be useful later.

The first two chapters provide foundations, including discussions of relations and functions, the number system, continuity and limits, and related topological properties. The Heine-Borel and Weierstrass-Bolzano theorems are established and then used in the discussions of

5 40 86

uniform continuity, the maximum value theorem, and the mean value theorems.

In Chapters 3 through 9 the emphasis is on topics generally regarded as necessary parts of an advanced calculus course. These include study of the definite integral, infinite series, multiple integration, partial differentiation, vector analysis, and the theory of inverse transformations and of change of variables in multiple integrals.

The last two chapters give a substantial introduction to advanced modern analysis. In Chapter 10 the theory of Fourier series is developed in the context of general orthonormal expansions. Convergence problems are studied carefully, with a variety of applications to wave and heat conduction problems. The basic theory of general measures and integration are developed in Chapter 11. Convergence and completeness theorems are discussed in general and then specialized to Lebesgue measure and integration.

Much of the first nine chapters is adapted from *University Mathematics* (Belmont: Wadsworth Publishing Company, 1963). Especially for help with this material, the author is grateful to the following past and present members of the mathematics department at Harvey Mudd College who have given generously of their time to contribute ideas and suggestions: Robert Borrelli, Courtney Coleman, John Greever, Robert Ives, George McCarty, Robert Seeley, Alden Pixley, Edward Posner, and Alvin White. Special appreciation is also due George Pedrick of Purdue University and Karl Stromberg of the University of Oregon. Further, the author is grateful to the Wadsworth Publishing Company for help in surveying opinions about the relative importance of topics for inclusion in the book. The author will be grateful for suggestions that may lead to improvements in the book.

CONTENTS

1

SETS AND NUMBERS

1-1. SETS

The concept of set is deeply embedded in our intuition. It occurs in all branches of science and life. The students in the freshman class, the children in a family, the buildings in New York City, the positive integers that are perfect squares—all constitute sets. Although we usually think of the members of a set as having some property in common, the only common property of members of a set might be that they all belong to this set. Thus, a set could consist of, say, the Empire State Building, the number 3, and the mayor of New Orleans. A set may itself be a member of another set. For example, if the United States and Russia are regarded as being sets of people, then these sets are both members of the United Nations.

The concept of set and the language of sets are very simple and intuitive and thus are particularly valuable for clarifying and simplifying other concepts. In mathematics, use of set theory has resulted in great enrichment, clarification, and generalization. The concept of set occurs so frequently in mathematics that the language of sets provides a very useful means for unification of mathematical concepts.

Sets often are described by giving a rule that determines whether any particular object is or is not a member of the set. One simple rule is provided when we list the members of the set. Thus, the set S whose members are the letter A and the numbers 1 and 2 can be described by the rule "x is a member of S if x is one of the objects A, 1, 2." A common practice is to list the members of a set between braces. The set whose members are the letter A and the numbers 1 and 2 is written as $\{A, 1, 2\}$, or $\{2, A, 1\}$, etc., the order in which the members are listed being immaterial. Another example of a rule for describing a

1

set is the rule that "x is a member of the set if x is an integer and $x^2 = 4$." Still another is the rule that "x is a member of the set if x is a man and x weighs more than 150 lb." These sets can be denoted by $\{x: x \text{ is an integer and } x^2 = 4\}$ and $\{x: x \text{ is a man and } x \text{ weighs more than } 150 \text{ lb}\}$. Stated after the colon in each case is the condition that x satisfies if it is a member of the set and does not satisfy if it is not a member. A partial listing of the members of a set can be used to indicate a rule. For example, the set of all positive even integers might be indicated by $\{2, 4, 6, \cdots\}$. However, caution is necessary, for one might also interpret $\{2, 4, 6, \cdots\}$ as being the set that is so arranged that the first and second members are 2 and 4 and any other member is the sum of the two preceding members.

It is permissible for a set not to have any members. Such a set can be described by many rules; e.g., it is the set $\{x: x \text{ is a number and } x \neq x\}$. A set that has no members is called the *empty set* or the *null set* and will be denoted by Φ. We often find the concept of empty set convenient in mathematics.

A set A is a *subset* of a set B if each member of A is a member of B. This does not exclude the possibility that A and B are the same sets. We shall say that sets A and B are *equal* and write $A = B$, if A and B are the same sets—that is, if each member of A is a member of B and if each member of B is a member of A. We shall write $A \subset B$ if A is a subset of B, and $x \in A$ if x is a member of A. One frequently reads $A \subset B$ and $x \in A$ as "A is contained in B" and "x belongs to A." A set A is called a *proper subset* of B if $A \subset B$, but $A \neq B$. It should be clear now that the following are true for any sets A, B, and C.

$$A \subset A. \qquad \Phi \subset A.$$

$$\text{If } A \subset B \text{ and } B \subset A, \text{ then } A = B.$$

$$\text{If } A \subset B \text{ and } B \subset C, \text{ then } A \subset C.$$

It is usual in a specific discussion for all sets to be subsets of one designated set, which (for that discussion) is called the *universal set*. Suppose a discussion involved the set of married men, the set of men more than 40 years old, and the set of men living in Africa. If the universal set were taken to be the set of all men, then the discussion could use any set each of whose members is a man. The universal set could also be the set of all human beings, or it could be the set of all men who are either married, or more than 40 years old, or living in Africa. The universal set must be explicitly described or be clear from the context. It will usually be denoted by the letter T. Then, for any set A used in a discussion with T the universal set, we have $A \subset T$. A description of a set is understood to designate the set of all members of T that fit the description. Thus, if T is the set of all integers, then $\{x: x^2 = 4\} = \{2, -2\}$. But if T is the set of all positive numbers, then $\{x: x^2 = 4\} = \{2\}$.

A convenient geometric visualization of sets can be obtained if we represent the universal set as a region in a plane and the other sets as regions within it. In Fig. 1-1, the universal set is the set of all

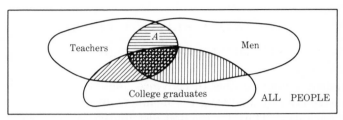

FIG. 1-1

people. The horizontally shaded region represents the set of all men who are also teachers. The vertically shaded region represents the set of all men who are college graduates. The diagonally shaded region represents the set of all college graduates who are teachers. Region A represents the set of all men who are teachers but are not college graduates.

> **DEFINITION 1-1.1.** The *union* of two sets A and B is the set C described by the rule that x is a member of C if x belongs to one or both of the sets A and B. The union of A and B is denoted by $A \cup B$.

> **DEFINITION 1-1.2.** The *intersection* of two sets A and B is the set D described by the rule that x is a member of D if x belongs to both of the sets A and B. The intersection of A and B is denoted by $A \cap B$.

The intersection of two sets is the common part of the two sets, and the union is formed when we consolidate the two sets into one set. Thus, the union of Hawaii, Alaska, and the previous 48 states is the present United States; the intersection of the "western states" and the "southern states" is Texas. In general, the union and intersection of sets A and B can be represented geometrically as in Fig. 1-2.

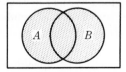 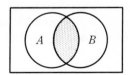

FIG. 1-2

It should be clear from Fig. 1-2 that for any sets A and B we have $A \subset (A \cup B)$ and $(A \cap B) \subset A$. We can also prove these statements by analyzing them directly. For example, an object belongs to $A \cap B$ if and only if it belongs to both A and B. Therefore, all objects that belong to $A \cap B$ also belong to A, and we conclude that $(A \cap B) \subset A$.

There are two useful theorems relating union and intersection of sets, which are called the *distributive laws* for sets:

$$A \cap (B \cup C) = (A \cap B) \cup (A \cap C),$$

$$A \cup (B \cap C) = (A \cup B) \cap (A \cup C).$$

The student should be able to convince himself of the truth of the distributive laws by analyzing the membership rules for the two sides of each equality. Thus, for the first distributive law, $x \in A \cap (B \cup C)$ means that x belongs to A and x belongs to at least one of the sets B and C, while $x \in (A \cap B) \cup (A \cap C)$ means that x either belongs to both A and B or to both A and C. Figure 1-3 illustrates how the truth of the

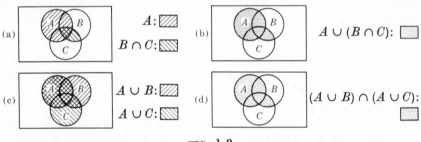

FIG. 1-3

second distributive law can be shown geometrically: diagram (a) shows the sets A and $B \cap C$ and (b) shows their union; diagram (c) shows the sets $A \cup B$ and $A \cup C$, whose intersection as shown in (d) is the same as the set $A \cup (B \cap C)$ of (b).

DEFINITION 1-1.3. Relative to a particular universal set T, the *complement* of a set A is the set described by the rule that x is a member of the set if x is a member of T and is not a member of A. The complement of A is denoted by $\sim A$.

Henceforth a universal set will always be specified for any discussion involving sets. The set $\sim A$ is frequently called "not A."

The following statements can be verified easily, it being understood that A and B can be any subsets of T:

$$\sim(\sim A) = A,$$

$$\sim \Phi = T, \qquad\qquad \Phi = \sim T,$$

$$(\sim A) \cup A = T, \qquad\qquad (\sim A) \cap A = \Phi,$$

$$A \subset B \text{ if and only if } A \cap (\sim B) = \Phi.$$

The following two statements are called *De Morgan's laws*. We can show that they are true by analyzing the membership rules for the sets on each side of the equality signs or by using geometric representations of the sets. The proof of the first of De Morgan's laws is illustrated in Fig. 1-4.

$$\textit{De Morgan's Laws:} \quad \begin{aligned} \sim(A \cup B) &= \sim A \cap \sim B \\ \sim(A \cap B) &= \sim A \cup \sim B \end{aligned}$$

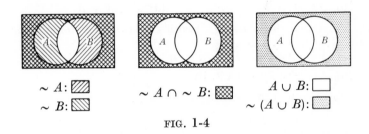

FIG. 1-4

PROBLEMS

1. Determine which of the following statements are true and which are false. In each case, the universal set is the set of numbers.

(a) $\{1, 3, 7\} \subset \{7, 1, 3\}$.

(b) $\{1, 2, 3\} \subset \{1, 2, 6, 3\}$.

(c) $\{0, 1, 2, 3\} \subset [\{1, 2, 3\} \cup \Phi]$.

(d) $\{x: x^2 = 1\} \subset \{x: x^3 = 1\}$.

2. Let the universal set be the set of numbers. For each of the following, determine whether the given statement is true and give reasons for your conclusion.

(a) $\{x: x^2 = 81\} \subset \{x: x+3 \text{ is an integer}\}$.

(b) $[\{x: x^2 - 3x + 2 = 0\} \cup \{x: x^2 + x = 0\}] \subset \{x: x^4 - 2x^3 - x^2 + 2x = 0\}$.

(c) $\{x^2: x \text{ is an integer}\} \subset \{x^2: \frac{1}{3}(x^2 - 1) \text{ is an integer}\}$.

3. Let T be the set of all dogs, H the set of all dogs that hate men, L the set of all large dogs, and W the set of all wild dogs. Without using set notation, describe the following sets.

(a) $(W \cup L) \cap H$.

(b) $W \cup (L \cap H)$.

(c) $(W \cup L) \cap (W \cup H)$.

(d) $(W \cap L) \cup H$.

(e) $(W \cup H) \cap (L \cup H)$.

(f) $W \cap (L \cup H)$.

(g) $(W \cap L) \cup (W \cap H)$.

(h) $\sim(W \cup L)$.

(i) $\sim(W \cap L)$.

(j) $\sim(W \cap \sim L)$.

4. Show that

$$\{x: |x| < 3\} = \sim[\{x: x \geq 3\} \cup \{x: x \leq -3\}]$$
$$= \{x: x < 3\} \cap \{x: x > -3\}.$$

5. Show that it is impossible to have sets A and B such that A has exactly 12 members, B exactly 18 members, $A \cap B$ exactly 6 members, and $A \cup B$ exactly 25 members.

6. Prove that the following statements are true for any set A contained in a universal set T.

(a) $\Phi \cup A = A$.

(b) $\Phi \cap A = \Phi$.

(c) $T \cup A = T$.

(d) $T \cap A = A$.

7. Prove that the following "associative laws" hold for any sets A, B, and C.

(a) $A \cup (B \cup C) = (A \cup B) \cup C$.

(b) $A \cap (B \cap C) = (A \cap B) \cap C$.

8. Prove each of the following theorems.

(a) If $B \subset A$, then $A \cup B = A$.

(b) If $A \cup B = A$, then $B \subset A$.

(c) If $A \subset B$, then $\sim B \subset \sim A$.

(d) If $A \subset B$, then for all C $(A \cap C) \subset (B \cap C)$.

(e) If $A \subset \Phi$, then $A = \Phi$.

(f) $A \cap (A \cup B) = A$.

(g) $A \cup (A \cap B) = A$.

(h) $(A \cap B) \cup (\sim A \cap B) = B$.

(i) $A \cup (\sim A \cap B) = A \cup B$.

(j) $A \cap (\sim A \cup B) = A \cap B$.

9. Let the *difference* $A - B$ be defined to be $A \cap (\sim B)$. Prove the following.

(a) $(A - B) \cup (A \cap B) = A$.

(b) $\sim(A - B) = (\sim A) \cup B$.

(c) $(A - B) \cap (A \cap B) = \Phi$.

(d) $(A - B) \cap (B - A) = \Phi$.

10.* Let the *symmetric difference* $A \nabla B$ be defined as $(A - B) \cup (B - A)$, where $A - B$ is defined as in problem 9. Prove the following.

(a) $A \nabla B = (A \cup B) \cap (\sim A \cup \sim B)$.

(b) $A \nabla B = (A \cup B) - (A \cap B)$.

(c) $A \nabla B = (\sim A) \nabla (\sim B)$.

(d) $(A \cup B) \nabla (P \cup Q) \subset (A \nabla P) \cup (B \nabla Q)$.

(e) $A \cap (B \triangledown C) = (A \cap B) \triangledown (A \cap C)$.

(f) $(A \triangledown B) \triangledown C = A \triangledown (B \triangledown C)$.

(g) $(A \triangledown C) \subset (A \triangledown B) \cup (B \triangledown C)$.

(h) If for some A it is true that $A \triangledown B = A \triangledown C$, then $B = C$.

11. Show that a set that has n members has 2^n subsets (a) by using mathematical induction, (b) by showing that the number of subsets is equal to the number of n-tuples $(\varepsilon_1, \varepsilon_2, \cdots, \varepsilon_n)$, where each ε_k is either $+1$ or -1.

1-2. RELATIONS

It is quite common to talk of objects being related, particularly when there is some clear rule that can be used to determine whether two specific objects are related. Thus, one might speak of two persons x and y being related in the sense of being brothers, or one might say that two animals are related if they have some specific biological similarity. In general, one might say that a relation is any rule by which it can be determined whether two objects are related or associated with each other. But the concepts of "rule" and "association" are vague. Just as members of a set need have no common property other than being members of the same set, a relation can be defined by simply designating which pairs of objects are related. Thus, the relation "mother of" can be thought of as being the set M of all pairs (x, y) for which x and y are people and x is the mother of y. Then the statement "$(x, y) \in M$" is equivalent to the statement "x is the mother of y." This example shows that it may be important to designate which is the first and which is the second member of a pair of related objects.

> **DEFINITION 1-2.1.** A *relation* is a set whose members are pairs of objects, these pairs being *ordered* in the sense that one member of the pair is designated as being the first and the other as being the second. We shall use the symbol (x, y) to denote the ordered pair for which the first object is x and the second object is y. The fact that (x, y) is a member of a relation R may be indicated by saying "x *is related to* y" or "$x\,R\,y$," or by writing $(x, y) \in R$ or xRy.

Before studying the theory of sets, the student probably felt that objects that belong to the same set should have some obvious common property, such as all being students in a French class, or all being rocks that weigh more than 5 lb, etc. However, it is difficult to define what is meant by a "suitable property" for determining set membership. There is a similar disadvantage to requiring some clear rule for determining whether objects are related. It is easy to give numerous

examples of relations with clear rules.   For example, one can think of x
and y as being related if y is the father of x.   Numbers x and y can be
said to be related if $x^2 + y^2 = 1$.   But since it is quite hopeless to describe
what types of rules are permissible, we choose instead to use Definition
1-2.1.   The only requirement that need be satisfied for x to be related
to y is that (x, y) be a member of the set that *is* the relation.   The
reader has already used such symbols as $<$ and $=$ to denote certain
relations.   Thus, $<$ is the relation R for which xRy means $x < y$, while
$=$ is the relation R for which $\alpha R\beta$ means $\alpha = \beta$.

DEFINITION 1-2.2.   The *domain* of a relation R is the set of all *first*
members of ordered pairs belonging to R; the *range* of R is the set of
all *second* members of ordered pairs belonging to R.

For example, if xRy means that x and y are numbers and
$x^2 + y^2 \leq 1$, then the domain and range of R are both equal to $\{t: |t| \leq 1\}$.
If xRy means that x and y are numbers and $|x| < -|y|$, then $R = \Phi$
and the domain and range of R are both empty.   If the domain and
range of R are sets of real numbers, then the *graph* of R is the set of
all points in the plane that have coordinates x and y for which $(x, y) \in R$.
In fact, we might describe the plane as the set of all ordered pairs (x, y)
such that x and y are real numbers.   Then we could say that a relation
R is the subset of the plane whose members are the points (x, y) for
which xRy, that is, the points that belong to R.   Figure 1-5 shows the
graphs of several relations.

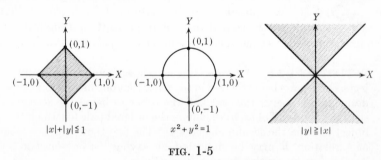

FIG. 1-5

There are three abstract properties that are used a great deal in
describing relations, which we shall now discuss.

A relation R for which the domain and the range are equal is said
to be *reflexive* if xRx is true whenever x belongs to the domain of R.†

---

† One might say that a relation is *reflexive with respect to a set S* if xRx is true whenever
$x \in S$.   For example, suppose that xRy means "x knows that y is a thief."   Then R
is reflexive with respect to the set of all thieves who are aware of their own behavior.

The inclusion relation for sets *is* reflexive, since $A \subset A$ is true for any set A. But if x and y are numbers and xRy means that y is the reciprocal of x, then $2R2$ is false and R *is not* reflexive.

If $(y, x) \in R$ whenever $(x, y) \in R$, then R is said to be *symmetric*. If x and y are numbers and xRy means that $|x-y| < 3$, then it follows from $|x-y| = |y-x|$ that R *is* symmetric. But if xRy means that x loves y, then R *is not* symmetric, unless the domain and range of R are chosen very carefully. It should be noted that the domain and range of a symmetric relation are necessarily equal. To show this, we note that if x is in the domain of a relation R, then there is at least one y such that $(x, y) \in R$. If R is symmetric, then $(y, x) \in R$, which implies that x is in the range of R. Similarly, if y is in the range of a symmetric relation R, then y is also in the domain.

A relation R is said to be *transitive* if $(x, z) \in R$ whenever there is an object y for which $(x, y) \in R$ and $(y, z) \in R$. If xRy means $x < y$, then R *is* transitive. But if xRy means that y is the father of x and if the domain of R is the set of all people, then R is not transitive. For if y is the father of x, and z is the father of y, then z *is not* the father of x.

DEFINITION 1-2.3. An *equivalence relation* is a relation that is reflexive, symmetric, and transitive.

Examples of equivalence relations are abundant. For example, some equivalence relations that have as domains the set of people presently living are: "is the same age as," "has the same mother as," and "lives in the same country as." For triangles, "is similar to," "is congruent to," and "has the same area as" are equivalence relations. Two equivalence relations for numbers are "is equal to" and "has the same square as."

There is a simple way to manufacture equivalence relations. Given a set T, we divide T into nonempty subsets, $S_1, S_2, \cdots$, in such a way that each member of T belongs to exactly one of these subsets. Then we define a relation R by stating that xRy means that x and y belong to the same subset of T. It is easy to verify that R is an equivalence relation. Conversely, Theorem 1-2.1 shows that if R is an equivalence relation, then R separates the members of T into nonoverlapping subsets. The set to which a member α of T belongs is simply the set of all members x of T for which $\alpha R x$.

DEFINITION 1-2.4. An *equivalence class* of an equivalence relation R is a set A for which there is a member α of A with $A = \{x : \alpha R x\}$.

THEOREM 1-2.1. The domain of an equivalence relation R is the union of the equivalence classes of R. If A and B are equivalence classes, then either $A \cap B = \Phi$ or $A = B$.

PROOF. If x is a member of the domain of an equivalence relation R, then it follows from R being *reflexive* that xRx. Thus, x belongs to at least one equivalence class; namely, the equivalence class $\{t : xRt\}$. Now suppose that $A = \{x : \alpha Rx\}$ and $B = \{x : \beta Rx\}$. We must show that $A = B$ if $A \cap B \neq \Phi$. Suppose $w \in A \cap B$, so that we have

$$\alpha Rw \quad \text{and} \quad \beta Rw.$$

Since R is *symmetric*, we have $wR\alpha$. If $x \in A$, then αRx. Then we have $wR\alpha$ and αRx, and it follows from R being *transitive* that wRx. But then βRw and wRx imply βRx, or $x \in B$. Thus, $A \subset B$. Similarly, $B \subset A$. Therefore, $A = B$.

ILLUSTRATION 1. Let T be the set of nonnegative integers and let xRy mean that $x - y$ is an integral multiple of 3; i.e., there is an integer k such that $3k = x - y$. It is very easy to show that R is reflexive and symmetric. To show that R is transitive, note that if xRy and yRz, then there are integers m and n such that $x - y = 3m$ and $y - z = 3n$. Then $(x - y) + (y - z) = x - z = 3(m + n)$, so that xRz. The relation R separates T into three nonoverlapping classes: $\{0, 3, 6, 9, \cdots\}$, $\{1, 4, 7, 10, \cdots\}$, and $\{2, 5, 8, 11, \cdots\}$.

Let R be a symmetric relation and let x and y be members of an ordered pair belonging to R. Then both (x, y) and (y, x) belong to R. For example, if xRy means that $x = 1/y$, then 3 and $\frac{1}{3}$ are members of an ordered pair and we have both $3R\frac{1}{3}$ and $\frac{1}{3}R3$. But if a relation is not symmetric, then a designation as to which member of an ordered pair is "first" and which "second" is very important. Given a set of ordered pairs, we might arbitrarily form a new set by interchanging the members of each ordered pair. Unless the relation is symmetric, this gives a new relation.

DEFINITION 1-2.5. The *inverse* of a relation R is the relation R^{-1} such that $(y, x) \in R^{-1}$ if and only if $(x, y) \in R$.

Clearly R^{-1} is the inverse of the relation R if and only if R is the inverse of R^{-1}. Also, if R and R^{-1} are inverses of each other, then the domain of R is the range of R^{-1} and the range of R is the domain of R^{-1}. If R is symmetric, then R is its own inverse. If R is a set of ordered pairs of numbers, then the graphs of R and R^{-1} are reflections of each other through the line $y = x$. As shown in Fig. 1-6, a point (a, b) in the graph of R is the reflection through the line $y = x$ of the point (b, a) in the graph of R^{-1}.

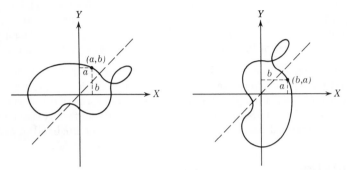

FIG. 1-6

PROBLEMS

1. In each of the following, determine whether R is reflexive, whether R is symmetric, and whether R is transitive. (*a*) x and y are men with brothers and xRy means that x is a brother of y. (*b*) x and y are people and xRy means that x and y live in the same congressional district. (*c*) x and y are numbers and xRy means that $|x-y| < 3$. (*d*) x and y are positive integers and xRy means that x divides y. (e) x and y are integers and xRy means that x and y are relatively prime; i.e., 1 is the only positive integer that divides both x and y. (f) x and y are numbers and xRy means that $x < y$. (g) x and y are numbers and xRy means that $x-y < 1$.

2. For each relation illustrated in Fig. 1-5, determine whether that relation is reflexive, whether it is symmetric, and whether it is transitive.

3. Let T be a set and let R be a relation whose domain is T and which is symmetric and transitive. Show that R is a reflexive relation and that T is both the domain and range of R.

4. Let R be the relation such that xRy means that the two people x and y are either of the same age, or of the same weight, or of both the same age and the same weight. (a) Explain why R is not transitive. (b) For each x, let S_x be the set of all y such that xRy. Explain why this does not define a separation of T into nonoverlapping subsets.

5. In each of the following, determine whether R is an equivalence relation defined on T. (*a*) T is the set of numbers and xRy means that $x \leq y$. (*b*) T is the set of numbers and xRy means that x is "approximately

equal" to y.   (*c*) T is the set of people who were born in hospitals and xRy means that x was born in the same hospital as y.   (*d*) T is the set of people who are married or have been married and xRy means that x has been or is the spouse of y.   (e) T is the set of people with homes and xRy means that x lives within one mile of y.   (f) T is the set of subsets of the positive integers and xRy means that x is the complement of y.   (g) T is the set of integers and xRy means that $x+y = 0$. (h) T is the set of lines in a plane and xRy means that x is parallel to y.

6. In each of the following, describe the inverse R^{-1} of the given relation R and state the domain and range of R^{-1}.   (a) xRy means that $y = x^2 + 1$, for x a real number.   (*b*) xRy means that $y = x(x+2)^{-1}$, for $x \neq -2$.   (c) xRy means that $y \leq x+1$, for x and y any real numbers. (d) For married people, xRy means that "x is the husband of y."

1-3. FUNCTIONS

The concept of function developed in a natural way along with the development of analytic geometry and calculus.   By the end of the eighteenth century, a function was regarded as being any formula involving variables and constants.   Soon after this, the development of mathematics led to investigations of more general types of relations among variables.   The following concept of function evolved as the result of attempts to furnish a definition that would include rather general relations among numbers: "A *variable* is a symbol that represents any one of a set of numbers; if two variables x and y are so related that whenever a value is assigned to x there is automatically assigned, by some rule or correspondence, a value to y, then y is a function of x."

We choose to define a function as a special type of relation— namely, a relation R such that xRy and xRz can both be true only if $y = z$.   The only essential differences between this definition and that of the preceding paragraph are that we avoid the use of such possibly ambiguous words as "rule" and "correspondence," and that the domain and range of R can be perfectly arbitrary sets rather than sets of numbers.

DEFINITION 1-3.1.   A *function*† is a relation R for which $y = z$ if $(x, y) \in R$ and $(x, z) \in R$.

---

† What we call a function is sometimes called a *single-valued function*, a relation then being called a *multiple-valued function*.   One would then say that R is an *n-valued function* if for some values of x there are n different values for y for which xRy, but for no x are there more than n such values for y.   In particular, if xRy means that x and y are numbers and $x^2 + 2y^2 = 4$, then $n = 2$ and R would be said to be a *double-valued function*.

Thus, a function is a set of ordered pairs for which no two ordered pairs have the same first member and different second members; that is, if the first member is specified, then the second member is uniquely determined.   Since for each member x of the domain of a function f there is exactly one member y of the range for which $(x, y) \in f$, it is permissible to speak of y as being *the value* of f at x.   It is quite common to call a function a *map* or a *transformation*, and say that the function *maps* or *sends* each point of the domain onto a point of the range, or that the function *transforms* each point of the domain into a point of the range. The member $f(x)$ of the range is said to be the *image* of x.   For a subset A of the domain, the set $S = \{f(x): x \in A\}$ is the *image* of A and f is said to map A *onto* S, or to map A *into* T if $S \subset T$.

A symbol is called a *variable* if it is used to designate an unspecified member of some set.   We may think of a variable as being a "place-holder" or a "blank" for the name of some member of the set. A *constant* is a symbol used to designate a member of a set that has only one member.   For example, suppose that, when studying the expression $xy + 3x + c$, it is understood that x or y can designate any number, but that there is exactly one (unspecified) number that c designates.   Then 3 and c are constants.

A symbol used to represent an unspecified member of the domain of a function is called an *independent variable*.   A *dependent variable* is a symbol used to represent an unspecified member of the range.   These definitions can be generalized, as we shall illustrate by means of examples.   Let f be the function whose domain is the set of points in a plane, while the value of f at the point whose coordinates are x and y is $x^2 + y^2$.   If the point whose coordinates are x and y is denoted by p and also by (x, y), then one might write $f(p) = x^2 + y^2$, or $f[(x, y)] = x^2 + y^2$. In this case, p is the independent variable.   However, it is also quite common to write $f(x, y) = x^2 + y^2$, and to speak of x and y as being independent variables and of f as being a *function of two variables*. Similarly, the function Γ, whose value for three sets A, B, and C is $A \cap (B \cup C)$, can be thought of as being a function of the single object (A, B, C), or as being a function of the three variables A, B, and C.   In either case, the value of Γ at (A, B, C) is written as $\Gamma(A, B, C)$.

If the domain of a function f is the set U and the range is the set V, then one might write

$$f\colon\ U \to V$$

and say that the function f maps the set U onto the set V.   This can be illustrated as shown in Fig. 1-7, where points in U represent members of the domain and points in V represent members of the range.   Each

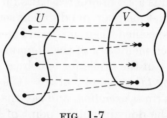

FIG. 1-7

point of U must map onto exactly one point of V, but more than one point of U may map onto the same point of V.

> **ILLUSTRATION 1.** Let f be the function that is the set of all ordered pairs (x, y) such that x and y are numbers with $0 \leq x \leq 2$ and $y = 1/(x+1)$. Then the domain is the set of all x such that $0 \leq x \leq 2$ and the range is the set of all y such that $\frac{1}{3} \leq y \leq 1$. If $(x, y) \in f$, then y is the "value" of the function f at x and is denoted by $f(x)$. One then writes
>
> $$y = f(x) \quad \text{or} \quad y = \frac{1}{x+1} \quad \text{or} \quad f(x) = \frac{1}{x+1}.$$
>
> The *graph* of f is shown in Fig. 1-8; it is the set of all points in the plane whose coordinates, x and y, satisfy the conditions $y = 1/(x+1)$ and $0 \leq x \leq 2$. Another way of illustrating the nature of this function is shown in Fig. 1-9; this method is similar to that of Fig. 1-7.

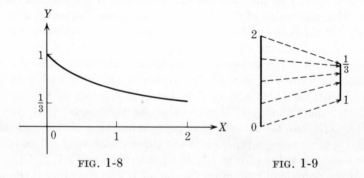

FIG. 1-8   FIG. 1-9

For convenience, abbreviations in notation will be used frequently. For example, one might speak of "the function $1/(x + 1)$," or of "the function $f(x)$," even though $1/(x + 1)$ and $f(x)$ denote the value of the function at x. If $f(x) = 1/(x + 1)$ for all $x \neq -1$, then the derivative of f is the function Df, or f', or df/dx, for which $(Df)(x)$, or $f'(x)$, is equal to $-1/(x + 1)^2$ if $x \neq -1$. For simplicity, one frequently makes such statements as "$-1/(x + 1)^2$ is the derivative of $1/(x+1)$," or "the derivative of $f(x)$ is $f'(x)$," which are technically inaccurate but can be regarded as being abbreviations of the following statements: "$-1/(c+1)^2$ is the value at c of the derivative of the function whose value at x is $1/(x+1)$ for all x," and "the value at x of the derivative of the function f is $f'(x)$."

ILLUSTRATION 2. A function f whose domain is the set of positive integers is called a *sequence*. Usually $f(n)$ is then denoted by a symbol such as a_n, and the objects in the range of f are said to be the *terms* of the sequence. The function S, for which $S(n)$ is the sum of the first n integers, is a particularly useful sequence. For this function,

$$S(n) = a_n = 1+2+3+\cdots+n = \tfrac{1}{2}n(n+1).$$

The terms of the range of S can then be indicated by using the suggestive notation

$$\{1, 3, 6, 10, 15, \cdots, \tfrac{1}{2}n(n+1), \cdots\}.$$

Another interesting sequence is the function ϕ for which $\phi(n)$ is the number of integers that are not greater than n and are relatively prime to n (two integers are relatively prime if 1 is the only positive integer that divides both of them). This function is called the ϕ-*function*, or *Euler's ϕ-function*. The terms are

$$\{1, 1, 2, 2, 4, 2, 6, 4, 6, 4, \cdots, \phi(n), \cdots\}.$$

For example, $\phi(6) = 2$, since 1 and 5 are the only integers not larger than 6 that are relatively prime to 6. Surprisingly, there is a concise formula for $\phi(n)$:

$$\phi(n) = n\left(1 - \frac{1}{p_1}\right)\left(1 - \frac{1}{p_2}\right)\cdots\left(1 - \frac{1}{p_k}\right),$$

where $p_1, \cdots, p_k$ are all the prime factors of n. For example,

$$\phi(60) = 60(1 - \tfrac{1}{2})(1 - \tfrac{1}{3})(1 - \tfrac{1}{5}) = 16.$$

The equality $f = g$ is to be interpreted as meaning that f and g are the same functions; i.e., they have the same domains and $f(x) = g(x)$ for all x in their common domain. Often one writes $f(x) \equiv g(x)$ instead of $f = g$ and calls it an *identity*. This is useful if one is using abbreviated notation for a function. For example, one might say that $1/\sqrt{x^2}$ and $1/|x|$ are *identically equal* and write

$$\frac{1}{\sqrt{x^2}} \equiv \frac{1}{|x|},$$

meaning that $f = g$, where f and g are the functions defined by $f(x)$ $= 1/\sqrt{x^2}$ when $x \neq 0$ and $g(x) = 1/|x|$ when $x \neq 0$.

The student has on many occasions added, multiplied, or divided functions. Let us review some of these ideas and state them in more detail, using the present definition of function. Let f and g be functions whose ranges are sets of numbers and let c be a number. Then the functions cf, $f+g$, fg, and $1/f$ are defined by means of the following equations:

$$y = (cf)(x) = c \cdot f(x), \tag{1-1}$$

$$y = (f+g)(x) = f(x) + g(x), \tag{1-2}$$

$$y = (fg)(x) = f(x) \cdot g(x), \tag{1-3}$$

$$y = \left(\frac{1}{f}\right)(x) = \frac{1}{f(x)}. \tag{1-4}$$

In each case, the domain is the set of all x for which the equation is meaningful. Thus, the domain of cf is equal to the domain of f. The domain of $f+g$ and the domain of fg are each equal to the intersection of the domain of f and the domain of g. The domain of $1/f$ is the set that contains all members x of the domain of f for which $f(x) \neq 0$. The functions $f-g$ and f/g are defined to be $f + (-g)$ and $(f) \cdot (1/g)$, respectively.

ILLUSTRATION 3. Let f and g be the functions defined by the equations

$$f(x) = \frac{x+1}{x-3} \quad \text{and} \quad g(x) = \frac{(x-3)(x+5)}{x-1},$$

where the domain of f is $\{x : x \neq 3\}$ and the domain of g is $\{x : x \neq 1\}$. Then

$$(f+g)(x) = \frac{x+1}{x-3} + \frac{(x-3)(x+5)}{x-1},$$

$$(fg)(x) = \left(\frac{x+1}{x-3}\right)\left(\frac{(x-3)(x+5)}{x-1}\right),$$

$$\left(\frac{f}{g}\right)(x) = \left(\frac{x+1}{x-3}\right)\left(\frac{(x-3)(x+5)}{x-1}\right)^{-1}.$$

Both the domain of $f+g$ and the domain of fg are the set of numbers not equal to 3 or 1. If x is not 3 or 1, then $(fg)(x) = (x+1)(x+5)/(x-1)$.

The expression $(x+1)(x+5)/(x-1)$ is equal to 16 when $x = 3$. But 3 is not in the domain of fg, since 3 is not in the domain of f and $(fg)(x)$ is defined to be $f(x)\cdot g(x)$. The domain of $(f/g)(x)$ is the intersection of the domain of f and the domain of $1/g$—that is, the set of numbers not equal to 3, 1, or -5. If x is not 3, 1, or -5, then

$$\left(\frac{f}{g}\right)(x) = \frac{x^2-1}{(x-3)^2(x+5)}.$$

Another important combination of two functions is the *composite function*. If f and g are two functions, then the composite function will be denoted by $f \circ g$ and is defined by means of the equation

$$(f \circ g)(x) = f[g(x)],$$

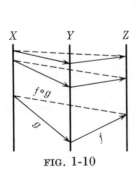

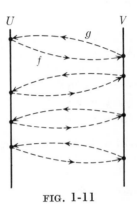

FIG. 1-10   FIG. 1-11

the domain being the set of all points x in the domain of g for which $g(x)$ is in the domain of f. There may be no points of the range of g that are contained in the domain of f, in which case the domain of $f \circ g$ is the empty set. The composite function of f and g can be represented geometrically as in Fig. 1-10. Points on the line X represent members of the domain of g and will be denoted by the variable x; members of the range of g or of the domain of f are both denoted by y and are represented by points on the line Y. The dashed lines illustrate the mapping by means of the function $f \circ g$ of points of X onto points of Z. We might then write $y = g(x)$, $z = f(y)$, and $z = f[g(x)]$.

A function is a relation for which no two ordered pairs have the same first member and different second members. If the inverse of a function is also a function, it must also be true that no two ordered pairs have the same second member and different first members. This means that if f and f^{-1} are both functions and if $(x, y) \in f$, then neither

x nor y occurs in any other ordered pair of f. Thus, each object in the domain of f is paired with exactly one object in the range of f. We then say that f is a *one-to-one correspondence* between its domain and its range.

Let us suppose that f and g are functions that are inverses of each other. Since $(x, y) \in f$ if and only if $(y, x) \in g$, we see that $y = f(x)$ if and only if $x = g(y)$. Thus, if x is in the domain of f and y is in the range of f, then $y = f[g(y)]$ and $x = g[f(x)]$. This is illustrated in Fig. 1-11: if a point x in U is mapped by f onto a point y of V, then y is mapped onto x by g. Thus, $(f \circ g)(x) = x$ for all x in U.

PROBLEMS

1. Each of the following equations defines a function. In each case, the domain is the set of all numbers x for which the equation gives a value for y. Determine the domain and range of the function and sketch its graph.

(a) $y = 3x + 7$.   (c) $y = 1/(x^2 - 1)$.

(b) $y = x^2 - 2x$.   (d) $y = (x - 2)/(x^2 + 1)$.

2. In each of the following, let the domain of the function described be the set of all numbers x for which $0 \leq x \leq 2$. Find the range of the function and sketch its graph.

(a) $y = 2x$.   (c) $y = 4x^3 - 6x^2 + 1$.

(b) $y = (x + 3)/(x - 4)$.   (d) $y = x^2 - x$.

3. Let f be the function defined by $f(x) = (2x + 3)/(x - 2)$ for $x \neq 2$. Show that f is a symmetric relation.

4. Show that, if a function f is a transitive relation and the domain and range of f are equal, then $f(x) = x$ for all x in the domain of f.

5. Find the 11th to 15th terms for the ϕ-function.

6. Let $A(n)$ be the number of primes not greater than n. Find the first 20 terms of the sequence A. [There is an interesting theorem (the *prime-number theorem*) which states that $A(n) \cdot (\ln n)/n \to 1$ as n increases.]

7. Find the values of $f \circ g$ and $g \circ f$ at -5, 0, and 2, if

(a) $f(x) = x + 2$; $g(x) = 3x - 1$;

(b) $f(x) = x + 7$; $g(x) = |x|$;

(c) $f(x) = 5x + 1$; $g(x) = |x| + 3x - 1$;

(d) $f(x) = \ln(x + 6)$; $g(x) = x + 1$.

8. Describe $f \circ g$ and $g \circ f$ if

(a) $f = \{(0, 1), (1, 2), (7, 3)\}$; $g = \{(2, 0), (3, 0), (1, 5)\}$;

(b) $f = \{(b, a), (c, a), (d, b)\}$; $g = \{(a, b)\}$;

(c) $f(x)$ is the father of x, with the domain of f the set of all people; $g(x)$ is the oldest brother of x, with the domain of g the set of all people who have at least one brother;

(d) $f(x)$ is the spouse of x, with the domain of f the set of married people; $g(x)$ is the mother of x, with the domain of g the set of all people;

(e) $f(x) = \ln(x+1)$ for $x > -1$; $g(x) = e^x$ for all x;

(f) $f(x) = x/(2x-3)$ for $x \neq \frac{3}{2}$; $g(x) = 5x+7$ for all x;

(g) for A and B subsets of a set T, $f[(A, B)] = A \cup B$ and $g(A) = \sim A$.

9. In each of the following, find the inverse g of f.

(a) $f(x) = 3x+2$ for all x.   (c) $f(x) = \ln(e^x+1)$ for all x.

(b) $f(x) = (x+7)/(2x-5)$ for $x \neq \frac{5}{2}$.   (d) $f(x) = \ln(x^2-2x+2)$ for $x \geqq 1$.

10. Determine a condition on a, b, c, and d which is satisfied if and only if f is its own inverse, where $ad - bc \neq 0$ and

$$f(x) = \frac{ax+b}{cx+d} \quad \text{when} \quad cx+d \neq 0.$$

1-4. NUMBERS

The most primitive concept involving numbers is the idea of one set having the *same number* of members as another. Counting began as a concept of *one-to-one correspondence*. A herd of cattle, for example, would be counted by pairing each cow with a pebble (or a notch on a stick, or one's fingers and toes), the number of cows being described by the pile of pebbles. Since it is much more difficult to conceive of the concept of "three" as an object than the concept of "three cows" or "three pebbles," it was a long time before numbers became abstracted from the objects with which they were associated. It was even more difficult, however, to conceive of the number zero. The introduction of zero was a major step in the development of positional value and arithmetic computation. Although positional value and zero were used in India before 800 A.D., their use in Europe was quite limited until after the twelfth century, and it was not until 1600 that these new methods of arithmetic computation had won a complete victory over the old methods, which used an abacus of some type.

The positive integers and zero are adequate for counting objects. For measuring such things as distance and volume, fractions are necessary and natural. Within experimental error, any two distances can be represented as multiples of some fractional part of the unit distance. Therefore, irrational numbers are not needed for measuring purposes. During the early development of Greek mathematics, it was assumed that any two line segments L_1 and L_2 are commensurable in the sense that there is a third line segment L_3 such that both L_1 and L_2 can be divided into pieces, each of which is congruent to L_3.

The Greek mathematician Pythagoras was born about 580 B.C. The members of a school and brotherhood he founded proved that there is no fraction whose square is 2. The discovery that $\sqrt{2}$ is not a rational number seemed to the Greeks to cause trouble with the basic assumption that everything depends on the integers. It was particularly upsetting to the Pythagoreans' theory of proportionality, which assumed that any two numbers are commensurable. This would imply, for instance, that the length of the side and the length of the diagonal of a square are commensurable, which was seen to be false.† The scandal was so great that attempts were made for a while to keep the fact secret. There was even a legend that one member of the Pythagorean brotherhood was drowned because he disclosed the secret to outsiders. Finally, in 370 B.C., Eudoxus reconciled the existence of irrational numbers and the theory of proportion in a way similar to modern treatments of irrational numbers.

This discussion gives a brief picture of the historical development of numbers. We shall discuss in detail only the part of the logical development of the number system that consists of the extension of the set of rational numbers to include all real numbers, since the definition of counting numbers and the discussions of extensions to include the rational numbers usually are regarded as belonging to a study of logic or algebra rather than of advanced calculus. The counting numbers may be defined as cardinal numbers of finite sets (including the empty set),‡ or the positive integers may be studied by use of Peano's axioms.§ As the set of counting numbers is enlarged to include all integers and then all rational numbers, more and more of the following axioms are satisfied:

---

† This is a consequence of the fact that $\sqrt{2}$ is an irrational number.

‡ See *University Mathematics* by R. C. James (Belmont, Calif.: Wadsworth Publishing Company, Inc., 1963), pp. 180–187, or *General Topology* by J. L. Kelley (Princeton, N.J.: D. Van Nostrand Publishing Co., 1955), pp. 271–280.

§ See *A Survey of Modern Algebra* (3rd ed.) by G. Birkhoff and S. MacLane (New York: The Macmillan Company, 1965), pp. 50–52.

N_1: For all x, y, and z,

$$x+y = y+x \quad \text{and} \quad x \cdot y = y \cdot x \quad \text{(Commutative laws)}$$

$$x+(y+z) = (x+y)+z \quad \text{and} \quad x \cdot (y \cdot z) = (x \cdot y) \cdot z$$
$$\text{(Associative laws)}$$

$$x \cdot (y+z) = (x \cdot y)+(x \cdot z). \qquad \text{(Distributive law)}$$

N_2: There are two different members, denoted by "0" and "1," which have the properties that, for all x,

$$x + 0 = x \quad \text{and} \quad x \cdot 1 = x.$$

N_3: For any x, there is a member $-x$ which has the property that

$$x + (-x) = 0.$$

N_4: For any x, other than 0, there is a member x^{-1} which has the property that

$$x \cdot x^{-1} = 1.$$

N_5: There is a subset P (whose members are said to be positive) such that P does not contain 0, and, for any x and y,

N_5': If $x \neq 0$, then $x \in P$ if and only if $-x \notin P$;

N_5'': If $x \in P$ and $y \in P$, then $x+y \in P$ and $x \cdot y \in P$.

The set of positive integers satisfies axiom N_1. The set of counting numbers satisfies axioms N_1 and N_2. The set of integers satisfies N_1 through N_3 and also N_5. The set of rational numbers satisfies all of axioms N_1 through N_5.

A *field* is a set F with which there are associated two functions, Σ and Π, with ranges contained in F, domains equal to the set of all ordered pairs (x, y) of members of F, and for which axioms N_1 through N_4 are satisfied when we denote $\Sigma(x, y)$ by $x+y$ and $\Pi(x, y)$ by $x \cdot y$. An *ordered field* is a field for which axiom N_5 is satisfied. For a field, subtraction and division can be defined by letting

$$x-y = x+(-y), \quad x/y = x \cdot y^{-1} \text{ if } y \neq 0.$$

The usual algebraic properties of numbers with which the student is familiar can be proved using only axioms N_1 through N_4, so they are valid for any field. For an ordered field, inequalities can be defined by letting $x < y$ mean that $y - x$ is positive, and the familiar properties of inequalities can be established. We shall leave the details of all this for a course in algebra.

The progress of mathematics has been hampered considerably by misconceptions and lack of understanding about the real numbers. This is illustrated by one of Zeno's paradoxes, which confused mathematicians for hundreds of years:

> Space and time being assumed to be made up of points and instants, let there be given three parallel rows of points, A, B, and C. Let C move to the right and A to the left at the rate of one point per instant, both relative to B; but then each point of A will move past two points of C in an instant, so that we can subdivide this, the smallest interval of time; and this process can be continued indefinitely, so that time cannot be made up of instants.†

Aristotle and the Greeks considered motion continuous and numbers discontinuous. Because of this, a satisfactory science of dynamics was impossible. Throughout the development of mathematics, confusion was rampant. The problem of the continuum (the real numbers) was often interpreted in terms of physical atomism. Some people assumed a finite number of points, others an infinite number of points; some postulated immediate contiguity and a discrete set of indivisibles. It was even claimed that although the line contains an infinite number of indivisibles, it is not made up of such indivisibles; others said that the continuum of real numbers is made up of an infinite number of infinitely divided continua.

The confusion illustrated by Zeno's paradox persisted for centuries, as can be seen in a quotation from Isaac Barrow, written in the seventeenth century:

> To every instant of time, or indefinitely small particle of time (I say instant or indefinite particle, for it makes no difference whether we suppose a line to be composed of points or of indefinitely small linelets; and so in the same manner, whether we suppose time to be made up of instants or indefinitely minute timelets); to every instant of time, I say, there corresponds some degree of velocity, which the moving body is considered to possess at the instant.‡

---

† See *The History of the Calculus and its Conceptual Development*, by Carl B. Boyer (New York: Dover Publications, 1949), p. 24 (*fn.*).

‡ Boyer, *op. cit.*, p. 180.

This confusion is also apparent in the belief of Leibniz that his calculus could be justified by mathematical considerations already understood and that therefore it was not necessary to fall back upon "metaphysical controversies such as the composition of the continuum."

The meaning of "continuity" or "completeness" of the set of real numbers (the *continuum* of real numbers) has taken centuries to develop. It is represented by what we call the *least upper bound axiom*. As we shall see, this axiom and related concepts are vitally important throughout the calculus.

> **DEFINITION 1-4.1.** Let S be a subset of an ordered field F. An *upper bound* for S is a member ω of F such that $x \leqq \omega$ whenever $x \in S$. The *least upper bound* of S is an upper bound that is less than all other upper bounds of S.

Common abbreviations for "least upper bound of S" are lub (S) and sup (S).†

> **DEFINITION 1.4.2.** A *lower bound* for a subset S of an ordered field F is a member ω of F such that $\omega \leqq x$ whenever $x \in S$. The *greatest lower bound* of S is a lower bound that is greater than all other lower bounds of S.

Common abbreviations for "greatest lower bound of S" are glb (S) and inf (S).† The rule "$x \in -S$ if and only if $-x \in S$" defines a set $-S$ for which the following are true statements: "ω is a lower bound for S if and only if $-\omega$ is an upper bound for $-S$," and "$\omega = \inf (S)$ if and only if $-\omega = \sup (-S)$." Thus, a nonempty set S has an upper bound if and only if $-S$ has a lower bound, and S has a least upper bound if and only if $-S$ has a greatest lower bound.

> **DEFINITION 1-4.3.** The set of *real numbers* is an extension of the set of rational numbers that satisfies axioms N_1 through N_5 and also satisfies the following logically equivalent axioms.
> N_6 (least upper bound axiom): If a nonempty subset S has an upper bound, then S has a least upper bound.
> N_6' (greatest lower bound axiom): If a nonempty subset S has a lower bound, then S has a greatest lower bound.

There are certain problems whose answers can be shown to exist by using the least upper bound axiom. A procedure that can be used in particular cases is to construct a set that has an upper bound and whose

---

† The abbreviation "sup" is derived from "supremum" and "inf" from "infimum."

least upper bound can be shown to be the desired number. This procedure is illustrated by the following examples.

ILLUSTRATION 1. We wish to show that there is a number whose square is 2. Let $S = \{x: x^2 \leq 2\}$ and let $\alpha = \sup (S)$. Note that $1 \leq \alpha \leq 2$, since $1^2 < 2$ and $2^2 > 2$. We wish to show that $\alpha^2 = 2$. If $\alpha^2 \neq 2$, then either $\alpha^2 < 2$ or $\alpha^2 > 2$. Suppose first that $\alpha^2 < 2$. Let ε be a positive number for which $0 < \varepsilon < 1$. Then

$$(\alpha+\varepsilon)^2 = \alpha^2 + 2\alpha\varepsilon + \varepsilon^2 < \alpha^2 + 5\varepsilon.$$

But if ε is chosen so that $5\varepsilon < 2 - \alpha^2$, then $(\alpha+\varepsilon)^2 < 2$, $\alpha+\varepsilon \in S$, and α is not an upper bound for S. A similar proof shows that it is false that $\alpha^2 > 2$.

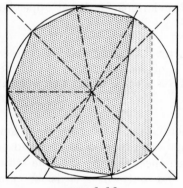

FIG. 1-12

ILLUSTRATION 2. The number π is defined as the ratio of the circumference of a circle to its diameter. To give meaning to this definition, the circumference of a circle must be defined and must be shown to have a ratio to the diameter which does not depend on the size of the circle. For a polygon inscribed in a circle of diameter d, we shall show that the perimeter of the polygon is less than $4d$. Thus, the lengths of inscribed polygons have the upper bound $4d$, and the circumference of a circle can be defined as the *least upper bound of the perimeters of all inscribed polygons*. We can show that $4d$ is an upper bound for these perimeters by taking a polygon inscribed in a circle and drawing a circumscribed square and those radial lines that pass through a vertex of the polygon or a vertex of the square. If for some of the vertices of the square the corresponding radial lines intersect the circle in points that are not vertices of the polygon, we increase the number of sides (and the perimeter) of the polygon so that these points are vertices. As illustrated in Fig. 1-12, two successive radial lines cut a segment from the new polygon which is shorter than the segment cut from the square. Therefore, the perimeter of the new polygon, and consequently the perimeter of the original polygon, is less than 4d, the perimeter of the square. We leave it to the student to convince himself that, for this definition of circumference, the ratio of circumference to diameter is the same for all circles. Methods of elementary geometry can be used to show that, if a circle has unit diameter, then

$$s_{2n} = [\tfrac{1}{2}(1 - \sqrt{1 - s_n^2})]^{1/2},$$

where s_n is the length of a side of a regular polygon of n sides inscribed in the circle. It can be proved to follow from the definition of π that, as n increases, the perimeter ns_n approaches π. This method was used by Archimedes (about 240 B.C.) to show that π is between 223/71 and 22/7. It was also used by many other persons. Ludolph van Ceulen (1540–1610) spent a large part of his life computing π to 35 decimal places, using a polygon having 2^{62} sides.

The following theorem is the basis for many applications of the least upper bound axiom. This theorem makes it possible to dispense with the explicit construction of sets that have least upper bounds, such as the sets used in the previous illustrations. A *monotone increasing* sequence is a sequence $\{a_n\}$ for which $a_k \leq a_{k+1}$ for each k, a *monotone decreasing* sequence is a sequence $\{a_n\}$ for which $a_k \geq a_{k+1}$ for each k, and a *monotone* sequence is a sequence that is either monotone increasing or monotone decreasing. A *bounded* sequence is a sequence $\{a_n\}$ for which there is a number M with $|a_k| \leq M$ for all k. A monotone increasing sequence is bounded if it has an upper bound, and a monotone decreasing sequence is bounded if it has a lower bound.

THEOREM 1-4.1. If the sequence $A = \{a_1, a_2, \cdots\}$ is monotone and bounded, then there is a number α for which $a_k \to \alpha$ as k increases. Also, $\alpha = \sup (A)$ if A is monotone increasing, and $\alpha = \inf (A)$ if A is monotone decreasing.

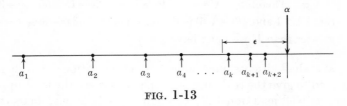

FIG. 1-13

PROOF. Let us analyze first what must be meant by "$a_k \to \alpha$ as k increases." If we choose a positive number ε as a tolerance [see Fig. 1-13], it must be true that $|\alpha - a_k|$ is smaller than this tolerance if k is sufficiently large. We need a formal proof, so let us express this

54086

LIBRARY
College of St. Francis
JOLIET, ILL.

in mathematical language: "Let ε be any positive number; then there must be a number K such that $|\alpha - a_k| < \varepsilon$ whenever $k > K$." Now let us proceed to the proof. We shall assume the sequence is monotone increasing and leave it to the reader to convince himself that a similar proof can be given if the sequence is monotone decreasing. Certainly we should let $\alpha = \sup(A)$. Then $a_k \leqq \alpha$ for each k. Now choose a positive number ε. Since $a_k \leqq a_{k+1}$ for each k, it follows that if we can find an a_k such that $a_k > \alpha - \varepsilon$, then we would have $a_r > \alpha - \varepsilon$ whenever $r > k$. Therefore, K can be any integer for which $a_K > \alpha - \varepsilon$. Such a K must exist, for otherwise $\alpha - \varepsilon$ is an upper bound for A, and α is not the smallest upper bound for A. This completes the proof that $a_k \to \alpha$ as k increases. The fact that there is no other number β for which $a_k \to \beta$ as k increases is a consequence of a theorem to be proved later [Theorem 2-5.1, page 86].

ILLUSTRATION 3. Suppose $A = \{a_1, a_2, \cdots\}$, where $a_1 = 1$ and $a_{n+1} = 1 + \sqrt{a_n}$ for each n. We wish to show that there is a number α such that $a_n \to \alpha$ as n increases. We also wish to find the value of α. Once it is known that α exists, it is customary to write

$$\alpha = 1 + \sqrt{1 + \sqrt{1 + \cdots}}.$$

Let us use mathematical induction to show that 3 is an upper bound for the set A. Clearly $a_1 < 3$. If $a_n < 3$, then $a_{n+1} = 1 + \sqrt{a_n} < 1 + \sqrt{3} < 3$. In order to use Theorem 1-4.1, we must also know that $a_{n+1} \geqq a_n$ for each n. Again we use mathematical induction. Note that $a_1 = 1$ and $a_2 = 2$, so that $a_2 > a_1$. But if $a_n > a_{n-1}$, then $\sqrt{a_n} > \sqrt{a_{n-1}}$ and

$$a_{n+1} = 1 + \sqrt{a_n} > 1 + \sqrt{a_{n-1}} = a_n.$$

Now we let α be the number such that $a_n \to \alpha$, which we have just shown exists. We will show later that $\sqrt{a_n} \to \sqrt{\alpha}$ as $a_n \to \alpha$ [see Illustration 2 of Section 2-6]. Since $a_{n+1} = 1 + \sqrt{a_n}$, it follows that $\alpha = 1 + \sqrt{\alpha}$. Therefore, $\sqrt{\alpha} = \alpha - 1$, $\alpha = \alpha^2 - 2\alpha + 1$, and $\alpha^2 - 3\alpha + 1 = 0$. Since $\alpha > 1$ and $\frac{1}{2}(3 + \sqrt{5})$ is the only solution of $x^2 - 3x + 1 = 0$ which is greater than 1, we must have $\alpha = \frac{1}{2}(3 + \sqrt{5})$.

We shall discuss now how the set of rational numbers can be extended to give the real numbers—i.e., to satisfy the least upper bound axiom as well as axioms N_1 through N_5. It is customary to extend the rational numbers by defining a set of objects called *real numbers* and labeling certain members of this set as rational numbers. The remaining numbers are called *irrational numbers*. The set of real numbers can be defined in several different ways, one of which is called

the method of *Dedekind cuts*.† For this method, a *(real) number* is an
ordered pair (A_1, A_2) of nonempty sets A_1 and A_2 whose members are
rational numbers and which have three properties:

    (i) $A_1 \cup A_2$ is the set of all rational numbers.

    (ii) If $x \in A_1$ and $y \in A_2$, then $x < y$.

    (iii) A_1 has no last member.

For example, the number usually denoted by $\sqrt{2}$ is the pair (A_1, A_2)
for which A_2 is the set of positive rational numbers x for which $x^2 > 2$,
and A_1 contains all other rational numbers.

Rather than working directly with ordered pairs (A_1, A_2) to define
addition and multiplication of real numbers, it is convenient to introduce the concept of Cauchy sequences.

> **DEFINITION 1-4.4.** A *Cauchy sequence of rational numbers* is a sequence
> $\{a_n\}$ of rational numbers with the property that, for any positive
> rational number ε, there is an integer N such that $|a_m - a_n| < \varepsilon$ if
> $m > N$ and $n > N$.

We shall think of Cauchy sequences of rational numbers as being
numerals that designate real numbers. A particular Cauchy sequence
$\{a_n\}$ designates the real number (A_1, A_2) for which A_1 is the set of all
rational numbers x for which there is a positive number ε and an integer
N with

$$x + \varepsilon < a_n \text{ if } n > N.$$

Two *equivalent Cauchy sequences* are Cauchy sequences $\{a_n\}$ and
$\{b_n\}$ such that for any $\varepsilon > 0$ there is an integer N with

$$|a_n - b_n| < \varepsilon \text{ if } n > N.$$

It is easy to show that two Cauchy sequences are equivalent if and only
if they are numerals for the same real number. Also, each real number
(A_1, A_2) is designated by at least one Cauchy sequence. To choose
such a sequence $\{a_n\}$ that designates (A_1, A_2), we can first let a_1 be an
arbitrary member of A_1. Then we let a_2 be the largest of the numbers
$a_1 + n^{-1}$, with n a positive integer, which belongs to A_1; a_3 be the largest

---

    † An interesting excerpt from Dedekind's original book on this subject, *Continuity and
Irrational Numbers*, appears in *The World of Mathematics*, compiled by James R.
Newman (New York: Simon and Schuster, Inc., 1960), pp. 528–537.

of the numbers $a_2 + n^{-1}$ which belongs to A_1; etc. The sequence defined in this way is a Cauchy sequence. To see this, we note that the sequence is increasing and therefore A_1 would contain all rational numbers if there were a positive number ε such that $a_m - a_n \geqq \varepsilon$ for infinitely many values of n with $m > n$. It is not difficult to show that $\{a_n\}$ designates (A_1, A_2).

> **ADDITION.** The *sum* of two real numbers $\{a_n\}$ and $\{b_n\}$ is the number $\{a_n + b_n\}$.

> **MULTIPLICATION.** The *product* of two real numbers $\{a_n\}$ and $\{b_n\}$ is the number $\{a_n b_n\}$.

These definitions of addition and multiplication must be shown to have meaning. First, we must know that $\{a_n + b_n\}$ and $\{a_n b_n\}$ are Cauchy sequences whenever $\{a_n\}$ and $\{b_n\}$ are Cauchy sequences. We shall show this for the product and leave the sum for the student. To do this, we note first that a Cauchy sequence is bounded [see problem 14]. Then we can let ε be an arbitrary positive number and choose integers N_1 and N_2 such that

$$|a_m - a_n| < \tfrac{1}{2}\varepsilon(1 + \sup |b_k|)^{-1} \text{ if } m > N_1 \text{ and } n > N_1,$$

$$|b_m - b_n| < \tfrac{1}{2}\varepsilon(1 + \sup |a_k|)^{-1} \text{ if } m > N_2 \text{ and } n > N_2.$$

If N is the larger of N_1 and N_2 and if $m > N$ and $n > N$, then

$$|a_m b_m - a_n b_n| = |a_m(b_m - b_n) + b_n(a_m - a_n)| < \tfrac{1}{2}\varepsilon + \tfrac{1}{2}\varepsilon = \varepsilon.$$

Thus $\{a_n b_n\}$ is a Cauchy sequence. Finally, to validate the definition of addition and multiplication we must also show that, if one Cauchy sequence in a sum (or a product) is replaced by an equivalent Cauchy sequence, then the sum (or the product) is replaced by an equivalent Cauchy sequence and therefore designates the same real number. We shall do this for the product and leave the sum for the student. Suppose $\{a_n\}$ and $\{\alpha_n\}$ are equivalent and $\{b_n\}$ is a third Cauchy sequence. Then, for an arbitrary positive rational number ε, there is an N such that $|a_n - \alpha_n| < \varepsilon(1 + \sup |b_n|)^{-1}$ if $n > N$. Then

$$|a_n b_n - \alpha_n b_n| = |a_n - \alpha_n| \, |b_n| < \varepsilon \text{ if } n > N.$$

This shows that $\{a_n b_n\}$ and $\{\alpha_n b_n\}$ are equivalent. Since we can replace one sequence and then the other, this proof implies that, if both Cauchy sequences in a product are replaced by equivalent Cauchy sequences, then the new product is equivalent to the original product.

With these definitions of addition and multiplication, it is clear that the commutative, associative, and distributive laws listed in axiom N_1 are satisfied. If we define 0 and 1 to be the real numbers designated by the Cauchy sequences $\{0, 0, \cdots\}$ and $\{1, 1, \cdots\}$ whose terms are all zeros and ones, respectively, then clearly $x + 0 = x$ and $x \cdot 1 = x$ for all real numbers x. Thus, N_2 is satisfied.

We can let $-\{a_n\}$ be the real number designated by $\{-a_n\}$, since clearly $\{-a_n\}$ and $\{-\alpha_n\}$ are equivalent if $\{a_n\}$ and $\{\alpha_n\}$ are equivalent. Then $x + (-x) = 0$ for all x and axiom N_3 is satisfied.

If $\{a_n\}$ does not designate 0—that is, if the sequences $\{a_n\}$ and $\{0, 0, \cdots\}$ are not equivalent—then there is a positive number ε and an integer N such that $|a_n| > \varepsilon$ if $n > N$ [see problem 15]. Now let the reciprocal $\{a_n\}^{-1}$ of the real number designated by $\{a_n\}$ be the real number designated by $\{0, 0, \cdots, 0, a_{N+1}^{-1}, a_{N+2}^{-1}, \cdots\}$. We leave to the student the problem of showing this is a Cauchy sequence. Then

$$\{a_n\} \cdot \{0, \cdots, 0, a_{N+1}^{-1}, a_{N+2}^{-1}, \cdots\} = \{0, \cdots, 0, 1, 1, \cdots\},$$

which is equivalent to $\{1, 1, \cdots\}$. Thus, $x \cdot x^{-1} = 1$ for all nonzero real numbers x, and axiom N_4 is satisfied.

The set of *positive real numbers* is defined as the set of all real numbers $\{A_1, A_2\}$ for which A_1 contains at least one positive rational number. The student should be able to show that this definition is equivalent to the statement that a number $\{a_n\}$ is positive if and only if there is a positive rational number ε and an integer N such that $a_n > \varepsilon$ if $n > N$. Then it follows easily that a nonzero number x is positive if and only if $-x$ is not positive and that $x + y$ and xy are positive if x and y are positive. Thus axiom N_5 is satisfied.

Now we know that the set of real numbers is an ordered field. To show that the least upper bound axiom is satisfied, one can show first that $(B_1, B_2) - (A_1, A_2)$ is positive, that is, $(A_1, A_2) < (B_1, B_2)$, if and only if $A_1 \subset B_1$ and $A_1 \neq B_1$. Then for a set S of real numbers, we let U_1 be the union of all sets A_1 for which there is a set A_2 such that (A_1, A_2) is a member of S. If S has an upper bound (B_1, B_2), then $A_1 \subset B_1$ if $(A_1, A_2) \in S$ and therefore $U_1 \subset B_1$. Therefore, U_1 is not the entire set of rational numbers and we let U_2 be the set of all rational numbers not in U_1. Also, if $(A_1, A_2) \in S$, then $A_1 \subset U_1$ and $(A_1, A_2) < (U_1, U_2)$. Therefore, (U_1, U_2) is an upper bound of S. If $(V_1, V_2) < (U_1, U_2)$, then $V_1 \subset U_1$ and $V_1 \neq U_1$. Let u be a member of $U_1 - V_1$. Then, for some (A_1, A_2) in S, we have $u \in A_1$ and therefore $(V_1, V_2) < (A_1, A_2)$. Thus, (V_1, V_2) is not an upper bound of S. This completes the proof that (U_1, U_2) is the least upper bound of S.

The final step in our discussion of the real numbers is to accept the convention that a rational number a is identified with the real number designated by the Cauchy sequence $\{a, a, \cdots\}$ whose terms are all a's. Then the set of rational numbers and the set of corresponding real numbers are indistinguishable except for the numerals used to denote them—addition, multiplication, inverses under addition and multiplication, and the positive set for the set of rational numbers become identified with the corresponding concepts for the set of corresponding real numbers.

PROBLEMS

1. Complete Illustration 1 by showing that if $S = \{x: x^2 \leqq 2\}$, then it is false that $[\sup (S)]^2 > 2$.

2.* Let $\{a_1, a_2, \cdots\}$ be a sequence with the properties that each a_n is positive and there is a number r with $0 < r < 1$ such that $a_{n+1} < ra_n$ for all n. Then this sequence is decreasing and it follows from Theorem 1-4.1 that there is a number α such that $a_n \to \alpha$ as n increases. Prove that $\alpha = 0$.

3. For each of the following, show that there is a number α for which $a_n \to \alpha$ as n increases. Find the value of α.

(*a*) $a_1 = 2$ and $a_{n+1} = 2 + \sqrt{a_n}$ for each n.

(*b*) $a_1 = 3$ and $a_{n+1} = 3 + \sqrt{a_n}$ for each n.

(c) $a_1 = 1$ and $a_{n+1} = 1 + 2\sqrt{a_n}$ for each n.

(*d*) $a_1 = \sqrt{2}$ and $a_{n+1} = (\sqrt{2})^{a_n}$ for each n. [Assume that 2 and 4 are the only positive solutions of $(\sqrt{2})^x = x$ and that $(\sqrt{2})^{a_n} \to (\sqrt{2})^\alpha$ as $a_n \to \alpha$.]

4. For each of the following, determine whether there is a number α for which $a_n \to \alpha$ as n increases. Determine the value of α if it exists.

(*a*) $a_n = 1 + \frac{1}{3} + (\frac{1}{3})^2 + (\frac{1}{3})^3 + \cdots + (\frac{1}{3})^{n-1}$ for each n.

(*b*) $b_n = 1 - \frac{1}{2} + (\frac{1}{2})^2 - (\frac{1}{2})^3 + \cdots + (-1)^{n+1}(\frac{1}{2})^{n-1}$.

(c) $a_1 = 1/\sqrt{2}$, $a_2 = \sqrt{2}$, and $a_{n+1} = a_{n-1} + 1/(a_n - a_{n-1})$ for each n.

(d)* $a_n = \frac{1}{2} + 2/2^2 + 3/2^3 + \cdots + n/2^n$. [*Hint:* Consider $a_n - \frac{1}{2}a_n$.]

5.* Let $\{a_1, a_2, \cdots\}$ be a sequence with the following properties:

(i) $a_n \leqq a_{n+2}$ if n is odd;

(ii) $a_n \geqq a_{n+2}$ if n is even;

(iii) $|a_n - a_{n-1}| \to 0$ as n increases.

Prove that there is a number α for which $a_n \to \alpha$ as n increases.

6. For each of the following, determine whether there is a number α for which $a_n \to \alpha$ as n increases. [At first, consider only a_n for which n is odd, or only a_n for which n is even.]

(a) $a_n = 1 - \frac{1}{2} + \frac{1}{3} - \frac{1}{4} + \cdots + (-1)^{n+1}1/n$.

(b) $a_n = 1 - 2 + 3 - 4 + \cdots + (-1)^{n+1}n$.

7. For each of the following, use problem 5 to show that there is a number α such that $a_n \to \alpha$ as n increases. Find the value of α.

(a) $a_1 = 1$ and $a_{n+1} = 1 + 1/a_n$ for each n. [*Hint:* One might use

$$a_{n+1} - a_n = \left(1 + \frac{1}{a_n}\right) - \left(1 + \frac{1}{a_{n-1}}\right) = \frac{a_{n-1} - a_n}{a_n \cdot a_{n-1}},$$

and a similar equality for $a_{n+2} - a_n$.]

(b) $a_1 = 2$ and $a_{n+1} = 2 + 1/a_n$ for each n.

(c) $a_1 = 1$ and $a_{n+1} = 1 + 1/(1 + a_n)$ for each n.

(d) $a_1 = 2$ and $a_{n+1} = 2 + 2/a_n$ for each n.

8. Compute the values of a_1, a_2, a_3, a_4, and a_5 for problem 7(c), and show without using any other approximations for $\sqrt{2}$ that

$$|\sqrt{2} - a_3| < \frac{1}{60} \quad \text{and} \quad |a_4 - \sqrt{2}| < \frac{1}{348}.$$

9. Compute the values of $a_1 - 1$, $a_2 - 1$, $a_3 - 1$, $a_4 - 1$, and $a_5 - 1$ for problem 7(d), and show without using any other approximations for $\sqrt{3}$ that

$$|\sqrt{3} - (a_3 - 1)| < \frac{1}{12} \quad \text{and} \quad |(a_4 - 1) - \sqrt{3}| < \frac{1}{44}.$$

10. Find, if it exists, the number approached by a_n if $a_1 = 1$ and $a_{n+1} = \frac{1}{4} + a_n^2$ for all n.

11. Show that, if x and y are positive real numbers, there is a positive integer n for which $nx > y$. [This is the *Archimedean property* of the real numbers. *Hint:* Use the least upper bound axiom to prove that y/x is not an upper bound for the set of positive integers.]

12. Show that for any real number x there is an integer n for which $n \leq x < n + 1$.

13. Prove that two Cauchy sequences of rational numbers are equivalent if and only if they designate the same real number.

14. Show that if $\{a_n\}$ is a Cauchy sequence of rational numbers, then there is a rational number M such that $|a_n| \leq M$ for all n.

15. Show that if a Cauchy sequence $\{a_n\}$ is not equivalent to the Cauchy sequence $\{0, 0, \cdots\}$, whose terms are all zeros, then there is a positive number ε and an integer N such that $|a_n| > \varepsilon$ if $n > N$.

16. Explain why the sum of real numbers (A_1, A_2) and (B_1, B_2) is the real number (S_1, S_2) for which

$$S_1 = \{x+y: x \in A_1 \text{ and } y \in B_1\}.$$

1-5. RATIONAL AND IRRATIONAL NUMBERS

One of the most useful applications of Theorem 1-4.1 is to the study of infinite decimals. For example, suppose we divide 3 by 11 and, instead of stopping at a particular step and stating the quotient and remainder, we continue the formal process of long division indefinitely and obtain the infinite decimal

$$0.272727\cdots 27\cdots.$$

If we let $a_1 = 0.2$, $a_2 = 0.27$, $a_3 = 0.272$, etc., then $a_n \to 3/11$ as n increases. In fact, $3/11 - a_n$ is positive and is less than 10^{-n}. Therefore, it is natural to write

$$\frac{3}{11} = 0.272727\cdots 27\cdots.$$

Now suppose we have an infinite decimal,

$$n + 0.d_1 d_2 d_3 d_4 \cdots d_k \cdots, \quad n \text{ an integer,}$$

and we wish to associate this symbol with a number. We shall let $a_1 = n + 0.d_1$, $a_2 = n + 0.d_1 d_2$, $a_3 = n + 0.d_1 d_2 d_3$, etc. Then $a_k \leq a_{k+1}$ for all k. Also, $a_k \leq n + 1$ for all k. Therefore, it follows from Theorem 1-4.1 that there is a number α such that $a_k \to \alpha$ as k increases. This number α is the number we associate with the infinite decimal. This means that the infinite decimal is a numeral which can be used to designate α, so that we can write

$$\alpha = n + 0.d_1 d_2 d_3 \cdots d_k \cdots.$$

Now we shall let α be any number and n be an integer such that $n \leq \alpha < n + 1$. We shall let d_1 be the largest of the digits $0, 1, \cdots, 9$ for which $n + 0.d_1 \leq \alpha$, and continue to choose successive digits in this way, so that d_2 is the largest digit for which $n + 0.d_1 d_2 \leq \alpha$, d_3 is the largest digit for which $n + 0.d_1 d_2 d_3 \leq \alpha$, etc. If we let $a_k = n + 0.d_1 d_2 \cdots d_k$, then $\alpha - a_k < 10^{-k}$ for each k. Therefore, $a_k \to \alpha$ as n increases, and we have

$$\alpha = n + 0.d_1 d_2 d_3 \cdots d_k \cdots.$$

We have seen that every infinite decimal designates a particular number. Now we have shown that every number determines at least one infinite decimal. [A number determines two infinite decimals only when it has a finite decimal representation—see problem 3.]

Let us now determine which decimals are rational numbers and which are irrational numbers. We saw that $3/11 = 0.272727\cdots$. Another example of an infinite decimal expansion generated by division of integers is

$$\frac{47}{56} = 0.839\ 285714\ 285714\cdots,$$

where the block of digits 285714 repeats indefinitely. A decimal is said to be *repeating* when it has a block of digits that repeats in this way. It will be left to the student to demonstrate that any rational number has a decimal expansion that is repeating. Let us now consider the particular repeating decimal

$$\beta = 1.379\ 12\ 12\ 12\cdots.$$

If we let $b_1 = 1.3$, $b_2 = 1.37$, $b_3 = 1.379$, etc., then β is the number for which $b_k \to \beta$ as k increases. Therefore, $10^3 b_k \to 10^3 \beta$ and $10^5 b_k \to 10^5 \beta$, so that

$$10^3\beta = 1379.12\ 12\ 12\cdots = 1379 + .12\ 12\ 12\cdots,$$

and

$$10^5\beta = 137912 + .12\ 12\ 12\cdots.$$

Therefore,

$$(10^5 - 10^3)\beta = 137912 - 1379,$$

or

$$\beta = \frac{136{,}533}{99{,}000} = \frac{45{,}511}{33{,}000}.$$

This shows that β is a rational number. We have discussed only one special case; however, the method by which we showed that β is a rational number can be generalized to prove that any repeating decimal represents a rational number. If the student completes this generalization and the proof needed for problem 1, he will have completed the proof of the following theorem.

THEOREM 1-5.1. A decimal expansion of a number is repeating if and only if the number is a rational number.

The foregoing discussion classified numbers as rational or irrational according to whether their decimal expansions are repeating or non-repeating. We shall now compare the "sizes" of the set of positive integers, the set of rational numbers, the set of irrational numbers, and the set of real numbers.† The most primitive method for comparing the sizes of two sets is by one-to-one correspondence. Two herds of cattle can be compared by pairing the cattle, one from each herd being put in each pair. The herds are said to have the same number of members, or the same counting number, if they are exhausted simultaneously. One-to-one correspondences are very effective in comparing sizes of finite sets. For finite sets A and B, exactly one of the following is true: there is a one-to-one correspondence between A and B; there is a one-to-one correspondence between A and a proper subset of B; there is a one-to-one correspondence between B and a proper subset of A. This is not true for nonfinite sets. For example, there is a natural one-to-one correspondence between the even positive integers and the odd positive integers. However, the even integers can be paired with some of the odd integers, as follows:

$$(2, 1), (4, 5), (6, 9), (8, 13), (10, 17), \cdots, (2n, 4n - 3), \cdots.$$

Then each even integer occurs in one of the pairs, but only alternate odd integers occur. This seems to indicate that there are more odd integers than even integers. Also, the pairing

$$(2, 1), (6, 3), (10, 5), (14, 7), (18, 9), \cdots, (4n - 2, 2n - 1), \cdots$$

seems to indicate that there are more even integers than odd integers. We shall call two sets (whether finite or not) *equinumerable* if there exists at least one one-to-one correspondence between the sets. For example, any two of these sets are equinumerable: the set of positive integers, the set of all integers, the set of all rational numbers. This can be demonstrated by the following indication of correspondences, where a positive integer (top line) corresponds to the integer (middle line) and to the rational number (bottom line) below it:

1	2	3	4	5	6	7	8	9	10	11	12	13	14	15	16 ⋯
0	1	−1	2	−2	3	−3	4	−4	5	−5	6	−6	7	−7	8 ⋯
0	−1	1	−2	$-\frac{1}{2}$	$\frac{1}{2}$	2	−3	$-\frac{1}{3}$	$\frac{1}{3}$	3	−4	$-\frac{3}{2}$	$-\frac{2}{3}$	$-\frac{1}{4}$	$\frac{1}{4}$ ⋯

$$(1\text{-}5)$$

---

† There is an interesting discussion of such questions in Newman, *op. cit.*, pp. 1593–1611.

The last row is formed by, first, listing the number $0/1$, which is of type m/n with $|m| + |n| = 1$; then listing in increasing order those of the numbers m/n with $|m| + |n| = 2$ that have not been listed previously; then listing in increasing order those of the numbers m/n with $|m| + |n| = 3$ that have not been listed previously; etc.

The concept of counting number can be extended to infinite sets. However, it is customary to use "cardinal number" instead of "counting number" when sets are not restricted to being finite. For any set S, we say that S has a property, called the *cardinal number of S*, that is shared by all sets that can be put into one-to-one correspondence with S. The numeral customarily used to denote the cardinal number of the positive integers is the symbol $\aleph_0$ (pronounced "aleph null"). Then the cardinal number of the set of all integers, or of the set of rational numbers, is also $\aleph_0$. A set with cardinal number $\aleph_0$ is said to be *countably infinite*.

It is customary to use the symbol c (for "continuum") to denote the cardinal number of the set of all (real) numbers. Let us prove that $\aleph_0 \neq$ c. If $\aleph_0 =$ c, then there exists at least one one-to-one correspondence between the set of positive integers and the set of all (real) numbers. We shall use a proof by contradiction to show that no such one-to-one correspondence exists. Let us assume one does exist and pick a particular one. For this particular one-to-one correspondence, we shall designate by r_n the number that corresponds to the positive integer n. Then each (real) number corresponds to some positive integer n and is denoted by r_n. We arrive at a contradiction by exhibiting a number α that does not correspond to any integer. Let α be defined by

$$\alpha = 0.d_1 d_2 d_3 d_4 \cdots,$$

where for each n the digit d_n is chosen to be one of the digits $0, 1, \cdots, 9$ which is not the nth digit in a decimal representation of r_n (r_n may have two decimal representations); to be specific, we can choose d_n as the smallest such digit. Then for each n we have $\alpha \neq r_n$, since r_n does not have a decimal representation that has the same nth digit as the chosen decimal representation of α. That is, α does not correspond to any integer. This completes the proof.

We shall let a and b denote the cardinal numbers of sets A and B. Then $a = b$ if and only if there is a one-to-one correspondence between A and B. We can now define $a < b$ as meaning that $a \neq b$ *and* that there is a one-to-one correspondence between A and a subset of B. A basic theorem about cardinal numbers, which we shall state and use but not prove, is as follows.

THEOREM 1-5.2. For any two cardinal numbers a and b, exactly one of the following statements is true: $a < b$, $a = b$, $a > b$.†

ILLUSTRATION 1. Let P be the set of positive real numbers and R be the set of real numbers. A one-to-one correspondence g between P and R can be defined by letting $g(x) = -x^{-1}$ if $x \leq -1$ and $g(x) = 2 + x$ if $x > -1$. Therefore the sets P and R are equinumerable.

ILLUSTRATION 2. Let A be the interval $\{x : 0 \leq x \leq 1\}$ and R be the set of real numbers. Since $f(x) = x$ defines a one-to-one correspondence f between A and a subset of R, we know that $a \leq r$ if a and r are the cardinal numbers of A and R. However, we can define a one-to-one correspondence g between R and a subset of A as follows: $g(x) = -\frac{1}{2}x^{-1}$ if $x \leq -1$, $g(x) = \frac{1}{2} + (3+x)^{-1}$ if $x > -1$. Therefore, $r \leq a$ and it follows from Theorem 1-5.2 that $a = r$ and the sets A and R are equinumerable.

ILLUSTRATION 3. Suppose we wish to show that there are "more" irrational numbers than rational numbers. As before, we denote the cardinal number of the set of rational numbers by $\aleph_0$. We shall let k denote the cardinal number of the set of irrational numbers [see problem 10]. We wish to show that $\aleph_0 < k$. Let us show first that $\aleph_0 \leq k$. We observe first that if r is a rational number, then $r + \sqrt{2}$ is an irrational number, since if $r + \sqrt{2} = s$ and s is a rational number, then $\sqrt{2} = s - r$ is a rational number. Now let r correspond to $r + \sqrt{2}$, for each rational number r. This gives a one-to-one correspondence of the set of all rational numbers and the set of all irrational numbers of type $r + \sqrt{2}$, where r is a rational number, and proves that $\aleph_0 \leq k$. Now we assume that $\aleph_0 = k$ and choose a particular one-to-one correspondence between the set of rational numbers and the set of irrational numbers. We use the first and third lines of (1-5) to define a function f as follows: If an irrational number x corresponds to a rational number that in 1-5 is below the positive integer n, we let $f(x) = 2n$. If a rational number x is below the positive integer n in (1-5), we let $f(x) = 2n - 1$. Then f is a one-to-one correspondence between the set of all (real) numbers and the set of positive integers (the irrational numbers correspond to the even integers and the rational numbers to the odd integers). We know this is impossible, so it follows that $\aleph_0 \neq k$.

---

† For a proof that *at most* one of these statements is true, see *General Topology* by J. L. Kelley (Princeton, N.J.: D. Van Nostrand Co., Inc., 1955), pp. 28–29. To show that *at least* one of the statements is true, one can show that any set can be linearly ordered so that all subsets have first members and that if two sets are so ordered, then one set is an "initial segment" of the other. See *Set Theory* by F. Hausdorff (New York: Chelsea Publishing Co., 1957), pp. 65–68; or "Neuer Beweis für die Wohlordnung" by E. Zermelo, *Math. Ann.*, **65** (1908), pp. 107–128.

PROBLEMS

1. Let m and n be integers. Prove that m/n has a repeating decimal expansion.

2. Express as a quotient of integers the rational number whose decimal expansion is

(*a*) $0.142857\ 142857\cdots$;   (*c*) $0.2\ 851\ 851\ 851\cdots$;

(b) $0.24\ 24\ 24\cdots$;   (d) $2.37\ 126\ 126\ 126\cdots$.

3. Let α be a number that has two different representations as infinite decimals. Show that one of these infinite decimals uses only zeros after some position, while the other uses only nines after some position.

4. Let $a = 0.131331333133331\cdots$, where each block of 3's contains one more 3 than the preceding block. Show that α is an irrational number.

5. Let x be a number that has a decimal representation $0.d_1d_2d_3\cdots$ for which $d_n = 0$ if n is a power of 2, and d_n is one of the digits $1, 2, \cdots, 9$ if n is not a power of 2. Show that x is an irrational number.

6. Show that if x and y are any two numbers with $x < y$, then there is a rational number ξ and an irrational number η such that $x < \xi < y$ and $x < \eta < y$.

7. Show that if sets A and B are equinumerable, and B and C are equinumerable, then A and C are equinumerable.

8. Show that $A \cup B$ is countable if both A and B are countable.

9. For each of the following, show that the two given sets are equinumerable.

(a) $\{x: 0 < x < 1\}$ and $\{x: 0 < x < 2\}$.

(b) $\{x: 0 < x < 1\}$ and $\{x: 0 \le x \le 1\}$.

(c) $\{x: 0 < x < 1\}$ and the set of positive numbers.

(d) $\{(x, y): x^2 + y^2 \le 1\}$ and $\{(x, y): |x| + |y| < 1\}$.

10. Let k be the cardinal number of the set of irrational numbers and c be the cardinal number of the set of all (real) numbers. Prove that $k = c$.

11. Two numbers written in decimal form, $0.x_1x_2x_3\cdots$ and $0.y_1y_2y_3\cdots$, determine a decimal $0.x_1y_1x_2y_2x_3y_3\cdots$ obtained by alternately choosing digits from the given numbers. Use this and Theorem 1-5.2 to show that the following sets are equivalent:

$\{x: 0 \le x \le 1\}$ and $\{(x, y): 0 \le x \le 1$ and $0 \le y \le 1\}$.

12. Let R be the set of positive integers and S the set whose members are finite subsets of R. Prove that R and S are equinumerable.

13. Let R be a set and S be the set of all subsets of R. Also let r and s be the cardinal numbers of R and S. (a) Prove that $r \neq s$. [*Hint:* Suppose that S is in one-to-one correspondence with R. Show that the subset A of R does not correspond to any member of R, if A is defined by the following rule: "$A \subset R$ and an x in R belongs to A if and only if it *does not* belong to the member of S that corresponds to x."] (b) Show that $r < s$. [This shows that there is no largest cardinal number.]

1-6. EXTENSIONS OF THE SET OF REAL NUMBERS

In Section 1-4, we discussed axioms N_1 through N_6 for the real numbers. Sets such as the set of rational numbers or the set of real numbers that satisfy all of axioms N_1 through N_5 are ordered fields [see the discussion, page 21]. Although we shall not prove it, it is true that *any two ordered fields that satisfy the least upper bound axiom are isomorphic*; i.e., there is a one-to-one correspondence between the fields for which addition and multiplication correspond. The next theorem is only a special case of the preceding statement, but it is interesting in that it shows we are at the end of the road. It is impossible to enlarge the number system any more without violating some of the axioms!

THEOREM 1-6.1. Suppose R and R_E are two sets which, with suitable addition and multiplication functions, satisfy axioms N_1 through N_6. Also assume that $R \subset R_E$ and that numbers x and y in R have the same sum and product, whether considered to be members of R or members of R_E. Then $R = R_E$.

We shall not give a formal proof of this theorem,† although the basic principle that can be used to construct a proof is simple: R and R_E contain in a natural way a subset we call the "rational numbers" in R (or R_E); also, between the set of infinite decimals that do not contain only 9's after some position and the set R (or R_E), there is a one-to-one correspondence for which x corresponds to the infinite decimal $n + 0.d_1 d_2 d_3 \cdots$ if and only if

$$x = \sup \{n, n.d_1, n.d_1 d_2, n.d_1 d_2 d_3, \cdots\}.$$

---

† For a proof, see James, *op. cit.*, p. 212.

Because of Theorem 1-6.1, it is not possible to enlarge the set of real numbers without sacrificing some of axioms N_1 through N_6. However, it is customary to speak of a system as being *an extension of the real numbers* if it contains the real numbers and if some of axioms N_1 through N_6 are satisfied. The set of complex numbers [to be studied in the next section] is an extension for which axioms N_1 through N_4 are satisfied. For the complex numbers, we sacrifice the possibility of defining a positive set (axiom N_5) to obtain an important extension of the set of real numbers that satisfies axioms N_1 through N_4. In the problems, an example is given of an extension for which all of the axioms except N_6 are satisfied [problem 7].

Let us now adjoin two objects to the set of real numbers and denote these objects by the symbols $+\infty$ and $-\infty$.† We extend addition and multiplication by the following definitions:

$$x + (+\infty) = (+\infty) + x = +\infty, \quad \text{if} \quad x \neq -\infty;$$

$$x + (-\infty) = (-\infty) + x = -\infty, \quad \text{if} \quad x \neq +\infty;$$

$$x \cdot (+\infty) = (+\infty) \cdot x = +\infty, \quad \text{if} \quad 0 < x \quad \text{or} \quad x = +\infty;$$

$$x \cdot (+\infty) = (+\infty) \cdot x = -\infty, \quad \text{if} \quad x < 0 \quad \text{or} \quad x = -\infty;$$

$$x \cdot (-\infty) = (-\infty) \cdot x = -\infty, \quad \text{if} \quad 0 < x \quad \text{or} \quad x = +\infty;$$

$$x \cdot (-\infty) = (-\infty) \cdot x = +\infty, \quad \text{if} \quad x < 0 \quad \text{or} \quad x = -\infty.$$

Furthermore, we define $+\infty$ as positive and $-\infty$ as negative. Although we shall not attempt to define the sum of $+\infty$ and $-\infty$, we use the following notational conventions and the equality

$$x - y = x + (-y)$$

to extend the concept of subtraction:

$$-(+\infty) = -\infty \quad \text{and} \quad -(-\infty) = +\infty.$$

Also, we do not define the product of 0 and either $+\infty$ or $-\infty$, but we use the following notational conventions and the equality

$$\frac{x}{y} = x \cdot y^{-1}$$

---

† The student should note that the set of cardinal numbers discussed in the preceding section is a natural extension of the set of counting numbers. The objects $+\infty$ and $-\infty$ are not cardinal numbers; they are merely two objects adjoined to the set of real numbers.

to extend the concept of division:

$$(+\infty)^{-1} = (-\infty)^{-1} = 0.$$

Of course, addition and multiplication could have been defined randomly. However, this extended real number system is to be used in the future and the conventions for addition and multiplication are chosen with this in mind.†

It is easy to see that we have been very destructive of axioms. In fact, only axioms N_2, N_5, and N_6 hold for this extended real number system. However, the situation is not as bad as it might seem. Axiom N_1 is not satisfied, since $x + y$ and $x \cdot y$ are not defined for all x and y. However, *all* the axioms can be salvaged if we change them so that the equalities involved are required to be true statements only when each member of the equality has meaning. (Note that the left members of the equalities in N_3 and N_4 do not have meaning if x is $+\infty$ or $-\infty$.) Of course, we could arbitrarily give values to $(+\infty)+(-\infty)$, $(-\infty)+(+\infty)$, $0 \cdot (+\infty)$, $(+\infty) \cdot 0$, $0 \cdot (-\infty)$, and $(-\infty) \cdot 0$. But then the cancellation laws for addition no longer hold [see also problems 1 and 4].

PROBLEMS

1. Let R^* be an extension of the real numbers for which axiom N_1 holds. In particular, this implies that $x + y$ and $x \cdot y$ have meaning and are members of R^* whenever x and y are members of R^*. Also assume that R^* has only a finite number of members that are not ordinary real numbers. Prove that neither of the following cancellation laws holds.

   (a) $x = y$ if $x + r = y + r$;

   (b) $x = y$ if $r \neq 0$ and $xr = yr$.

2. Show that the extended real number system that contains $+\infty$ and $-\infty$ satisfies axiom N_5 and that, for this extended real number system, every set of numbers has a least upper bound.

---

† We wish $x + y$ and $x \cdot y$ to be "continuous" in a sense to be discussed in the next chapter. This means, for example, that $\alpha + (+\infty) = +\infty$ if α is an ordinary real number, since $x + y$ is a large positive number if x is near α and y is a large positive number. However, $0 \cdot (+\infty)$ is not defined, since the restriction that x is near zero and y is a large positive number gives no information as to the size of $x \cdot y$.

3. For the extended real number system that contains $+\infty$ and $-\infty$, show that

(a) $(+\infty)-x = +\infty$ if $x \neq +\infty$;

(b) $x-(+\infty) = -\infty$ if $x \neq +\infty$;

(c) $(-\infty)-x = -\infty$ if $x \neq -\infty$;

(d) $x-(-\infty) = +\infty$ if $x \neq -\infty$;

(e) $+\infty/x = +\infty$ and $-\infty/x = -\infty$
   if x is an ordinary positive real number;

(f) $+\infty/x = -\infty$ and $-\infty/x = +\infty$
   if x is an ordinary negative real number;

(g) $x/(+\infty) = x/(-\infty) = 0$ if x is an ordinary real number.

4. For the extended real number system that contains $+\infty$ and $-\infty$, suppose that the definitions of addition and multiplication are extended by letting

$$(+\infty)+(-\infty) = (-\infty)+(+\infty) = 0,$$

$$0\cdot(+\infty) = (+\infty)\cdot 0 = 0\cdot(-\infty) = (-\infty)\cdot 0 = 1.$$

Then axioms N_2 through N_6 are satisfied.   (a) Show that neither of the associative laws is satisfied.   (b) Show that the distributive law is not satisfied.   [*Note:* For these and other reasons, we will *not* use these extensions of the definitions of addition and multiplication.]

5. Suppose we define an extension of the real number system with exactly one additional member.   Let us denote this new member by θ and give the following definitions [often θ is denoted by ∞]:

$$x+\theta = \theta+x = \theta \quad \text{if} \quad x \neq \theta; \qquad x\cdot\theta = \theta\cdot x = \theta \quad \text{if} \quad x \neq 0.$$

Also, we use the notational conventions

$$-(\theta) = \theta, \quad \theta^{-1} = 0, \quad x+(-y) = x-y, \quad \text{and} \quad x\cdot y^{-1} = x/y,$$

whenever $x+(-y)$ and $x\cdot y^{-1}$ have meaning.   For each of the following, show that the equality is a true statement if x, y, and z are chosen so that both members of the equality have meaning.

(a) $x+(y+z) = (x+y)+z$.

(b) $x(yz) = (xy)z$.

(c) $x(y+z) = xy+xz$.

(d) $-(x-y) = y-x$.

(e) $-(x/y) = (-x)/y$.

(f) $(xz)/(yz) = x/y$.

6. Let S be the set of all formal expressions in x (polynomials) of type

$$p(x) = a_0+a_1 x+a_2 x^2+\cdots+a_n x^n,$$

whose coefficients are real numbers.   Let addition and multiplication of polynomials be defined in the usual way.   Then it is easy to show that axioms N_1 through N_3 are satisfied.   (a) Show that N_4 is not satisfied. (b) Let the set P of *positive* members of S be those nonzero polynomials for which the term of highest degree has a positive coefficient. Show that axiom N_5 is satisfied. Determine whether N_6 is satisfied.

7. Let S be the set of all formal expressions in x of type

$$r(x) = \frac{a_0 + a_1 x + a_2 x^2 + \cdots + a_n x^n}{b_0 + b_1 x + b_2 x^2 + \cdots + b_m x^m},$$

where the coefficients are real numbers and not all the coefficients in the denominator are zero. Let equality, addition, and multiplication be defined in the obvious ways. Then it can be shown that axioms N_1 through N_4 are satisfied. (a) Let the set P of positive members of S be those members of S for which the ratio of the coefficients of the highest degree terms in numerator and denominator is positive. For example, $(3-5x)/(-2-7x)$ is positive. Show that axiom N_5 is satisfied. Determine whether N_6 is satisfied. (b) Show that if ω is a positive member of S and the numerator of ω is of higher degree than the denominator, then there is no integer n such that $n > \omega$.

8. The ordered field S of problem 7 contains all ordinary real numbers since we can let $a_k = b_k = 0$ if $k > 0$ and $b_0 = 1$. Show that (a) $1/x$ is positive and less than all positive real numbers; (b) x is greater than all real numbers.

1-7. COMPLEX NUMBERS

The point in the (x, y)-plane with coordinates x and y can be designated by the symbol (x, y). An ordered pair of numbers determines a point. An ordered pair of numbers also determines a *complex number*. If the ordered pair is (x, y), then the complex number usually is denoted by $x + yi$. Complex numbers differ from points in that operations of addition and multiplication will be defined for complex numbers. A symbol of type $a + 0i$ is called a *real number* and is identified with the number a. Therefore, when the operations of addition and multiplication are defined for complex numbers, one should check to see that the definitions of addition and multiplication for complex numbers do not conflict with the usual addition and multiplication of numbers when the complex numbers are real numbers. We shall follow the usual convention and say that the symbol $0 + bi$ is a *pure imaginary number* when $b \neq 0$ and write it as bi. The use of the word "imaginary" is a firmly established convention in mathematics. However, it is an unfortunate convention, for bi is no more imaginary than the point $(0, b)$.

A complex number $x + yi$ will be represented in a plane by the point whose rectangular coordinates are x and y. When the plane is used in this way, we refer to it as the *complex plane*. The real numbers are then represented by points on the x-axis and pure imaginary numbers by points on the y-axis.

Two complex numbers are said to be *equal* if and only if as ordered pairs they have the same first members and the same second members. That is,

$$x_1 + y_1 i = x_2 + y_2 i \text{ if and only if } x_1 = x_2 \text{ and } y_1 = y_2. \qquad (1\text{-}6)$$

DEFINITION 1-7.1. The *sum of two complex numbers* is given by the formula

$$(x_1 + y_1 i) + (x_2 + y_2 i) = (x_1 + x_2) + (y_1 + y_2)i.$$

DEFINITION 1-7.2. The *absolute value* of the complex number $x + yi$ is the number $(x^2 + y^2)^{1/2}$ and is denoted by the symbol $|x + yi|$.

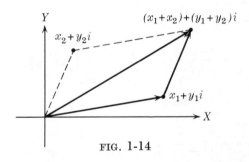

FIG. 1-14

The absolute value of $x + yi$ is equal to the distance between the origin and the point (x, y). Also, if we represent complex numbers by arrows, then we can add $x_1 + y_1 i$ and $x_2 + y_2 i$ geometrically, as indicated in Fig. 1-14. The arrow from the origin to $x_2 + y_2 i$ is moved parallel to itself so that its initial point is at the terminal point of the arrow from the origin to $x_1 + y_1 i$. Then these two arrows and the arrow from the origin to the sum of $x_1 + y_1 i$ and $x_2 + y_2 i$ form a triangle. Since the length of a side of a triangle is not larger than the sum of the lengths of the other two sides, we have the *triangle inequality for complex numbers*:

$$|z_1 + z_2| \leq |z_1| + |z_2|. \qquad (1\text{-}7)$$

DEFINITION 1-7.3. The *product of two complex numbers* is given by the formula

$$(x_1 + y_1 i)(x_2 + y_2 i) = (x_1 x_2 - y_1 y_2) + (x_1 y_2 + x_2 y_1)i. \qquad (1\text{-}8)$$

We have defined addition of complex numbers so that the numbers are added as if they were polynomials in i. It is also useful to note that the definition of multiplication is equivalent to stating that $x_1 + y_1 i$ and $x_2 + y_2 i$ are multiplied as if they were polynomials in i, except that i^2 is to be replaced by -1. It follows from these observations that addition and multiplication of complex numbers are *commutative* and *associative* and that the *distributive law* is satisfied. Let us check some of the other properties of the real numbers that were listed as axioms N_1 through N_6 in Section 1-4. Clearly, N_2 is satisfied, since

$$(x + yi) + 0 = x + yi \quad \text{and} \quad (x + yi) \cdot 1 = x + yi$$

for any complex number $x + yi$. Also, $(x + yi) + [-x + (-y)i] = 0$. The only property among N_1 through N_4 about which there remains any question is the existence for any nonzero complex number z of a complex number z^{-1} such that $zz^{-1} = 1$. Although $(x + yi)^{-1}$ is not known to have meaning, we might attempt to discover its value by formal manipulation:

$$\frac{1}{x + yi} = \frac{x - yi}{(x + yi)(x - yi)} = \frac{x - yi}{x^2 + y^2} = \left(\frac{x}{x^2 + y^2}\right) - \left(\frac{y}{x^2 + y^2}\right)i.$$

The last expression is a complex number and

$$(x + yi)\left[\left(\frac{x}{x^2 + y^2}\right) - \left(\frac{y}{x^2 + y^2}\right)i\right] = \frac{x^2 + y^2}{x^2 + y^2} = 1.$$

Therefore, axiom N_4 is satisfied if we let

$$(x + yi)^{-1} = \left(\frac{x}{x^2 + y^2}\right) - \left(\frac{y}{x^2 + y^2}\right)i.$$

Now we can define division by

$$\frac{x_1 + y_1 i}{x_2 + y_2 i} = (x_1 + y_1 i)(x_2 + y_2 i)^{-1}, \quad \text{if} \quad x_2 + y_2 i \neq 0.$$

For any field, we have

$$\frac{xs}{ys} = (xs)(ys)^{-1} = (xs)s^{-1}y^{-1} = x(ss^{-1})y^{-1} = xy^{-1} = \frac{x}{y},$$

if neither y nor s is zero. This provides a method for reducing the quotient of two complex numbers to the standard form, $x + yi$. For example,

$$\frac{2+3i}{4-5i} = \frac{(2+3i)(4+5i)}{(4-5i)(4+5i)} = \frac{-7+22i}{16+25} = -\frac{7}{41} + \frac{22}{41}i.$$

Now trouble develops. We can show that there does not exist a set P of "positive" complex numbers which satisfies the requirements of axiom N_5. Then the concept of "inequality" cannot be defined in terms of a set of "positive" numbers, and axiom N_6 has no meaning. We shall use an indirect proof, assuming that the set P exists. Since either $1 \in P$ or $-1 \in P$ and the product of two members of P belongs to P, it follows that $1 \in P$. Also, either $i \in P$ or $-i \in P$, and therefore either $i^2 \in P$ or $(-i)^2 \in P$. Since $i^2 = (-i)^2 = -1$, it follows that $-1 \in P$. This is impossible, since axiom (N_5') requires that $1 \in P$ if and only if -1 does not belong to P.

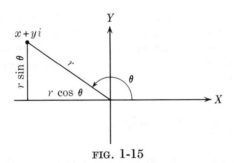

FIG. 1-15

The polar coordinates of a point with rectangular coordinates x and y are any two numbers r and θ for which

$$x = r \cos \theta \quad \text{and} \quad y = r \sin \theta. \tag{1-9}$$

If r and θ satisfy (1-9) and r is positive, then the *polar form* of the complex number $x + yi$ is $r(\cos \theta + i \sin \theta)$, where θ is an angle with initial side on the positive x-axis and terminal side on the ray from the origin through the point (x, y) [see Fig. 1-15]. Such an angle θ is said to be an *argument*† of the complex number $z = x + yi$ and is denoted by arg (z). Of course, a complex number has many arguments. When

---

† The use of "argument" in this sense is firmly established, though it is not particularly desirable since "argument" is also used as a synonym for "independent variable" and might as reasonably refer to r as to θ.

it is immaterial which argument is used, there is no harm in using the ambiguous notation arg (z). Otherwise, a definite choice must be made for the argument. For example, one might agree that arg (z) is to be chosen so that $-\pi < \arg(z) \leqq \pi$. The polar form is very useful for studying multiplication and division of complex numbers. If

$$z_1 = r_1(\cos\theta_1 + i\sin\theta_1) \quad \text{and} \quad z_2 = r_2(\cos\theta_2 + i\sin\theta_2),$$

then

$$z_1 z_2 = r_1 r_2 [(\cos\theta_1\cos\theta_2 - \sin\theta_1\sin\theta_2)$$
$$+ i(\sin\theta_1\cos\theta_2 + \cos\theta_1\sin\theta_2)].$$

It follows from this and the addition formulas for $\cos(\theta_1 + \theta_2)$ and $\sin(\theta_1 + \theta_2)$ that

$$z_1 z_2 = r_1 r_2 [\cos(\theta_1 + \theta_2) + i\sin(\theta_1 + \theta_2)]. \tag{1-10}$$

This is the polar form of the complex number with absolute value $r_1 r_2$ and argument $\theta_1 + \theta_2$. In other words, *the product of two complex numbers is the number whose absolute value and argument are obtained by multiplying the absolute values and adding the arguments of the given numbers.* If z_2 is nonzero, then

$$\frac{z_1}{z_2} = w \text{ if and only if } z_1 = z_2 w.$$

Therefore, *the quotient of two complex numbers is the number whose absolute value and argument are obtained by dividing the absolute values and subtracting the arguments of the given numbers.*

ILLUSTRATION 1. Suppose $z_1 = 1 + i$ and $z_2 = -1 + \sqrt{3}\,i$. These complex numbers are plotted in Fig. 1-16. In polar form, they are

$$z_1 = \sqrt{2}\,(\cos\tfrac{1}{4}\pi + i\sin\tfrac{1}{4}\pi), \qquad z_2 = 2\,(\cos\tfrac{2}{3}\pi + i\sin\tfrac{2}{3}\pi).$$

Then direct multiplication of $1 + i$ and $-1 + \sqrt{3}\,i$ gives

$$z_1 z_2 = -(\sqrt{3} + 1) + (\sqrt{3} - 1)i,$$

and multiplying absolute values and adding arguments gives

$$z_1 z_2 = 2\sqrt{2}\,(\cos\tfrac{11}{12}\pi + i\sin\tfrac{11}{12}\pi).$$

This means that

$$2\sqrt{2} \cos \tfrac{11}{12}\pi = -(\sqrt{3}+1) \quad \text{and} \quad 2\sqrt{2} \sin \tfrac{11}{12}\pi = \sqrt{3}-1.$$

Also,

$$\frac{z_1}{z_2} = \frac{1+i}{-1+\sqrt{3}\,i} = \frac{(1+i)(-1-\sqrt{3}\,i)}{(-1+\sqrt{3}\,i)(-1-\sqrt{3}\,i)} = \frac{(\sqrt{3}-1)-(\sqrt{3}+1)i}{4},$$

or

$$\frac{z_1}{z_2} = \frac{\sqrt{2}}{2}\left[\cos\left(-\tfrac{5}{12}\pi\right)+i\sin\left(-\tfrac{5}{12}\pi\right)\right].$$

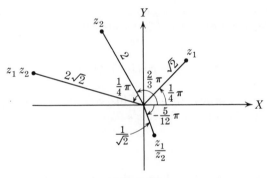

FIG. 1-16

Let us now define $e^{i\theta}$ as $\cos\theta + i\sin\theta$, when θ is a real number. Since $e^{i\theta}$ has had no meaning before now except when $\theta = 0$, we are free to define its value in any way we wish, as long as $e^{i\theta} = 1$ when $\theta = 0$. However, this definition is motivated by a number of facts, some of which we shall now discuss.

If we put $r_1 = r_2 = 1$ in Eq. (1-10), we have $z_1 = e^{i\theta_1}$, $z_2 = e^{i\theta_2}$, and

$$e^{i\theta_1}e^{i\theta_2} = e^{i(\theta_1+\theta_2)}. \tag{1-11}$$

This gives us an extension of one of the familiar laws of exponents. We can also show that, for n an integer,

$$(e^{i\theta})^n = e^{in\theta}. \tag{1-12}$$

Let us first use mathematical induction to prove Eq. (1-12) for n a positive integer. If $n = 1$, then (1-12) becomes $e^{i\theta} = e^{i\theta}$. If (1-12) is not true for all positive integers, we can let n be the first positive integer for which it is false. Then $n-1 \geq 1$ and

$$(e^{i\theta})^{n-1} = e^{i(n-1)\theta}.$$

After multiplying both members of this equation by $e^{i\theta}$, we can use Eq. (1-11) to obtain

$$(e^{i\theta})^n = e^{i(n-1)\theta}e^{i\theta} = e^{in\theta}.$$

This proves Eq. (1-12) for all positive integers. Now we can extend the usual definition for zero exponent, so that $z^0 = 1$ for any nonzero complex number z. Then (1-12) is valid when $n = 0$. It is also valid when n is a negative integer, if we understand that $z^{-n} = 1/z^n$ when $z \neq 0$. To complete the argument, it is necessary to note that this meaning of negative exponents is consistent with the definition of $e^{i\theta}$, or that

$$e^{i\theta} \cdot e^{-i\theta} = \cos 0 + i \sin 0 = 1,$$

and $e^{-i\theta}$ is the reciprocal of $e^{i\theta}$. This completes the proof of (1-12). Equation (1-12) is called *de Moivre's Theorem* when it is written as

$$(\cos \theta + i \sin \theta)^n = \cos n\theta + i \sin n\theta. \tag{1-13}$$

ILLUSTRATION 2. To find the cube roots of the complex number $8i$, we first write $8i$ in polar form as

$$8(\cos \tfrac{1}{2}\pi + i \sin \tfrac{1}{2}\pi) \quad \text{or} \quad 8e^{i(\frac{1}{2}\pi)}.$$

The problem is to find all complex numbers $z = r(\cos \theta + i \sin \theta) = re^{i\theta}$ such that $z^3 = 8i$. This means that

$$r^3(\cos 3\theta + i \sin 3\theta) = 8(\cos \tfrac{1}{2}\pi + i \sin \tfrac{1}{2}\pi)$$

or

$$r^3 e^{i(3\theta)} = 8e^{i(\frac{1}{2}\pi)}.$$

Therefore, r must be 2, and 3θ must be $\tfrac{1}{2}\pi$ or differ from $\tfrac{1}{2}\pi$ by an integral multiple of 2π. There is then an integer k for which

$$3\theta = \tfrac{1}{2}\pi + 2k\pi \quad \text{or} \quad \theta = \tfrac{1}{6}\pi + \frac{2k\pi}{3}. \tag{1-14}$$

Possible values for θ are $\tfrac{1}{6}\pi$, $\tfrac{5}{6}\pi$, and $\tfrac{3}{2}\pi$. All other values given by

(1-14) differ from one of these by an integral multiple of 2π. There are then three cube roots of $8i$:

$$2e^{i(\pi/6)} = \sqrt{3}+i, \quad 2e^{i(5\pi/6)} = -\sqrt{3}+i, \quad 2e^{i(3\pi/2)} = -2i.$$

These are plotted in Fig. 1-17. The smallest positive argument of $\sqrt{3}+i$ is one-third the smallest positive argument of $8i$, while this and the other cube roots are equally spaced around the circle $|z| = 2$.

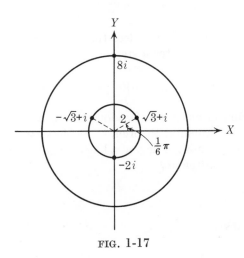

FIG. 1-17

The set of complex numbers behaves beautifully with respect to the existence of roots, since any nonzero complex number has exactly n different nth roots. There is another remarkable property of complex numbers, the *fundamental theorem of algebra*.

THEOREM 1-7.1 (FUNDAMENTAL THEOREM OF ALGEBRA).[†]
Suppose

$$p(z) = a_n z^n + a_{n-1} z^{n-1} + \cdots + a_1 z + a_0$$

is a polynomial whose coefficients are complex numbers, with $a_n \neq 0$ and $n \geq 1$. Then there is at least one complex number that is a zero of this polynomial.

This theorem and the factor theorem can be used to show that *any polynomial whose coefficients are complex numbers can be factored into*

[†] For an elementary proof of this theorem, see James, *op. cit.*, pp. 359–360.

n *first-degree factors.* For, if z_1 is a zero of a polynomial $p(z)$, then $z - z_1$ is a factor and

$$p(z) = (z - z_1)p_1(z),$$

where $p_1(z)$ is of one degree less than $p(z)$. If $p_1(z)$ is not a constant, then $p_1(z)$ has a zero z_2 and

$$p(z) = (z - z_1)(z - z_2)p_2(z),$$

where the degree of $p_2(z)$ is two less than the degree of $p(z)$. If $p(z)$ is of degree n, we obtain after n steps

$$p(z) = a_n(z - z_1)(z - z_2) \cdots (z - z_n).$$

If a zero z_i occurs in exactly k factors, then z_i is said to be of *multiplicity* k. The fundamental theorem of algebra can then be extended to state that a polynomial of degree n has n zeros, *if each zero is counted to the degree of its multiplicity.*

PROBLEMS

1. Find all real-number values of x and y for which
   (a) $x + 4i = (1 + yi)^2$; (c) $(x + yi)^2 = 5 + 12i$.
   (b) $(x + yi)^2 = i$;

2. Show that $|z_2 - z_1|$ is the distance between points representing complex numbers z_1 and z_2.

3. Sketch and describe the following sets of complex numbers.
   (a) $\{z: |z| = 3\}$. (c) $\{z: |z - 1| = |z + i|\}$.
   (b) $\{z: |z - 2| = 5\}$.

4. Let $z = x + iy$. Write the relation $|(z - i)/(z + i)| = 3$ in terms of x and y and describe its graph.

5. Let $P = \{(x + yi): (x > 0) \text{ or } (x = 0 \text{ and } y > 0)\}$. Show that P has the following properties.
   (a) If $z \neq 0$, then $z \in P$ if and only if $-z \notin P$.
   (b) If $z_1 \in P$ and $z_2 \in P$, then $(z_1 + z_2) \in P$.

6. Let $z_1 < z_2$ mean $z_2 - z_1 \in P$, where P is the set of problem 5. Show that, for all complex numbers z_1, z_2, and z_3,

(a) $z_1 + z_3 < z_2 + z_3$ if $z_1 < z_2$,

(b) $z_1 < z_3$ if $z_1 < z_2$ and $z_2 < z_3$;

but that

(c) there are numbers z_1, z_2, and z_3 such that $z_3 \in P$, $z_1 < z_2$, and $z_2 z_3 < z_1 z_3$,

(d) there are numbers z_1 and z_2 such that $0 < z_1 < z_2$ and $z_2^2 < z_1^2$.

7. Explain the fallacy in the following argument:

$$\text{``}1 = \sqrt{1} = \sqrt{(-1)(-1)} = \sqrt{-1}\,\sqrt{-1} = i \cdot i = -1.\text{''}$$

8. Write each of the following complex numbers in the form $x + yi$.

(**a**) $e^{\pi i}$.

(**c**) $(\cos \tfrac{1}{3}\pi + i \sin \tfrac{1}{3}\pi)^{15}$.

(**b**) $\sqrt{2}\, e^{-\frac{1}{4}\pi i}$.

(**d**) $(\cos \tfrac{1}{6}\pi - i \sin \tfrac{1}{6}\pi)^{26}$.

9. Express the following complex numbers in the form $re^{i\theta}$.

(a) $4 - 4i$.

(**d**) $(2 - 2i)(3 - \sqrt{3}\, i)$.

(**b**) $7i$.

(e) $3 + 4i$.

(c) $\dfrac{1+i}{-1+i}$.

(**f**) $\dfrac{(\sqrt{3}+i)^2}{1-i}$.

10. Find the three cube roots of

(**a**) $+1$;

(b) $-27i$.

11. Find the four fourth roots of

(**a**) $-i$;   (b) $+1$;   (c) -1.

12. Find the six solutions of the equation $z^6 + 2z^3 + 2 = 0$.

13. Since

$$(\cos \theta + i \sin \theta)^2 = (\cos^2 \theta - \sin^2 \theta) + 2i \sin \theta \cos \theta$$

and

$$(\cos \theta + i \sin \theta)^2 = \cos 2\theta + i \sin 2\theta,$$

we have

$$(\cos^2 \theta - \sin^2 \theta) + 2i \sin \theta \cos \theta = \cos 2\theta + i \sin 2\theta,$$

or

$$\cos 2\theta = \cos^2 \theta - \sin^2 \theta \quad \text{and} \quad \sin 2\theta = 2 \sin \theta \cos \theta.$$

(a) Use this method to show that

$$\cos 3\theta = \cos^3 \theta - 3 \cos \theta \sin^2 \theta$$

and

$$\sin 3\theta = 3 \cos^2 \theta \sin \theta - \sin^3 \theta.$$

(b) Express $\cos 4\theta$ and $\sin 4\theta$ in terms of $\sin \theta$ and $\cos \theta$.

14. Show that if $p(z)$ is a polynomial whose coefficients are real numbers, then $p(z)$ can be written as the product of factors that are of the first or second degree and have real coefficients.

15. Let z_1, z_2, and z_3 be three complex numbers for which

$$|z_1| = |z_2| = |z_3| = 1 \quad \text{and} \quad z_1 + z_2 + z_3 = 0.$$

Show that z_1, z_2, and z_3 are vertices of an equilateral triangle. [*Hint:* Choose a suitable angle θ and rotate by multiplying by $e^{j\theta}$.]

16. Let z_1, z_2, and z_3 be three complex numbers for which

$$\frac{z_1 - z_3}{z_2 - z_3}$$

is a real number. Show that z_1, z_2, and z_3 are collinear—i.e., they all lie on a single line in the complex plane.

17. Let z_1, z_2, and z_3 be three different complex numbers for which $(z_1 - z_3)/(z_2 - z_3)$ is a pure imaginary number. Show that z_1, z_2, and z_3 are vertices of a right triangle.

2

TOPOLOGY AND
FUNCTIONS

The development of mathematics frequently has been hindered because new ideas were excluded that at the time of their appearance could not be given strict logical interpretations. For example, the Greeks excluded the very concepts that led to calculus—continuity, the infinite, and the infinitesimal.† During the seventeenth century, many mathematicians avoided the use of analytic geometry because it did not meet their demands for rigor, which they had inherited from the Greeks. When calculus first appeared, many mathematicians shunned the new subject because its logical basis at that time was very weak.

On the other hand, even when an adequate logical basis has existed, mathematics has been hampered because mathematicians have failed to give concepts the precision and formality available to them. For example, Zeno's paradoxes, because of their lack of precision, caused great confusion in Greek mathematics. Similarly, vagueness in defining basic concepts used in calculus caused havoc long after the time of Leibniz and Newton. This might have been avoided if the two had been more precise in stating their limit methods and had developed more understanding of continuity and motion.

Certainly, suggestive ideas should not be barred simply because they lack rigor; nevertheless, it is clear that there should not be indiscriminate use of methods and concepts that seemingly have no logical foundation. A logical basis ultimately must be found if hopeless confusion is to be avoided. In the beginning of calculus, infinity,

---

† An *infinitesimal relative to a point* p is a function such that $\lim_{x \to p} f(x) = 0$. However, until recently, many mathematicians talked of "infinitely small quantities." Even Leibniz admitted once that one could not prove or disprove the existence of infinitely small quantities. Unfortunately, students sometimes develop such misconceptions and their progress is slowed as a result.

motion, limit, continuity, derivative, and definite integral were used without being adequately defined or understood. As a result there was a great deal of confusion of thought and casting about for alternative methods. It required the work of Cauchy, Weierstrass, and others to define these ideas precisely enough so that they became generally acceptable.

There is no need for students today to fall prey to the confusion that once plagued mathematicians, since the basic concepts of calculus are now thoroughly understood and can be presented in logical form. The chief purpose of this chapter is to formulate some of these concepts, particularly some of the basic and most useful topological concepts such as those of continuity and limit.

2-1. MORE ABOUT SETS

For most of the discussion of this chapter, we shall make frequent use of the distance between points. Let us denote the distance between points p and q by $d(p, q)$. The most basic properties of distance that we shall need are included in the following definition.

> **DEFINITION 2-1.1.** A *metric space* is a set X and a function d whose domain is the set of all ordered pairs (p, q) of members of X, whose range is a set of nonnegative real numbers, and for which
>
> (i) $d(p, q) = 0$ if and only if $p = q$;
>
> (ii) $d(p, q) = d(q, p)$ for all p and q;
>
> (iii) $d(p, r) \leqq d(p, q) + d(q, r)$ for all p, q, and r.

Although there are many metric spaces that are not subsets of Euclidean spaces [see problem 16], most examples used in this text are subsets of Euclidean spaces, e.g., lines, planes, and curves. Hereafter, we shall use the symbol R^3 for three-dimensional Euclidean space. Until Chapter 8, whenever we use the concept "metric space," the student may substitute "subset of R^3" if he wishes, although it would be instructive to check that only properties of metric spaces are used.

Two points might be said to be close together when the distance between them is less than .01 ft; but, for some purposes, such points might not be regarded as close enough, and a closeness of less than .0001 ft might be demanded. Two towns might be said to be close in the sense that the distance between them is less than 50 miles, or in the sense that they are in the same county, or in the sense that they are in the same state. Thus, "closeness" is not meaningful until a particular criterion is stated. For any set, we can designate certain subsets as being *neighborhoods* and use neighborhoods to express precisely ideas involving closeness. Then we can speak of objects as being in the same neighborhood and avoid the ambiguity of statements that objects are merely "close together."

> **DEFINITION 2-1.2.** Let p be a point in a metric space T. If $\varepsilon > 0$, then the *ε-neighborhood of p in T* is the set of all points x in T for which $d(x, p) < \varepsilon$. A *neighborhood of p in T* is a subset of T that, for some $\varepsilon > 0$, contains the ε-neighborhood of p.

The reason T was assumed to be a metric space is that distance is a convenient concept to use when defining neighborhoods. If T is a more general set, then certain subsets of T can arbitrarily be designated neighborhoods. For some purposes, one need know little more than this about neighborhoods. Since it is beyond the scope of this text to discuss the concept of neighborhood in full generality, we shall for the most part use only metric spaces. In this chapter, all sets are understood to be metric spaces unless they are described otherwise.

Often metric spaces used will be subsets of a line, a curve, or a plane. A neighborhood of a point p in T is a subset of T which, for some positive ε, includes all points whose distance from p is less than ε but may include other points of T. If T is a line, then an ε-neighborhood of a point p in T is a line segment without end points and of length 2ε with center at p. Any such segment is a neighborhood of p, and, more generally, any set that contains such a line segment is a neighborhood of p. Thus, if I_ε is an ε-neighborhood of a point p in a line T and A is any subset of T, then $I_\varepsilon \cup A$ is a neighborhood of p in T. If T is a plane, then the ε-neighborhood of p in T is the interior of the disk with radius ε and center at p; if U_ε is such a disk and A is any subset of T, then $U_\varepsilon \cup A$ is a neighborhood of p in T.

The concept of open set as given by the following definition is closely related to the concept of neighborhood. In fact, if a set S is open in T, then S is a neighborhood in T of each of its points [see problem 1].

> **DEFINITION 2-1.3.** A set *open in a set T* is a subset S of T such that each point of S has a neighborhood in T that is contained in S.

> **DEFINITION 2-1.4.** A set *closed in a set T* is a subset S of T such that each point of $T - S$ has a neighborhood in T that contains no points of S.

The student is familiar with the concepts of closed and open intervals. Partly for review and partly to establish conventions, we give the following definition. In this definition, we understand that we are considering intervals as subsets of the set of real numbers. With R the set of real numbers, the student should check that an open interval is open in R and a closed interval is closed in R.

DEFINITION 2-1.5. An *interval* is a set S of numbers having the property that, if x_1 and x_2 are two numbers that belong to S, then all numbers between x_1 and x_2 belong to S. This means that an interval is of one of the following types:

I. A *closed* interval, which is an interval that contains all of its end points. It may have two end points, a and b, and contain all numbers x for which $a \leq x \leq b$, in which case we denote the interval by the symbol $[a, b]$. It may have only one end point a and contain all numbers x for which $x \leq a$, or all numbers x for which $x \geq a$. Finally, it may have no end points and either contain all numbers or contain no numbers.

II. An *open* interval, which is an interval that does not contain any of its end points. It may have two end points, a and b, and contain all numbers x for which $a < x < b$, in which case we denote the interval by the symbol (a, b). It may have only one end point a and contain all numbers x for which $x < a$, or all numbers x for which $x > a$. Finally, it may have no end points and either contain all numbers or contain no numbers.

III. An interval that is *neither open nor closed*, which is an interval that has two end points, a and b, and consists either of all numbers x for which $a \leq x < b$, or of all numbers x for which $a < x \leq b$. We denote such intervals by the symbols $[a, b)$ and $(a, b]$, respectively, using the parenthesis to indicate the missing end point.

As in the preceding definition, it is customary to speak of sets as being "open" or "closed" rather than "open in T" or "closed in T," when it is clear from the context which set is intended to be used for T. For example, if we are studying a particular curve C, we might speak of an "open subset" of the curve rather than a "subset open in C."

In everyday usage, the words "open" and "closed" are antonyms. This is not true when they are applied to intervals or to sets in general. A set may be neither open nor closed, or it may be both open and closed. However, the following theorem gives a close relation between open and closed sets. We shall not give a formal proof, since Definitions 2-1.3 and 2-1.4 have been phrased so as to make this theorem a direct consequence of these definitions.

THEOREM 2-1.1. If S is a subset of a set T, then S is open in T if and only if $T - S$ is closed in T.

We shall now introduce some more concepts that will be useful in the future and that may help now in understanding the preceding definitions and theorem. If S is a subset of a set T, then an *interior point* of S with respect to T is a point p that has a neighborhood in T that is contained in S; an *exterior point* of S with respect to T is a point p that has a neighborhood in T that contains no points of S; and a *boundary point* of S with respect to T is a point p such that each neighborhood of p in T contains points of S and points of $T - S$. The *boundary* of S with respect to T is the set of all boundary points of S with respect to T. In simple cases, this concept of boundary is the same as the intuitive concept of edge or circumference. It should be clear that a boundary point of S is a point that is neither an interior point nor an exterior point. Also, an open set is a set that contains none of its boundary points and a closed set is a set that contains all its boundary points. A set that contains some but not all of its boundary points is neither open nor closed.

DEFINITION 2-1.6. A *cluster point*† of a set S is a point p such that each neighborhood of p contains points of S other than p. For a subset S of a set T, the *closure* of S in T is the union of S and the set of its cluster points in T.

As for boundary points, a cluster point of a set may or may not belong to the set itself. If a cluster point of S is in T and does not belong to the subset S, then it is a boundary point of S with respect to T and the set S is not closed in T. Thus, if a set is closed, it contains all its cluster points. However, any boundary point that does not belong to S is a cluster point of S, so it also is true that a set S is closed in T if it contains all its cluster points in T. This gives us the first of the following theorems.

THEOREM 2-1.2. A subset of a set T is closed in T if and only if it contains all its cluster points in T.

THEOREM 2-1.3. The closure of a set is closed.

PROOF. We must show that if S is a subset of a set T and $\bar{S}$ is the closure of S in T, then $\bar{S}$ contains all of its cluster points in T. Let p be such a cluster point and U be a neighborhood of p in T. Then there is an ε for which the ε-neighborhood of p in T is contained in U. To show that $p \in \bar{S}$, we shall show that if $p \notin S$ then p is a cluster point of S and

---

† Other terms used are *limit point* and *accumulation point*.

therefore belongs to $\bar{S}$. For this, we need only show that U contains a point of S. Since p is a cluster point of $\bar{S}$, there is a point q of $\bar{S}$ in the ε-neighborhood of p. Then $q \in U$. If $q \notin S$, then q is a cluster point of S and the ε-neighborhood of p is a neighborhood of q and therefore contains points of S [see problem 3].

The concept of connected set is of great use in mathematics. Intuitively, a connected set is a set without "breaks" or "gaps"— that is, a set that cannot be split into two pieces that are in some sense "separated." It will be very important for us to have a precise definition.

DEFINITION 2-1.7. A *disconnected set* is a set S that can be represented as the union of two nonempty sets, each of which is open in S. A *connected set* is a set that is not disconnected.

THEOREM 2-1.4. A set S of real numbers is disconnected if and only if there is a number θ not in S that is between members of S.

PROOF. Let us suppose first that S is a set of real numbers and that there is a number θ that does not belong to S but has members of S on both sides. Let A be the set of all members of S that are less than θ and let B be the set of all members of S that are greater than θ. Then neither A nor B is empty. If $x < \theta$, then the set $S \cap (x-1, \theta)$ is a neighborhood of x in S that contains no members of B; whereas, if $x > \theta$, the set $S \cap (\theta, x+1)$ is a neighborhood of x in S that contains no members of A. Therefore, A and B are open in S. This completes the proof that S is disconnected if there is a number θ that does not belong to S but is between members of S. Now we must show that, if a set S of real numbers is disconnected, then there is a number θ not in S that is between members of S. Suppose S is a disconnected set of real numbers. Then there are nonempty sets A and B such that $S = A \cup B$ and each of A and B is open in S. Since A and B are nonempty, there are numbers a and b such that $a \in A$ and $b \in B$. Clearly, there is no loss of generality in assuming that $a < b$. Let

$$A_b = \{x: x \in A \text{ and } x < b\},$$

and let θ be the least upper bound of A_b. Then $a \leq \theta \leq b$. Since A_b has no smaller upper bound than θ, we know that for each positive number ε the ε-neighborhood of θ contains members of A_b. Since the set B is open in S, this implies that $\theta \in A$ if $\theta \in S$. Thus, if $\theta \notin A$, then θ is a number not in S that is between members a and b of S. But if $\theta \in A$, then since A is open in S there is a positive number ε for which the ε-neighborhood of θ contains no points of B. Also, no points of A_b

are larger than θ. Therefore, all numbers in the interval $(\theta, \theta + \varepsilon)$ are between the members a and b of S but are not in S.

THEOREM 2-1.5. A set of real numbers is connected if and only if it is an interval.

This theorem follows directly from Definition 2-1.5 and Theorem 2-1.4. It gives a very simple description of all disconnected sets on a line—namely, those sets that have two "pieces" that are separated by a point not in the set. No similar criterion can be given for sets of two or three dimensions. However, we can give some simple, sufficient conditions for sets of two or three dimensions to be disconnected and

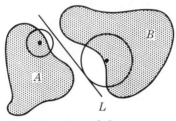

FIG. 2-1

some simple, sufficient conditions for such sets to be connected. A plane set is disconnected if it is divided into two pieces by a line that contains no points of the set. To show that, let us suppose that a plane set S contains no points of a line L. We choose a particular side of L and let A be the subset of S whose members are on this side of L. Then we let B be the subset of S whose members are on the other side of L. Any point of A (or B) has a circular neighborhood containing no points on the other side of L, and therefore A and B are open in S [see Fig. 2-1]. Similarly, a three-dimensional set is disconnected if it is divided into two pieces by a plane. There are some obvious generalizations of these facts. For example, any plane set divided into two pieces by a circle or a polygon is disconnected. In particular, the union of the interior and exterior of a circle is disconnected.

A *convex set* is a set S such that any two points of S can be joined by a line segment all of whose points are in S. Examples of convex sets are the interior of a rectangle and the interior of a sphere. All convex sets are connected. To illustrate this, let us suppose that S is convex and disconnected. Then $S = A \cup B$, where A and B are nonempty and each point of A or B has a neighborhood that contains no points of the other set. We then choose a point a in A and a point b in B and connect a to b by a line segment L. Then L is contained in $S = A \cup B$. We let $A_L = A \cap L$ and $B_L = B \cap L$. The sets A_L and B_L are nonempty, since $a \in A_L$ and $b \in B_L$. Any point of A_L has a neighborhood that contains no points of B, and therefore contains no points of B_L. Similarly, any point of B_L has a neighborhood that contains no points of A_L. Thus, L is disconnected. This contradicts the fact that any interval on a line is connected [Theorem 2-1.5] and completes the proof that all convex sets are connected.

PROBLEMS

1.* Show that a subset S of a set T is open in T if and only if S is a neighborhood of each of its points.

2. Show that for some sets T there are neighborhoods of points in T that are not open in T.

3.* Explain why an ε-neighborhood of a point is an open set and also is a neighborhood of each of its members.

4. Let T be the set $[0, 1] \cup (2, 3)$. List the subsets of T that have the property of being both open and closed in T.

5. Prove that S' is closed if S' is the set of cluster points of a set S.

6.* Prove that $A \cup B$ and $A \cap B$ are closed in T if A and B are closed in T.

7.* Prove that $A \cup B$ and $A \cap B$ are open in T if A and B are open in T.

8. (a) Give an example for which the union of an infinite number of closed sets is not closed. (b) Give an example for which the intersection of an infinite number of open sets is not open.

9.* Prove that the union of any number of open sets is open and the intersection of any number of closed sets is closed.

10. Describe the boundaries of the following sets with respect to the set of real numbers.

    (*a*) The interval $[2, 7)$.

    (b) The set of rational numbers.

    (c) The set $(1, 3) \cup (3, 5)$.

11. Describe the boundaries of the following sets with respect to the (x, y)-plane.

(*a*) The x-axis.

(b) $\{(x, y): x^2 + y^2 < 1\}$.

(c) $\{(x, y): x^2 + y^2 < 1\} \cup \{(x, y): (x-2)^2 + y^2 < 1\}$.

(d) $\{(x, y): x^2 + y^2 < 1 \text{ and } x \text{ and } y \text{ are rational}\}$.

12. Suppose $S \subset T$. Explain why a point p of T has exactly one of the properties: "p is an interior point of T," "p is an exterior point of T," and "p is a boundary point of T."

13. For each of the following, explain why S is connected or disconnected. (a) S contains 10 distinct points. (b) S is the graph of $x^2 + y^2 = 1$. (c) S is a polygonal curve (a succession of line segments, joined end-to-end). (d) S has the property that any two points of S can be connected by a polygonal curve that is entirely in S.

14. For each of the following, determine whether the given set S is connected. (*a*) S is the graph of $x^2 + y^2 = 1$ with the point $(1, 0)$ deleted. (b) S is the union of a square and a diagonal of the square, with the two corners not on this diagonal deleted. (*c*) S is the graph of $y = x(x^2 - 1)^{-1}; x \neq \pm 1$. (d) S is the range of f, where $f(x) = x(x^2 - 1)^{-1}$ for $x \neq \pm 1$. (*e*) S is the union of $\{(0, y): 1 \leq y \leq 2\}$, the graph of $y = 0$, and the graphs of $x = 1/n$ for n a nonzero integer.

15.* Prove that any open connected set S in R^3 has the property that any two of its points can be joined by a polygonal curve (a curve consisting of line segments joined end-to-end) contained in S. [*Hint:* For a point a in S, let A be the set of all points that can be joined to a by a polygonal curve in S and $B = S - A$.]

16. Verify that each of the following is a metric space. (a) An arbitrary set S, with $d(p, p) = 0$ for all p and $d(p, q) = 1$ if $p \neq q$. (b) The set M of all functions whose domains are the set $\{a, b, c, d, e\}$ and whose ranges are subsets of the set of real numbers, with $d(f, g)$ the largest value of $|f(p) - g(p)|$ for p one of the objects a, b, c, d, e.

2-2. CONTINUOUS FUNCTIONS

Many common words are used in mathematics in specialized ways. Often the mathematical meaning is similar to the common meaning; however, mathematical meanings are precise, whereas common meanings seldom are. The word "continuous" is one example of this. Students tend to assume more about what "continuous" means than is implied by the mathematical definition. Generally, the term "continuous function" is associated with a picture of a smooth, unbroken curve or surface. It is true that if a function is continuous at each point of an interval, the graph of the function is an unbroken curve;

but it need not be smooth.   Smoothness is related to differentiability, and a function may be continuous without being differentiable.   A continuous function that is not differentiable may be so "crinkly" as to make correct geometric visualization of it quite impossible.

Continuity is one of the most basic and important concepts of mathematics and science and will be used often in this text.   In order to make effective use of continuity, we shall give a precise definition and describe some of the basic properties of continuous functions.

Roughly speaking, a function f is continuous at a point p in its domain if $f(p)$ can be approximated satisfactorily by computing $f(x)$ for x sufficiently close to p—that is, if $f(x)$ can be made "arbitrarily close" to $f(p)$ by taking x "sufficiently close" to p.   We shall now phrase this precisely, using the convention that for a function f the *inverse image* of a set V is the set $\{x: f(x) \in V\}$.

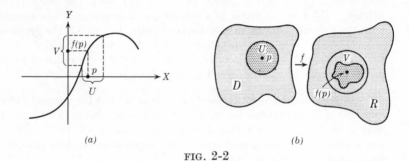

(a)   (b)

FIG. 2-2

DEFINITION 2-2.1.   Suppose f is a function with domain D and range R.   A *point of continuity* of f is a point p in D for which it is true that, whenever V is a neighborhood of $f(p)$ in R, the inverse image of V is a neighborhood of p in D.   A *point of discontinuity* of f is a point of D that is not a point of continuity.   A *continuous function* is a function that is continuous at each point of its domain.   A *discontinuous function* is a function that has at least one point of discontinuity.

It is important to understand that the requirement in this definition that the inverse image of V be a neighborhood of p is equivalent to the requirement that there exist a neighborhood U of p such that $f(x) \in V$ whenever $x \in U$.   In fact, we could require U to be the δ-neighborhood of p for some δ, but sometimes this is inconvenient. The meaning of Definition 2-2.1 is illustrated in Fig. 2-2.   Diagram (a) shows the graph of a function whose domain and range are sets of numbers; (b) is a type of set diagram that can be used to illustrate the meaning of continuity in general.   Given a neighborhood V of $f(p)$, there must exist a neighborhood U of p such that f maps each point of U onto a point of V. That is, $f(x) \in V$ if $x \in U$. The images of points of U are represented by the similarly shaded part of V.

The following theorem relieves us of the burden of dealing with an *arbitrary* neighborhood V of $f(p)$ in R.

THEOREM 2-2.1. Suppose f is a function with domain D and range R. Then f is continuous at a point p of D if and only if, for each $\varepsilon > 0$, the inverse image of the ε-neighborhood of $f(p)$ in R is a neighborhood of p in D.

PROOF. By definition, a function is continuous at a point p of its domain if and only if, for any neighborhood V of $f(p)$ in the range R of f, the inverse image of V is a neighborhood of p in D. Therefore, if f is continuous at p and V_ε is the ε-neighborhood of $f(p)$ in R, then the inverse image of V_ε is a neighborhood of p in D. To complete the proof, we need to show that f is continuous at p if, for each $\varepsilon > 0$, the inverse image of the ε-neighborhood of $f(p)$ in R is a neighborhood of p in D. To do this, we shall let V be an arbitrary neighborhood of $f(p)$ in R. Then it follows from Definition 2-1.1 that there is an $\varepsilon > 0$ such that $V_\varepsilon \subset V$, where V_ε is the ε-neighborhood of $f(p)$ in R. Since the inverse image of V_ε is a neighborhood of p in D, there is a positive number δ such that the δ-neighborhood of p in D is contained in the inverse image of V_ε and therefore also in the inverse image of V. Thus, the inverse image of V is a neighborhood of p in D. Since V was an arbitrary neighborhood of $f(p)$ in R, this proves that f is continuous at p.

ILLUSTRATION 1. If a function f is continuous at p, then $f(p)$ can be approximated by computing the value of f at a point in a suitable neighborhood of p. The size of the neighborhood can be expected to depend on the accuracy one requires of the approximation. For example, suppose the distance in feet an object has fallen in t sec is given by the formula $s = 16t^2$, and that we wish to determine s with an error that is less than $\frac{1}{10}$ ft. Since velocity increases with time, the error in measuring time must be less than the number δ for which the object falls $\frac{1}{10}$ ft between times t and $t + \delta$. That is,

$$[16(t+\delta)^2 - 16t^2] = \tfrac{1}{10} \quad \text{or} \quad 2t\delta + \delta^2 = \tfrac{1}{160}.$$

The distance the object falls in $\frac{1}{10}$ sec increases as the initial time increases. That is, the permissible error in measuring time decreases as time increases. Let us assume that $t \leq 2$. Then $4\delta + \delta^2 = 1/160$ and $\delta = .0016-$. That is, if we measure the time with an error of less than $.0016-$ sec, and if the time is 2 sec or less, then the error in determining distance by use of the formula $s = 16t^2$ is less than $\frac{1}{10}$ ft. If all we know about t is that $t \leqq 10$, then we must require the error in measuring time to be less than .00031+ sec.

One might not be able to determine a physical quantity within a desired accuracy because of the inability to obtain the accuracy needed when measuring the variables. But one may still feel that tolerance limits exist which would assure the desired accuracy. Continuity is the precise formulation of such a feeling.

The postage functions provide familiar examples of functions that are discontinuous at some points of their domains. For parcel post, the domain of the postage function is an interval of type $\{x: 0 < x \leqq M\}$, where M is the number such that the post office is willing to accept only packages that weigh M lb or less. The cost $P(x)$ of mailing a package that weighs x lb to a particular city is discontinuous at many integers. Everyone is familiar with the fact that it is impossible to tell the precise cost of mailing a package that appears to weigh 2 lb. The postage varies considerably according to whether the postal clerk decides the package weighs 2 lb or less, or more than 2 lb.

ILLUSTRATION 2. We shall let f be the function defined by $f(x) = |x|$, where x can be any real number. This function might be said to "bend" the real line at the origin and "fold" the negative part along the positive part. The function f is continuous everywhere. To show this, we shall let p be any real number and ε be a positive number. We can easily see that, if V_ε is the ε-neighborhood of $f(p)$, then $f(x) \in V_\varepsilon$ if $x \in U_\varepsilon$, where U_ε is the ε-neighborhood of p. Therefore, f is continuous at p.

ILLUSTRATION 3. We shall let f be the function whose domain is the (x, y)-plane and which is defined by the equality $f(x, y) = (3x, 3y)$. Then the range of f is also the (x, y)-plane. Geometrically, this function "stretches" the plane. In fact, if p_1 and p_2 are any two points in the plane, then $f(p_1)$ and $f(p_2)$ are on the rays from the origin to p_1 and p_2, and three times as far from the origin as p_1 and p_2, respectively. As follows from the similar triangles of Fig. 2-3, the distance between $f(p_1)$ and $f(p_2)$ is three times the distance between p_1 and p_2. Thus, the function f "stretches" the distance between any two points by a factor of three. If V_ε is the ε-neighborhood of a point $f(p)$, then we can let U be the $\frac{1}{3}\varepsilon$-neighborhood of p and have $f(x)$ in V_ε whenever x is in U.

The following theorem gives a useful criterion for a function to be continuous, i.e., to be continuous at all points of its domain.

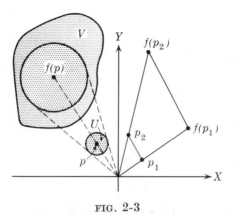

FIG. 2-3

THEOREM 2-2.2. A function f with domain D and range R is continuous if and only if the inverse image of each open set in R is open in D.

PROOF. Let f be a function and D and R the domain and range of f. If f is continuous and V is an open set in R, then V is a neighborhood of each of its points, and it follows from Definition 2-2.1 that the inverse image of V is a neighborhood of each of its points and therefore is open in D [see problem 1 of Section 2-1]. To complete the proof, we must show that f is continuous if the inverse image of each open set in R is open in D. Let p be any point in D and for an arbitrary positive number ε let V_ε be the ε-neighborhood of $f(p)$. Then V_ε is open in R and therefore the inverse image of V_ε is open in D and is a neighborhood of p in D. It then follows from Theorem 2-2.1 that f is continuous at p.

The following theorem gives a basic relation between the concepts of continuity and connectedness. This theorem states that a continuous function cannot map a connected set onto a disconnected set. On the other hand, a discontinuous function may map a connected set onto a disconnected set. For example, the function f such that $f(x)$ is the greatest integer not larger than x [Fig. 2-4] maps the real line (the domain of f) onto the integers (the range of f). The function g, defined by $g(x) = 1/x$ when $x \neq 0$ and $g(0) = 1$, is discontinuous at $x = 0$. The graph consists of three "pieces," as shown in Fig. 2-5 (one piece is a single point). The range of g is the y-axis with only the point $y = 0$ missing. If the definition of g is changed so that $g(0) = 0$, then the range of g is connected. However, this change in the value of $g(0)$ does not change the fact that g is discontinuous at $x = 0$. This shows that there are discontinuous functions whose domains and ranges are both connected.

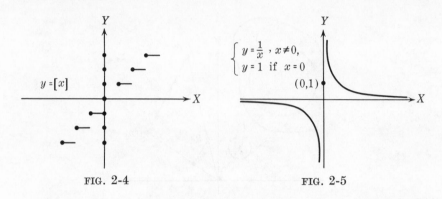

FIG. 2-4 FIG. 2-5

THEOREM 2-2.3. If f is a continuous function, then the image of any connected set in the domain of f is connected.

PROOF. We shall let D be a connected set in the domain of f and let R be the set of all points $f(p)$ where $p \in D$. Our proof is indirect, starting with the assumption that R is disconnected. We shall let $R = A \cup B$, where $A \cap B = \Phi$ and A and B are nonempty and each is open in R [see Fig. 2-6]. Now we let D_A and D_B be the inverse images of A and B. Since A and B are nonempty and are in the range of f, the sets D_A and D_B also are nonempty. Since $A \cap B = \Phi$, we have $D_A \cap D_B = \Phi$. Also, it follows from Theorem 2-2.2 that D_A and D_B are open in D. Thus, D is disconnected.

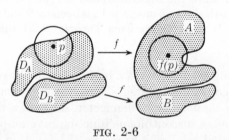

FIG. 2-6

In addition to immediate practical applications of the concept of continuity, continuous functions have many useful properties. Because of the wealth of continuous functions used in mathematics, the detailed study of some of these properties is extremely important. One of the best illustrations of these properties is the theorem that states that if a continuous function maps a closed interval onto a set of points on a line, then the range is also a closed interval. An equivalent statement of this theorem is that if f is a continuous function whose domain and range are sets of numbers and whose domain is a closed interval $[a, b]$, then (i) if k is a number between $f(a)$ and $f(b)$, there is a number ξ between a and b for which $f(\xi) = k$ (*intermediate value theorem*); (ii) there is a number ξ at which f has an absolute maximum (*maximum value theorem*), and a number η at which f has an absolute minimum. Both the intermediate value theorem and the maximum value theorem, which we shall prove in Section 2-8, demonstrate the hidden strength of continuity and will be useful in later chapters of the text.

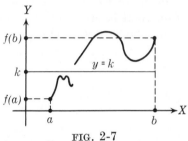

FIG. 2-7

THEOREM 2-2.4 (INTERMEDIATE VALUE THEOREM). Suppose f is a continuous function whose domain contains the closed interval $[a, b]$ and whose range is a set of real numbers. If $f(a) \neq f(b)$ and k is a number between the numbers $f(a)$ and $f(b)$, then there is a number ξ in the open interval (a, b) for which $f(\xi) = k$.

PROOF. Let us suppose that k is between $f(a)$ and $f(b)$ and is not in the range of f [Fig. 2-7]. Then f maps the interval $[a, b]$ onto a set S on the y-axis that contains $f(a)$ and $f(b)$ but does not contain k. Since S does not contain k, it is not an interval and is not connected [see Theorem 2-1.5]. We know this is impossible if f is continuous [Theorem 2-2.3].

ILLUSTRATION 4. If a line has the equation $ax + by + c = 0$, it is easy to show that there are points not on the line for which $ax + by + c$ is positive, and points for which $ax + by + c$ is negative. We wish to show that if p and q are points on the same side of the line, then $ax + by + c$ has the same sign at p as at q. We shall denote the coordinates of p by x_1 and y_1, and the coordinates of q by x_2 and y_2. If we let

$$f(t) = ax(t) + by(t) + c,$$

where $x(t) = x_1 + t(x_2 - x_1)$ and $y(t) = y_1 + t(y_2 - y_1)$, then f is a continuous function of t. For t between 0 and 1, $x(t)$ and $y(t)$ are the coordinates of a point on the line segment joining p and q. But $f(0)$

and $f(1)$ are the values of $ax+by+c$ at p and q, respectively. If these differ in sign, it follows from the intermediate value theorem that there is a point between p and q for which $ax+by+c = 0$. This is impossible if p and q are on the same side of the line.

The intermediate value theorem suggests a method for finding approximations to solutions of an equation of type $f(x) = 0$, where f is continuous. For if we find two numbers a and b such that $f(a)$ and $f(b)$ have opposite signs, then there is a number ξ between a and b for which $f(\xi) = 0$. This number ξ is said to be a *zero* of the function f. Now one can try other numbers between a and b, shortening the interval in which the solution must be located. This process can be continued indefinitely.

PROBLEMS

1. An object falls $16t^2$ ft in t sec. Find the largest number c, and a simple approximation of c, such that, if the error Δt in measuring time is less than c, then the error in the estimated distance will be less than (*a*) $\frac{1}{10}$ ft, when $t \leq 1$; (*b*) $\frac{1}{10}$ ft, when $t \leq 10$; (*c*) ε ft, when $t \leq k$. [*Hint:* For (a), show that the maximum error for an error of Δt in t occurs when $t = 1$, so that we need to have $\Delta t(32+16\,\Delta t) < \frac{1}{10}$. Assuming that $\Delta t < \frac{1}{160}$, it follows that Δt is small enough if $\Delta t < \frac{1}{321}$.]

2. Determine what error Δx in x will make an error in $1/x$ of less than $\frac{1}{10}$, when (*a*) $x > 10$; (b) $x > \frac{1}{2}$; (*c*) $x > \frac{1}{100}$.

3. For each of the following, show that the function f is continuous at c.
   (a) $c = 5$ and $f(x) = 3$ for all x.
   (b) $c = 2$ and $f(x) = 5x$ for all x.
   (c) $c = 3$ and $f(x) = x^2$ for all x.
   (d) $c = 7$ and $f(x) = 1/(x+1)$ when $x \neq -1$.
   (e) $c = \pi$ and $f(x) = $ (the greatest integer not larger than x).

4. Show that f is *not* continuous at c if
   (a) $c = 0$, $f(x) = 1/x$ when $x \neq 0$, and $f(0) = 15$;
   (b) $c = 2$ and $f(x) = $ (the greatest integer not larger than x).

5. For each of the following, describe a function that has exactly one point of discontinuity and whose domain and range are as indicated.
   (a) $D = [0, 1]$; $R = [0, 2]$.
   (b) $D = [0, 2]$; $R = [0, 1) \cup (1, 2]$.

6. In each of the following, f is to be a continuous function with the indicated domain and range. Choose such a function and give a geometric description or an algebraic formula by which you can determine the value of f at particular points.

(a) $D = \{x: x \geq 0\}$; $R = [0, 1)$.

(b) $D = (1, 3)$; $R = $ the x-axis.

(c) $D = [0, 1] \cup (2, 3] \cup (4, 5]$; $R = [0, 3]$.

(d) D is the (x, y)-plane and R is the set of all (x, y) such that neither x nor y is negative.

(e) D is the interior of the circle of unit radius in the (x, y)-plane with center at the origin and R is the interior of the square bounded by the lines $x = \pm 1$, $y = \pm 1$.

(f) D is the interior of the sphere of unit radius with center at $(0, 0, 0)$ and R is all of three-dimensional space.

7. Prove that a function f is continuous at p when there is a positive number r such that, given any number ε for which $0 < \varepsilon < r$, the inverse image of the ε-neighborhood of $f(p)$ in the range of f is a neighborhood of p in the domain of f.

8. For each of the following, use Theorem 2-2.3 to determine whether the function f is discontinuous (has at least one point of discontinuity), or explain why it is impossible to do this.

(*a*) $f(x) = x^2$ for all x.

(*b*) $f(x) = x^{-2}$ if $x \neq 0$; $f(0) = 0$.

(*c*) $f(x) = |x|^{3/2}$ if $x \neq 0$; $f(0) = 3$.

(d) $f(x) = x^2(x^2 - 1)^{-1}$ if $x \neq \pm 1$, $f(+1) = f(-1) = 1$.

(e) $f(x) = 1$ if x is rational, $f(x) = 0$ if x is irrational.

(f) $f(x) = x$ if x is rational, $f(x) = 1 + x$ if x is irrational.

9. Give an example of a continuous function whose range is connected and whose domain is disconnected.

10. Let f be a continuous function whose domain is the circumference of a circle and whose range is a line segment. Prove that f does not have an inverse. [*Hint:* Consider what happens if a point p is removed from the circle.]

11. Let f be a function whose domain is the closed interval $[0, 1]$ and whose range is a square with its interior. Prove that f^{-1} is discontinuous if it exists.

12. Let f be a function whose range is the circumference of a circle and whose domain is a disk (a circle and its interior). Prove that f is discontinuous or f is not one-to-one.

13. For each of the following, describe a continuous function that has the given domain and range, or explain why such a function does not exist.

(a) $D = [0, 1] \cup [2, 3)$; $R = [0, 1]$.

(b) $D = [0, 1]$; $R = [0, 1] \cup [2, 3)$.

(c) $D = [0, 2]$; $R = [0, 1) \cup (1, 2]$.

14. Explain why a polynomial of odd degree has at least one real zero.

15. Sketch the graph of the equation $y = 32x^5 - 160x - 3$ and show that there are exactly three real zeros. Find the value of each, accurate to one decimal place.

16. For each of the following, determine all real zeros of the given polynomial. Answers should be accurate to one decimal place.

(*a*) $x^3 - 3x - 1$.   (c) $3x^4 + 4x^3 - 12x^2 + 20$.

(*b*) $x^3 + 2x^2 - 8$.   (d) $2x^5 + 8x^4 + 3x^3 + 12x^2 + x + 4$.

17. Let f be a function whose domain is $[a, b]$ and for which $f(a) > a$ and $f(b) < b$. Prove there is an x for which $f(x) = x$.

18. Suppose f is a continuous function on the interval $[0, 1]$ and that $f(0) = f(1)$. Prove each of the following.

(a) There are numbers a and b in $[0, 1]$ such that $f(a) = f(b)$ and $b - a = \frac{1}{2}$. [*Hint:* Consider the function g defined by $g(x) = f(x + \frac{1}{2}) - f(x)$ for $0 \le x \le \frac{1}{2}$.]

(b) If $\theta = 1/n$ for some positive integer n, then there are numbers a and b in $[0, 1]$ such that $f(a) = f(b)$ and $b - a = \theta$. [*Note:* If $0 < \theta < 1$ and there is no integer n such that $\theta = 1/n$, then there is a continuous function f for which $f(0) = f(1)$ and there are no numbers a and b in $[0, 1]$ with $f(a) = f(b)$ and $b - a = \theta$.]

19. Let f be a continuous function whose domain is connected. Explain why there is a point ξ such that $f(\xi) = k$, if there are points p and q such that $f(p) < k < f(q)$.

2-3. THE HEINE-BOREL THEOREM

The Heine-Borel theorem is a very useful tool in analysis. For the real numbers, it is logically equivalent to the least upper bound axiom and to the fact that the real line is connected, as well as to other concepts that will be discussed in Section 2-10. In this section, we shall prove the Heine-Borel theorem and make an important application. First we need some definitions. We shall say that a set A is *covered* by a collection Σ of sets, or that Σ is a *cover* of A, if and only if A is contained in the union of the members of Σ. For the Heine-Borel theorem, we shall consider only covers whose members are open sets.

ILLUSTRATION 1. Let A be the interval $(0, 1]$ and let Σ be the sequence of open intervals

$$\left\{ \left(\frac{1}{2}, 2\right), \left(\frac{1}{3}, 1\right), \left(\frac{1}{4}, \frac{1}{2}\right), \left(\frac{1}{5}, \frac{1}{3}\right), \cdots, \left(\frac{1}{n+1}, \frac{1}{n-1}\right), \left(\frac{1}{n+2}, \frac{1}{n}\right), \cdots \right\}.$$

Then each point of A belongs to at least one of these intervals. This cover cannot be reduced by discarding some members of Σ, since for each n the number $1/n$ belongs only to the interval $(1/n+1, 1/n-1)$. Another cover is the sequence Σ^* of open intervals

$$\left\{ \left(\frac{1}{2}, 2\right), \left(\frac{1}{3}, 2\right), \cdots, \left(\frac{1}{n+1}, 2\right), \cdots \right\}.$$

However, in this case many intervals can be discarded and still leave a cover of A. In fact, we still have a cover if and only if an infinite number of intervals remain. If we introduce an open interval that contains 0, then it is possible to cover T using this interval and a finite number of members of Σ or a finite number of members of Σ^*.

DEFINITION 2-3.1. A *compact* set is a set A with the property that, if A is covered by a collection Σ of sets each of which is open in A, then there is a finite subcollection of Σ that covers A.

Unlike the properties of being closed or open, whether a set A is compact does not depend on the space T in which we might embed A. Actually, it is immaterial in Definition 2-3.1 whether we require the members of the cover to be open in A or open in some set that contains A. Let us state this as a formal theorem. This theorem will allow us, when studying compactness of sets in a plane, for example, to use covers by sets that are open in the plane.

THEOREM 2-3.1. Each of the following is a necessary and sufficient condition for a set A to be compact.
  (i) There is a set S containing A with the property that if A is covered by a collection Σ of sets, each of which is open in S, then there is a finite subcollection of Σ that covers A.
  (ii) All sets T that contain A have the property that if A is covered by a collection Σ of sets, each of which is open in T, then there is a finite subcollection of Σ that covers A.

PROOF. If A is compact, we can establish (i) by letting S be A. Let us show now that (i) implies (ii). Suppose T is an arbitrary set that contains A, and S is a set for which (i) is satisfied. Let Σ be a cover of A, each of whose members is open in T. If U is an arbitrary member of Σ and $x \in U \cap A$, then there is an ε-neighborhood of x whose intersection with T is contained in U. Let U^* be the union of the intersections with S of all such neighborhoods of points in $U \cap A$. Then U^* is open in S, since it is the union of sets open in S [see problem 9 of Section 2-1]. Also, $U \cap A = U^* \cap A$, since $U^* \cap A \subset U \cap A$ follows from U^* being the union of neighborhoods whose intersections with T are contained in U, and $U \cap A \subset U^* \cap A$ follows from each x in $U \cap A$ being the center of some of these neighborhoods. Thus, the sets of type U^* form a cover Σ^* of A to which (i) applies. A reduction of Σ^* to a finite cover determines a corresponding reduction of Σ to a finite cover. The last step of the proof is to note that (ii) implies A is compact, since in (ii) we can let T be A.

DEFINITION 2-3.2. A *bounded set* is a set A for which there is a number M and a point p such that $d(p, r) \leqq M$ if $r \in A$.

Note that "having a boundary" and "being bounded" are not related concepts—in fact, all sets have boundaries (possibly empty). If T is a closed subset of R^3, then a subset of T is closed in T if and only if it is closed in R^3. Thus, in the following theorem, "closed in R^3" can be interpreted as "closed in a line" (or "closed in a plane") if T is a subset of a line (or a plane).

THEOREM 2-3.2 (HEINE-BOREL). A subset T of R^3 is compact if it is bounded and closed in R^3.†

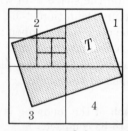

FIG. 2-8

PROOF. To simplify notation, we shall give the proof for a subset of a plane and let the student convince himself that essentially the same argument could be used in space. We shall use a proof by contradiction, assuming that T is a bounded closed subset of a plane and that T has a cover Σ of sets such that each is open in T and no finite subcollection of Σ covers T. Since T is bounded, there is a square that contains T. We divide a square containing T into four congruent squares, as indicated in Fig. 2-8. At least one of these squares has the

† The converse also is true; see Problems 2 and 3.

property that its intersection with T is not covered by a finite subcollection of Σ. Let S_1 be the first such square. Now we divide S_1 into four congruent squares in the same way and let S_2 be the first of these squares whose intersection with T is not covered by a finite subcollection of Σ. This can be continued indefinitely. If now we let x_n and y_n be the coordinates of the lower left corner of S_n, then the sequences $\{x_1, x_2, \cdots\}$ and $\{y_1, y_2, \cdots\}$ are monotone increasing and bounded. If we let

$$\sup\{x_n\} = \xi, \quad \sup\{y_n\} = \eta, \quad \text{and} \quad p = (\xi, \eta), \tag{2-1}$$

then it follows that $p \in S_n$ for all n. To show this, we need only observe that if there is an n for which $p \notin S_n$, then $d(p, S_n) > 0$. This contradicts (2-1) since $d(p, S_m) \geqq d(p, S_n)$ if $m > n$. Clearly, all of the sets S_n contain points of T, so that p is a cluster point of T and belongs to T because T is closed. Therefore, there is a member U of Σ that contains p. Since U is open in T, there is an n for which $S_n \cap T \subset U$. This is impossible, since $S_n \cap T$ is not covered by any finite subcollection of Σ and therefore not by the single member U.

Suppose f is a function whose range is a set of numbers. We say that f is continuous on a set S contained in the domain of f if f is continuous at each point of S—that is, if *for each point c of S* it is true that, for each positive number ε, there exists a positive number δ such that

$$|f(x) - f(c)| < \varepsilon \quad \text{if} \quad d(x, y) < \delta \tag{2-2}$$

and x is in the domain of f. If, for a given ε and c, a suitable value exists for δ, then any smaller positive number can also be used. Thus the choice of δ is never unique. The following illustration shows that the value of δ may depend on the point c as well as on the number ε.

ILLUSTRATION 2. If we let $f(x) = 1/x$ when $x \neq 0$, then

$$|f(x) - f(c)| = \left|\frac{1}{x} - \frac{1}{c}\right| = \frac{|x - c|}{|xc|}.$$

This can be made small by making $|x - c|$ sufficiently small, but exactly how small we must make $|x - c|$ clearly depends on the size of c. Let us find an explicit expression for the number δ of (2-2), without specifying the value of ε. This will prove that δ can be found, whatever the value of ε. For each number $c \neq 0$, we need to find a positive number $\delta(c)$ such that

$$\left|\frac{1}{x} - \frac{1}{c}\right| < \varepsilon \quad \text{if} \quad |x - c| < \delta(c).$$

Since the absolute value of the slope of the graph of f decreases when x is positive [see Fig. 2-9], it follows that when $c > 0$ we can let $\delta(c)$ be the number for which

$$f[c - \delta(c)] = \frac{1}{c - \delta(c)} = \frac{1}{c} + \varepsilon \quad \text{or} \quad \delta(c) = \frac{c^2 \varepsilon}{1 + c\varepsilon}.$$

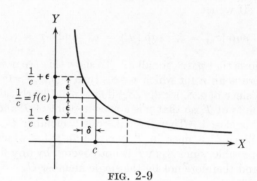

FIG. 2-9

In fact, this is the largest number that can be used for δ in (2-2). Since $\lim_{c \to 0} \delta(c) = 0$, there is no positive number that can be used for δ in (2-2) independently of the value of c. It is customary to describe this situation by saying that f is *not* uniformly continuous on any interval $(0, r)$, where $r > 0$.

DEFINITION 2-3.3. Given a set S, a function *uniformly continuous on S* is a function f with the property that, for each positive number ε, there exists a positive number δ such that

$$|f(p) - f(q)| < \varepsilon \quad \text{if} \quad d(p, q) < \delta \tag{2-3}$$

and p and q are points of S.

In Illustration 2 we discussed the function $f(x) = 1/x$, which is continuous at all numbers except zero. This function is uniformly continuous on any set $S = \{x : x \geq r\}$, where $r > 0$. But f is not uniformly continuous on the set of all positive numbers, even though f is continuous at each positive number. However, for certain sets, it is true that any function that is continuous on the set is also uniformly continuous on the set. This is true for compact sets.

THEOREM 2-3.3. Suppose f is a function whose range is a set of real numbers and that S is a compact set contained in the domain of f. If f is continuous at each point of S, then f is uniformly continuous on S.

PROOF. Suppose S is a compact set. If f is continuous at each point of S, then, for any point p_0 of S and any positive number ε, there is a positive number $\delta(p_0)$ such that, for all r in the domain of f,

$$|f(p_0) - f(r)| < \tfrac{1}{2}\varepsilon \quad \text{if} \quad d(p_0, r) < \delta(p_0). \tag{2-4}$$

Once such a number $\delta(p_0)$ has been found, any positive number smaller than $\delta(p_0)$ is also a suitable choice of $\delta(p_0)$. Let ε be a positive number and assume that a definite choice of $\delta(p)$ has been made for each point p in S. Now define a cover Σ of S by letting Σ be the set of all open sets of type

$$U_p = \{r : d(p, r) < \tfrac{1}{2}\delta(p)\},$$

where $p \in S$. Choose a finite subset of Σ, $\{U_{p_1}, U_{p_2}, \cdots, U_{p_n}\}$, that covers S, and let δ be the smallest of $\tfrac{1}{2}\delta(p_1), \tfrac{1}{2}\delta(p_2), \cdots, \tfrac{1}{2}\delta(p_n)$. Now let r and s be two arbitrary points of S for $d(r, s) < \delta$. Then there is a k for which $1 \leq k \leq n$ and $r \in U_{p_k}$. Since $d(p_k, r) < \tfrac{1}{2}\delta(p_k)$ and $d(r, s) < \delta \leq \tfrac{1}{2}\delta(p_k)$, we have

$$d(p_k, r) < \delta(p_k) \quad \text{and} \quad d(p_k, s) < \delta(p_k),$$

so that it follows that

$$|f(p_k) - f(r)| < \tfrac{1}{2}\varepsilon, \quad |f(p_k) - f(s)| < \tfrac{1}{2}\varepsilon,$$

and $|f(r) - f(s)| < \varepsilon$. Since ε was arbitrary, this proves that f is uniformly continuous on S.

PROBLEMS

1. Give an example of an open cover of the interval $[0, 4)$ that has no finite subcover.

2.* Let S be an unbounded metric space. Describe a cover Σ of S by open sets for which no finite subcollection of Σ covers S.

3.* Let S be a subset of a metric space T and suppose that S is not closed in T. Describe a cover Σ of S by open sets for which no finite subcollection of Σ covers S.

4. Prove that a subset of a line is closed in the line if and only if it is closed in R^3.

5. Let E be the extension of the set of real numbers that contains $+\infty$ and $-\infty$, as discussed in Section 1-6. A *neighborhood* of $+\infty$ is a set V that contains $+\infty$ and for which there is a number α such that $x \in V$ if $x > \alpha$. Similarly, a *neighborhood* of $-\infty$ is a set V that contains $-\infty$ and for which there is a number α such that $x \in V$ if $x < \alpha$. Prove that a subset of E is compact if and only if it is closed in E.

6. Construct a compact set of real numbers that has a countably infinite number of cluster points.

7. For each of the following functions and the specified set S, find a positive number δ such that, for each p and q in S, $|f(p)-f(q)| < \varepsilon$ if $|p-q| < \delta$.

   (**a**) $f(x) = 7x+3$, S is the set of real numbers, $\varepsilon = \frac{1}{10}$.

   (b) $f(x) = x^2$, $S = [-5, 6]$, $\varepsilon = \frac{1}{2}$.

   (**c**) $f(x) = 1/(x+5)$, $S = \{x: x \geq -1\}$, $\varepsilon = \frac{1}{4}$.

8. Let $g(x) = x^2$ for all x. Explain why g is not uniformly continuous on the set of all real numbers.

9. For each of the following, determine whether the given function is uniformly continuous on the set S indicated. Explain.

   (**a**) $f(x, y) = x^2+y^2$; $S = \{(x, y): |x| \leq 1 \text{ and } |y| \leq 1\}$.

   (**b**) $f(x, y) = 2x+3y$; S the (x, y)-plane.

   (**c**) $f(x, y) = xy$; S the (x, y)-plane.

10. Let f be uniformly continuous on intervals A and B of the x-axis. (a) Explain why f is uniformly continuous on $A \cup B$ if $A \cap B \neq \Phi$. (b) Explain why f need not be uniformly continuous on $A \cup B$ if $A \cap B = \Phi$.

11. Let f be uniformly continuous on a set A and also on a set B. Show that f is uniformly continuous on $A \cup B$ if there is a positive number Δ such that

$$|r-s| > \Delta \quad \text{if} \quad r \in A \quad \text{and} \quad s \in B.$$

12. Let A be a compact subset of R^3 and B be a closed subset of R^3. Prove that, if a function f is continuous on A and uniformly continuous on B, then f is uniformly continuous on $A \cup B$. [*Hint:* Find a δ that works in (2-3) when both p and q are in B or both are in $(A \cup B) \cap S$, where S is a suitable ball that contains A.]

13. Let S be a set that is not closed in R^3. Describe a function that is continuous on S but not uniformly continuous on S.

14. Describe a set S that is not bounded but which has the property that each function continuous on S is uniformly continuous on S.

15.* Let f be continuous on the closed interval $[a, b] = \{x: a \leq x \leq b\}$. Show that for any positive number ε there is a polygonal function g

such that $|f(x)-g(x)| < \varepsilon$ if $x \in [a, b]$. [A *polygonal function* is a function whose graph consists of a finite number of line segments, joined end-to-end.]

16.* Prove the following strengthened form of Theorem 2-3.3: "Suppose f is a function whose range is a set of real numbers and that S is a compact set contained in the domain of f. If f is continuous at each point of S, then for any $\varepsilon > 0$ there is a $\delta > 0$ such that

$$|f(r)-f(s)| < \varepsilon \quad \text{if} \quad d(r, s) < \delta$$

and r belongs to the domain of f and $s \in S$.

2-4. DEFINITION OF LIMIT

The concept of limit is basic to all of calculus.   Lack of understanding of this concept and lack of an adequate definition hampered the development of mathematics from the time of the Greeks until long after the time of Leibniz and Newton.   The following quotation from Newton illustrates the confusion of thought that resulted from lack of a precise definition of limit:

> But the answer is easy: for by the ultimate velocity is meant that with which the body is moved, neither before it arrives at its last place, when the motion ceases, nor after; but at the very instant when it arrives. . . . And, in like manner, by the ultimate ratio of evanescent quantities is to be understood the ratio of the quantities, not before they vanish, nor after, but that with which they vanish.†

Even later, Simon Antoine Jean Lhuilier (1750–1840) claimed that if a variable quantity at all stages has a certain property, then its limit has the same property.‡   The falsity of this is demonstrated by the fact that an *irrational* number can be the limit of a sequence of *rational* numbers, that a discontinuous function can be the limit of a sequence of continuous functions, and that a circle is the limit of a sequence of inscribed polygons.   In 1894 Vivanti made the confused statement that it is immaterial whether one calls the circle the limit of a polygon as the sides are indefinitely decreased in length, or whether one looks upon the circle as a polygon with an infinite number of infinitesimal sides.§

---

† See *The History of the Calculus and its Conceptual Development* by Carl B. Boyer (New York: Dover Publications, 1949), p. 216.

‡ See Boyer, *op. cit.*, p. 256.

§ *Il concetto d'infinitesimo e la sua applicazione alla matematica* by G. Vivanti (Mantua: 1894), p. 39.

Similarly confused ideas are often present in the minds of students and desperately need correction if mathematics is to be understood.

It is the purpose of this section to place the notion of limit on a sound foundation. Because there are many different phenomena called "limit processes," we shall give a rather abstract definition of limit. At first, this definition may seem difficult to understand or appreciate because it is so general. However, it has the tremendous advantage of being general enough so that all the different "limit processes" we wish to study are special cases of the "limit" described by our one definition. Yet, as will be seen in the next section, the definition is also restricted enough that it can be used to prove several useful and important theorems about limits. This use of a general definition enables us to discuss simultaneously a number of concepts traditionally treated separately, thus not only saving time, but, even more important, allowing us to see exactly what these various concepts of limit have in common and where they differ. Before giving the general definition of limit, let us consider some special cases.

Such statements as "$f(x) \to l$ as $x \to p$" can be read as "$f(x)$ approaches l as x approaches p." We can write this as

$$\lim_{x \to p} f(x) = l, \tag{2-5}$$

and read it as "the limit of $f(x)$ as x approaches p is l." We might interpret this to mean that $f(x)$ is near l if x is sufficiently close to p. By using the concept of "neighborhood," we can say more precisely that Eq. (2-5) means that for any neighborhood V of l there is a neighborhood U of p such that, if A is the set U with the point p deleted, then $f(x) \in V$ if $x \in A$.

ILLUSTRATION 1. Suppose we let $f(x) = x^3 - 3$ and we wish to show that $\lim_{x \to 2} f(x) = 5$. We shall let V be any neighborhood of 5 and let ε be a positive number such that V contains the interval $(5 - \varepsilon, 5 + \varepsilon)$. We then show that there is a neighborhood U of 2 such that $f(x)$ is in the interval $(5 - \varepsilon, 5 + \varepsilon)$ if $x \in U$ and $x \neq 2$. The graph of $y = x^3 - 3$ is shown in Fig. 2-10. The essential fact to us is that y increases as x increases. It is clear that there are numbers a and b such that $a < 2 < b$ and $a^3 - 3 = 5 - \varepsilon, b^3 - 3 = 5 + \varepsilon$. Then $f(a) = 5 - \varepsilon < f(x) < 5 + \varepsilon = f(b)$ if $a < x < b$, so that $|f(x) - 5| < \varepsilon$ if $x \in (a, b)$. Thus we can let U be the interval (a, b).

For sequences, such statements as "$a_k \to \alpha$ as k increases" may be written as

$$\lim_{k \to +\infty} a_k = \alpha. \tag{2-6}$$

Roughly, Eq. (2-6) means that a_k is near α if k is sufficiently large. The precise meaning of this statement is that, if V is any neighborhood of α, then there is a positive number N such that

$$a_k \in V \quad \text{if} \quad k > N. \tag{2-7}$$

We could let $A = \{k : k > N\}$ and write (2-7) as

$$a_k \in V \quad \text{if} \quad k \in A.$$

If Eq. (2-6) is true in this sense, we say that the sequence $\{a_k\}$ is *convergent*.

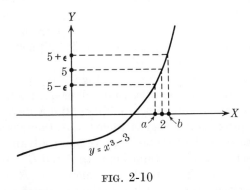

FIG. 2-10

ILLUSTRATION 2. We shall let $a_k = k(2k+3)^{-1}$. We wish to show that $\lim_{k \to +\infty} a_k = \frac{1}{2}$. We let V be any neighborhood of $\frac{1}{2}$ and let ε be a positive number such that V contains the interval $(\frac{1}{2} - \varepsilon, \frac{1}{2} + \varepsilon)$. We must show that there is a number N such that $|\frac{1}{2} - a_k| < \varepsilon$ if $k > N$. We have

$$\frac{1}{2} - a_k = \frac{1}{2} - \frac{k}{2k+3} = \frac{\frac{3}{2}}{2k+3}.$$

It follows from this that $|\frac{1}{2} - a_k| < \varepsilon$ if

$$\left| \frac{\frac{3}{2}}{2k+3} \right| < \varepsilon \quad \text{or} \quad 2k+3 > \frac{3}{2\varepsilon} \quad \text{or} \quad k > \frac{3}{4\varepsilon} - \frac{3}{2}.$$

Thus, we can let $N = 3/(4\varepsilon) - \frac{3}{2}$.

We have given precise meaning to statements (2-5) and (2-6). This is very important if such statements are to be used in mathematical discussions. However, there are many other types of limits and we seek a single definition of limit by which (2-5) and (2-6), as well as all the other types of limits we shall use, will be special cases. Let us analyze the similarities of (2-5) and (2-6). First, in each case we used a neighborhood V and replaced the statements "$f(x)$ is near l" and "a_k is near α" by the statements "$f(x) \in V$" and "$a_k \in V$," respectively. In general, the statement "the limit of $f(x)$ is l" will mean that for any neighborhood V of l the object $f(x)$ is in V if the object x is in a suitable set, which we shall call a "stage." Intuitively, we might say that $f(x)$ will be near l if an appropriate restriction is placed on x, such as that x is in an advanced "stage" of some process. For example, the statement $\lim_{x \to p} f(x) = l$ means that for any neighborhood V of l the number $f(x)$ will be in V if x is sufficiently close to p—i.e., if x is in a suitable set A, where A is a neighborhood of p with p deleted (the set A is called a stage). Similarly, the statement $\lim_{k \to +\infty} a_k = \alpha$ means that, for any neighborhood V of α, there is a number N such that $a_k \in V$ if $k > N$. In this case, we might call the set $A = \{k \colon k > N\}$ a stage and use such stages to specify how large k must be.

In general, the sets to be called stages can be chosen somewhat freely, but there are two properties that will be quite important in later discussions: (1) a stage must not be empty; (2) if a stage C is defined as being *more advanced* than a stage A when $C \subset A$, then for any two stages A and B there must be a stage that is more advanced than either A or B. The set $A \cap B$ is contained in both A and B. We shall require that $A \cap B$ be a stage if A and B are stages, $A \cap B$ then being more advanced than either A or B. Clearly, the two types of stages we have discussed have these properties.

DEFINITION 2-4.1. A *system of stages* is a collection S of nonempty subsets of a set T for which $A \cap B$ is a member of S whenever A and B are members of S. The members of a system of stages are called *stages*.

DEFINITION 2-4.2. Suppose D is the domain of a function f and S is a system of stages for which each stage contains at least one point of D. Also suppose that there is a number l with the property that, for any neighborhood V of l, there is a stage A such that, for each x in the domain of f,

$$f(x) \in V \quad \text{if} \quad x \in A.$$

Such a number l is said to be the *limit of f with respect to S* and is denoted by $\lim_S f$.

Although this definition allows considerable freedom in the choice of subsets that are to be designated as stages, there are certain types of limits for which we wish to introduce special notation and to establish a convention as to which sets are to be called stages. The first case we shall consider is a generalization of Eq. (2-5).

I. *Deleted neighborhoods.* A deleted neighborhood of a point p is a set W for which $p \notin W$ and $\{p\} \cup W$ is a neighborhood of p. We shall let f be a function whose domain D is a set of points in R^3 and let p be a point (not necessarily in D) for which each deleted neighborhood of p contains points of D. Also, S will be the system of stages consisting of the deleted neighborhoods of p. If W_1 and W_2 are deleted neighborhoods of p, then $W_1 \cap W_2$ is a deleted neighborhood of p, and therefore the requirements of Definition 2-4.1 are satisfied. Now we define $\lim_{x \to p} f(x) = l$ as meaning $\lim_S f = l$. We can then say that $\lim_{x \to p} f(x) = l$ means that, for any neighborhood V of l, there is a neighborhood U of p such that, for all x in the domain of f,

$$f(x) \in V \quad \text{if} \quad x \in U \quad \text{and} \quad x \neq p. \tag{2-8}$$

If we recall that, for each neighborhood V of a point p, there is a positive number ε such that V contains the ε-neighborhood of p, then it is easily seen that our definition can be reworded as follows: "$\lim_{x \to p} f(x)$ is a number l which has the property that, for any positive number ε, there is a positive number δ such that, for all x in the domain of f,

$$d[f(x), l] < \varepsilon \quad \text{if} \quad 0 < d(x, p) < \delta." \tag{2-9}$$

ILLUSTRATION 3. We shall let $f(x) = 3x^2 - 5x + 1$ for all numbers x. We wish to show that $\lim_{x \to 2} f(x) = 3$. This means we must show that, if ε is a positive number, then there exists a positive number δ such that

$$|f(x) - 3| < \varepsilon \quad \text{if} \quad |x - 2| < \delta \quad \text{and} \quad x \neq 2.$$

Since $f(2) = 3$, there is no need to insist that x is not equal to 2. Note that

$$|f(x) - 3| = |3x^2 - 5x - 2| = |x - 2| \cdot |3x + 1|.$$

Now we choose a positive number, say $\frac{1}{3}$, and note that if $|x - 2| < \frac{1}{3}$ then $\frac{5}{3} < x < \frac{7}{3}$ and $|3x + 1| < 8$. We let δ be the smaller of $\frac{1}{3}$ and $\varepsilon/8$. If $|x - 2| < \delta$, then

$$|f(x) - 3| = |x - 2| \cdot |3x + 1| < \delta \cdot |3x + 1| < 8\delta \leqq \varepsilon.$$

ILLUSTRATION 4. We shall let $g(x) = 1/x$ when $x \neq 0$. We wish to show that $\lim_{x \to 0} g(x)$ does not exist. Let us use an indirect proof, assuming that there is a number l for which $\lim_{x \to 0} g(x) = l$. Then for the particular positive number 1 there must be a positive number δ such that

$$\left| l - \frac{1}{x} \right| < 1 \quad \text{if} \quad |x| < \delta \quad \text{and} \quad x \neq 0.$$

But now we let x be a number such that $0 < x < \delta$ and $x < 1/(|l|+1)$. Then

$$\frac{1}{x} > |l| + 1 \quad \text{and} \quad \left| l - \frac{1}{x} \right| > 1.$$

II. *Neighborhoods of infinity.* We shall let $+\infty$ and $-\infty$ be the objects adjoined to the set of real numbers to form the "extension of the set of real numbers" discussed in Section 1-6. A *neighborhood* of $+\infty$ is a set V that contains $+\infty$ and for which there is a number α such that $x \in V$ if $x > \alpha$. Similarly, a *neighborhood of* $-\infty$ is a set V that contains $-\infty$ and for which there is a number α such that $x \in V$ if $x < \alpha$.

Now the previous discussion of deleted neighborhoods and the definition of the statement "$\lim_{x \to p} f(x) = l$" can be generalized to include the cases for which l is $+\infty$ or $-\infty$ and/or p is $+\infty$ or $-\infty$. Thus we have definitions of such statements as $\lim_{x \to +\infty} f(x) = 3$, $\lim_{x \to 5} f(x) = -\infty$, and $\lim_{x \to +\infty} f(x) = -\infty$. For example, "$\lim_{x \to +\infty} f(x) = l$" means "For any neighborhood V of l there is a number α such that $f(x) \in V$ if $x > \alpha$ and x is in the domain of f." Roughly speaking, we might state this as "$f(x)$ gets 'arbitrarily close' to l as x gets 'arbitrarily large.'" It should be noted that this definition is consistent with the discussion of limits of sequences preceding Illustration 2, since for a deleted neighborhood of $+\infty$ we consider only those numbers that are both in this deleted neighborhood and in the domain of the function. For a sequence, this means that we consider only positive integers.

ILLUSTRATION 5.   Suppose we wish to show that

$$\lim_{x \to +\infty} \frac{2x - 1}{x + 3} = 2.$$

To do this, we show that for any positive number ε there is a number α such that

$$\left| 2 - \frac{2x - 1}{x + 3} \right| < \varepsilon \quad \text{if} \quad x > \alpha.$$

We let ε be an arbitrary positive number. Since

$$\left| 2 - \frac{2x-1}{x+3} \right| = \left| \frac{7}{x+3} \right|,$$

we want to have $7(x+3)^{-1} < \varepsilon$ or $x+3 > 7/\varepsilon$. This will be true if $x > (7/\varepsilon) - 3$. Therefore, we can let $\alpha = (7/\varepsilon) - 3$.

Problems 4, 5, and 10 introduce three other useful types of limits which are special cases of our general definition. Problems 10 through 13 introduce several examples which should be of help in learning the abstract definitions of "system of stages" and "$\lim_S f$," though they are not intended to be useful for later work.

PROBLEMS

1. Prove that

(a) $\lim\limits_{x \to 1} (7x+3) = 10;$

(c) $\lim\limits_{x \to 1} \left(\dfrac{x^2}{x^2+x+1} \right) = \dfrac{1}{3}.$

(b) $\lim\limits_{x \to -1} \left(\dfrac{1}{x-2} \right) = -\dfrac{1}{3};$

2. Prove that

(a) $\lim\limits_{n \to +\infty} (3n+7)^{-1} = 0;$

(c) $\lim\limits_{n \to +\infty} \dfrac{n!}{n^n} = 0;$

(b) $\lim\limits_{n \to +\infty} \left(\dfrac{2n}{3n+1} \right) = \dfrac{2}{3};$

(d) $\lim\limits_{n \to +\infty} \dfrac{(10)^n}{n!} = 0.$

3. For each of the following, give an explanation of the indicated equality.

(a) $\lim\limits_{n \to +\infty} [(n^2+1)^{\frac{1}{2}} - n] = 0.$

(b) $\lim\limits_{n \to +\infty} [(n^2+n)^{\frac{1}{2}} - n] = \frac{1}{2}.$

(c) $\lim\limits_{n \to +\infty} \left(\dfrac{1}{n^2} + \dfrac{2}{n^2} + \dfrac{3}{n^2} + \cdots + \dfrac{n}{n^2} \right) = \dfrac{1}{2}.$

(d) $\lim\limits_{n \to +\infty} n^2 2^{-n} = 0.$

4.* Let $\lim_{x \to c-} f(x) = l$ mean $\lim_S f = l$, where a set A is a stage belonging to S if there is a number $a < c$ for which $A = \{x : a < x < c\}$. Then

l is said to be the *left-hand limit*, or the *limit on the left*, of f at c. Explain the following.

(a) $\lim\limits_{x \to 0-} \dfrac{1}{1+2^{1/x}} = 1.$

(b) $\lim\limits_{x \to 0-} \dfrac{x}{|x|} = -1.$

(c) $\lim\limits_{x \to 3-} [x] = 2$, where $[x]$ denotes the greatest integer not greater than x.

5. * Let $\lim\limits_{x \to c+} f(x) = l$ mean $\lim_S f = l$, where a set A is a stage belonging to S if there is a number $a > c$ for which $A = \{x: c < x < a\}$. Then l is said to be the *right-hand limit*, or the *limit on the right*, of f at c. Explain the following.

(a) $\lim\limits_{x \to 0+} \dfrac{1}{1+2^{1/x}} = 0.$

(b) $\lim\limits_{x \to 0+} \dfrac{x}{|x|} = 1.$

(c) $\lim\limits_{x \to 3+} [x] = 3$, where $[x]$ denotes the greatest integer not greater than x.

6. * Explain why $\lim\limits_{x \to c} f(x)$ exists if and only if both $\lim\limits_{x \to c+} f(x)$ and $\lim\limits_{x \to c-} f(x)$ exist and are equal. [See problems 4 and 5.]

7. Explain in detail why the following are true statements.

(a) $\lim\limits_{x \to +\infty} \dfrac{2x-1}{5x+2} = \dfrac{2}{5}.$

(c) $\lim\limits_{x \to +\infty} \dfrac{1}{1+2^x} = 0.$

(b) $\lim\limits_{x \to -\infty} \dfrac{1}{1+2^x} = 1.$

(d) $\lim\limits_{x \to +\infty} \dfrac{x^2}{2^x} = 0.$

8. Explain in detail why the following are true statements.

(a) $\lim\limits_{x \to 2} \left| \dfrac{1}{x-2} \right| = +\infty.$

(b) $\lim\limits_{x \to 0} \dfrac{x+3}{|x^2-x|} = +\infty.$

(c) $\lim\limits_{x \to 3+} \dfrac{1}{3-x} = -\infty$ [see problem 5].

9. * Let $\lim\limits_{|x| \to +\infty} f(x) = l$ mean that $\lim_S f(x) = l$, where a set A is a member of the system of stages S if and only if there is a number α such that $x \in A$ if $|x| > \alpha$. Explain why the following are true statements or show that they are not.

(*a*) $\lim\limits_{|x| \to +\infty} \dfrac{x^3}{x+3} = +\infty.$

(*c*) $\lim\limits_{|x| \to +\infty} \dfrac{x+1}{2x^2+3} = 0.$

(*b*) $\lim\limits_{|x| \to +\infty} \dfrac{x}{2x+1} = \dfrac{1}{2}.$

(*d*) $\lim\limits_{|x| \to +\infty} \dfrac{x^2+1}{2x+3} = +\infty.$

(*e*) $\lim\limits_{|x| \to +\infty} \dfrac{1}{1+2^x} = 0.$

10. For each of the following, determine whether it is true that $\lim_S (x^2 + x) = 2$ and explain your conclusion. (***a***) S is the system of deleted neighborhoods of the number 1. (***b***) Each stage of S is the union of a deleted neighborhood of $+\infty$ and a deleted neighborhood of 1. (***c***) The sets $\{1, 2, 3, 4\}$, $\{1, 2, 3\}$, $\{1, 2\}$, and $\{1\}$ are the stages of S. (***d***) The sets $\{1, 2, 3, 4\}$, $\{1, 2, 3\}$, and $\{1, 2\}$ are the stages of S.

11. For each of the following, determine whether $\lim_S (x^2 - 10x)$ exists and determine the value of this limit if it exists. Explain. (***a***) S is the system of deleted neighborhoods of the number 12. (***b***) The sets $\{0, 2, 4, 6\}$, $\{0, 4, 6\}$, and $\{4, 6\}$ are the stages of S. (***c***) The sets $\{0, 2, 3\}$ and $\{3\}$ are the stages of S.

12. Let the universal set be the set of positive integers and let S be the system of stages for which A is a stage if and only if $\sim A$ is finite. (a) Show that $A \cap B$ is a stage if A and B are stages.

For each of the following, determine the number l, if one exists, for which $\lim_S f = l$. (***b***) $f(n) = 1/(n+3)$. (***c***) $f(n) = 1/$(the number of different primes that divide n).

13. Let the universal set be the set of positive integers and let S be the system of stages for which A is a stage if and only if there is an integer k such that A is the set of all positive integers divisible by k.

(a) Show that $A \cap B$ is a stage if A and B are stages.

For each of the following, determine the number l, if one exists, for which $\lim_S f = l$.

(***b***) $f(n) = 1/(n+3)$.

(***c***) $f(n)$ is the greatest common divisor of n and 12.

(***d***) $f(n) = 1/$(the number of different primes that divide n).

2-5. SOME THEOREMS ABOUT LIMITS

In the preceding section, we saw many different types of limits, all of which are special cases of one very general definition of $\lim_S f = l$. We shall now justify the study of that definition by using it to prove some important theorems about limits. Each theorem is, of course, valid for all special cases considered. The first theorem brings out what is perhaps the most fundamental of all properties of limits. The definition of "system of stages" was largely determined by what tools are necessary for the proofs of these theorems. The student has been using these theorems for years. However, we now have the logical and mathematical foundations to give explicit proofs. The methods of these proofs are particularly important, since similar methods will be used in proving theorems that are not so familiar.

THEOREM 2-5.1. Suppose f is a function whose domain and range are metric spaces. If α and β are limits of f with respect to the same system of stages, then $\alpha = \beta$.

This theorem may seem very obvious. However, one should keep in mind that the definition that α is a value of $\lim_S f$ means that a certain complicated condition holds for $S, f,$ and α. The problem is to make sure that this same condition does not also hold for $S, f,$ and β. Of course, we have used "$=$" in writing "$\lim_S f = l$" in anticipation of this theorem.

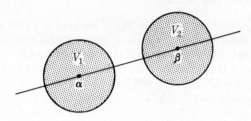

FIG. 2-11

PROOF OF THEOREM 2-5.1. Let us assume that $\alpha \neq \beta$ and that V_1 and V_2 are neighborhoods of α and β, respectively, such that $V_1 \cap V_2 = \Phi$. For example, if α and β are ordinary real numbers, then we could let [Fig. 2-11]

$$V_1 = \{y: d(y, \alpha) < \tfrac{1}{3} \cdot d(\alpha, \beta)\},$$

$$V_2 = \{y: d(y, \beta) < \tfrac{1}{3} \cdot d(\alpha, \beta)\}.$$

We choose A and B as stages such that, for each x in the domain of f,

$$f(x) \in V_1 \quad \text{if} \quad x \in A \quad \text{and} \quad f(x) \in V_2 \quad \text{if} \quad x \in B.$$

We let $C = A \cap B$. Then x belongs to both A and B if $x \in C$. Thus, if $x \in C$, then $f(x) \in V_1$ and $f(x) \in V_2$, so that $f(x) \in V_1 \cap V_2$. This is impossible, since C contains points of the domain of f and $V_1 \cap V_2$ is empty.

The next theorem also is easy to prove. It is very useful for problems such as the following. Suppose we wish to prove that $\lim_{n \to +\infty} n^{-1} \cos n = 0$. Then we can use the facts that $\lim_{n \to +\infty} n^{-1} = 0$ and $\lim_{n \to +\infty} -n^{-1} = 0$. The desired conclusion then follows directly from Theorem 2-5.2. Suppose we wish to prove that $\lim_{n \to +\infty} (\sin^2 n) 2^{-n} = 0$. We need only know that $\lim_{n \to +\infty} 2^{-n} = 0$ in order to use Theorem 2-5.2 [see problem 2, page 30], since $\lim_{n \to +\infty} 0 = 0$.

THEOREM 2-5.2 (HAM SANDWICH THEOREM). Suppose f and h are functions whose ranges are sets of real numbers. Also suppose S is a system of stages and that

$$\lim_S f = \lim_S h = \ell.$$

If g is a function for which there is a stage A such that

$$f(x) \leqq g(x) \leqq h(x) \quad \text{if} \quad x \in A,$$

then $\lim_S g = \ell$.

PROOF. We must show that, for any neighborhood U of ℓ, there is a stage D such that $g(x) \in U$ if $x \in D$. Let ε be a positive number for which the ε-neighborhood of ℓ is contained in U. Since both $\lim_S f$ and $\lim_S h$ are equal to ℓ, there are stages B and C such that

$$|f(x) - \ell| < \varepsilon \quad \text{if} \quad x \in B, \qquad |h(x) - \ell| < \varepsilon \quad \text{if} \quad x \in C.$$

Now let $D = A \cap B \cap C$. If $x \in D$, then

$$f(x) \leqq g(x) \leqq h(x), \quad |f(x) - \ell| < \varepsilon, \quad \text{and} \quad |h(x) - \ell| < \varepsilon.$$

These inequalities imply that $|g(x) - \ell| < \varepsilon$, so we have

$$g(x) \in U \quad \text{if} \quad x \in D.$$

THEOREM 2-5.3. Suppose that f and g are functions whose ranges are sets of numbers and that S is a system of stages. If $\lim_S f = \alpha$ and α and c are ordinary real numbers, then

$$\lim_S (cf) = c\alpha. \tag{2-10}$$

If also $\lim_S g = \beta$ and β is an ordinary real number, and if each stage contains at least one point in the domain of both f and g, then

$$\lim_S (f+g) = \alpha + \beta, \tag{2-11}$$

$$\lim_S (f \cdot g) = \alpha \cdot \beta, \tag{2-12}$$

$$\lim_S \left(\frac{f}{g}\right) = \frac{\alpha}{\beta} \quad \text{if} \quad \beta \neq 0. \tag{2-13}$$

We shall prove Eqs. (2-10) and (2-13), and leave (2-11) and (2-12) for the student. To prove Eq. (2-10), we need to show that, for any positive number ε, there is a stage A such that, for each x in the domain of f,

$$|cf(x) - c\alpha| < \varepsilon \quad \text{if} \quad x \in A. \tag{2-14}$$

If $c = 0$, A can be any stage. Assume $c \neq 0$. Since $\lim_S f = \alpha$ and $\varepsilon/|c|$ is a positive number, there is a stage A such that, for each x in the domain of f,

$$|f(x) - \alpha| < \frac{\varepsilon}{|c|} \quad \text{if} \quad x \in A.$$

We can multiply both members of this inequality by $|c|$ and obtain Eq. (2-14).

To prove Eq. (2-13), we show that, for any positive number ε, there is a stage C such that, for each x in the domain of f,

$$\left| \frac{f(x)}{g(x)} - \frac{\alpha}{\beta} \right| < \varepsilon \quad \text{if} \quad x \in C.$$

Note that

$$\left| \frac{f(x)}{g(x)} - \frac{\alpha}{\beta} \right| = \left| \frac{\beta f(x) - \alpha g(x)}{\beta g(x)} \right| = \left| \frac{\beta[f(x) - \alpha] + \alpha[\beta - g(x)]}{\beta g(x)} \right|$$

$$\leq \left| \frac{f(x) - \alpha}{g(x)} \right| + \left| \frac{\alpha[\beta - g(x)]}{\beta g(x)} \right|. \tag{2-15}$$

Now we choose a positive number ε and complete the proof by finding a stage C for which each of the last two terms is less than $\frac{1}{2}\varepsilon$, if $x \in C$. Since $\beta \neq 0$, there are stages A and B such that

$$|f(x) - \alpha| < \tfrac{1}{4}\varepsilon|\beta| \quad \text{if} \quad x \in A,$$

$$|\beta - g(x)| < \frac{\varepsilon\beta^2}{4|\alpha| + 2\varepsilon|\beta|} \quad \text{if} \quad x \in B. \tag{2-16}$$

If $x \in B$, then $|\beta - g(x)| < \frac{1}{2}|\beta|$ and therefore

$$|g(x)| > \tfrac{1}{2}|\beta| \quad \text{if} \quad x \in B.$$

Let $C = A \cap B$. Then $|g(x)| > \frac{1}{2}|\beta|$ and $|f(x) - \alpha| < \frac{1}{4}\varepsilon|\beta|$ if $x \in C$, so that

$$\left| \frac{f(x) - \alpha}{g(x)} \right| < \tfrac{1}{2}\varepsilon \quad \text{if} \quad x \in C.$$

Now we use (2-16) and the fact that $|g(x)| > \frac{1}{2}|\beta|$ if $x \in C$, to obtain

$$\left| \frac{\alpha[\beta - g(x)]}{\beta g(x)} \right| < \frac{|\alpha|\varepsilon\beta^2}{(4|\alpha| + 2\varepsilon|\beta|)\frac{1}{2}\beta^2} < \frac{|\alpha|\varepsilon}{2|\alpha| + \varepsilon|\beta|} < \frac{1}{2}\varepsilon \quad \text{if} \quad x \in C.$$

For the extended real number system that contains $+\infty$ and $-\infty$, it could be said that we were guided in defining the operations of addition, multiplication, and division by the desire to prove Theorem 2-5.3 valid when α and β are $+\infty$ or $-\infty$. In any case, our definitions do work in this way. However, the student should be cautioned that there are other extensions of the real number system for which theorems similar to the following theorem can be proved [the extension given by problem 5, page 41, is of particular interest].

> **THEOREM 2-5.4.** Conclusions (2-10) through (2-13) of Theorem 2-5.3, are valid if one or more of c, α, and β is $+\infty$ or $-\infty$, provided the operations in the right members are defined.

It is important to realize that there are many cases for which this theorem cannot be used. For example, Eq. (2-11) cannot be used if $\alpha = +\infty$ and $\beta = -\infty$, Eq. (2-12) cannot be used if $\alpha = +\infty$ and $\beta = 0$, and Eq. (2-13) cannot be used if $\alpha = \beta = +\infty$. We shall prove only one case of this theorem, leaving the rest for the student. Let us suppose that

$$\lim_S f = +\infty \quad \text{and} \quad \lim_S g = \beta, \tag{2-17}$$

where $\beta > 0$, and that each stage contains a point in the domain of $f \cdot g$. We shall prove that

$$\lim_S (f \cdot g) = +\infty.$$

To do this, we must show that for any number K there is a stage C such that, for all x in the domain of $f \cdot g$,

$$f(x)g(x) > K \quad \text{if} \quad x \in C.$$

Since β may be $+\infty$, we choose β^* such that $0 < \beta^* < \beta$. Then it follows from Eqs. (2-17) that there is a stage A and a stage B such that

$$f(x) > \frac{K}{\beta^*} \quad \text{if} \quad x \in A$$

and

$$g(x) > \beta^* \quad \text{if} \quad x \in B.$$

We let $C = A \cap B$. If $x \in C$, then

$$f(x)g(x) > \left(\frac{K}{\beta*}\right)(\beta*) = K.$$

PROBLEMS

1. (a) Explain why $\lim_{x \to 3} c = c$ if c is any number, and why $\lim_{x \to 3} x = 3$.
(b) Use Theorem 2-5.3 and the results of part (a) to evaluate the limits

$$\lim_{x \to 3} (7x - 5), \quad \lim_{x \to 3} (2x - 5)^7(3x - 8)^9, \quad \lim_{x \to 3} \frac{2x - 1}{x + 2}.$$

2. For each of the following, evaluate the limit in the extended real number system or explain why it does not exist.

(a) $\lim_{x \to 0} x + x^{-2}$.

(d) $\lim_{n \to +\infty} \left(\frac{1}{n}\right)2^n$.

(b) $\lim_{x \to +\infty} \frac{x^2 - 1}{x - 1}$.

(e) $\lim_{x \to 2} \frac{x}{x - 2}$.

(c) $\lim_{|x| \to +\infty} (x^2 + 4)^{1/2} - |x|$.

(f) $\lim_{x \to 0} \frac{1/x}{1/|x|}$.

3. Let f and g be defined by $f(1) = 0$, $f(2) = 3$, $f(3) = 6$; $g(1) = 2$, $g(2) = 0$, $g(3) = 3$. In each of the following, evaluate $\lim_S f$, $\lim_S g$, $\lim_S f \cdot g$, and $\lim_S f/g$ if it exists. (a) The sets $\{1, 2, 3\}$ and $\{3\}$ are the stages of S. (b) The sets $\{1, 2, 3\}$, $\{1, 2\}$, and $\{2\}$ are the stages of S.

2-6. CONTINUITY AND LIMITS

A point p in a set S is an *isolated point* of S if there is a neighborhood of p that contains no points of S other than p. Continuity at nonisolated points of the domain of a function is very closely related to the theory of limits. The precise connection is stated in the following theorem, the proof of which requires little more than an analysis of the definition of continuity.

THEOREM 2-6.1. A function is continuous at all isolated points of its domain. A necessary and sufficient condition for a function to be continuous at a nonisolated point p of its domain is that

$$\lim_{x \to p} f(x) = f(p).$$

PROOF. A point of continuity of a function f is a point p of the domain of f which has the property that, for any neighborhood V of $f(p)$, there is a neighborhood U of p such that, for all x in the domain of f,

$$f(x) \in V \quad \text{if} \quad x \in U. \tag{2-18}$$

Since $\lim_{x \to p} f(x)$ was defined in terms of stages that are intersections of the domain of f with deleted neighborhoods of p, $\lim_{x \to p} f(x) = f(p)$ means that, for any neighborhood V of $f(p)$, there is a neighborhood U of p such that, for all x in the domain of f,

$$f(x) \in V \quad \text{if} \quad x \in U \quad \text{and} \quad x \neq p.$$

Stages are required to contain points of the domain; hence, this definition of limit is meaningful only if each neighborhood of p contains a point of the domain of f other than p (i.e., p is *not* an isolated point). Since $f(p) \in V$, the requirement that x not be p is superfluous and we may conclude that, if p is not an isolated point, then f is continuous at p if and only if $\lim_{x \to p} f(x) = f(p)$. If p is an isolated point of the domain of f, then p has a neighborhood U whose intersection with the domain of f contains only the one point p. Then f is continuous at p, since (2-18) is true for U and any neighborhood V of $f(p)$.†

We shall use Theorem 2-6.1 to discuss the nature of the discontinuities of a function whose domain and range are sets of numbers. A nonisolated number c in the domain of a function f is a discontinuity if and only if

$$\lim_{x \to c} f(x) = f(c)$$

is not a true statement. It is not a true statement (I) if $\lim_{x \to c} f(x)$ does not exist; or (II) if $\lim_{x \to c} f(x)$ exists, but $\lim_{x \to c} f(x) \neq f(c)$.

    I. There are various cases for which c is not an isolated point and $\lim_{x \to c} f(x)$ does not exist. (i) It is not difficult to show that if f is not bounded near c (i.e., if for each number α and each neighborhood U of c there is an x in U such that $|f(x)| > \alpha$), then $\lim_{x \to c} f(x)$ does not exist. We then say that c is an *infinite discontinuity* of f [see (a) and (b) of Fig. 2-12]. (ii) If the left and right limits of f at c both exist, but are not equal [see problem 6 of Section 2-4], then c is said to be a *jump discontinuity* of f [see (c) and (d) of Fig. 2-12]. (iii) $\lim_{x \to c} f(x)$

---

    † Since continuity of a function at an isolated point of its domain is a consequence of the fact the point is isolated, continuity at an isolated point has only formal significance; i.e., it gives no information about the function that cannot be deduced using only the fact the point is isolated.

can fail to exist without c being either an infinite or a jump discontinuity [as indicated for $c = 0$ by (e) and (f) of Fig. 2-12]. Such a discontinuity is sometimes called an _oscillating discontinuity_.

II. If $\lim_{x \to c} f(x)$ exists, but $\lim_{x \to c} f(x) \neq f(c)$, then c is a _removable discontinuity_. This means that it is possible to change the definition of the function at the one point c in such a way that this point is not a discontinuity of the new function. In this case, the value of f at c is "poorly chosen." If the choice had been the number $\lim_{x \to c} f(x)$, then f would have been continuous at c.

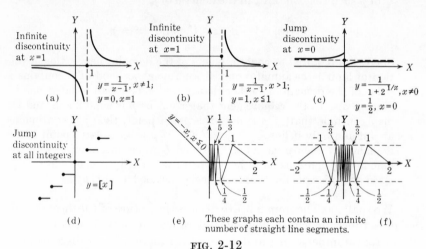

FIG. 2-12

With the definition we have given for a point of discontinuity, a function is neither continuous nor discontinuous at points not in its domain. For example, the function defined by $f(x) = 1/x$ if $x \neq 0$ is continuous at all points of its domain and therefore has no points of discontinuity. This function is noncontinuous on the x-axis in the sense that it is false that the function is continuous at all points of this line, but the function is not "discontinuous" unless it is given a value at $x = 0$. In such cases, it is customary to ignore the logical inconsistency (or to imagine the domain has been enlarged) and say that the function is discontinuous. Similarly, a function such as the function g, defined by

$$g(x) = \frac{x^2 - 1}{x - 1} = x + 1 \quad \text{if} \quad x \neq 1,$$

is often said to be continuous (meaning continuous on the entire set of real numbers), with the understanding that the function has been given the "obvious" value of 2 at $x = 1$.

Theorem 2-6.1 states that one can evaluate limits at points of
continuity by direct substitution. Thus, for limits of type $\lim_{x \to p} f(x)$,
the evaluation of the limit is particularly easy if f is continuous and p
is in the domain of f. For such limits, the theorem about sums,
products, and quotients of limits [Theorem 2-5.3] can be restated in a
useful form. Suppose f and g are functions whose ranges are sets of
real numbers, and p is a point at which $\lim_{x \to p} f(x)$ and $\lim_{x \to p} g(x)$
both exist. If p is not an isolated point of the domain of any of the
functions involved, then

$$\lim_{x \to p} \; cf(x) \;=\; c[\lim_{x \to p} f(x)] \quad \text{for any number } c; \qquad (2\text{-}19)$$

$$\lim_{x \to p} \; [f(x) + g(x)] \;=\; \lim_{x \to p} \; f(x) + \lim_{x \to p} \; g(x); \qquad (2\text{-}20)$$

$$\lim_{x \to p} \; [f(x)g(x)] \;=\; [\lim_{x \to p} \; f(x)][\lim_{x \to p} \; g(x)]; \qquad (2\text{-}21)$$

$$\lim_{x \to p} \; \left(\frac{f(x)}{g(x)}\right) \;=\; \frac{\lim_{x \to p} f(x)}{\lim_{x \to p} g(x)} \quad \text{if} \quad \lim_{x \to p} \; g(x) \neq 0. \qquad (2\text{-}22)$$

THEOREM 2-6.2. If f and g are functions that are continuous at a
point p, then $cf, f+g,$ and fg are continuous at p. Also, f/g is continuous
at p if p is in the domain of f/g, that is, if $g(p) \neq 0$.

PROOF. A function is automatically continuous at all isolated points
of its domain. An isolated point p of the domain of either f or g that
belongs to the domain of any one of $f+g$, fg, or f/g is also an isolated
point of that domain. Hence, there is no loss of generality in assuming
that p is not an isolated point of any domain involved. Then the
theorem is a direct consequence of equalities (2-19) through (2-22).

Now suppose that k is a number and f is the function such that
$f(x) = k$ for all x. Then f is continuous, since the inverse image of any
nonempty open set in the range is the entire domain and therefore is
open in the domain [see Theorem 2-2.2]. The function g such that
$g(x) = x$ for all x is continuous, since the domain and range are equal and
the inverse image of any open set in the range is the same open set in
the domain. Then because the product of two continuous functions is
continuous, it follows that kx, kx^2, kx^3, etc., are all continuous. The
sum of two continuous functions is continuous; therefore, it follows
that $a_0 + a_1 x, a_0 + a_1 x + a_2 x^2, a_0 + a_1 x + a_2 x^2 + a_3 x^3$, etc., are continuous.
That is, any polynomial function is continuous. Since the quotient of
two continuous functions is continuous, the quotient of two polynomials
is continuous. A quotient of two polynomials is called a *rational function*.

THEOREM 2-6.3. Any polynomial function is continuous. A rational function is continuous and its domain is the set of all numbers for which the denominator is nonzero.

The student will have had enough experience using the basic definitions of limit to realize that the establishment of a limit by direct use of the definition can be quite complicated and difficult. The two preceding theorems enable us to determine many limits without making direct use of the definitions.

ILLUSTRATION 1. If we let $f(x) = (x^2 + 3x - 4)/(x - 1)$ when $x \neq 1$, then

$$\lim_{x \to c} f(x) = \frac{c^2 + 3c - 4}{c - 1} = c + 4,$$

when $c \neq 1$. Also, $f(x) = x + 4$ when $x \neq 1$, so $\lim_{x \to 1} f(x) = 5$. However, 1 is not in the domain of f. If $f(x)$ had been defined as equal to $(x^2 + 3x - 4)/(x - 1)$ when $x \neq 1$ and equal to 5 when $x = 1$, then f would have been continuous at 1.

The next three theorems will make it possible to enlarge greatly the set of functions known to be continuous, without in each case facing the difficulties of using the definition of continuity.

THEOREM 2-6.4. Suppose f is a function whose domain is an interval of numbers. If f is either increasing throughout its domain or decreasing throughout its domain, then f has an inverse and the inverse is continuous.†

PROOF. We know that a function f has an inverse if and only if there do not exist two distinct points r and s in the domain of f for which $f(r) = f(s)$. If f is either increasing or decreasing, then such points r and s do not exist, so it follows that f has an inverse. Let D and R be the domain and range of f. To complete the proof, we can show that the inverse image under f^{-1} of any open set in D is an open set in R [see Theorem 2-2.2]. This is the same as showing that f maps open sets in D onto open sets in R. Suppose S is an open set in D. If $c \in S$, then there is a positive number ε such that

$$D \cap (c - \varepsilon, c + \varepsilon) \subset S.$$

If $c - \varepsilon$ and $c + \varepsilon$ both belong to D, then it follows from the fact that f is either increasing or decreasing that the interval $\big(f(c - \varepsilon), f(c + \varepsilon)\big)$ is a

---

† Note that it is not assumed that f is continuous, but compare with problem 2 of Section 2-9.

neighborhood of $f(c)$ that is contained in the image of S [see Fig. 2-13]. If only $c-\varepsilon$ does not belong to D, then $c-\varepsilon$ is a lower bound for D and $R \cap (-\infty, f(c+\varepsilon))$ is contained in the image of S. If only $c+\varepsilon$ does not belong to D, then $R \cap (f(c-\varepsilon), +\infty)$ is contained in the image of S. If neither $c-\varepsilon$ nor $c+\varepsilon$ is contained in D, then R is the image of S. Thus, there is a neighborhood of $f(c)$ in R that is contained in the image of S. Therefore, the image of S is open in R.

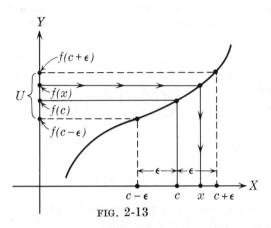

FIG. 2-13

ILLUSTRATION 2. Suppose we let $f(x) = x^2$ if $x > 0$. Then the inverse of f is the function g such that $g(x) = x^{1/2}$ if $x > 0$, where $x^{1/2}$ denotes the positive square root of x. Since f is increasing and its domain is an interval, it follows from Theorem 2-6.4 that g is continuous.

THEOREM 2-6.5. If the domain of a continuous function f is compact and f has an inverse, then the inverse is continuous.

PROOF. Let f be a function with an inverse, i.e., f is one-to-one. Also assume that the domain D of f is compact. To prove f^{-1} is continuous, we need only prove that f maps open sets onto open sets [see Theorem 2-2.2]. Let U be open in D and let U^* denote the image of U in the range R of f. Also, let p be a member of U, and let Σ^* be a cover of R that consists of U^* and all open sets in R not containing $f(p)$. Then the cover Σ of D that consists of the inverse images of members of Σ^* is a cover of D by open sets. Since D is compact, this cover can be reduced to a finite cover Σ_0 of D. The images of the sets in Σ_0 constitute a finite cover Σ_0^* of R. All of the sets in Σ_0^* except possibly U^* are open and the number of these sets is finite, so there is a neighborhood V of $f(p)$ in R that contains only points of U^*. Thus U^* is open in R. [Also see problem 7 of Section 2-8.]

The next theorem is very important, though easy to prove, and provides another useful tool for determining whether functions are continuous. We recall that the symbol $f \circ g$ denotes the composite function defined by

$$(f \circ g)(x) = f[g(x)],$$

where x is a point in the domain of g such that $g(x)$ is in the domain of f.

THEOREM 2-6.6. If g is continuous at the point p and f is continuous at the point $g(p)$, then $f \circ g$ is continuous at the point p.

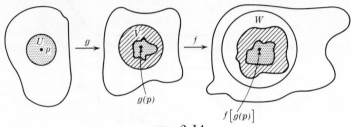

FIG. 2-14

PROOF. Little more than a picture [Fig. 2-14] is needed to prove this theorem. Suppose that g is continuous at p and that f is continuous at $g(p)$. To demonstrate that $f \circ g$ is continuous at p, we must show that, for any neighborhood W of $f[g(p)]$, there is a neighborhood U of p in the domain of $f \circ g$ whose points map onto points of W by $f \circ g$; that is,

$$f[g(x)] \in W \quad \text{if} \quad x \in U.$$

Now let W be a neighborhood of $f[g(p)]$. Since f is continuous at $g(p)$, there is a neighborhood V of $g(p)$ such that f maps each point of V onto a point of W. Since g is continuous at p, there is a neighborhood U of p such that g maps points of U onto points of V. But now, if $x \in U$, it follows that $g(x) \in V$ and that $f[g(x)] \in W$. Thus, $f \circ g$ maps points of U onto points of W.

We know that, if n is a positive integer and $f(x) = x^n$ for all x, then the function f is continuous. If the domain of f is taken to be the interval containing all positive numbers, then f is increasing and therefore has a continuous inverse g, for which $g(x) = x^{1/n}$. If now we let m be an integer (positive or negative) and let the function h be defined by $h(x) = x^m$ for $x > 0$, then h is continuous. It follows from Theorem 2-6.6 that $h \circ g$ is continuous, where

$$(h \circ g)(x) = (x^{1/n})^m = x^{m/n} \quad \text{if} \quad x > 0.$$

This proves the following theorem for the case r is rational.

THEOREM 2-6.7. If r is a real number and $f(x) = x^r$ for $x > 0$, then f is continuous at all points of its domain.†

Now we can use the theorems about the sum, product, quotient, and composition of continuous functions to enlarge the class of continuous functions. For example, the function F is continuous if

$$F(x) = \frac{(3x^2 + 16)^{\frac{2}{3}} - x + 1}{(x+5)^{\frac{1}{2}} + x^2 - 7x}$$

when $x \geq -5$ and the denominator is nonzero. In particular,

$$\lim_{x \to 4} F(x) = \frac{(64)^{\frac{2}{3}} - 4 + 1}{9^{\frac{1}{2}} + 16 - 28} = \frac{13}{-9}.$$

If the student doubts the significance of the theorems about continuity, he should try to make direct use of the definition of continuity to establish continuity of this function.

PROBLEMS

1. Evaluate the following.

(**a**) $\lim_{x \to 0} \dfrac{x^2 - 2x}{x}$.

(**c**) $\lim_{x \to 3} \dfrac{2x^2 - 7x + 4}{x^3 - 9x + 2}$.

(**b**) $\lim_{x \to 0} \dfrac{(x+4)^3 - 64}{x}$.

(**d**) $\lim_{x \to 1} \dfrac{x - 1}{x^2 + x - 2}$.

2. Show that $\lim_{x \to +\infty} f(x) = \lim_{x \to 0+} f(1/x)$ [see II (Neighborhoods of Infinity) and problem 5 of Section 2-4] and use this to show that

(a) $\lim_{x \to +\infty} \dfrac{x^2 - 3x + 1}{2x^2 + 7x + 9} = \dfrac{1}{2}$;

(b) $\lim_{x \to +\infty} \dfrac{a_0 + a_1 x + \cdots + a_n x^n}{b_0 + b_1 x + \cdots + b_m x^m} = \begin{cases} a_n/b_n & \text{if } n = m; \\ 0 & \text{if } n < m; \\ \text{is not an ordinary real number} \\ \text{if } n > m. \end{cases}$

---

† Continuity of $\ln x$ for $x > 0$ and of e^x for all x follows from Theorem 2-6.4 and the fact that both $\ln x$ and e^x are increasing and have interval domains. Then continuity of x^a for a an arbitrary real number and $x > 0$ follows from Theorem 2-6.6 and the equality $x^a = e^{a \ln x}$.

3. For each of the following, determine all points of discontinuity of the given function.   Explain.

$$\text{(a) } f(x) = \frac{x}{x+2} \quad \text{if} \quad x \neq -2. \quad \text{(b) } f(x) = \frac{x+2}{x^2+1} \quad \text{for all } x.$$

$$\text{(c) } f(x) = \frac{x}{x^3+x} \quad \text{if} \quad x \neq 0, \ f(0) = \tfrac{1}{2}.$$

4. Suppose that $f(x) = (x^2 - 2x - 3)/(x-3)$ if $x \neq 3$.   What value should be assigned to $f(3)$ in order to make f continuous at 3?

5. Let f be a function that is continuous at p.   Prove that if $f(p) > 0$, there is a neighborhood U of p such that $f(x) > 0$ if $x \in U$.

6. Explain why $\lim_{x \to p} f(x)$ does not exist if there is no neighborhood U of p on which $|f(x)|$ is bounded.

7. A function whose domain and range are sets of numbers is said to be *continuous on the left* at c if $\lim_{x \to c-} f(x) = f(c)$, and *continuous on the right* at c if $\lim_{x \to c+} f(x) = f(c)$ [see problems 4, 5, and 6 of Section 2-4]. Determine which of the functions whose graphs are indicated in (a), (b), and (d) of Fig. 2-12 are continuous on the left at 1, and which are continuous on the right at 1.   Do likewise for the graphs in (c), (e), and (f) of Fig. 2-12 at 0.

8. Find all discontinuities in the domains of the following functions and determine whether they are infinite discontinuities, jump discontinuities or neither.   In each case, determine whether the function is continuous on the right and whether it is continuous on the left at its discontinuities.

(a) $f(x) = [(1+x)^2 - 1]/x$ if $x \neq 0, f(0) = \tfrac{1}{2}$.
(b) $f(x) = [(3+x)^2 - 9]/x$ if $x \neq 0, f(0) = 6$.
(c) $f(x) = (x^3+1)/(x^2-1)$ if $x^2 \neq 1, f(1) = 7, f(-1) = -\tfrac{3}{2}$.
(d) $f(x) = [x]/x$ if $x \neq 0, f(0) = 0$.
(e) $f(x) = [(4+x)^{3/2} - 8]/x$ if $x > -4$ and $x \neq 0, f(0) = 3$.

9. Let f be defined in the following manner:

$$\begin{cases} f(x) = 0 & \text{if } x \text{ is irrational}; \\ f(x) = 1/q & \text{if } x = p/q, \end{cases}$$

where q is a positive integer and p/q is in lowest terms.   Show that f is continuous at all irrational values of x and discontinuous at all rational values of x.

10.* Let f be a function whose range is a set of numbers.   Show that f is continuous at a point p if and only if for any positive number ε there is a neighborhood U of p such that, for all r and s in the domain of f, $|f(r) - f(s)| < \varepsilon$ if $r \in U$ and $s \in U$.

11. For each of the following, evaluate the limit and explain why your answer is correct.

(a) $\lim\limits_{x \to 4} x^{\frac{1}{2}}$.

(c) $\lim\limits_{x \to 3} \left(\dfrac{x+1}{x-2}\right)^{\frac{3}{2}}$.

(b) $\lim\limits_{x \to 2} \left(\dfrac{x^2+5}{x^3-7}\right)^{\frac{1}{2}}$.

(d) $\lim\limits_{x \to 9} \left(\dfrac{x^{\frac{1}{2}}+x-8}{x+7}\right)^{\frac{3}{2}}$.

2-7. DIFFERENTIATION

The concept of limit developed in this chapter can be used to state the definition of derivative in the following familiar form.

DEFINITION 2-7.1. Suppose f is a function whose domain and range are sets of numbers. The *derivative* of f is the function f' for which a number c is in the domain of f' if and only if

$$\lim_{x \to c} \frac{f(x)-f(c)}{x-c} \tag{2-23}$$

exists, the value of this limit being $f'(c)$. The function f is *differentiable* at c if and only if c is in the domain of f'.

In order for Eq. (2-23) to have meaning, all deleted neighborhoods of c must contain points of the domain of f. A case that will often be of special interest to us is that for which the domain of the function is a closed interval $[a, b]$. Then the values at a and at b of the derivative can be determined by using the two formulas

$$\lim_{x \to a+} \frac{f(x)-f(a)}{x-a} = f'(a)$$

and

$$\lim_{x \to b-} \frac{f(x)-f(b)}{x-b} = f'(b).$$

It is customary to define one-sided derivatives; the *derivative on the right* and the *derivative on the left* are defined by

$$f'_+(c) = \lim_{x \to c+} \frac{f(x)-f(c)}{x-c}$$

and

$$f'_-(c) = \lim_{x \to c-} \frac{f(x)-f(c)}{x-c},$$

respectively, when these limits exist. For example, if $f(x) = [x]$, meaning that $f(x)$ is the greatest integer not larger than x, then

$$f'_+(1) = \lim_{x \to 1+} \frac{[x]-1}{x-1} = \lim_{x \to 1+} \frac{0}{x-1} = 0.$$

The methods now at our disposal make it possible to give careful proofs of the following familiar theorems about differentiation.

THEOREM 2-7.1.   If the function f is differentiable at c, then f is continuous at c.

PROOF.   To show that f is continuous at c, we must show that $\lim_{x \to c} f(x) = f(c)$, or that $\lim_{x \to c} [f(x) - f(c)] = 0$.   If $f'(c)$ exists, then

$$f'(c) = \lim_{x \to c} \frac{f(x) - f(c)}{x - c}. \tag{2-24}$$

It follows from Eq. (2-24) and the theorem about limit of a product [Theorem 2-5.3, Eq. (2-12)] that

$$\lim_{x \to c} [f(x) - f(c)] = \left[\lim_{x \to c} \frac{f(x) - f(c)}{x - c} \right] \left[\lim_{x \to c} (x - c) \right] = f'(c) \cdot 0 = 0.$$

The following theorem is a natural extension of Theorem 2-6.4.

THEOREM 2-7.2.   Suppose the domain of f is an interval, that f is either increasing throughout its domain or decreasing throughout its domain, and that g is the inverse of f.   If $f'(x)$ exists and is nonzero, and if $y = f(x)$ or $x = g(y)$, then $g'(y)$ exists and $g'(y) = 1/[f'(x)]$.

PROOF.   We shall let x be a point such that $f'(x)$ exists and is nonzero and we shall use the notation

$$\begin{cases} f(x) = y, \\ g(y) = x; \end{cases} \qquad \begin{cases} f(x + \Delta x) = y + \Delta y, \\ g(y + \Delta y) = x + \Delta x. \end{cases}$$

Then

$$f(x) = \lim_{\Delta x \to 0} \frac{\Delta y}{\Delta x}.$$

It follows from the theorems on limits of quotients [Theorem 2-5.3, Eq. (2-13)] that

$$\lim_{\Delta x \to 0} \frac{1}{\Delta y/\Delta x} = \frac{1}{f'(x)}$$

or

$$\lim_{\Delta x \to 0} \frac{\Delta x}{\Delta y} = \frac{1}{f'(x)}. \tag{2-25}$$

To complete the proof, we need to show that

$$\lim_{\Delta y \to 0} \frac{\Delta x}{\Delta y} = \frac{1}{f'(x)}.$$

This will follow from Eq. (2-25) if we can show that $\lim_{\Delta y \to 0} \Delta x = 0$. To do this, we assume that the domain of f is an interval and f is either increasing throughout its domain or decreasing throughout its domain. For any $\varepsilon > 0$, this assumption implies that

$$|\Delta y| \geq |f(x+\varepsilon) - f(x)| \quad \text{if} \quad \Delta x \geq \varepsilon$$

and

$$|\Delta y| \geq |f(x) - f(x-\varepsilon)| \quad \text{if} \quad \Delta x \leq -\varepsilon.$$

Thus, $|\Delta x| < \varepsilon$ if $|\Delta y|$ is less than the smaller of $|f(x+\varepsilon) - f(x)|$ and $|f(x) - f(x-\varepsilon)|$. This shows that

$$\lim_{\Delta y \to 0} \Delta x = 0.$$

ILLUSTRATION 1. Let $f(x) = 2x^2 + 8$ for $x > 0$, and $g(y) = (\frac{1}{2}y - 4)^{1/2}$ when $y > 8$. Then

$$(f \circ g)(y) = f[g(y)] = f[(\tfrac{1}{2}y - 4)^{1/2}] = 2(\tfrac{1}{2}y - 4) + 8 = y,$$

so that f and g are inverses of each other. Clearly,

$$f'(x) = 4x \quad \text{and} \quad g'(y) = \frac{1}{4(\frac{1}{2}y - 4)^{1/2}},$$

so that

$$g'(y) = \frac{1}{4(\frac{1}{2}y - 4)^{1/2}} = \frac{1}{4g(y)} = \frac{1}{4x} = \frac{1}{f'(x)}.$$

ILLUSTRATION 2. We shall let $f(x) = \ln x$ and $g(y) = e^y$, where the domain of f (range of g) is the set of all positive numbers, and the range of f (the domain of g) is the set of all numbers. Then $y = \ln x$ if and only if $x = e^y$. Therefore, f and g are inverses of each other. Figure 2-15 indicates that the graphs of $y = \ln x$ and $y = e^x$ are reflections of each other in the line $y = x$ and that the graphs are both increasing. The equation $f'(x)g'(y) = 1$ now becomes $(D_x \ln x)(D_y e^y) = 1$, or $(1/x)e^y = 1$, where x and y are numbers for which $y = \ln x$ and $x = e^y$.

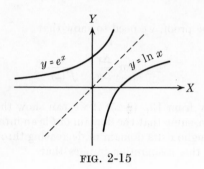

FIG. 2-15

PROBLEMS

1. Evaluate the following derivatives, using Definition 2-7.1 and theorems about limits. Do not use differentiation formulas.

(a) $D_x(3x^2 + 5x - 1)$.   (c) $D_x(3x - 1)^5$.

(b) $D_x(2x - 3)^{-1}$.   (d) $D_x[x(3x^2 + 1)^{-1}]$.

2. Evaluate each of the following.

(a) $\lim_{x \to 1} (x + 7)^{2/3}$.   (c) $\lim_{x \to 2} \dfrac{(x + 2)^{1/2} - 1}{x - 1}$.

(b) $\lim_{x \to 0} \dfrac{(x + 4)^{3/2} - 8}{x}$.   (d) $\lim_{x \to 0} \dfrac{(x + 1)^{5/2} - 1}{x}$.

3. For each of the following, find the inverse g of f and verify that $f'(x)g'(y) = 1$ when $y = f(x)$.

(a) $f(x) = 3x + 6$; all x.   (c) $f(x) = \frac{1}{2}x^2 + 3$; $x > 0$.

(b) $f(x) = x^n$; $x > 0$.   (d) $f(x) = (3x + 7)/(2x - 1)$; $x \ne \frac{1}{2}$.

4. For each of the following, find the inverse g of f and verify that $f'(x)g'(y) = 1$ when $y = f(x)$.

(a) $f(x) = (x + 7)/(2x - 5)$; $x \ne \frac{5}{2}$.

(b) $f(x) = \ln (e^x + 1)$; all x.

(c) $f(x) = \ln (x^2 - 2x + 2)$; $x \ge 1$.

5. In each of the following, f is a differentiable function such that x and y satisfy the given equation if x and y are related so that $y = f(x)$. Determine $D_x y$ and $D_y x$ and show that $D_x y \cdot D_y x = 1$.

(a) $3x + 5y = 7$.   (c) $xy + x^3 + xy^2 = 3$.

(b) $x^2 + 9y^2 = 16$.   (d) $x^2 y + xy^3 + 7x^3 + 9y = 1$.

6. Let f be the absolute value function $f(x) = |x|$.   Explain why f is continuous at $x = 0$, but is not differentiable at this point.

7. Let f be defined by $f(x) = |x| + |x-1|$.   Sketch the graph of f and explain why f is continuous everywhere but is not differentiable at $x = 0$ or at $x = 1$.

2-8. THE MAXIMUM VALUE AND MEAN VALUE THEOREMS

We shall first prove a more general theorem than the maximum value theorem and then use this theorem to obtain the maximum value theorem.   Then we shall discuss some applications of the maximum value theorem and of Theorem 2-8.1.

THEOREM 2-8.1.   If a function f is continuous on a compact set A, then the image of A is compact.

PROOF.   Let B be the image of A and let Σ be a collection of sets that covers B, with each member of Σ open in B.   Let Σ^* be the collection of all inverse images of sets in Σ.   Then each member of Σ^* is open in A [see Theorem 2-2.2] and Σ^* covers A.   Since A is compact, there is a finite subcollection of Σ^* that covers A [see Definition 2-3.1].   The images of the members of this finite subcollection form a finite subcollection of Σ that covers B.   Therefore, B is compact.

THEOREM 2-8.2 (MAXIMUM VALUE THEOREM).   Suppose f is a function that is continuous on a compact set A.   Also suppose that the range of f is a set of numbers.   Then f has an upper bound on A and there is a point p of A such that $f(p)$ is the absolute maximum of f on A.

PROOF.   Let B be the image of A.   Since A is compact, it follows from Theorem 2-8.1 that B is compact.   Therefore, B is bounded [see problem 2, page 75].   That is, f is bounded on A.   Let m be the least upper bound of f on A.   That is, m is the smallest number such that $f(p) \leq m$ for all p in A.   Then m is a cluster point of B, since if some neighborhood of m contains no numbers in B then B has a smaller upper bound than m.   Therefore, m belongs to B, since B is closed in the set of real numbers [see problem 3, page 75].

We shall now discuss Rolle's theorem and two mean value theorems with which the student may be familiar.   However, we now have tools that we can use to establish these facts carefully.

THEOREM 2-8.3 (ROLLE'S THEOREM).   Suppose f is a function that is differentiable at all points of the open interval (a, b) and is continuous at a and b.   If $f(a) = f(b)$, then there is at least one number ξ in the open interval (a, b) such that $f'(\xi) = 0$.

PROOF. Note first that if f is differentiable at a point x, then f is continuous at x [see Theorem 2-7.1]. Thus, the function f of this theorem is continuous on the closed interval $[a, b]$. Although for most applications we make there would be no objection to assuming that the function is also differentiable at a and at b, this assumption is unnecessary for the proof of the theorem and it is customary to assume only that f is continuous at a and b. Note first that if $f(x) = f(a)$ for all x in the interval $[a, b]$, then $f'(x) = 0$ for $a < x < b$ and ξ can be any number in (a, b). Now assume that there is a point x of $[a, b]$ for which $f(x) \neq f(a)$. If $f(x) > f(a)$, then f has an absolute maximum that is attained at some point inside $[a, b]$, while if $f(x) < f(a)$, then f has an absolute minimum that is attained at some point inside $[a, b]$. If $f(\xi)$ is an absolute maximum, then $[f(\xi+h)-f(\xi)]/h$ is nonnegative if h is negative and nonpositive if h is positive. This implies

$$f'(\xi) = \lim_{h \to 0} \frac{f(\xi+h)-f(\xi)}{h} = 0.$$

Similarly, $f'(\xi) = 0$ if $f(\xi)$ is an absolute minimum.

Intuitively, Rolle's theorem states that if a function f is differentiable on (a, b) and is continuous at a and b, and if the total change of f is zero, then the instantaneous rate of change is zero somewhere. It will be seen that the mean value theorem [Theorem 2-8.5] states a similar fact: "If a function is differentiable on an interval (a, b), and continuous at a and b, then the average rate of change of f on this interval is equal to the instantaneous rate of change at some point ξ, so that $f(b)-f(a) = (b-a)f'(\xi)$." Rather than proving the mean value theorem directly, we shall prove a generalization, which is just as easy to prove as the mean value theorem, and which will be useful later to develop "L'Hôpital's rule."

THEOREM 2-8.4 (DOUBLE MEAN VALUE THEOREM†). Suppose f and g are functions that are differentiable at all points of the open interval (a, b) and are continuous at a and b. Also suppose that $g(a) \neq g(b)$ and that there is no point of (a, b) at which f' and g' are both zero. Then there is at least one number ξ in the open interval (a, b) such that

$$\frac{f(b)-f(a)}{g(b)-g(a)} = \frac{f'(\xi)}{g'(\xi)}. \tag{2-26}$$

---

† Also called the *second mean value theorem, Cauchy's mean value formula*, and the *generalized* (or *extended*) *mean value theorem*.

PROOF. Let us consider the graph C of the parametric equations $x = g(t), y = f(t), a \leq t \leq b$, as indicated in Fig. 2-16. Let us pass a line L through the end points, $(g(a), f(a))$ and $(g(b), f(b))$, of the curve C. This line has an equation of type

$$y = mx + \beta, \quad \text{where} \quad m = \frac{f(b) - f(a)}{g(b) - g(a)}.$$

Also, the directed distance $d(t)$ measured along a vertical line segment from the line L to a point (x, y) on C is given by

$$d(t) = y - (mx + \beta) = f(t) - mg(t) - \beta.†$$

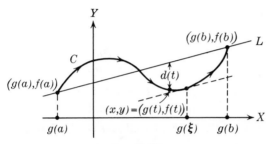

FIG. 2-16

Since f and g are differentiable at points of the open interval (a, b) and continuous at a and b, this is also true of the function d. And since $d(a) = d(b) = 0$, Rolle's theorem is applicable and there is a number ξ between a and b such that $d'(\xi) = 0$; that is, $f'(\xi) - mg'(\xi) = 0$. Since $f'(\xi)$ and $g'(\xi)$ are not both zero, it follows that $g'(\xi) \neq 0$ and

$$m = \frac{f'(\xi)}{g'(\xi)} \quad \text{or} \quad \frac{f(b) - f(a)}{g(b) - g(a)} = \frac{f'(\xi)}{g'(\xi)}.$$

Now we let the function g in the double mean value theorem be such that $g(t) = t$ for all t. Then the hypothesis $g(a) \neq g(b)$ becomes $a \neq b$. Also, the hypothesis that there is no point at which f' and g' are both zero is satisfied, since $g'(t) = 1$ for all t. The double mean value theorem then becomes Theorem 2-8.5.

THEOREM 2-8.5 (MEAN VALUE THEOREM). Suppose f is a function that is differentiable at all points of the open interval (a, b) and is

---

† Of course, $d(t)$ is proportional to the perpendicular distance from L to (x, y) so that a number ξ at which d has an absolute maximum (or minimum) determines a point at which the curve C is at greatest distance from the line L.

continuous at a and b.　Also, suppose that $a \neq b$.　Then there is at least one number ξ in the open interval (a, b) such that

$$\frac{f(b)-f(a)}{b-a} = f'(\xi) \quad \text{or} \quad f(b)-f(a) = (b-a)f'(\xi). \qquad (2\text{-}27)$$

This theorem is a special case of Theorem 2-8.4 and therefore needs no additional proof, although the usual direct proof may be obtained from the proof of Theorem 2-8.4 by replacing $g'(\xi)$ by 1 and $g(t)$, $g(a)$, and $g(b)$ by t, a and b, respectively, wherever they occur.

PROBLEMS

1. Find a number ξ for which $f(b)-f(a) = (b-a)f'(\xi)$ and $a < \xi < b$, if
　(*a*) $f(x) = x^2$　for all x, $a = 0$, $b = 2$;
　(*b*) $f(x) = 1/x$　for $x > 0$, $a = \frac{1}{2}$, $b = 3$;
　(*c*) $f(x) = x^3 - x$　for all x, $a = -3$, $b = -1$;
　(*d*) $f(x) = x^3 - 9x^2 + 15$　for all x, $a = -2$, $b = 1$.

2. In each of the following cases, the function has no absolute maximum. Explain why this does not contradict the maximum value theorem.
　(a) $f(x) = x^4;\ 0 \leq x < 2$.　　　　(c) $f(x) = x^2/(1+x^2)$　for all x.
　(b) $f(x) = \begin{cases} 1/x & \text{if } 0 < x \leq 1; \\ 0 & \text{if } x = 0. \end{cases}$　(d) $f(x) = \begin{cases} x & \text{if } 0 \leq x < 1; \\ 1-x & \text{if } 1 \leq x \leq 2. \end{cases}$

3. In each of the following, f has no absolute maximum.　Explain why this does not contradict the maximum value theorem.
　(a) $f(x, y) = 2x - y$　for all (x, y).
　(b) $f(x, y) = (x^2 + y^2)$　if $0 < x^2 + y^2 \leq 1$.
　(c) $f(x, y) = x + 2y$　if $0 \leq x < 1$　and　$0 \leq y \leq 2$,
　　　or if $0 \leq x \leq 2$　and　$0 \leq y \leq 1$.

4. Let f be a function whose range is a set of real numbers.　Prove that, if f is continuous on a compact set A, then f is bounded on A.　Do this by using the cover of A that contains all sets of type $\{x: f(x) < n\}$, where n is a positive integer.

5. Let A be a subset of R^3 with the property that each function continuous on A with its range a set of real numbers maps A onto a bounded set.　Prove that A is compact by using the Heine-Borel theorem and proving that (a) A is bounded; (b) A is closed in R^3. [*Hint:* If $p \notin A$ and p is a cluster point of A, consider the function f with $f(x) = \{d(x, p)\}^{-1}$.]

6. Let f be a continuous function whose range is a set of numbers. Prove that if A is a connected compact set, then the image of A is a closed bounded interval.

7. Suppose a continuous function f has an inverse and the domain D of f is compact. Prove that f^{-1} is continuous by showing that, if f^{-1} is not continuous at $f(p)$, then there is a positive number ε such that the function g defined by

$$g(r) = \frac{1}{d[f(p), f(r)]}$$

is not bounded on $\{r: d(p, r) \geq \varepsilon\} \cap D$.   [See Theorem 2-6.5.]

8. Let $f(x) = |x|$ for all x. Show that if $a < 0 < b$ then there is no number for which $f(b) - f(a) = (b - a)f'(\xi)$. Why is this not a counterexample for the mean value theorem?

9. Let $f(x) = x^{\frac{1}{3}}$ for all x. Note that $f(a) < 0 < f(b)$ if $a < 0 < b$.

(a) Explain why the mean value theorem cannot be used with the function f when $a < 0 < b$ to prove the existence of a number ξ for which $f(b) - f(a) = (b - a)f'(\xi)$.

(b) Show that if $a < 0 < b$, then the mean value theorem can be used with the function $g(y) = y^3$ to prove the existence of a number ξ between a and b for which $f(b) - f(a) = (b - a)f'(\xi)$.

10. Let f be a function for which there exists a function F with $F'(x) = f(x)$ for $a \leq x \leq b$. Also assume $f(a) < f(b)$ and k is a number between $f(a)$ and $f(b)$.

(a) Explain why there is a positive number h less than $b - a$ for which

$$\frac{F(a+h) - F(a)}{h} < k < \frac{F(b) - F(b-h)}{h}.$$

(b) Use the intermediate value theorem to show that for this value of h there is a number x_0 for which

$$a < x_0 < b - h \quad \text{and} \quad \frac{F(x_0 + h) - F(x_0)}{h} = k.$$

(c) Show that there is a number ξ in (a, b) such that $f(\xi) = k$. [Compare this to the intermediate value theorem of Section 2-2.]

2-9.   APPLICATIONS OF MEAN VALUE THEOREMS

The following corollaries are very important in elementary calculus. Their proofs depend heavily on the mean value theorem. Theorem 2-9.1 is another application of the mean value theorem.

It gives us a test for uniform continuity that complements Theorem 2-3.3 and also is helpful in understanding the meaning of uniform continuity.

COROLLARY 1. A function is increasing on an interval if its derivative is positive at all points of the interval; it is decreasing on an interval if its derivative is negative at all points of the interval.

COROLLARY 2. If f and g are functions such that $f'(x) = g'(x)$ for all x in an interval I, then there is a number c such that $f(x) = g(x) + c$ for all x in I.

PROOFS. For Corollary 1, let us suppose the derivative of f is positive at all points of an interval I and that r and s are in I, with $r < s$. Then it follows from the mean value theorem that there is a number ξ such that $r < \xi < s$ and

$$f(s) - f(r) = (s-r)f'(\xi).$$

Since $f'(\xi) > 0$, we have $f(s) - f(r) > 0$. Similarly, f is decreasing if f' is negative at all points of I.

To prove Corollary 2, we suppose $f'(x) = g'(x)$ for all x in an interval I and then choose a particular number a in I. For any x in I, there is a number ξ in I with

$$[f(x) - g(x)] - [f(a) - g(a)] = (x-a)[f'(\xi) - g'(\xi)].$$

Since $f'(\xi) = g'(\xi)$, this gives us $f(x) - g(x) = c$, where $c = f(a) - g(a)$.

THEOREM 2-9.1. Suppose f is a function that is differentiable at each point of an interval I. If there is a number M for which $|f'(x)| \leq M$ when $x \in I$, then f is uniformly continuous on I.

PROOF. We need to show that, if ε is a positive number, then there exists a positive number δ such that

$$|f(r) - f(s)| < \varepsilon \quad \text{if} \quad |r-s| < \delta$$

and r and s are points of I. In order to show that δ can be found, whatever the value of ε, we shall find δ as a function of ε without specifying the value of ε. The first step is to use the mean value theorem, noting that for any points r and s of I there is a number ξ between r and s for which

$$f(r) - f(s) = f'(\xi)(r-s).$$

Since $|f'(\xi)| \leqq M$, it follows from $|f(r)-f(s)| = |f'(\xi)| \cdot |r-s|$ that $|f(r)-f(s)| \leqq M |r-s|$ and that

$$|f(r)-f(s)| < \varepsilon \quad \text{if} \quad |r-s| < \frac{\varepsilon}{M}.$$

Thus, ε/M is a suitable value of δ and the proof is complete.

For many functions, this theorem gives an adequate test of uniform continuity. For example, let $f(x) = 1/x$ if $x \neq 0$. Then $f'(x) = -1/x^2$ and $|f'(x)|$ is not bounded. However, we can choose a positive number r and note that, if $x \geqq r$, then $|f'(x)| \leqq 1/r^2$. Therefore, f is uniformly continuous on the set $S = \{x : x \geqq r\}$.

ILLUSTRATION 1. Suppose we let $g(x) = x^2$ for all x. Then $g'(x) = 2x$. Although $|g'(x)|$ is not bounded, we can choose a positive number K and note that, if $|x| \leqq K$, then $|g'(x)| \leqq 2K$. Therefore, g is uniformly continuous on the interval $[-K, K]$.

The major application of the double mean value theorem will be in the proof of L'Hôpital's rule. However, before stating this rule, we shall consider two illustrative examples.

ILLUSTRATION 2. Suppose we wish to determine whether

$$\lim_{x \to 0} \frac{\ln(1+x) - x}{x^2} \tag{2-28}$$

exists and, if it exists, that we want to know its value. To use the double mean value theorem, we shall let $f(x) = \ln(1+x) - x$ and $g(x) = x^2$. Then $f(0) = g(0) = 0$ and Eq. (2-26), with $a = 0$ and $b = x$, gives us

$$\frac{\ln(1+x) - x}{x^2} = \frac{f'(\xi)}{g'(\xi)} = \frac{(1+\xi)^{-1} - 1}{2\xi} = \frac{-\xi}{2\xi(1+\xi)} = \frac{-1}{2(1+\xi)}.$$

Since ξ is between 0 and x, it follows that ξ approaches zero as x approaches zero and that $-1/[2(1+\xi)]$ approaches $-\frac{1}{2}$ as x approaches zero. Therefore, (2-28) exists and equals $-\frac{1}{2}$.

ILLUSTRATION 3. Suppose we wish to determine whether

$$\lim_{x \to +\infty} \frac{\ln x}{x}$$

exists and, if it exists, that we want to know its value. To use the double mean value theorem, we shall let $f(x) = \ln x$ and $g(x) = x$. Then for positive numbers x and α, there is a number ξ between x and α such that

$$\frac{\ln x - \ln \alpha}{x - \alpha} = \frac{1}{\xi}.$$

Therefore, as x and α increase, $(\ln x - \ln \alpha)/(x - \alpha)$ approaches zero and

$$\frac{\ln x}{x} \left[\frac{1 - \ln \alpha / \ln x}{1 - \alpha / x} \right] \to 0. \tag{2-29}$$

If we let $\alpha^2 = x$, then when $x > 1$ we have

$$\frac{\ln x}{x} \left[\frac{1 - \ln \alpha / \ln x}{1 - \alpha / x} \right] = \frac{\ln x}{x} \left[\frac{1 - \frac{1}{2}}{1 - 1/\alpha} \right] > \frac{1}{2} \left(\frac{\ln x}{x} \right),$$

so it follows from Eq. (2-29) that

$$\lim_{x \to +\infty} \frac{\ln x}{x} = 0.$$

LEMMA. Suppose that f and g are functions for which there is a positive number η such that f and g are differentiable at all points of the open interval $(a, a+\eta)$, there is no point of $(a, a+\eta)$ at which f' and g' are both zero, and one of the following is true:

(i) $\lim_{x \to a+} f(x) = \lim_{x \to a+} g(x) = 0.$

(ii) $\lim_{x \to a+} |f(x)| = \lim_{x \to a+} |g(x)| = +\infty.$

If $\lim_{x \to a+} f'(x)/g'(x)$ exists, then $\lim_{x \to a+} f(x)/g(x)$ exists and

$$\lim_{x \to a+} \frac{f(x)}{g(x)} = \lim_{x \to a+} \frac{f'(x)}{g'(x)}.$$

PROOF. We must use a slightly different technique than that indicated by Illustration 2, since $f(a)$ and $g(a)$ are not assumed to exist. If $\lim_{x \to a+} f'(x)/g'(x)$ exists, then each interval of type $(a, a+k)$ contains at least one point x in the domain of f'/g' [see Definition 2-4.2]; at such a point x, $g'(x) \neq 0$, so that g is not identically zero on $(a, a+k)$. For a number x in $(a, a+k)$ with $g(x) \neq 0$, we shall let α be another number in $(a, a+k)$ for which $g(\alpha) \neq g(x)$. Then it follows from the double mean value theorem that there is a number ξ such that

$$\frac{f(x)-f(\alpha)}{g(x)-g(\alpha)} = \frac{f'(\xi)}{g'(\xi)}, \tag{2-30}$$

where ξ is between α and x. Suppose that $\lim_{x \to a+} f'(x)/g'(x)$ exists and equals l. Then for any positive number ε there is an open interval $(a, a+\delta)$ such that

$$\left| \frac{f'(x)}{g'(x)} - l \right| < \varepsilon \quad \text{if} \quad x \in (a, a+\delta). \tag{2-31}$$

It then follows from Eqs. (2-30) and (2-31) that

$$\left| \frac{f(x)-f(\alpha)}{g(x)-g(\alpha)} - l \right| < \varepsilon \quad \text{if} \quad x \in (a, a+\delta) \quad \text{and} \quad \alpha \in (a, a+\delta). \tag{2-32}$$

In case (i), $\lim_{\alpha \to a+} [f(x)-f(\alpha)]/[g(x)-g(\alpha)] = f(x)/g(x)$, and it follows from Eq. (2-32) that

$$\left| \frac{f(x)}{g(x)} - l \right| \leqq \varepsilon.$$

Therefore, $\lim_{x \to a+} f(x)/g(x) = l$.

In case (ii), we first observe that if, for some positive integer $n > 1$, x is chosen close enough to a that $|f(\alpha)| < |f(x)|/n$ and $|g(\alpha)| < |g(x)|/n$, then

$$\frac{n}{n+1} |f(x)-f(\alpha)| < |f(x)| < \frac{n}{n-1} |f(x)-f(\alpha)|,$$

$$\frac{n}{n+1} |g(x)-g(\alpha)| < |g(x)| < \frac{n}{n-1} |g(x)-g(\alpha)|,$$

and

$$\frac{n-1}{n+1} \left| \frac{f(x)-f(\alpha)}{g(x)-g(\alpha)} \right| < \left| \frac{f(x)}{g(x)} \right| < \frac{n+1}{n-1} \left| \frac{f(x)-f(\alpha)}{g(x)-g(\alpha)} \right|.$$

We leave it to the student to use this inequality and show that, since $f(x)/g(x)$ and $[f(x)-f(\alpha)]/[g(x)-g(\alpha)]$ have the same sign, the absolute value of their difference is not greater than $2/(n-1)$ multiplied by $|[f(x)-f(\alpha)]/[g(x)-g(\alpha)]|$, or $2/(n-1)$ multiplied by $|l|+\varepsilon$ [see (2-32)]. Therefore, it follows from (2-32) that

$$\left| \frac{f(x)}{g(x)} - l \right| < \frac{2}{n-1} (|l|+\varepsilon) + \varepsilon < \frac{2|l|}{n-1} + 2\varepsilon,$$

if $n > 3$. We could have chosen n large enough that the last member of this inequality is less than 3ε. Since ε was arbitrary, it follows that $\lim_{x \to a+} f(x)/g(x) = l$.

The number a in this lemma could be $-\infty$. Also, a similar lemma can be proved for limits on the left (in this case, the number a could be $+\infty$). Since a limit exists if and only if the limits on both the right and left exist and are equal [see problem 6, page 84], the theorem that follows is a direct consequence of our lemma and the similar unstated lemma for limits on the left.

THEOREM 2-9.2 (L'HÔPITAL'S RULE). Suppose f and g are functions such that f and g are both differentiable at all points of a deleted neighborhood of a which contains no point at which f' and g' are both zero (a can be $+\infty$ or $-\infty$), and that one of the following is true:

(i) $\lim_{x \to a} f(x) = \lim_{x \to a} g(x) = 0$;

(ii) $\lim_{x \to a} |f(x)| = \lim_{x \to a} |g(x)| = +\infty$.

If $\lim_{x \to a} f'(x)/g'(x)$ exists, then $\lim_{x \to a} f(x)/g(x)$ exists and

$$\lim_{x \to a} \frac{f(x)}{g(x)} = \lim_{x \to a} \frac{f'(x)}{g'(x)}.$$

ILLUSTRATION 4. Suppose we wish to evaluate

$$\lim_{x \to 0} \frac{(1+x)^{\frac{1}{2}} - 1 - \frac{1}{2}x}{x^2}.$$

We know that this limit exists and is equal to

$$\lim_{x \to 0} \frac{\frac{1}{2}(1+x)^{-\frac{1}{2}} - \frac{1}{2}}{2x},$$

provided this limit exists. The numerator and denominator of this expression both approach zero as x approaches zero, so we use L'Hôpital's rule again and assert that both of the previous limits exist and are equal to

$$\lim_{x \to 0} \frac{-\frac{1}{4}(1+x)^{-\frac{3}{2}}}{2} = -\frac{1}{8}.$$

PROBLEMS

1. Explain why $f'(x) \geq 0$ at all points of an interval if f is increasing on the interval, and why $f'(x) \leq 0$ at all points of an interval if f is decreasing on the interval. Is this exactly the converse of Corollary 1 ?

2. Let f be a continuous function whose domain is an interval of numbers. Prove that if f has an inverse then either f is increasing throughout its domain or f is decreasing throughout its domain.

3. For each of the following functions and the specified interval I, find a number δ such that, for r and s in I,

$$|f(r) - f(s)| < \varepsilon \quad \text{if} \quad |r - s| < \delta.$$

  (a) $f(x) = x^{\frac{1}{3}}$; $I = \{x: 1 \leq x \leq 8\}$; $\varepsilon = \frac{1}{10}$.
  (b) $f(x) = 1/x^2$; $I = \{x: x \geq 2\}$; $\varepsilon = \frac{1}{8}$.
  (c) $f(x) = e^x$; $I = \{x: x \leq 2\}$; $\varepsilon = e$.

4. Let $f(x) = x(\ln x)$ if $x > 0$ and $f(0) = 0$. Show that f is uniformly continuous on the closed interval $[0, 1]$, but that $f'(x)$ is not bounded on $[0, 1]$. Explain why this does not contradict Theorem 2-9.1.

5. For each of the following, determine whether the given function is uniformly continuous on the set S indicated. Explain.

  (a) $f(x) = \ln x$; $S = \{x: x > 0\}$.
  (b) $f(x) = \ln x$; $S = \{x: x > 1\}$.
  (c) $f(x) = x^2 \ln |x|$; $S = \{x: 0 < |x| < 1\}$.
  (d) $f(x) = x^2$ if $|x| \leq 1$; $f(x) = x^{\frac{4}{5}}$ if $|x| > 1$, S the x-axis.

6. For each of the following, use L'Hôpital's rule to evaluate the limit.

  (a) $\displaystyle\lim_{x \to 0} \frac{(1 + 3x)^{\frac{1}{2}} - (1 - 2x)^{\frac{1}{2}}}{x}$.
      (e) $\displaystyle\lim_{x \to 0} \frac{e^x + e^{-x} - 2}{3x^2}$.

  (b) $\displaystyle\lim_{x \to 0} \frac{(1 - x)^{\frac{1}{2}} + x - (1 + x)^{\frac{1}{2}}}{x^3}$.
    (f) $\displaystyle\lim_{x \to +\infty} \frac{\ln (x + 1) - \ln (x - 1)}{x^{-1}}$.

  (c) $\displaystyle\lim_{x \to 1} \frac{(x - 1)^2}{2x^3 - 2x^2 + x - 1}$.
    (g) $\displaystyle\lim_{x \to 0} \frac{\ln (1 + x) - \ln (1 - x)}{x}$.

  (d) $\displaystyle\lim_{x \to +\infty} \frac{x(\ln x)}{e^x}$.
      (h) $\displaystyle\lim_{x \to 0} \frac{x \cos x - \sin x}{x^3}$.

7. Justify each of the following equalities.

  (a) $\displaystyle\lim_{x \to +\infty} \frac{3x^3 + 5x - 1}{5x^3 + 7x^2 + 2} = \frac{3}{5}$.
    (c) $\displaystyle\lim_{x \to +\infty} x^n e^{-x} = 0$,
                         n a positive integer.

  (b) $\displaystyle\lim_{x \to 0} \frac{3x^3 + 5x - 1}{5x^3 + 7x^2 + 2} = -\frac{1}{2}$.
    (d) $\displaystyle\lim_{x \to +\infty} \frac{(\ln x)^n}{x} = 0$,
                         n a positive integer.

8. Use L'Hôpital's rule to evaluate the following limits.

(a) $\lim\limits_{x \to 0+} \dfrac{x^{1/2} - x}{x^{1/2} + x}$.　　(b) $\lim\limits_{x \to 0+} \dfrac{x^{3/2} e^x}{\ln (1 + x)}$.　　(c) $\lim\limits_{x \to 0+} \dfrac{\ln x}{1 + 2^{1/x}}$.

9. Evaluate each of the following.

(a) $\lim\limits_{x \to 0+} x(\ln x)$.   [*Hint:* Write $x(\ln x)$ as a quotient.]

(b) $\lim\limits_{x \to 0+} x(\ln x)^2$.

(c) $\lim\limits_{x \to 0+} \ln (1 - x) \cdot \ln x$.

(d) $\lim\limits_{|x| \to +\infty} \dfrac{2^x}{1 + 3^x}$.

10. Explain why it is true for both case (i) and case (ii) of Theorem 2-9.2 that

$$\lim_{x \to a} \frac{f(x)}{g(x)} = +\infty \quad \text{if} \quad \lim_{x \to a} \frac{f'(x)}{g'(x)} = +\infty.$$

11. For each of the following, use problem 10 and/or L'Hôpital's rule to evaluate the given limit.

(a) $\lim\limits_{x \to +\infty} \dfrac{x^2 + 3}{x - 7}$.　　　　　(c) $\lim\limits_{x \to 1/2} \dfrac{\ln 2x}{2x - 1}$.

(b) $\lim\limits_{x \to 0} \dfrac{e^x + e^{-x} - 2}{x^4}$.　　(d) $\lim\limits_{x \to 0+} \dfrac{e^{3x} - 1}{x^2}$.

2-10. MORE TOPOLOGICAL CONCEPTS

We have seen that the least upper bound axiom can be used to prove that monotone bounded sequences have limits [Theorem 1-4.1] and that an interval is connected [see the proof of Theorem 2-1.4]. The convergence of monotone bounded sequences also was used to prove the Heine-Borel theorem. In this section, we shall introduce some more topological concepts and relate them to the preceding facts.

DEFINITION 2-10.1. A *nested* sequence of sets is a sequence of sets $\{S_n\}$ with the property that $S_{k+1} \subset S_k$ for all k.

THEOREM 2-10.1. Let T be a metric space. Then each of the following is a necessary and sufficient condition for T to be compact.
  (i) Each nested sequence of closed nonempty subsets of T has a nonempty intersection.
  (ii) (BOLZANO-WEIERSTRASS PROPERTY.) Each infinite subset of T has a cluster point in T.

(iii) Each sequence whose terms are members of T has a subsequence that converges to a point of T.

PROOF. We shall first use an indirect proof to show that T has property (i) if T is compact, starting with the assumption that there is a nested sequence $\{S_n\}$ of closed nonempty subsets of T that has an empty intersection. Since $\bigcap_1^{+\infty} S_n = \Phi$, each point of T belongs to $T - S_n$ for some n and the sets $\{T - S_n\}$ constitute a cover of T by open sets. It follows from the nested property that this cover cannot be reduced to a finite cover, since if $T - S_k$ is the last member of such a finite cover then no point of the nonempty set S_k belongs to a member of the finite cover. Therefore, T is not compact.

To prove that (i) implies (ii), we let S be an infinite subset of T. Then we choose a sequence $\{p_n\}$ of members of S and define a sequence of sets $\{S_n\}$ by letting $S_n = \{p_n, \ p_{n+1}, \cdots\}$ for all n. Then $\bigcap_1^{+\infty} S_n$ is empty and none of the sets $\{S_n\}$ is empty, so it follows from (i) that there is an m for which S_m is not closed in T. This implies that S_m has a cluster point in T. This point also is a cluster point of S.

The proof that (ii) implies (iii) is easy. Given a sequence $\{x_n\}$ with $x_n \in T$ for all n, we let x be a cluster point of $\{x_n\}$ that belongs to T. Then we choose the desired subsequence $\{y_n\}$ inductively by the rule that y_n is the first member of $\{x_n\}$ with the property that

$$d(x, y_n) < \varepsilon_n,$$

where ε_n is the smaller of n^{-1} and the smallest of the distances $d(x, y_1), \cdots, d(x, y_{n-1})$. The reader should check that this defines a subsequence of $\{x_n\}$ that converges to x.

It remains to complete a circle of implications by proving that T is compact if T satisfies (iii). We use an indirect proof, starting with the assumption that T is not compact, so that there is a cover Σ of T by open sets that cannot be reduced to a finite cover. The argument is similar to that used in the proof of Theorem 2-3.2. For no positive integer n can there be an infinite subset of T with every two points at distance at least $1/n$, since a sequence with this property cannot have a convergent subsequence. Therefore, for each n, there is a largest finite set T_n with the property that every point is at least at distance $1/n$ from every other point. For at least one x_n in T_n, the n^{-1}-neighborhood of x_n cannot be covered by a finite number of members of Σ, since T is contained in the union of such neighborhoods. Let x be the limit of a subsequence of $\{x_n\}$, let U be a member of Σ that contains x, and let ε be a positive number such that U contains the ε-neighborhood of x. Then, for some p, we have $d(x, x_p) < \frac{1}{2}\varepsilon$ and $p^{-1} < \frac{1}{2}\varepsilon$, so that the p^{-1}-neighborhood of x_p is contained in U. This is impossible, since the p^{-1}-neighborhood of x_p cannot be covered by a finite number of members of Σ and certainly not by only one member of Σ.

THEOREM 2-10.2. Each Cauchy sequence in R^3 is convergent.

PROOF. Let $\{p_n\}$ be a Cauchy sequence in R^3. That is, for every positive number ε there is an N such that

$$d(p_n, p_m) < \varepsilon \quad \text{if} \quad m > N \quad \text{and} \quad n > N.$$

Since $\{p_n\}$ is a Cauchy sequence, it is bounded [see problem 1]. It then follows from the Bolzano-Weierstrass property that the closure of $\{p_n\}$ has a cluster point, so that $\{p_n\}$ itself has a cluster point p. We shall show that p is the limit of $\{p_n\}$. For an arbitrary positive number ε, we must show that there is an N such that

$$d(p, p_m) < \varepsilon \quad \text{if} \quad m > N.$$

First, we choose N so that

$$d(p_n, p_m) < \tfrac{1}{2}\varepsilon \quad \text{if} \quad m > N \quad \text{and} \quad n > N.$$

Then we use the fact that p is a cluster point of $\{p_n\}$ to choose p_k so that

$$d(p, p_k) < \tfrac{1}{2}\varepsilon \quad \text{and} \quad k > N.$$

It follows from the triangle inequality and these inequalities that

$$d(p, p_m) < d(p, p_k) + d(p_k, p_m) < \varepsilon \quad \text{if} \quad m > N.$$

We conclude this section with an omnibus theorem listing a number of properties that are equivalent to the least upper bound axiom for an ordered field. Any one of these could have been used in place of the least upper bound axiom as an axiom for the real numbers.

Every ordered field contains a subset isomorphic to the set of rational numbers. In the rest of this section, the usual rational-number numerals are used to designate the corresponding members of an ordered field. An ordered field being *Archimedian* means that for any positive numbers x and y there is a positive integer n with $nx > y$ [see problem 11, p. 31]. Each of (i) through (vi) of Theorem 2-10.3 implies F is Archimedian. However, there are non-Archimedian ordered fields for which all Cauchy sequences are convergent. The importance of the Archimedian hypothesis in (vii) should be clear from the proof of Theorem 2-10.3, which makes heavy use of the equivalence of the Archimedian property and the convergence of the sequence $\{1/n\}$ [also see problem 4].

THEOREM 2-10.3.   For an ordered field F, any two of the following are equivalent.

  (i) If a nonempty subset S of F has an upper bound, then S has a least upper bound.
 (ii) All intervals in F are connected.
(iii) Each monotone bounded sequence in F is convergent.
 (iv) A subset of F is compact if it is bounded and closed in F.
  (v) Each nested sequence of closed bounded nonempty subsets of F has a nonempty intersection.
 (vi) Each bounded infinite subset of F has a cluster point in F.
(vii) The field F is Archimedian and each Cauchy sequence in F is convergent.

PROOF.   As explained in the first paragraph of this section, we have already shown that (i) implies both (ii) and (iii).   This simply means that the set of real numbers has properties (ii) and (iii).   Hereafter, we do not know that the ordered field F satisfies the least upper bound axiom (i).   However, F is to be considered as our set of "numbers" that are used in treating F as a "metric" space, with

$$d(x, y) = |x-y|.$$

With this interpretation, the proof of Theorem 2-3.2 (Heine-Borel) can be restated for one dimension to prove that (iii) implies (iv).† Similarly, the first two paragraphs of the proof of Theorem 2-10.1 show that (iv) implies (v) and that (v) implies (vi).   The proof of Theorem 2-10.2 shows that (vi) implies each Cauchy sequence in F is convergent. To complete the proof, we shall show that (vi) implies F is Archimedian, (vii) implies (i), and that (ii) implies (i).

To use (vi) to prove that F is Archimedian, we let x and y be arbitrary positive members of F.   If $nx \leq y$ for all n, then the set $\{nx\}$ is bounded and has a cluster point ξ.   Then there are unequal integers r and s with

$$d(\xi, rx) < \tfrac{1}{2}x \quad \text{and} \quad d(\xi, sx) < \tfrac{1}{2}x.$$

This implies $\mathrm{d}(rx, sx) < x$, which is contradicted by

$$d(rx, sx) = |r-s|x \geq x.$$

Therefore there is an n with $nx > y$.

---

† Note that in the proof of the Heine–Borel theorem the Archimedian property was used on page 73 to conclude that the edge of S_n approaches zero and $S_n \cap T \subset U$ for some n.   However, the Archimedian property follows from the convergence of $\{1/n\}$ [see problem 4].

To show that (vii) implies (i), we let S be an arbitrary bounded subset of F and use the Archimedian property to conclude that there is a largest integer n for which there is an s in S with $s \geqq n$. Then we consider the sequence

$$\{n + .d_1, \ n + .d_1 d_2, \ n + .d_1 d_2 d_3, \cdots\}, \tag{2-33}$$

for which d_1 is the largest of the digits $0, 1, \cdots, 9$ for which there is an s in S, with $s \geqq n + .d_1$; d_2 is the largest of the digits $0, 1, \cdots, 9$ for which there is an s in S, with $s \geqq n + .d_1 d_2$; etc. For any positive member ε of F, it follows from the Archimedian property that there is a positive integer n, with $n\varepsilon > 1$ and $1/n < \varepsilon$. Since $10^{-n} < 1/n$, the sequence (2-33) is a Cauchy sequence and therefore has a limit α. Then α is an upper bound of S, since if $s > \alpha$ and $s \in S$ then there is a positive integer n, with $n(s - \alpha) > 1$ and $s - \alpha > 10^{-n}$. Then the nth digit d_n in (2-33) could have been larger than it is. Also, there is no smaller upper bound of S than α, since if $\beta < \alpha$ and $10^{-n} < \alpha - \beta$ then $n + .d_1 \cdots d_n > \beta$.

We now have a complete circle of implications from (i) through (vii) and back to (i), with (ii) omitted. We know that (i) implies (ii). We shall complete the proof by showing that (ii) implies (i). To do this, we shall use only the hypothesis that F itself is connected. Let S be an arbitrary nonempty subset of F with an upper bound and let

$$A = \{x \colon x < s \text{ for some member } s \text{ of } S\},$$

$$B = \{x \colon x \geqq s \text{ if } s \in S\}.$$

Clearly, $A \cap B$ is empty and $A \cup B = F$. Since S is nonempty, A is nonempty. For each s of S, the set $\{x \colon x < s\}$ is open. Thus, A is the union of open sets and therefore is open [see problem 9, page 60]. Since S has an upper bound, B is not empty. Since F is connected, B is not open and contains a cluster point ω of A. Since $\omega \in B$, ω is an upper bound of S. Since every neighborhood of ω contains points of A, ω is a least upper bound of A.

PROBLEMS

1. Show that every Cauchy sequence of points in R^3 is bounded.

2. Give an example of a nested sequence of bounded nonempty sets that have an empty intersection.

3. Give an example of a nested sequence of closed nonempty sets that have an empty intersection.

4. Show that each of the following is a necessary and sufficient condition for an ordered field F to be Archimedian.

(a) The set of positive integers in F is not bounded.

(b) $\lim_{n \to +\infty} 1/n = 0$.

(c) The sequence $\{1/n\}$ is convergent.

5. Without using the Heine-Borel theorem or any of the theorems of this section, prove the following theorems about an Archimedian ordered field F.

(a) If each monotone bounded sequence in F is convergent, then every nonempty subset S of F with an upper bound has a least upper bound.

(b) If all bounded closed subsets of F are compact, then each monotone bounded sequence in F is convergent.

(c) If each nested sequence of closed bounded subsets of F has a nonempty intersection, then all bounded closed subsets of F are compact.

6.* A *Cauchy net* is a function f and a system of stages S such that each stage contains at least one point in the domain of f and for each positive number ε there is a stage A such that

$$|f(x) - f(y)| < \varepsilon \quad \text{if} \quad x \in A \quad \text{and} \quad y \in A.$$

Suppose (f, S) is a Cauchy net and the range of f is in R^3. Prove that $\lim_S f$ exists.

3

AREA AND
INTEGRATION

Although the Greeks did not develop the concept of derivative, the principles of definite integration were involved in the *method of exhaustion* of Eudoxus and Archimedes, who discovered several formulas for area equivalent to simple integration formulas. The method of exhaustion is similar to the method of "inner sums" and "outer sums," which we shall use to study area.†

Francesco Cavalieri (1598–1647) revived the methods of the Greeks 2000 years later in his *method of indivisibles*, which has been extended and improved by other mathematicians to assume the form of the summation process used today.

The development of the concept of differentiation began with attempts to solve the problem of finding tangents to curves. There is reason to think that the first person to realize the relation between differentiation and integration was Barrow, though the creation of a symbolism and systematic set of formal analytical rules was provided independently by Newton, who was Barrow's pupil, and Leibniz. In his *method of fluxions*, Newton used *fluent* and *fluxion* for what we now call *function* and *derivative*, and denoted the derivative by putting a dot over the letter representing the function. Leibniz introduced the notation for derivatives and integrals that is commonly used today— namely, dy/dx and $\int_a^b f(x)\, dx$.

During the early development of calculus, the trend was away from precision of thought toward free use of imagination. Such concepts as infinity, the infinitesimal, motion, and continuity were used without being adequately defined. Although this imaginative approach may

---

† Problem 10, page 140, makes direct use of the method of exhaustion.

have helped develop some of the fundamentals of calculus, it also led
to a great deal of confusion of thought and to the invention of many
alternative methods. It was not until Augustin Cauchy (1789–1857),
Karl Weierstrass (1815–1897), and others gave continuity, limit,
derivative, and definite integral precise definitions that these concepts
became generally acceptable.

In order to understand and properly define definite integral and examine its properties, we must first study the concepts of length and area.

3.1 LENGTH

The length of an interval with end points a and b is $|b-a|$,
whether or not the interval contains its end points. Two intervals
are said to *overlap* if and only if some interior point of one of the intervals belongs to the other. Although the student may not be accustomed
to doing so, we might think of the length of a union of intervals as the
sum of the lengths, if no two of the intervals overlap. We shall have
use for generalizations of length to even more general sets of points.

> **DEFINITION 3-1.1.** Suppose B is a set of points on a line and
> $\{I_1, I_2, \cdots, I_n\}$ is a finite set of bounded intervals such that no two
> intervals overlap and each interval is contained in B. Also suppose
> a_i and b_i are the end points of the interval I_i. Then $\sum |b_i - a_i|$ is a
> 1-D *inner sum* for the set B. (A sum is said to be zero if there are no
> terms.)

> **DEFINITION 3-1.2.** Suppose B is a set of points on a line and
> $\{I_1, I_2, \cdots, I_n\}$ is a finite set of bounded intervals whose union contains
> B. Also suppose a_i and b_i are the end points of the interval I_i. Then
> $\sum |b_i - a_i|$ is a 1-D *outer sum* for the set B.

> **DEFINITION 3-1.3.** A *one-dimensional set of points that has* 1-D *content*
> is a set of points on a line for which there exists at least one 1-D outer
> sum and
>
> $$\text{sup (inner sums)} = \text{inf (outer sums)}.$$

The 1-D *content* (or *length*) of a set having 1-D content is the common
value of [sup (inner sums)] and [inf (outer sums)].

What we call length is often called *Jordan measure* or *Jordan
content.*† Instead of the expressions "1-D content," "2-D content,"

---

† See C. Jordan, *Cours d'Analyse de l'Ecole Polytechnique* (Paris: Gauthier-Villars,
1909), pp. 28–31.

and "3-D content," we shall use the more familiar and colorful words "length," "area," and "volume." Since the reader may be accustomed to using "length" only for line segments or curves, it may take some effort to adjust to thinking of the length of a disconnected set.

We shall now study the meaning of our definition of length and develop methods of determining length that are more practical than direct use of the preceding definition. The proof of the following theorem is very simple and will be left to the student. The theorem is very useful. The analogous theorems for area and volume are very difficult to prove.

THEOREM 3-1.1. If B is a bounded set of points on a line and s_* and s^* are inner and outer sums for B, then $s_* \leqq s^*$.

ILLUSTRATION 1. Let I be an interval with end points a and b for which $a < b$. Then $b-a$ is an outer sum for I, and it follows from Theorem 3-1.1 that $b-a$ is an upper bound for the set of inner sums. If $\varepsilon < b-a$, then $[a+\frac{1}{2}\varepsilon, b-\frac{1}{2}\varepsilon] \subset I$ and $b-a-\varepsilon$ is an inner sum for I. Therefore,

$$\sup (\text{inner sums}) = b-a.$$

Since $b-a$ is an outer sum and each inner sum is a lower bound for the set of outer sums, it follows that inf (outer sums) $= b-a$, I has length, and the length of I is $b-a$.

ILLUSTRATION 2. Let B be the set of rational numbers in the interval $[0, 1]$. If an interval is contained in B, then it contains no irrational numbers and therefore has zero length. Therefore, sup (inner sums) $= 0$. Now let $\{I_1, I_2, \cdots, I_n\}$ be a set of intervals whose union contains B. There is no loss of generality in assuming each interval is closed, since adding end points to an interval does not change the length of the interval. Then $\bigcup I_i$ is closed [see problem 6, page 60]. Therefore, if $p \in [0, 1]$, but $p \notin \bigcup I_i$, then p has a neighborhood that contains no members of $\bigcup I_i$. This is impossible, since all neighborhoods of p contain members of B. Thus, $\bigcup I_i$ contains $[0, 1]$. It follows from this and Illustration 1 that for B we have inf (outer sums) $= 1$. Thus, B does not have length.

DEFINITION 3-1.4. A *system of intervals* on a line is a set of nonoverlapping intervals whose union is the line and for which there is a positive lower bound to the lengths of the intervals. A system of intervals *has mesh* if and only if there is an upper bound to the lengths of the intervals. The *mesh* is the least upper bound of the lengths.

We shall use the convention that, for a set B, the *inner sum determined by a particular system of intervals* is the sum determined by those intervals of the system that are contained in B; and, for a set B, the *outer sum determined by a particular system of intervals* is the sum determined by those intervals that contain at least one point of B. The following theorem gives us two criteria for determining whether a set has length. These criteria are much easier to use than that given by Definition 3-1.3. Later, they will be generalized to area and volume.

THEOREM 3-1.2. For a one-dimensional bounded set B, each of the following is a necessary and sufficient condition for B to have length.
    (i) For each positive number ε, there exists an inner sum s_* and an outer sum s^* such that $s^* - s_* < \varepsilon$.
   (ii) For each positive number ε, there is a positive number δ such that, if s_* and s^* are the inner and outer sums determined by a system of intervals with mesh less than δ, then $s^* - s_* < \varepsilon$.

PROOF. First we shall prove that condition (i) is satisfied if B has length. Since [sup (inner sums)] is the smallest upper bound for the set of inner sums, it follows that [sup (inner sums)] $- \frac{1}{2}\varepsilon$ is not an upper bound for the set of inner sums. Therefore, there is an inner sum s_* such that

$$s_* > \text{sup (inner sums)} - \tfrac{1}{2}\varepsilon. \tag{3-1}$$

Similarly, there is an outer sum s^* such that

$$s^* < \text{inf (outer sums)} + \tfrac{1}{2}\varepsilon. \tag{3-2}$$

If B has length, then sup (inner sums) $=$ inf (outer sums). It then follows from (3-1) and (3-2) that $s^* - s_* < \varepsilon$.

Now we shall prove that (ii) is satisfied if (i) is satisfied. For an arbitrary positive number ε, we use (i) and choose inner and outer sums σ_* and σ^* for which $\sigma^* - \sigma_* < \frac{1}{2}\varepsilon$. Suppose m intervals $\{I_1, \cdots, I_m\}$ are used in σ_* and n intervals $\{J_1, \cdots, J_n\}$ are used in σ^*. Let $\delta = \frac{1}{8}\varepsilon/(m+n)$. Now let us select a system of intervals with mesh less than δ and let s_* and s^* be the inner and outer sums for B determined by this system. Each interval contained in an I_i is used in s_*; each interval used in s_* is used in s^*; and each interval used in s^* contains a point of at least one J_i. Therefore, we have

$$\sigma_* - 2m\delta < s_* \leqq s^* < \sigma^* + 2n\delta. \tag{3-3}$$

Since $\delta = \frac{1}{8}\varepsilon/(m+n)$, it follows from $\sigma^* - \sigma_* < \frac{1}{2}\varepsilon$ and (3-3) that $\sigma^* - \frac{3}{4}\varepsilon < \sigma_* - \frac{1}{4}\varepsilon < s_* \leqq s^* < \sigma^* + \frac{1}{4}\varepsilon$ and $s^* - s_* < \varepsilon$.

We can now complete the proof by showing that B has length if (ii) is satisfied. From Theorem 3-1.1, we know that any outer sum for B is an upper bound for the set of inner sums and any inner sum is a lower bound for the set of outer sums. Therefore, [sup (inner sums)] and [inf (outer sums)] both exist, and we need only show they are equal. Note first that [sup (inner sums)] is the smallest of all the upper bounds for the set of inner sums and is therefore a lower bound for the set of outer sums, so that

$$\text{sup (inner sums)} \leqq \text{inf (outer sums)}.$$

Now suppose we let s_* and s^* be any inner and outer sum for B. It follows from

$$\text{inf (outer sums)} \leqq s^*, \qquad \text{sup (inner sums)} \geqq s_*,$$

that

$$\text{inf (outer sums)} - \text{sup (inner sums)} \leqq s^* - s_*.$$

If for each positive number ε there is an inner sum s_* and an outer sum s^* for which $s^* - s_* < \varepsilon$, then

$$\text{inf (outer sums)} - \text{sup (inner sums)}$$

is a nonnegative number that is less than each positive number and therefore must be zero.

THEOREM 3-1.3. If A and B are sets that have length, then $A \cap B$, $B - A$, and $A \cup B$ have length. If $A \cap B = \Phi$, then the length of $A \cup B$ is the sum of the lengths of A and B.

PROOF. First we choose a positive number ε and use (ii) of Theorem 3-1.2 to obtain a system of intervals with small enough mesh so that, if a_*, a^* and b_*, b^* are the resulting inner and outer sums for A and B, respectively, then

$$a^* - a_* < \tfrac{1}{2}\varepsilon \quad \text{and} \quad b^* - b_* < \tfrac{1}{2}\varepsilon.$$

For this system of intervals, let s^* and s_* be the outer and inner sums for $A \cap B$. An interval is used in forming this outer sum for $A \cap B$, but not for the inner sum, only if it contains points of both A and B, but is not contained in $A \cap B$. Therefore, such intervals either are used for a^* and not for a_*, or for b^* and not for b_*, so that

$$s^* - s_* \leqq (a^* - a_*) + (b^* - b_*) < \varepsilon.$$

It then follows from (i) of Theorem 3-1.2 that $A \cap B$ has length. Since $B - A = B - (A \cap B)$, there is no loss of generality in assuming that $A \subset B$ when we prove $B - A$ has area. If σ_* and σ^* are inner and outer sums for $B-A$ determined by our system of intervals, we then have

$$b_* - a^* \leqq \sigma_* \leqq \sigma^* \leqq b^* - a_*$$

and $\sigma^* - \sigma_* \leqq (b^* - b_*) + (a^* - a_*) < \varepsilon$. Thus, $B - A$ has length. Since $A \cup B = A \cup (B-A)$, there is no loss of generality in assuming that $A \cap B = \Phi$ when proving $A \cup B$ has length. If τ_* and τ^* are inner and outer sums for $A \cup B$ determined by our system of intervals, we then have

$$a_* + b_* \leqq \tau_* \leqq \tau^* \leqq a^* + b^*,$$

and therefore $\tau^* - \tau_* < \varepsilon$. Thus, $A \cup B$ has length. Moreover, the length of $A \cup B$ is between $a_* + b_*$ and $a^* + b^*$ and therefore is the sum of the lengths of A and B.

The following theorem gives a simple and elegant criterion for a set to have length. The proof uses set operations justified by the preceding theorem.

THEOREM 3-1.4. A set B has length if and only if for each positive number ε there are sets A and C that have length and for which $A \subset B \subset C$ and the length of $C - A$ is less than ε.

PROOF. If B has length, then A and C can both be B. Conversely, let us suppose that we have sets A and C with length and that $A \subset B \subset C$ and the length of $C - A$ is less than ε. Then we can choose inner and outer sums a_* and a^* for A, and c_* and c^* for C, such that $a^* - a_* < \varepsilon$ and $c^* - c_* < \varepsilon$. Then

$$a_* > (\text{length of } A) - \varepsilon, \qquad c^* < (\text{length of } C) + \varepsilon. \qquad (3\text{-}4)$$

Since $C = A \cup (C - A)$ and the length of $C - A$ is less than ε, we know that the difference between the length of C and the length of A is less than ε. Therefore, from (3-4) we have $c^* - a_* < 3\varepsilon$. Since ε was an arbitrary positive number and a_* and c^* are inner and outer sums for B, it follows from (i) of Theorem 3-1.2 that B has length.

PROBLEMS

1. Explain why a set B is bounded if B has length.

2. For a set B with length, let $\ell(B)$ denote the length of B. Show that, if A, B, and C have length, then

(a) $\ell(A \cup B) = \ell(A) + \ell(B) - \ell(A \cap B)$;

(b) $\ell(A \cup B \cup C) = \ell(A) + \ell(B) + \ell(C)$
$- \ell(A \cap B) - \ell(A \cap C) - \ell(B \cap C) + \ell(A \cap B \cap C)$.

3. In the notation of problem 2, show that if A and B have length then

(a) $\ell(A \cup B) = \ell(A - B) + \ell(A \cap B) + \ell(B - A)$;

(b) $\ell(B - A) = \ell(B) - \ell(A)$ if $A \subset B$.

4. For a bounded set B on a line, let $\bar{\ell}(B)$ denote inf (outer sums for B) and $\underline{\ell}(B)$ denote sup (inner sums for B). Show that if A and B are bounded then

(a) $\bar{\ell}(A \cup B) + \bar{\ell}(A \cap B) \leq \bar{\ell}(A) + \bar{\ell}(B)$;

(b) $\underline{\ell}(A \cup B) + \underline{\ell}(A \cap B) \geq \underline{\ell}(A) + \underline{\ell}(B)$.

5.* Prove that a bounded set B on a line has length if and only if the boundary of B has length and the length is zero.

6.* The *Cantor set* C is the set of all numbers in the interval $[0, 1]$ that are not in the open middle third of $[0, 1]$ and not in the open middle third of any interval obtained by dividing $[0, 1]$ into three equal intervals, then dividing each of these intervals into three equal intervals, etc. Prove that

(a) C is compact and has length zero;

(b) $x \in C$ if and only if x has a representation in the ternary system (number base 3) of type $.d_1 d_2 \cdots$, where each d_n is either 0 or 2;

(c) C is not countably infinite.

7.* Let $B = [0, 1] - \bigcup_{j=1}^{+\infty} S_j$, where S_1 is the open interval of length 2^{-2} centered in $[0, 1]$ and, in general, S_n has length 2^{-n-1} and is the union of 2^{n-1} equal intervals centered in the 2^{n-1} intervals whose union is $[0, 1] - \bigcup_{j=1}^{n-1} S_j$. Prove the following.

(a) B is compact but does not have length.

(b) B is not countable.

3-2. AREA

The student already is familiar with the process of estimating the area of a geometric figure. By drawing a system of equidistant horizontal lines and equidistant vertical lines, one may estimate the area as the sum of the areas of squares contained in the region. But this estimate will be either correct or too small. Suppose, then, we were to use the squares that are either entirely or partially contained in the region. This will lead to an estimate for the area that is either

correct or too large.   If the squares are small enough, we can expect
the error to be small in both cases.

The definition of area we shall use for sets of points in a plane is
suggested by this method of "counting squares."   We shall use the
convention that a rectangle is the intersection of the set of points that
are between or on two parallel or coincident lines L_1 and L_2 and the
set of points that are between or on two parallel or coincident lines
M_1 and M_2, where L_1 and M_1 are perpendicular.   Thus, a line segment,
or a point, will be said to constitute a rectangle.   Two rectangles are
said to *overlap* if and only if some interior point of one of the rectangles
belongs to the other.

DEFINITION 3-2.1.   Suppose B is a set of points in a plane and
$\{R_1, R_2, \cdots, R_n\}$ is a finite set of rectangles, no two of which overlap
and each of which is contained in B.   Also suppose b_i and h_i are the
lengths of two adjacent sides of the rectangle R_i.   Then $\sum b_i h_i$ is a
2-D inner sum for the set B.   (A sum is said to be zero if there are no
terms.)

DEFINITION 3-2.2.   Suppose B is a set of points in a plane and
$\{R_1, R_2, \cdots, R_n\}$ is a finite set of rectangles whose union contains B.
Also suppose b_i and h_i are the lengths of two adjacent sides of the
rectangle R_i.   Then $\sum b_i h_i$ is a *2-D outer sum* for the set B.

DEFINITION 3-2.3.   A *plane set of points that has area* is a set of points
in a plane for which there exists at least one 2-D outer sum and

$$\text{sup (inner sums)} = \text{inf (outer sums)}.$$

The *area* (or 2-D *content*) of a set having area is the common value of
[sup (inner sums)] and [inf (outer sums)].

This provides a natural definition of area.   It also is a definition
that will be easy to use in developing methods for determining area,
after some theorems about area have been proved.   Moreover, it is
clear that the area of a set is not changed either by translation or by
rotation.   We shall establish basic facts about area that are similar
to those discussed for length.   The following theorem is very important.
Unlike the similar theorem for subsets of a line [Theorem 3-1.1], this
theorem is difficult to prove and the proof will not be given.†

THEOREM 3-2.1.   If B is a bounded set of points in a plane and s_* and
s^* are inner and outer sums for B, then $s_* \leqq s^*$.

---

† For a proof, see James, *op. cit.*, pp. 394–396.

The theorems to follow give practical and useful criteria for determining whether a given set has area. Calculus provides more tools for doing this.

THEOREM 3-2.2. If B is a bounded set of points in a plane, then B has area if and only if for each positive number ε there exists an inner sum s_* and an outer sum s^* such that

$$s^* - s_* < \varepsilon.$$

If B has area, then $s_* \leqq$ (area of B) $\leqq s^*$ for any inner sum s_* and any outer sum s^*.

PROOF. We shall prove first that, if a set B has area, then for each positive number ε there exists an inner sum s_* and an outer sum s^* such that $s^* - s_* < \varepsilon$. Since [sup (inner sums)] is the smallest upper bound for the set of inner sums, [sup (inner sums)] $- \frac{1}{2}\varepsilon$ is not an upper bound for the set of inner sums. Therefore, there is an inner sum s_* such that

$$s_* > \text{sup (inner sums)} - \tfrac{1}{2}\varepsilon. \tag{3-5}$$

Similarly, there is an outer sum s^* such that

$$s^* < \text{inf (outer sums)} + \tfrac{1}{2}\varepsilon. \tag{3-6}$$

If B has area, then sup (inner sums) = inf (outer sums). It then follows from (3-5) and (3-6) that $s^* - s_* < \varepsilon$.

Now we shall show that B has area if, for each positive number ε, there exists an inner sum s_* and an outer sum s^* such that $s^* - s_* < \varepsilon$. It follows from Theorem 3-2.1 that any outer sum for B is an upper bound for the set of inner sums, and any inner sum is a lower bound for the set of outer sums. Therefore,

$$\text{[sup (inner sums)]} \quad \text{and} \quad \text{[inf (outer sums)]}$$

both exist, and we need only show they are equal. Note first that [sup (inner sums)] is the smallest of all the upper bounds for the set of inner sums and is therefore a lower bound for the set of outer sums, so that

$$\text{sup (inner sums)} \leqq \text{inf (outer sums)}.$$

Now suppose we let s_* and s^* be any inner and outer sum for B. It follows from

$$\text{inf (outer sums)} \leqq s^*, \qquad \text{sup (inner sums)} \geqq s_*,$$

that

$$\text{inf (outer sums)} - \text{sup (inner sums)} \leqq s^* - s_*.$$

If for each positive number ε there is an inner sum s_* and an outer sum s^* for which $s^* - s_* < \varepsilon$, then

$$\text{inf (outer sums)} - \text{sup (inner sums)}$$

is a nonnegative number that is less than each positive number and therefore must be zero.

To complete the proof, we need to show that if B has area then $s_* \leq (\text{area of } B) \leq s^*$ for any inner sum s_* and any outer sum s^*. This follows directly from the facts that the area of B is equal to

$$[\text{sup (inner sums)}]$$

and therefore is not less than any inner sum, and the area of B is equal to $[\text{inf (outer sums)}]$ and therefore is not greater than any outer sum.

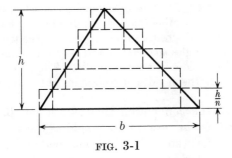

FIG. 3-1

One of the most direct consequences of Theorem 3-2.2 is the fact that a rectangle has area. For if a rectangle R has adjacent sides of length b and h, then bh is both an inner and an outer sum. With $bh = s_* = s^*$, we have $s^* - s_* = 0$ and $s^* - s_* < \varepsilon$ for all positive numbers ε. Therefore, R has area. Since $s_* \leq (\text{area of } R) \leq s^*$, the area of R is equal to bh. A more substantial application of Theorem 3-2.2 can be made to prove that a triangle has area and to establish the formula for the area. For the triangle of Fig. 3-1, suppose we choose a positive integer n and draw horizontal lines as shown so as to divide the triangle into n strips, each of width h/n. All the rectangles have altitudes of length h/n. The "outer" rectangles have bases b/n, $2b/n$, $3b/n$, $\cdots$, nb/n. The outer sum for these rectangles is therefore

$$s^* = \frac{h}{n}\left(\frac{b}{n} + \frac{2b}{n} + \frac{3b}{n} + \cdots + \frac{nb}{n}\right) = \frac{bh}{n^2}(1 + 2 + \cdots + n)$$

$$= \frac{bh}{2n^2}\, n \cdot (n+1) = \frac{1}{2}\, bh\left(1 + \frac{1}{n}\right).$$

The "inner" rectangles have widths $0, b/n, \cdots, (n-1)b/n$, so that the inner sum for these rectangles is

$$s_* = \frac{h}{n}\left(0 + \frac{b}{n} + \frac{2b}{n} + \cdots + \frac{(n-1)b}{n}\right) = \frac{bh}{n^2}[1 + 2 + \cdots + (n-1)]$$

$$= \frac{bh}{2n^2}(n-1)n = \frac{1}{2}bh\left(1 - \frac{1}{n}\right).$$

The difference of these outer and inner sums is bh/n. If ε is a positive number and $n > bh/\varepsilon$, then $bh/n < \varepsilon$ and $s^* - s_* < \varepsilon$. It now follows from Theorem 3-2.2 that the triangle has area. Also, it is clear that $\frac{1}{2}bh$ is the only number that is between $\frac{1}{2}bh(1 - 1/n)$ and $\frac{1}{2}bh(1 + 1/n)$ for all positive integers n. Therefore, the area is equal to $\frac{1}{2}bh$.

DEFINITION 3-2.4. A *system of rectangles* is a set of rectangles formed by two families of parallel lines, which divide the plane into rectangles for which there is a positive lower bound to the lengths of the sides. A system of rectangles *has mesh* if and only if there is an upper bound to the lengths of sides of the rectangles. The *mesh* is the least upper bound of the lengths of sides of rectangles in the system.

We shall use the convention that, for a set B, the *inner sum determined by a particular system of rectangles* is the sum determined by those rectangles of the system that are contained in B; and, for a set B, the *outer sum determined by a particular system of rectangles* is the sum determined by those rectangles that contain at least one point of B.

THEOREM 3-2.3. A set B has area if and only if for any positive number ε there is a positive number δ such that, if s_* and s^* are the inner and outer sums determined by a system of rectangles with mesh less than δ, then

$$s^* - s_* < \varepsilon.$$

PROOF. It is known that a set B has area if, for any positive number ε, there are inner and outer sums s_* and s^* such that $s^* - s_* < \varepsilon$ [see Theorem 3-2.2]. Therefore, the inequality of the present theorem is a sufficient condition for B to have area. If we suppose that B has area, it follows from Theorem 3-2.2 that, if ε is a positive number, then there is an inner sum σ_* and an outer sum σ^* for which

$$0 \leqq \sigma^* - \sigma_* < \tfrac{1}{2}\varepsilon,$$

where these inner and outer sums are not known to be determined by a system of rectangles. To complete the proof, we shall use σ_* and σ^*

to show that there is a positive number δ such that, if s_* and s^* are inner and outer sums determined by a system of rectangles with mesh less than δ, then $s^* - s_* < \varepsilon$. Suppose $R_1, \cdots, R_m$ and $S_1, \cdots, S_n$ are the rectangles for which

$$\sigma_* = \sum_{i=1}^{m} b_i h_i, \qquad \sigma^* = \sum_{i=1}^{n} b'_i h'_i,$$

where b_i and h_i are lengths of adjacent sides of R_i, and b'_i and h'_i are lengths of adjacent sides of S_i. It follows that there is a positive number δ such that the inner sum for R_i, determined by any system of rectangles whose mesh is less than δ, differs from $b_i h_i$ by less than $\frac{1}{4}\varepsilon/m$ $(i = 1, 2, \cdots, m)$, and the outer sum for S_i, determined by any system of rectangles whose mesh is less than δ, differs from $b'_i h'_i$ by less than $\frac{1}{4}\varepsilon/n$ $(i = 1, 2, \cdots, n)$.† Let us select a system of rectangles with mesh less than δ and let s_* and s^* be the inner and outer sums for B determined by this system. Each rectangle contained in one of $R_1, \cdots$, R_m is used in s_*; each rectangle used in s_* is used in s^*; and each rectangle used in s^* is used for the outer sum of at least one S_i. Therefore we have

$$\sum_{i=1}^{m} \left(b_i h_i - \frac{\varepsilon}{4m} \right) < s_* \leqq s^* < \sum_{i=1}^{n} \left(b'_i h'_i + \frac{\varepsilon}{4m} \right).$$

Since

$$\sum_{i=1}^{m} \left(b_i h_i - \frac{\frac{1}{4}\varepsilon}{m} \right) = \sigma_* - \tfrac{1}{4}\varepsilon, \qquad \sum_{i=1}^{n} \left(b'_i h'_i + \frac{\frac{1}{4}\varepsilon}{n} \right) = \sigma^* + \tfrac{1}{4}\varepsilon,$$

and $\sigma^* - \sigma_* < \tfrac{1}{2}\varepsilon$, it follows that $s^* - s_* < \varepsilon$.

The proof of the next theorem will be omitted, since it is identical to the proof of Theorem 3-1.3 except that systems of rectangles are used instead of systems of intervals.

THEOREM 3-2.4. If A and B are sets that have area, then $A \cap B$, $B - A$, and $A \cup B$ have area. If $A \cap B = \Phi$, then the area of $A \cup B$ is the sum of the areas of A and B.

For a plane set T that has area, a *partition* of T is a set $\{T_1, T_2, \cdots, T_n\}$ whose members are subsets of T that have area, whose union is T, and for which $T_i \cap T_j$ has zero area if $i \neq j$. The

---

† If such a δ exists for each R_i and each S_i, the smallest one can be used for all R_i and S_i. For a proof that δ exists for a particular rectangle, see James, *op. cit.*, Lemma 1, page 394.

fineness of a partition is the number

sup $\{d(p, q): p$ and q in the same set of the partition$\}$.

We shall use the convention that, for a set B, the *inner sum determined by a partition* of a set T that contains B is the sum of the areas of all members of the partition that are contained in B, and the *outer sum determined by a partition* of a set T that contains B is the sum of the areas of all members of the partition that contain points of B.

THEOREM 3-2.5. For a bounded plane set B, each of the following is a necessary and sufficient condition for B to have area.

(i) For each positive number ε, there are sets A and C that have area and for which $A \subset B \subset C$ and the area of $C - A$ is less than ε.

(ii) For each positive number ε, there is a positive number δ such that $s^* - s_* < \varepsilon$ if s_* and s^* are the inner and outer sums determined by a partition with fineness less than δ of a set containing B.

PROOF. First note that (i) is satisfied trivially if B has area, since we can then let $A = B = C$. Also, it follows from Theorem 3-2.2 that B has area if (ii) is satisfied. Therefore, we need only show that (ii) is satisfied if (i) is satisfied. To do this, we let ε be an arbitrary positive number and A and C be sets with area for which $A \subset B \subset C$ and the area of $C - A$ is less than $\frac{1}{6}\varepsilon$. We know from Theorem 3-2.3 that there is a system of rectangles for which the inner sum a_* and the outer sum c^* determined for A and C, respectively, differ from the areas of A and C by less than $\frac{1}{6}\varepsilon$. Then a_* and c^* are inner and outer sums for B. Since $C = A \cup (C - A)$ and the area of $C - A$ is less than $\frac{1}{6}\varepsilon$, the areas of A and C differ by less than $\frac{1}{6}\varepsilon$. Thus, $c^* - a_* < \frac{1}{2}\varepsilon$. Let δ be defined as a positive number small enough that $\frac{1}{4}\varepsilon$ is larger than the area of the set of all points that are as close as δ to at least one point on the boundary of a rectangle used in c^*. Now let T be a set with area that contains B and let $\Pi = \{T_1, T_2, \cdots, T_n\}$ be a partition of T with fineness less than δ. If a rectangle R is used in forming a_*, then any interior point of R that is as far as δ from the boundary of R belongs to one of the members of Π that is contained in R. Thus, if s_* is the inner sum for B determined by Π, then

$$s_* > a_* - \tfrac{1}{4}\varepsilon.$$

If a member T_k of Π contains a point of B, then all points of T_k are either inside or not farther than δ from the boundary of a rectangle used in c^*. Therefore,

$$s^* < c^* + \tfrac{1}{4}\varepsilon.$$

Since $c^* - a_* < \frac{1}{2}\varepsilon$, we now have $s^* - s_* < \varepsilon$.

PROBLEMS

1. Prove that any line segment has zero area.

2. Prove that any finite set of points has zero area.

3. Prove that if B has zero area and $A \subset B$, then A has area and the area of A is zero.

4. Suppose B is a countable set. Explain why every inner sum for B is zero, and B either has zero area or does not have area.

5. Explain why a set is bounded if it has area.

6. For a set B with area, let $\alpha(B)$ denote the area of B. Show that if A, B, and C have area then
   (a) $\alpha(A \cup B) = \alpha(A) + \alpha(B) - \alpha(A \cap B)$;
   (b) $\alpha(A \cup B) = \alpha(A - B) + \alpha(A \cap B) + \alpha(B - A)$;
   (c) $\alpha(B - A) = \alpha(B) - \alpha(A)$ if $A \subset B$.

7. For a bounded plane set B, let $\bar{\alpha}(B)$ denote inf (outer sums for B) and $\underline{\alpha}(B)$ denote sup (inner sums for B). Show that, if A and B are bounded, then
   (a) $\bar{\alpha}(A \cup B) + \bar{\alpha}(A \cap B) \leqq \bar{\alpha}(A) + \bar{\alpha}(B)$;
   (b) $\underline{\alpha}(A \cup B) + \underline{\alpha}(A \cap B) \geqq \underline{\alpha}(A) + \underline{\alpha}(B)$.

8. Suppose that B is the set that contains the interval $[0, 1]$ of the x-axis and contains the segment from the point $(p/q, 0)$ to the point $(p/q, 1/q)$ whenever p and q are relatively prime positive integers with $p \leqq q$. Show that B has area and the area of B is zero.

9. Suppose that B is the set that contains the interval $[0, 1]$ of the x-axis and contains the segment from the point $(x, 0)$ to the point $(x, 1)$ whenever x is a rational number. Show that B does not have area. [*Hint:* Show that any outer sum for B is at least 1.]

10. Prove the usual formulas for the areas of parallelograms and trapezoids.

11.* Prove that a bounded plane set B has area if and only if the boundary of B has area and the area is zero.

3-3. SETS WITH AREA

Suppose f is a function for which $f(x) \geqq 0$ for all x in the interval $[a, b]$, where $a \leqq b$. We shall refer to the following set W as "the region under the graph of f from a to b":

$$W = \{(x, y): a \leqq x \leqq b \text{ and } 0 \leqq y \leqq f(x)\}.$$

The first theorem of this section states that a sufficient condition for W to have area is that f be monotone or f be continuous. We shall also establish necessary and sufficient conditions for W to have area.

DEFINITION 3-3.1. A *monotone increasing function* on an interval I is a function f with the property that $f(x_1) \leq f(x_2)$ whenever x_1 and x_2 are numbers in I such that $x_1 \leq x_2$. A *monotone decreasing function* on an interval I is a function f with the property that $f(x_1) \geq f(x_2)$ whenever $x_1 \leq x_2$. A *monotone function* is a function that is either monotone increasing or monotone decreasing.

THEOREM 3-3.1. If $f(x) \geq 0$ whenever $a \leq x \leq b$, then each of the following is a sufficient condition for the region under the graph of f from a to b to have area.
  (i) f is monotone on $[a, b]$.
  (ii) f is continuous on $[a, b]$.

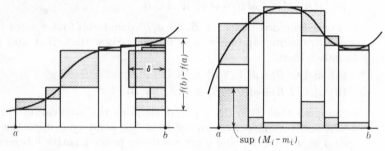

FIG. 3-2

PROOF. Let us assume that f is monotone increasing. It will be clear that a similar proof would apply if f were monotone decreasing. Let us form inner and outer rectangles in vertical strips, as shown in the first diagram of Fig. 3-2. Since f is monotone increasing, the top of each outer rectangle is the top of the next inner rectangle. Hence, if each of the rectangles that represents the difference between an outer rectangle and the corresponding inner rectangle is replaced by a congruent rectangle placed along the line $x = b$, as illustrated, these rectangles will extend from $f(a)$ to $f(b)$. Therefore, the difference between these outer and inner sums is not larger than

$$[f(b) - f(a)]\delta,$$

where δ is the width of the widest strip. Whatever positive number ε is chosen, it is possible to choose δ so small that this difference is less than ε. Therefore the given region has area.

Now suppose f is continuous at all points of the interval $[a, b]$. Then

f is uniformly continuous on $[a, b]$.   Therefore, if ε is a positive number, then there is a positive number δ such that

$$|f(r)-f(s)| < \frac{\varepsilon}{b-a} \quad \text{if} \quad |r-s| < \delta.$$

If we use vertical strips of width less than δ, as shown in the second diagram of Fig. 3-2, then $M_i - m_i < \varepsilon/(b-a)$ if M_i and m_i are the largest and smallest values of $f(x)$ for x in the ith strip.   That is, the altitudes of all the shaded rectangles are less than $\varepsilon/(b-a)$.   This is illustrated in Fig. 3-2 by dropping all the shaded rectangles onto the x-axis.   Since these rectangles all have altitudes less than $\varepsilon/(b-a)$, the sum of their areas is less than $[\varepsilon/(b-a)](b-a) = \varepsilon$.   Therefore, ε is greater than the difference between this particular outer and inner sum, so we can conclude from Theorem 3-2.2 that the region under f from a to b has area.

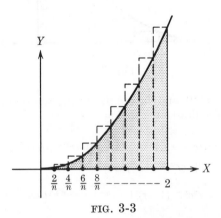

FIG. 3-3

ILLUSTRATION 1.   Suppose $f(x) = x^2$ for $0 \leq x \leq 2$.   If the interval from 0 to 2 is divided into n equal intervals, as shown in Fig. 3-3, then the area of the first outer rectangle is $(2/n)(2/n)^2$; the area of the second is $(2/n)(2 \cdot 2/n)^2$; the area of the third is $(2/n)(3 \cdot 2/n)^2$; etc. Therefore, the outer sum is

$$\frac{8}{n^3} (1^2 + 2^2 + 3^2 + \cdots + n^2).$$

It follows from the identity,

$$1^2 + 2^2 + \cdots + n^2 = \tfrac{1}{6}n(n+1)(2n+1),$$

that this is equal to

$$\frac{8}{6n^2} (2n^2 + 3n + 1) = \frac{4}{3} \left(2 + \frac{3}{n} + \frac{1}{n^2}\right),$$

which approaches $\frac{8}{3}$ as n increases. This is the area of the illustrated region.

ILLUSTRATION 2. Suppose we let $f(x) = x^n$ for $0 \leq x \leq c$, where n is a positive integer, and choose a number r in the interval $(0, 1)$ and a positive integer k. We also divide the interval from c to 0 by the points

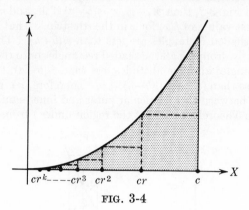

FIG. 3-4

$c, cr, cr^2, \cdots, cr^k, 0$, and denote by $s(r, k)_*$ the sum of the areas of the inner rectangles illustrated in Fig. 3-4. Then

$$s(r, k)_* = (c - cr)(cr)^n + (cr - cr^2)(cr^2)^n + (cr^2 - cr^3)(cr^3)^n + \cdots$$
$$+ (cr^{k-1} - cr^k)(cr^k)^n$$
$$= r^n c^{n+1}(1 - r)[1 + r^{n+1} + r^{2(n+1)} + \cdots + r^{(k-1)(n+1)}]$$
$$= r^n c^{n+1}(1 - r)\frac{1 - r^{k(n+1)}}{1 - r^{n+1}}$$
$$= \frac{r^n c^{n+1}(1 - r^{k(n+1)})}{1 + r + r^2 + \cdots + r^n}.$$

We know that this inner sum approaches the area as the length of the longest subdivision approaches zero. We shall show that this area is equal to $c^{n+1}/(n+1)$. The first subdivision is of length cr^k. The length of any other subdivision is the product of $c(1 - r)$ and a power of r; hence, the longest of the other subdivisions is the last one, which is of length $c(1 - r)$. Therefore either the first or the last interval is the longest. We can make the last interval small by making r near 1, and then make the first interval small by making k large. If we choose a positive "tolerance" ε, then we can choose r so near 1, and then choose k so large, that $r^n/(1 + r + r^2 + \cdots + r^n)$ will be near enough to $1/(n+1)$, and $r^{k(n+1)}$ near enough to zero, that $s(r, k)_*$ will differ from

$c^{n+1}/(n+1)$ by less than ε. Therefore, the area is exactly equal to $c^{n+1}/(n+1)$.

DEFINITION 3-3.2. Let T be a nonempty subset of the domain D of a function f. The number

$$\Omega_f(T) = \sup\{|f(r)-f(s)|: r \in T \text{ and } s \in T\} \tag{3-7}$$

is the *oscillation* of f on the set T. If every neighborhood of x contains points of D, then the *oscillation of f at x* is the number

$$\omega_f(x) = \inf\{\Omega_f(D \cap N): N \text{ a neighborhood of } x\}. \tag{3-8}$$

THEOREM 3-3.2. Suppose f is nonnegative on $[a, b]$. If the region W under the graph of f from a to b has area, then for each positive number η the set $0_\eta = \{x: \omega_f(x) \geqq \eta\}$ has zero length.

PROOF. Suppose W has area. Then we form vertical strips as in Fig. 3-2, with the strips narrow enough that the difference between the sum of the outer rectangles and the sum of the inner rectangles is less than ε. That this is possible follows from Theorem 3-2.3. If $x \in 0_\eta$ and x as a point on the x-axis is interior to one of the strips, then the difference between the areas of the outer and inner rectangles in this strip is at least as large as the product of η and the width of the strip. Therefore, if L is the sum of the lengths of the strips that have interior points in 0_η, then $\eta \cdot L < \varepsilon$. Since we have excluded only a finite number of points by requiring x to be interior to a strip, we can conclude that the length of the set 0_η is less than ε/η. Since η is fixed and ε is arbitrary, 0_η has zero length.

THEOREM 3-3.3. Suppose f is bounded and nonnegative on $[a, b]$. If, for each positive number η, the set $0_\eta = \{x: \omega_f(x) \geqq \eta\}$ has zero length, then the region W under the graph of f from a to b has area.

PROOF. Since f is bounded, there is a number M for which $f(x) \leqq M$ if $x \in [a, b]$. Let ε be an arbitrary positive number and let η be a positive number such that

$$\eta < \frac{\frac{1}{2}\varepsilon}{b-a}.$$

Since the length of 0_η is zero, we can cover 0_η with a finite set $\{I_1, I_2, \cdots, I_m\}$ of nonoverlapping open intervals the sum of whose lengths is less than $\frac{1}{2}\varepsilon/M$ [see problem 5]. Then for each point x in $[a, b] - \bigcup I_k$, $\omega_f(x) < \eta$ and x is the center of an open interval J_x for which

$$\Omega_f(J_x) < \eta.$$

The set $[a, b] - \bigcup I_k$ is closed and bounded. Therefore, it follows from the Heine-Borel theorem that the cover by such sets J_x contains a finite cover. By discarding pieces of members of this finite cover, we can obtain a set of intervals $\{K_1, K_2, \cdots, K_n\}$ such that

$$\{I_1, I_2, \cdots, I_m, K_1, K_2, \cdots, K_n\}$$

is a set of intervals that covers $[a, b]$ and for which no two intervals overlap. Now we use these intervals as the bases of vertical strips as illustrated in Fig. 3-2. The sum of the widths of all the intervals $I_1, \cdots, I_m$ is less than $\frac{1}{2}\varepsilon/M$, so the sum of the areas of outer rectangles in these strips is less than $(\frac{1}{2}\varepsilon/M)M = \frac{1}{2}\varepsilon$. The difference between the altitudes of the outer and inner rectangles in one of the remaining strips is less than η, so the sum of the differences between the areas of outer and inner rectangles in such strips is less than $\eta(b-a) < \frac{1}{2}\varepsilon$. Therefore, the difference between the sum of the areas of all outer rectangles and the sum of the areas of all inner rectangles is less than ε. It then follows from Theorem 3-2.2 that W has area.

The following concept of "set of measure zero" gives an interesting and useful tool to use in connection with the two preceding theorems. The next lemma and theorem provide this link.

DEFINITION 3-3.3. A set of 1-D *measure zero* is a set B on a line such that for each positive number ε there is a sequence of intervals $\{I_1, I_2, \cdots\}$ such that $B \subset \bigcup I_k$ and $\sum_{k=1}^{n} |I_k| < \varepsilon$ for all n, where $|I_k|$ is the length of I_k.

LEMMA. A point p in the domain of a function f is a discontinuity of f if and only if $\omega_f(p) > 0$.

PROOF. We need merely observe that f is discontinuous at p if and only if there exists a positive number ε such that every δ-neighborhood of p contains points r and s for which $|f(r) - f(s)| \geqq \varepsilon$ [see problem 10, page 98]; that is, if and only if $\omega_f(p) \geqq \varepsilon$.

THEOREM 3-3.4. Suppose f is bounded and nonnegative on $[a, b]$. Then each of the following is a necessary and sufficient condition for W to have area, where W is the region under the graph of f from a to b.
  (i) For each positive number η, the set $0_\eta = \{x \colon \omega_f(x) \geqq \eta\}$ has zero length.
  (ii) The set of discontinuities of f is of measure zero.

PROOF. It follows from Theorems 3-3.2 and 3-3.3 that (i) is a necessary and sufficient condition for W to have area. To show that (i) and (ii) are logically equivalent, we let D be the set of discontinuities of f and use the lemma to see that

$$D = \bigcup_{n=1}^{+\infty} 0_{1/n}.$$

If (i) is satisfied, then each $0_{1/n}$ has length zero. Then, for any positive number ε and each n, there is a finite set of intervals $\{I_1^n, I_2^n, \cdots, I_{p_n}^n\}$ that covers $0_{1/n}$ and for which $\sum |I_k^n| < \varepsilon/2^n$. Then the sequence

$$\{I_1^1, I_2^1, \cdots, I_{p_1}^1; I_1^2, \cdots, I_{p_2}^2; \cdots; I_1^n, \cdots, I_{p_n}^n; \cdots\}$$

covers D and the sum of the lengths of any finite number of these intervals is less than ε. Thus, D is of measure zero. Now suppose D is of measure zero. For an arbitrary positive number ε, let

$$\{J_1, J_2, J_3, \cdots\} \tag{3-9}$$

be a sequence of open intervals that covers D and for which $\sum_{k=1}^{n} |J_k| < \varepsilon$ for all n [see problem 6]. If r is a member of the set

$$[a, b] - 0_\eta = \{x : \omega_f(x) < \eta\},$$

then $\omega_f(r) < \eta$ and there is an open interval V containing r with $\Omega_f(V) < \eta$. Then $\omega_f(s) < \eta$ if $s \in V$, and therefore $V \subset [a, b] - 0_\eta$. This shows that $[a, b] - 0_\eta$ is open. Therefore, 0_η is closed and it follows from the Heine-Borel theorem that (3-9) contains a finite cover of 0_η. The sum of the lengths of the intervals in this finite cover is an outer sum for 0_η that is less than ε. Since ε was arbitrary, 0_η has length and the length is zero.

PROBLEMS

1. Use outer sums to determine the area of the region between the x-axis and the graph of $y = x^2$ and between the lines whose equations are $x = 0$ and $x = 5$.

2. Use inner sums and equal subdivisions to determine the area of the region that is under the graph of $y = x^3$ and between the lines whose equations are $x = 0$ and $x = 3$. [*Hint:* Use the identity $1^3 + 2^3 + 3^3 + \cdots + n^3 = \frac{1}{4}n^2(n+1)^2$.]

3. Let $A(t)$ be the area of the region that is under the graph of $y = 1/x$ and between the lines whose equations are $x = 1$ and $x = t$. Form an outer sum using the points of subdivision $1, r, r^2, \cdots, r^n$, where $r^n = t$.

Show that this outer sum is equal to $n(r-1)$ if $r>1$ and to $n(1-r)/r$ if $0<r<1$. Use this to show that $A(t^2)=2A(t)$.

4. Show that every countable set on a line has measure zero but that there is a countable set that does not have length.

5. Let B be a set on a line. Show that, if B has zero length, then for any positive number ε there is a cover of B that consists of a finite number of *open* intervals the sum of whose lengths is less than ε.

6. Let S be a set of measure zero on a line. Show that for any positive number ε there is a sequence $\{I_1, I_2, \cdots\}$ of *open* intervals that covers S and for which $\sum_{k=1}^{n} |I_k| < \varepsilon$ for all n.

7. Suppose B is a closed bounded set of measure zero. Explain why B has length and the length of B is zero.

8.* Suppose each member of the sequence $\{A_1, A_2, \cdots\}$ is of measure zero. Prove that $\bigcup_1^{+\infty} A_i$ is of measure zero.

9. Show that $\omega_f(x)$ of Definition 3-3.2 is equal to

$$\lim_{h \to 0+} \Omega_f[D \cap \{r: d(r, x) < h\}].$$

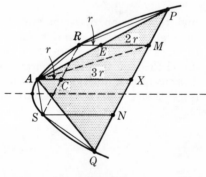

FIG. 3-5

10. For the parabola of Fig. 3-5, the axis is parallel to the lines RM, AX, and SN; the points X, M, and N are the midpoints of the segments PQ, PX, and XQ.

(a) Show that RS is parallel to PQ and that if $AC=r$, then $AX=4r$. [*Hint:* Show that RS is parallel to PQ by first showing that if a parabola has the equation $y^2=kx$, then the slope of the chord between points with ordinates y_1 and y_2 is equal to $k/(y_1+y_2)$. Then show that $AX=(y_1-y_2)^2/(4k)$ if P and Q have ordinates y_1 and y_2, and note that the difference of the ordinates at R and S is one-half the difference of the ordinates at P and Q.]

(b) Use the fact proved in (a) to show that $EM = 2r$ and $RE = r$. Then show that

$$\text{area } (\triangle REP) = \tfrac{1}{2} \text{ area } (\triangle EMP);$$

$$\text{area } (\triangle AER) = \tfrac{1}{2} \text{ area } (\triangle AME);$$

$$\text{area } (\triangle APR) = \tfrac{1}{4} \text{ area } (\triangle AXP).$$

(c) Show that area $[(\triangle APR) \cup (\triangle ASQ)] = \tfrac{1}{4}$ area $(\triangle AQP)$. Make successive applications of this fact to show that the area of the parabolic segment is approximately equal to

$$[\text{area } (\triangle AQP)][1 + \tfrac{1}{4} + (\tfrac{1}{4})^2 + (\tfrac{1}{4})^3 + \cdots + (\tfrac{1}{4})^n]$$

if n is sufficiently large, and that the area of the parabolic segment is equal to $\tfrac{4}{3}[\text{area } (\triangle AQP)]$. [*Note:* This is an illustration of Archimedes' method of exhaustion.]

3-4. THE DEFINITE INTEGRAL

The definite integral is important both because of its relation to the concept of area and because it can be used to express many other physical and mathematical quantities, such as volume, mass, mean, moment of inertia, work, and potential energy. Because of the

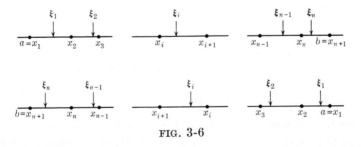

FIG. 3-6

possibility of representing a definite integral as a difference of areas, the theory of area we have developed will be very useful for studying definite integrals.

To define the definite integral, we shall use such types of sums as

$$\sum_{i=1}^{n} f(\xi_i)(x_{i+1} - x_i),$$

where the numbers x_i and ξ_i are arranged between a and b as shown in Fig. 3-6. To give a precise definition, we must introduce several new concepts.

DEFINITION 3-4.1. A *partition* of an interval with end points a and b is an ordered set $\{x_1, x_2, \cdots, x_{n+1}\}$ such that $a = x_1$, $b = x_{n+1}$, and the numbers $x_1, x_2, \cdots, x_{n+1}$ are monotone increasing if $a \leq b$ and monotone decreasing if $a \geq b$. The *fineness* of a partition $\{x_1, x_2, \cdots, x_{n+1}\}$ is the largest of the numbers $|x_{i+1} - x_i|$ for $1 \leq i \leq n$.

DEFINITION 3-4.2. For an interval with end points a and b, a *partition with selection* is an ordered pair

$$s = (\{x_1, x_2, \cdots, x_{n+1}\}, \quad \{\xi_1, \xi_2, \cdots, \xi_n\}) \qquad (3\text{-}10)$$

whose first member is a partition $\{x_1, x_2, \cdots, x_{n+1}\}$ of the given interval and whose second member is an ordered set $\{\xi_1, \xi_2, \cdots, \xi_n\}$ with the property that, for each i, the number ξ_i is in the closed interval with end points x_i and x_{i+1}.

DEFINITION 3-4.3. Suppose f is a function whose domain includes the closed interval with end points a and b, and that we use the following equality to define a function R whose domain is the set of all partitions with selection of this interval:

$$R(s) = \sum_{i=1}^{n} f(\xi_i)(x_{i+1} - x_i).$$

This sum is called a *Riemann sum.*

Now we shall let $\delta(s)$ denote the fineness of the partition in the partition with selection (3-10) and let S be the system of stages whose stages are those sets A for which there is a positive number Δ such that

$$A = \{s \colon \delta(s) < \Delta\}.$$

Then we may define $\lim_{\delta \to 0} \sum_{i=1}^{n} f(\xi_i)(x_{i+1} - x_i) = l$, or $\lim_{\delta \to 0} R(s) = l$, to mean that $\lim_S R = l$, where R is the function of Definition 3-4.3.

DEFINITION 3-4.4. A *Riemann integrable function* on an interval with end points a and b is a function f such that, for this interval,

$$\lim_{\delta \to 0} \sum_{i=1}^{n} f(\xi_i)(x_{i+1} - x_i)$$

exists. For an integrable function f, the value of this limit is the (*Riemann*) *definite integral* of f between a and b and is denoted by the symbol

$$\int_a^b f(x)\, dx. \qquad (3\text{-}11)$$

The symbol $\int$, called an *integral sign*, is an elongated "S." The ordinary summation symbol "$\sum$" is the Greek "S." Because of the close relation between integrals and sums, this similarity in notation is quite appropriate. The definite integral could be represented more briefly by $\int_a^b f$; however, we shall write $f(x)$ in place of f when this is convenient. It must be understood that the use of dx and the use of $f(x)$ instead of f are superfluous from the standpoint of denoting the definite integral; however, they will prove useful in the future. The symbol x is a *dummy variable* in the sense that it could be replaced by any other symbol without changing the meaning of (3-11).

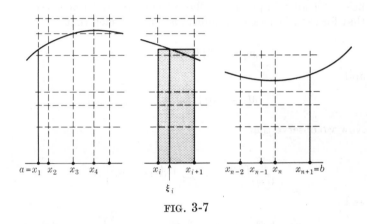

FIG. 3-7

THEOREM 3-4.1. Suppose $a \leq b$ and f is nonnegative on $[a, b]$. Then f is Riemann integrable on $[a, b]$ if and only if the region under the graph of f from a to b has area. If f is Riemann integrable on $[a, b]$, then $\int_a^b f(x)\, dx$ is equal to this area.

PROOF. Suppose the interval $[a, b]$ is divided into subintervals by the vertical lines of a system of rectangles, as in Fig. 3-7. If s_* and s^* are the inner and outer sums for this system of rectangles, then

$$s_* \leq \sum_{i=1}^{n} f(\xi_i)(x_{i+1} - x_i) \leq s^*, \tag{3-12}$$

for any numbers ξ_i in the respective intervals. We shall assume first that the region W under the graph of f has area. Then it follows from Theorem 3-2.3 that, for any positive number ε, there is a number Δ such that $s^* - s_* < \varepsilon$ if the mesh of the system of rectangles is less than Δ. It then follows from (3-12) that

$$\left| (\text{area of } W) - \sum_{i=1}^{n} f(\xi_i)(x_{i+1} - x_i) \right| < \varepsilon,$$

if $[a, b]$ is partitioned into subintervals shorter than Δ. Therefore, the limit of $\sum_{i=1}^{n} f(\xi_i)(x_{i+1} - x_i)$ exists and is equal to the area of W.

Now we assume that f is Riemann integrable. Then for $\varepsilon > 0$, we can choose a partition of $[a, b]$ such that

$$\left| \int_a^b f(x)\, dx - \sum_{i=1}^{n} f(\xi_i)(x_{i+1} - x_i) \right| < \tfrac{1}{2}\varepsilon, \qquad (3\text{-}13)$$

for any numbers ξ_i in the respective subintervals of $[a, b]$. We shall leave it to the student to show [problem 6] that there is a number K such that $|f(x)| \leq K$ for all x in $[a, b]$. Since $f(x)$ is bounded above and below for all x in $[a, b]$, it follows from the least upper bound axiom that for each i there are numbers m_i and M_i such that

$$m_i = \inf \{f(x) \colon x_i \leq x \leq x_{i+1}\},$$

and

$$M_i = \sup \{f(x) \colon x_i \leq x \leq x_{i+1}\}.$$

Now we observe that

$$\left| \int_a^b f(x)\, dx - \sum_{i=1}^{n} m_i(x_{i+1} - x_i) \right| \leq \tfrac{1}{2}\varepsilon,$$

and

$$\left| \int_a^b f(x)\, dx - \sum_{i=1}^{n} M_i(x_{i+1} - x_i) \right| \leq \tfrac{1}{2}\varepsilon, \qquad (3\text{-}14)$$

since if in either case it were necessary to replace $\leq$ by $>$, then the numbers ξ_i in (3-13) could be chosen so that $<$ in (3-13) should be replaced by $>$. It follows from inequalities (3-14) that

$$\sum_{i=1}^{n} M_i(x_{i+1} - x_i) - \sum_{i=1}^{n} m_i(x_{i+1} - x_i) \leq \varepsilon.$$

For the set W, $\sum m_i(x_{i+1} - x_i)$ and $\sum M_i(x_{i+1} - x_i)$ are inner and outer sums, respectively. Therefore it follows from Theorem 3-2.2 that W has area.

This theorem makes it clear that, from a strictly logical viewpoint, we could define the area of the region under the graph of f from a to b as $\int_a^b f(x)\, dx$. However, the region under the graph of a function is a set and the area of this set should not be changed by translations or rotations. It is clear that area as defined in Definition 3-2.3 is not

changed by translation or rotation. This question is not so easily
discussed if area is defined as an integral. Moreover, many sets with
area in the sense of Definition 3-2.3 cannot be represented as the region
under the graph of a function, wherever the coordinate axes are placed.

PROBLEMS

1. Use only the theory already developed in this chapter to evaluate
the following integrals.

(**a**) $\int_1^5 3 \, dt.$ (**b**) $\int_2^4 s \, ds.$ (**c**) $\int_{-1}^4 (3y+2) \, dy.$ (**d**) $\int_{-1}^2 |x| \, dx.$

2. Show that

(**a**) $0 \leq \int_0^\pi \sin x^{\frac{1}{2}} \, dx \leq \pi;$ (**b**) $2 \leq \int_0^2 \sqrt{1 + x^3} \, dx \leq 6.$

3. Let $f(x)$ equal 1 if x is rational, and equal 0 if x is irrational. Show
that $\int_0^1 f(x) \, dx$ does not exist.

4. Let $f(x) = 1/|q|$ if $x = p/q$ and p and q are relatively prime integers,
and $f(x) = 0$ if x is an irrational number. Prove that $\int_0^1 f(x) \, dx$ exists
and equals zero.

5. Let $f(x) = x$ if there are positive integers m and n such that $x = m \cdot 2^{-n}$;
otherwise, let $f(x) = 0$. Determine whether $\int_0^1 f(t) \, dt$ exists. Give
reasons.

6. Let f be a function that is integrable on $[a, b]$. Prove that there is
a number K such that $|f(x)| \leq K$ if $a \leq x \leq b$.

7.* Assume that $a \neq b$ and that f is a continuous function such that
$\int_a^b f(x) \, dx$ is zero and $f(x) \geq 0$ if $x \in [a, b]$. Prove that $f(x) = 0$ if
$x \in [a, b]$.

3-5. SOME PROPERTIES OF DEFINITE INTEGRALS

For Theorem 3-4.1 of the previous section and the discussion that
followed this theorem, we used only nonnegative functions. We shall
now establish several properties of Riemann integrals not subject to
this restriction, and use some of them to generalize Theorem 3-4.1 to
functions that have both positive and negative values.

(A) $\int_a^b f(x) \, dx = - \int_b^a f(x) \, dx$ *if either of these integrals exists.* This
follows from the fact that a partition of the interval from a to b is also

a partition of the interval from b to a. If the same values of ξ_i are used in each case, then

$$\sum_{i=1}^{n} f(\xi_i)(x_{i+1} - x_i) \quad \text{and} \quad \sum_{i=1}^{n} f(\xi_i)(x_i - x_{i+1})$$

are negatives of each other and one approaches $\int_a^b f(x) \, dx$, while the other approaches $\int_b^a f(x) \, dx$.

(B) *If $\int_a^b f(x) \, dx$ exists, then $\int_a^b cf(x) \, dx = c \int_a^b f(x) \, dx$ for every number c.* From Definition 3-4.4 we have

$$c \int_a^b f(x) \, dx = c \lim_{\delta \to 0} \sum_{i=1}^{n} f(\xi_i)(x_{i+1} - x_i)$$

$$= \lim_{\delta = 0} \sum_{i=1}^{n} cf(\xi_i)(x_{i+1} - x_i) = \int_a^b cf(x) \, dx.$$

(C) $\int_a^b [f(x) + g(x)] \, dx = \int_a^b f(x) \, dx + \int_a^b g(x) \, dx$ *if the latter two integrals exist.* Again, we may make direct use of Definition 3-4.4, obtaining

$$\int_a^b f(x) \, dx + \int_a^b g(x) \, dx = \lim_{\delta \to 0} \sum_{i=1}^{n} f(\xi_i)(x_{i+1} - x_i)$$

$$+ \lim_{\delta \to 0} \sum_{i=1}^{n} g(\xi_i)(x_{i+1} - x_i)$$

$$= \lim_{\delta \to 0} \left[\sum_{i=1}^{n} f(\xi_i)(x_{i+1} - x_i) + \sum_{i=1}^{n} g(\xi_i)(x_{i+1} - x_i) \right]$$

$$= \lim_{\delta \to 0} \sum_{i=1}^{n} [f(\xi_i) + g(\xi_i)](x_{i+1} - x_i)$$

$$= \int_a^b [f(x) + g(x)] \, dx.$$

We shall now return to the discussion of the existence of $\int_a^b f(x) \, dx$, without the restriction that $f(x) \geq 0$ for all x. Given a function f defined on an interval $[a, b]$ with $a \leq b$, we shall let the functions f^+ and f^- be defined as indicated in Fig. 3-8. The function f^+ has the same value as f when this value is positive or zero, and is zero when f is negative. The function f^- has the value $-f(x)$ when $f(x)$ is negative or zero, and is zero when $f(x)$ is positive. We shall call f^+ the *positive part* of f and f^- the *negative part* of f. The formulas that define f^+ and f^- are

$$f^+(x) = \tfrac{1}{2}[|f(x)| + f(x)] \quad \text{and} \quad f^-(x) = \tfrac{1}{2}[|f(x)| - f(x)].$$

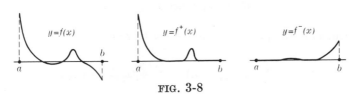

FIG. 3-8

THEOREM 3-5.1. Suppose f is a function whose domain contains the interval $[a, b]$, where $a \leq b$. Each of the following is a necessary and sufficient condition for f to be Riemann integrable on $[a, b]$:

(i) f^+ and f^- are integrable on $[a, b]$;

(ii) the region W between the x-axis and the graph of f and between the lines $x = a$ and $x = b$ has area.

If f is integrable, then $\int_a^b f(x)\, dx$ is equal to the area of the region under the graph of f^+ from a to b *minus* the area of the region under the graph of f^- from a to b, that is, the area of the part of W above the x-axis *minus* the area of the part of W below the x-axis.

PROOF. It follows from Theorem 3-4.1, and known properties of area, that (i) and (ii) are equivalent. Suppose that $\int_a^b f^+(x)\, dx$ and $\int_a^b f^-(x)\, dx$ both exist. Since $f(x) = f^+(x) - f^-(x)$, it then follows from (B), with $c = -1$, and (C), that $\int_a^b f(x)\, dx$ exists and that

$$\int_a^b f(x)\, dx = \int_a^b f^+(x)\, dx - \int_a^b f^-(x)\, dx.$$

Because of Theorem 3-4.1, we can say that the integrals in the right member of this equality are the areas of the regions from a to b under the graphs of f^+ and f^-, respectively. To complete the proof, we must show that $\int_a^b f^+(x)\, dx$ and $\int_a^b f^-(x)\, dx$ both exist if $\int_a^b f(x)\, dx$ exists. To do this, it is sufficient to show that the regions under the graphs of f^+ and f^- from a to b have area, since one can then apply Theorem 3-4.1 to conclude that the integrals of these functions exist. The proof is similar to the latter part of the proof of Theorem 3-4.1. For $\varepsilon > 0$, we can choose a partition of $[a, b]$ such that

$$\left| \int_a^b f(x)\, dx - \sum_{i=1}^n f(\xi_i)(x_{i+1} - x_i) \right| < \tfrac{1}{2}\varepsilon,$$

for any numbers ξ_i in the respective subintervals of $[a, b]$. For each i, we let

$$m_i = \inf \{f(x): x_i \leq x \leq x_{i+1}\}$$

and

$$M_i = \sup \{f(x): x_i \leq x \leq x_{i+1}\}.$$

Then, as in the proof of Theorem 3-4.1, we have

$$\sum_{i=1}^{n} M_i(x_{i+1}-x_i) - \sum_{i=1}^{n} m_i(x_{i+1}-x_i) \leq \varepsilon. \qquad (3\text{-}15)$$

Now let $M_i^* = M_i$ if $M_i \geq 0$ and $M_i^* = 0$ if $M_i < 0$, and let $m_i^* = m_i$ if $m_i \geq 0$ and $m_i^* = 0$ if $m_i < 0$. This has the effect of replacing

$$(M_i - m_i)(x_{i+1}-x_i)$$

in (3-15) by zero if $M_i \leq 0$, replacing it by a smaller term if $M_i > 0 > m_i$, and leaving it unchanged if $m_i \geq 0$. Therefore,

$$\sum_{i=1}^{n} M_i^*(x_{i+1}-x_i) - \sum_{i=1}^{n} m_i^*(x_{i+1}-x_i) \leq \varepsilon. \qquad (3\text{-}16)$$

The left member of inequality (3-16) is the difference between an outer and an inner sum for the region under the graph of f^+ from a to b. Therefore, it follows from Theorem 3-2.2 that this region has area. Similarly, the region under the graph of f^- from a to b has area.

Now we shall use Theorem 3-5.1 to establish some more properties of integrals.

(D) $\int_a^a f(x)\,dx = 0$. The regions under f^+ and f^- from a to a both have area and the area of each is zero. Therefore, $\int_a^a f(x)\,dx = 0 - 0 = 0$.

(E) $\int_a^b f(x)\,dx + \int_b^c f(x)\,dx = \int_a^c f(x)\,dx$ *if the first two integrals exist.* Let us consider the equality

$$\int_a^b f^+(x)\,dx + \int_b^c f^+(x)\,dx = \int_a^c f^+(x)\,dx. \qquad (3\text{-}17)$$

It follows from (A) and Theorem 3-5.1 that the first two integrals exist if the first two integrals in (E) exist. Also, $\int_a^b f^+(x)\,dx$ is the area of the region under the graph of f^+ from a to b if $a \le b$, or the negative of this area if $a > b$. With a similar interpretation of $\int_b^c f^+(x)\, dx$, we may conclude from the properties of area developed in Section 3-2 that the left member of Eq. (3-17) is the area of the region under the graph of f^+ from a to c if $a \le c$, or the negative of this area if $a > c$. This and Theorem 3-4.1 imply that $\int_a^c f^+(x)\, dx$ exists and has the same value. Similarly,

$$\int_a^b f^-(x)\, dx + \int_b^c f^-(x)\, dx = \int_a^c f^-(x)\, dx. \qquad (3\text{-}18)$$

Now we can get (E) by subtracting corresponding members of (3-17) and (3-18) and using Theorem 3-5.1.

(F) $\int_a^b |f(x)|\, dx$ *exists if* $\int_a^b f(x)\, dx$ *exists.* Our proof uses the equality $|f(x)| = f^+(x) + f^-(x)$. We know that if $\int_a^b f(x)\, dx$ exists, then f^+ and f^- are integrable. Now we can use property (C) to establish the existence of $\int_a^b [f^+(x) + f^-(x)]\, dx$, which is equal to $\int_a^b |f(x)|\, dx$.

If both f^+ and f^- are continuous at a point x, then f is continuous at x. That is, if f is discontinuous at x, then at least one of f^+ or f^- is discontinuous at x. Therefore, if D, D^+, and D^- denote the sets of discontinuities of f, f^+, and f^-, respectively, then $D \subset (D^+ \cup D^-)$. Also, a point of continuity of f is a point of continuity of both f^+ and f^-, so we have $D^+ \subset D$ and $D^- \subset D$. Thus,

$$D = D^+ \cup D^-. \qquad (3\text{-}19)$$

Therefore, if D is of measure zero, then both D^+ and D^- are of measure zero. Also, if both D^+ and D^- are of measure zero, then D is of measure zero [see problem 8, page 140]. Thus, each of the following is a necessary and sufficient condition for D to be of measure zero:
  (i) Both D^+ and D^- are of measure zero.
  (ii) Both the region under the graph of f^+ and the region under the graph of f^- have area [see (ii) of Theorem 3-3.4].
  (iii) Both f^+ and f^- are integrable [Theorem 3-4.1].
From Theorem 3-5.1, we then have the following theorem.

THEOREM 3-5.2. Suppose f is a bounded function whose domain contains the interval $[a, b]$. Then f is Riemann integrable on $[a, b]$ if and only if the set of discontinuities of f in $[a, b]$ is of measure zero.

At times it will be convenient to evaluate integrals over sets that have length but are not intervals. The next definition gives a simple technique for doing this. Later, when discussing double and triple integrals, we shall use partitions of sets with area and of sets with volume. After reading Chapter 5, the student might find it interesting to formulate a definition of a partition of a set with length and a definition of integral over a set with length, analogous to the definitions of double and triple integrals. It is not difficult to show that the resulting definition is equivalent to Definition 3-5.1.

DEFINITION 3-5.1. Suppose R is a set that has length. A *Riemann integrable function* on R is a function f for which ϕ is integrable in the sense of Definition 3-4.4 on an interval containing R, where ϕ is the function defined by $\phi(x) = f(x)$ if $x \in R$ and $\phi(x) = 0$ if $x \notin R$. If f is integrable on R and $R \subset [a, b]$, then

$$\int_R f(x)\, dx = \int_a^b \phi(x)\, dx.$$

It is clear that this definition is consistent with Definition 3-4.4 when R is an interval. Also, it follows immediately from Definition 3-5.1 that Theorem 3-5.1 can be restated, replacing $[a, b]$ by R and (ii) by the statement that "f is integrable on R if and only if the region W between R and the graph of f has area."

Suppose f is continuous on a set R except in a set of measure zero and that R has length. If $\phi(x) = f(x)$ when $x \in R$ and $\phi(x) = 0$ when $x \notin R$, then the set of discontinuities of ϕ also is of measure zero [see problem 12]. Thus, the following theorem follows from Theorem 3-5.2.

THEOREM 3-5.3. Suppose R is a set that has length and that f is a bounded function whose domain contains the set R. Then f is Riemann integrable on R if and only if the set of discontinuities of f in R is of measure zero.

PROBLEMS

1. Suppose that f is a function whose domain contains the interval $[a, b]$ and that $f(x) = 0$ for all but a finite number of values of x. Show that $\int_a^b f(x)\, dx$ exists and is equal to zero.

2. Suppose that $f(x) = 1$ if x is rational and $f(x) = -1$ if x is irrational. Show that $\int_a^b f(x)\, dx$ does not exist. [*Note:* f is a function such that $\int_a^b |f(x)|\, dx$ exists and $\int_a^b f(x)\, dx$ does not exist.]

3. Give an example of a function f for which f^+ is integrable and f is not integrable.

4.* Prove that if $\int_a^b h(x)\,dx$ exists, then $\left|\int_a^b h(x)\,dx\right| \le \left|\int_a^b |h(x)|\,dx\right|$.

5.* Let f and g be integrable functions on $[a, b]$ for which $f(x) \le g(x)$ for all x. Show that if $a \le b$, then

$$\int_a^b f(x)\,dx \le \int_a^b g(x)\,dx.$$

6. Suppose f is integrable on $[a, b]$. (a) Prove that there are numbers m and M such that $m \le f(x) \le M$ if $x \in [a, b]$. (b) Prove that

$$m(b-a) \le \int_a^b f(x)\,dx \le M(b-a),$$

if $a < b$ and $m \le f(x) \le M$ when $x \in [a, b]$.

7.* Suppose f is integrable on $[a, b]$. (a) Prove that f is integrable on $[a, x]$ if $a \le x \le b$. (b) Let F be defined by $F(x) = \int_a^x f(t)\,dt$. Prove that F is continuous on $[a, b]$.

8. Suppose f is continuous on $[a, b]$ except in a set of measure zero and explain why

$$\lim_{n \to +\infty} \frac{b-a}{n} \sum_{k=1}^n f\left(a + \frac{k(b-a)}{n}\right) = \int_a^b f(x)\,dx.$$

9. Suppose f is a function whose domain contains the interval $[a, b]$ and that f is bounded on $[a, b]$ and continuous except at a countable number of discontinuities. Prove that f is integrable on $[a, b]$.

10. Suppose f is a function whose domain is a set R that has length. Prove that f is integrable on R if and only if the graph of f has area.

11. Prove that if a function f is monotone on the interval $[a, b]$ then its set of discontinuities in $[a, b]$ either is finite or is countably infinite.

12.* Suppose the domain of f is a set D of real numbers and that D has length. Let $\phi(x) = f(x)$ if $x \in D$ and $\phi(x) = 0$ if $x \notin D$. Let A and B be the sets of discontinuities of f and ϕ, respectively, and prove (a) the set of numbers that are discontinuities of ϕ and not of f has length zero [see problem 5, page 126]; (b) A is of measure zero if and only if B is of measure zero.

3-6. THE FUNDAMENTAL THEOREM OF CALCULUS

The fundamental theorem of calculus relates differentiation and integration and shows that in a certain sense integration is the inverse of differentiation. We shall state and prove two forms of the fundamental theorem and show the relation between these forms. It is easy to show that if $\int_a^b f(t)\,dt$ exists, then $\int_a^x f(t)\,dt$ exists and is continuous if x is in the interval $[a, b]$ [see problem 7 of the last section]. The *indefinite integral* of f is then defined as the function F for which $F(x) = \int_a^x f(t)\,dt$ for all x in $[a, b]$.

THEOREM 3-6.1 (FIRST FORM OF THE FUNDAMENTAL THEOREM OF CALCULUS). Suppose the function f is Riemann integrable on $[a, b]$ and that F is the indefinite integral defined by

$$F(x) = \int_a^x f(t)\,dt, \tag{3-20}$$

for x in the interval $[a, b]$. If x_0 is in the interval $[a, b]$ and f is continuous at x_0, then F is differentiable at x_0 and

$$F'(x_0) = f(x_0).$$

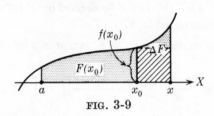

FIG. 3-9

PROOF. We shall make direct use of the definition of derivative. For x_0 a point of continuity of f, and $\Delta F = F(x) - F(x_0)$, we have

$$\Delta F = \int_a^x f(t)\,dt - \int_a^{x_0} f(t)\,dt = \int_{x_0}^x f(t)\,dt$$

$$= \int_{x_0}^x \{f(x_0) + [f(t) - f(x_0)]\}\,dt$$

$$= f(x_0)(x - x_0) + \int_{x_0}^x [f(t) - f(x_0)]\,dt.$$

In Fig. 3-9, the diagonally shaded part of ΔF represents the term $f(x_0)(x - x_0)$. With $\Delta x = x - x_0$, we have

$$\frac{\Delta F}{\Delta x} = f(x_0) + \frac{\int_{x_0}^x [f(t) - f(x_0)]\,dt}{x - x_0}.$$

To complete the proof, we need to show that

$$\lim_{x \to x_0} \frac{\int_{x_0}^x [f(t) - f(x_0)]\,dt}{x - x_0} = 0. \tag{3-21}$$

Since f is continuous at x_0, for any positive number ε there is a positive number δ such that

$$|f(t)-f(x_0)| < \varepsilon \quad \text{if} \quad |t-x_0| < \delta.$$

Now we choose x so that $|x-x_0| < \delta$ and use the fact that for no function h is $\left|\int_a^b h(x)\, dx\right|$ larger than $\left|\int_a^b |h(x)|\, dx\right|$ [see problem 4 of the last section] to obtain

$$\left|\frac{\int_{x_0}^x [f(t)-f(x_0)]\, dt}{x-x_0}\right| \leqq \frac{\left|\int_{x_0}^x |f(t)-f(x_0)|\, dt\right|}{|x-x_0|}.$$

Now we use $|f(t)-f(x_0)| < \varepsilon$ to obtain the following inequality [see problem 5 of the last section]:

$$\left|\frac{\int_{x_0}^x [f(t)-f(x_0)]\, dt}{x-x_0}\right| \leqq \frac{\left|\int_{x_0}^x \varepsilon\, dt\right|}{|x-x_0|} = \frac{\varepsilon|x-x_0|}{|x-x_0|} = \varepsilon.$$

This establishes Eq. (3-21) and completes the proof of the theorem.

If we assume that the function f of Theorem 3-6.1 is continuous at all points of the interval $[a, b]$ and that F^* is an antiderivative of f, then it follows that on $[a, b]$ the function f is the derivative of both F^* and the function F defined by Eq. (3-20).   Therefore, there is a number c such that

$$\int_a^x f(t)\, dt = F^*(x)+c$$

if $x \in [a, b]$ [see Corollary 2, page 108].   If we let $x = a$, we see that $c = -F^*(a)$, so that

$$\int_a^x f(t)\, dt = F^*(x) - F^*(a).$$

Now we can let $x = b$, to obtain

$$\int_a^b f(t)\, dt = F^*(b) - F^*(a),$$

where F^* is any antiderivative of f.   This will be the conclusion of the second form of the fundamental theorem.   However, the assumption that f is continuous at all points of $[a, b]$ is more stringent than necessary. To avoid this assumption and to introduce a new method of proof, we shall state and prove the second form of the fundamental theorem independently of the first form.

THEOREM 3-6.2 (SECOND FORM OF THE FUNDAMENTAL THEOREM OF CALCULUS). Suppose the function f is Riemann integrable on $[a, b]$ and that there is a function F such that $F'(x) = f(x)$ for *all* x of $[a, b]$. Then

$$\int_a^b f(t)\, dt = F(b) - F(a).$$

PROOF. If we use the notation of Section 3-4, then

$$\int_a^b f(x)\, dx = \lim_{\delta \to 0} \sum_{i=1}^n f(\xi_i)(x_{i+1} - x_i).$$

Therefore, if ε is a positive number, there is a partition $\{x_1, x_2, \cdots, x_{n+1}\}$ such that

$$\left| \int_a^b f(x)\, dx - \sum_{i=1}^n f(\xi_i)(x_{i+1} - x_i) \right| < \varepsilon, \qquad (3\text{-}22)$$

whatever the values of ξ for the respective intervals. Since F is differentiable on $[a, b]$, we can use the mean value theorem and choose ξ_i as a number for which

$$F(x_{i+1}) - F(x_i) = F'(\xi_i)(x_{i+1} - x_i). \qquad (3\text{-}23)$$

Since $F'(\xi_i) = f(\xi_i)$, we have

$$\sum_{i=1}^n f(\xi_i)(x_{i+1} - x_i) = \sum_{i=1}^n [F(x_{i+1}) - F(x_i)] = F(x_{n+1}) - F(x_1)$$

$$= F(b) - F(a).$$

Then Eq. (3-22) becomes $\left| \int_a^b f(x)\, dx - [F(b) - F(a)] \right| < \varepsilon$. This is true for all positive numbers ε only if $\int_a^b f(t)\, dt = F(b) - F(a)$.

For most applications, the difference between the hypothesis that f is continuous (first form) and the hypothesis that f has an antiderivative (second form) is not very significant, since for most functions the student will encounter the derivatives are continuous. However, there are functions for which this is not true. For example, if F is defined by

$$F(x) = x^2 \sin \frac{1}{x} \quad \text{if} \quad x \neq 0 \quad \text{and} \quad F(0) = 0,$$

then

$$F'(x) = 2x \sin \frac{1}{x} - \cos \frac{1}{x} \quad \text{if} \quad x \neq 0,$$

and

$$F'(0) = \lim_{x \to 0} \frac{x^2 \sin 1/x - 0}{x - 0} = \lim_{x \to 0} x \sin \frac{1}{x} = 0.$$

The function F' is not continuous at the origin. However, $\int_a^b F'(x)\,dx$ exists for any a and b, since F' has only one point of discontinuity and is bounded. Thus, it follows from the second form of the fundamental theorem that

$$\int_{-1}^1 F'(x)\,dx = F(1) - F(-1) = 2 \sin 1.$$

This conclusion cannot be reached by direct application of the first form, since F' is not continuous at $x = 0$.

The following theorem justifies the usual method of change of variables in a definite integral. The proof uses the two forms of the fundamental theorem of calculus and the familiar chain rule for differentiation.† Another type of proof is discussed in Section 8-1.

THEOREM 3-6.3. Suppose u is a function whose derivative is continuous at all points of a closed interval I_α^β with end points α and β. If $a = u(\alpha)$ and $b = u(\beta)$, and if f is continuous at x whenever $x = u(t)$ and $t \in [\alpha, \beta]$, then

$$\int_a^b f(x)\,dx = \int_\alpha^\beta f[u(t)]u'(t)\,dt.$$

PROOF. Since u is continuous, it follows from the intermediate value theorem that the range of u contains the closed interval with end points a and b. Therefore, f is continuous on this interval and $\int_a^b f(x)\,dx$ exists. Since f and u are both continuous and u' is continuous, it follows that $(f \circ u)u'$ is continuous on I_α^β and that $\int_\alpha^\beta f[u(t)]u'(t)\,dt$

---

† A formal proof of the chain rule is given in Section 6-2.

exists. We know from the first form of the fundamental theorem of calculus that f has an antiderivative F and that

$$\int_a^b f(x)\, dx = F(b) - F(a).$$

Suppose we let the function G be defined by $G(t) = F[u(t)]$ for $t \in I_\alpha^\beta$. Then

$$G'(t) = F'[u(t)]u'(t) = f[u(t)]u'(t),$$

which means that G is an antiderivative of $f[u(t)]u'(t)$. Then it follows from the second form of the fundamental theorem of calculus that

$$\int_\alpha^\beta f[u(t)]u'(t)\, dt = G(\beta) - G(\alpha) = F[u(\beta)] - F[u(\alpha)]$$

$$= F(b) - F(a) = \int_a^b f(x)\, dx.$$

The familiar mean value theorem for derivatives [Theorem 2-8.5] has a natural formulation in terms of integrals. If a function F is differentiable at all points of an interval $[a, b]$, then it follows from the mean value theorem for derivatives that there is a number ξ in the open interval (a, b) such that

$$F(b) - F(a) = (b - a)F'(\xi).$$

If we let f denote F', then this can be written as

$$\int_a^b f(t)\, dt = (b - a)f(\xi).$$

THEOREM 3-6.4 (FIRST MEAN VALUE THEOREM FOR INTEGRALS).
Suppose the function f is integrable on $[a, b]$ and that there is a function F such that $F'(x) = f(x)$ for *all* x of $[a, b]$. Then there is a number ξ in the open interval (a, b) such that

$$\int_a^b f(x)\, dx = f(\xi)(b - a).$$

THEOREM 3-6.5 (SECOND MEAN VALUE THEOREM FOR INTEGRALS).
Suppose functions f and h are continuous on the interval $[a, b]$ and that $h(x)$ has the same sign at all points of $[a, b]$ at which it is nonzero. Then there is a number ξ in the open interval (a, b) such that

$$\int_a^b f(t)h(t)\, dt = f(\xi) \int_a^b h(t)\, dt. \tag{3-24}$$

PROOF.   We shall assume that $a < b$ and that $h(x) \geq 0$ if $x \in [a, b]$.   Any other case can be reduced to this case by changing the sign of h, or the sign of each integral in Eq. (3-24), or the sign of h and the sign of each integral.   Since f is continuous on $[a, b]$, it has a smallest value m and a largest value M.   Then

$$m \cdot h(x) \leq f(x)h(x) \leq M \cdot h(x),$$

and it follows from our geometric interpretation of definite integrals in terms of area that

$$m \int_a^b h(t) \, dt \leq \int_a^b f(t)h(t) \, dt \leq M \int_a^b h(t) \, dt.$$

If $m \int_a^b h(t) \, dt = \int_a^b f(t)h(t) \, dt$, then $\int_a^b [f(t) - m]h(t) \, dt = 0$ and, for each t, either $f(t) = m$ or $h(t) = 0$ [see problem 7, page 145].   If in this case $f(x) = m$ for some x in (a, b), then this value of x can be used for ξ in (3-24); otherwise, $h(t) \equiv 0$ and we can let ξ be any number in (a, b). The case $\int_a^b f(t)h(t) \, dt = M \int_a^b h(t) \, dt$ can be treated similarly.   Now suppose that

$$m \int_a^b h(t) \, dt < \int_a^b f(t)h(t) \, dt < M \int_a^b h(t) \, dt.$$

Since m and M are values of the function f, it follows from the intermediate value theorem that there is a number ξ such that $f(\xi)$ is the number between m and M that satisfies (3-24).   Moreover, ξ can be chosen *between* a point at which f has the value m and a point at which f has the value M, so that ξ can be in the open interval (a, b).

PROBLEMS

1. Evaluate each of the following. [*Hint:* In some cases, it may be helpful to let F denote an antiderivative of the integrand.]

(**a**) $D_x \int_1^x (\ln t) \, dt.$

(**d**) $D_x \int_1^{x^2} (\ln t) \, dt.$

(**b**) $D_t \int_0^2 \dfrac{1}{1+t^2} \, dt.$

(**e**) $D_x \int_x^{x^2} e^{-t^2} \, dt.$

(**c**) $D_x \int_x^2 \dfrac{\sin t}{t} \, dt; \ x > 0.$

(**f**) $\int_0^{\sqrt{\pi}} D_t(\cos^5 t^{1/2}) \, dt.$

2. An object moves in a straight line in such a way that it has a velocity v for which $\int_{t_1}^{t_2} v(t)\, dt$ exists. Explain why the average velocity between t_1 and t_2 is equal to

$$\frac{\int_{t_1}^{t_2} v(t)\, dt}{t_2 - t_1}.$$

3. Let f be a function continuous on $[a, b]$, where $a < b$. Find the value of w for which G has its smallest value, where

$$G(w) = \int_a^b [f(x) - w]^2\, dx.$$

4. For each of the following, evaluate the limit by writing it as a definite integral and then using the fundamental theorem of calculus.

(**a**) $\displaystyle \lim_{n \to +\infty} \sum_{k=1}^{n} \frac{k^2}{n^3}$.

(**c**) $\displaystyle \lim_{n \to +\infty} \sum_{k=1}^{n} \frac{2n}{(n+2k)^2}$.

(**b**) $\displaystyle \lim_{n \to +\infty} \sum_{k=1}^{n} \left(\sin \frac{k\pi}{n} \right) \frac{\pi}{n}$.

(**d**) $\displaystyle \lim_{n \to +\infty} \sum_{k=1}^{n} \frac{(n+2k)^4}{n^5}$.

5. Let $f(x) = \cos x$ for all x. Show that each antiderivative of f is of the form $\sin x + c$ for some number c. Show that $\sin x + c$ is an indefinite integral of f if and only if $|c| \leqq 1$. [*Note:* This shows that an antiderivative of a function is not always an indefinite integral of the function.]

6. Let $f(x) = 1$ if $x > 0$, $f(0) = 0$, and $f(x) = -1$ if $x < 0$. If $F(x) = |x|$ for all x, then $F'(x) = f(x)$ if $x \neq 0$. Show that

$$\int_{-1}^{0} f(x)\, dx = F(0) - F(-1) \quad \text{and} \quad \int_{0}^{1} f(x)\, dx = F(1) - F(0).$$

Explain why neither form of the fundamental theorem can be used directly to show this.

7. Let F be defined by $F(x) = x^{3/2}(\sin 1/x)$ if $x > 0$ and $F(0) = 0$. Show that $F'(x)$ exists for $x \geqq 0$, but that $\int_0^1 F'(x)\, dx$ does not exist. [*Note:* This shows that not all functions that have antiderivatives are integrable.]

8. Suppose f' is continuous on $[a, b]$. Explain carefully why $\int_a^b f'(x)\, dx = f(b) - f(a)$.

9. (a) Explain why the first mean value theorem for integrals remains true if the requirement that "f is Riemann integrable on $[a, b]$ and there is a function F such that $F'(x) = f(x)$ for *all* x of $[a, b]$" is replaced by "f is continuous on $[a, b]$." (b) Prove this form of the theorem

without using the mean value theorem for derivatives. [*Hint:* Let m and M be the smallest and largest values of f and use the intermediate value theorem.]

10. Consider the following five statements that might apply to a function on an interval $[a, b]$: (1) f is continuous on $[a, b]$; (2) f is uniformly continuous on $[a, b]$; (3) f is differentiable on $[a, b]$; (4) f has an anti-derivative on $[a, b]$; (5) $\int_a^b f(x)\, dx$ exists. There are 20 implications of type "p implies q," where each of p and q is one of statements (1) through (5), but p and q are not the same statement. Determine which of these implications are true and summarize in a table.

11. Suppose f is integrable on the interval $[a, b]$ and that the function F has the property that, whenever $a \leq r < s \leq b$, there is a number ξ in $[r, s]$ for which

$$F(s) - F(r) = f(\xi)(s - r).$$

Prove that $\int_a^b f(x)\, dx = F(b) - F(a)$ and that $F'(x) = f(x)$ on (a, b).

3-7. IMPROPER INTEGRALS

For a Riemann integral of a function of one variable to exist, the function must be bounded and the interval of integration must be bounded. We shall consider methods for extending the definition of integral so that certain unbounded functions are integrable and suitable functions can be integrated over unbounded intervals. An "integral" that exists in one of the senses to be discussed in this section, but not in the sense of the previous definition, is an *improper integral*.

We have seen that there is a close connection between area and integrals. For this reason, it is convenient to extend the definition of area before defining improper integrals.

DEFINITION 3-7.1.   An *unbounded plane set with area* is an unbounded set R that has the two properties:
    (i) $R \cap S$ has area whenever S is a bounded set that has area.
    (ii) The following set has an upper bound:

$$\{(\text{area of } R \cap S)\colon S \text{ a bounded set with area}\}.$$

When R has area, the least upper bound of this set is the *area* of R.

If we apply the preceding definition to a bounded set R, then R will have area in the new sense if and only if it has area in the old sense. Furthermore, we get the same values for the area of R.

However, it appears from Definition 3-7.1 that, in order to show that R has area, we must consider $R \cap S$ for all bounded sets with area. The next theorem enables us to simplify this procedure.

THEOREM 3-7.1. Suppose that R is an unbounded set and that $\{S_1, S_2, \cdots\}$ is a sequence of bounded sets with area such that $S_k \cap R$ has area and $S_k \subset S_{k+1}$ for all k. Also suppose that, for any bounded set S, there is a k such that $(S \cap R) \subset (S_k \cap R)$. Then

$$(\text{area of } R) = \lim_{k \to +\infty} (\text{area of } S_k \cap R), \qquad (3\text{-}25)$$

where one member of this equality exists if and only if the other exists.

PROOF. We shall let A_k denote the area of $S_k \cap R$. Since $\{A_k\}$ is a monotone increasing sequence, $\lim_{k \to +\infty} A_k$ exists if and only if the sequence $\{A_k\}$ has an upper bound. Also, for any bounded set S with area, there is a k such that $S \cap R$ is a subset of $S_k \cap R$. Since $S_k \cap R$ and S each have area, and $S \cap R = S \cap (S_k \cap R)$, it follows that $S \cap R$ has area. Therefore, (i) of Definition 3-7.1 is satisfied. Also, when $S \cap R$ is a subset of $S_k \cap R$, we have

$$(\text{area of } S \cap R) \leqq A_k.$$

Therefore, (ii) of Definition 3-7.1 is satisfied if and only if $\lim_{k \to +\infty} A_k$ exists. This is the same as saying that one member of (3-25) exists if and only if the other exists. If $\lim_{k \to +\infty} A_k = l$, then l is the least upper bound of the set $\{A_k\}$ and is therefore the least upper bound of the areas of sets of type $S \cap R$, where S has area. This completes the proof.

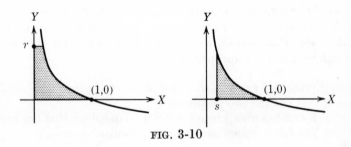

FIG. 3-10

ILLUSTRATION 1. Let us consider the graph of $y = x^{-\frac{1}{3}} - 1$ for $x > 0$, as shown in Fig. 3-10. Since $x^{-\frac{1}{3}} - 1$ is not bounded on the interval $(0, 1]$, the integral on $[0, 1]$ does not exist even if a value is assigned to y when $x = 0$. The shaded region in the first diagram has area equal to

$$\int_0^r \frac{1}{(y+1)^3}\, dy = \left[\frac{-1}{2(y+1)^2}\right]_0^r = \frac{1}{2} - \frac{1}{2(r+1)^2}.$$

This approaches $\frac{1}{2}$ as r increases and we can conclude from Theorem 3-7.1 that the area of the region under the graph of $x^{-\frac{1}{3}}-1$ from 0 to 1 exists and equals $\frac{1}{2}$. The shaded region in the second diagram of Fig. 3-10 has area equal to

$$\int_s^1 (x^{-\frac{1}{3}}-1)\,dx = [\tfrac{3}{2}x^{\frac{2}{3}}-x]_s^1 = \tfrac{1}{2}-\tfrac{3}{2}s^{\frac{2}{3}}+s,$$

and

$$\lim_{s\to 0}\ (\tfrac{1}{2}-\tfrac{3}{2}s^{\frac{2}{3}}+s) = \tfrac{1}{2}.$$

This procedure is justified by the following theorem.

THEOREM 3-7.2. Suppose f is a function that is Riemann integrable on the interval $[k, b]$ if $a < k \leqq b$. Also suppose that $f(x) \geqq 0$ if $a < x \leqq b$ and that R denotes the region under the graph of f from a to b. Then

$$\lim_{r\to a+}\int_r^b f(x)\,dx = (\text{area of } R),$$

if either member of this equality exists.

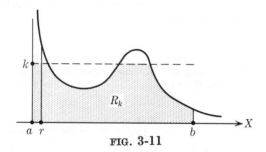

FIG. 3-11

PROOF. If we let S_k denote the rectangle bounded by $y = 0, y = k, x = a$, and $x = b$, and let $R_k = S_k \cap R$, as indicated in Fig. 3-11, then it follows that R_k has area.† Also, since (area of R_k) $\leqq k(r-a)+\int_r^b f(x)\,dx$, we have

$$(\text{area of } R_k) \leqq \lim_{r\to a+}\int_r^b f(x)\,dx,$$

---

† This can be shown as follows. For $\varepsilon > 0$, choose r so that $k(r-a) < \varepsilon$. If $R_{k,r}$ is the part of R_k whose points are on or to the right of the line $x = r$, then $R_{k,r}$ has area because it is the intersection of a rectangle and the region under the graph of the integrable function f between r and b. Also, $R_k - R_{k,r}$ is contained in a rectangle of area $k(r-a)$. That R_k has area now follows from (i) of Theorem 3-2.5, with $A = R_{k,r}$ and C the union of $R_{k,r}$ and this rectangle of area $k(r-a)$.

if this limit exists. Therefore, if this limit exists, then it follows from Theorem 3-7.1 that R has area and that the area of R is the least upper bound of the areas of all the R_k's, so that

$$\text{(area of } R) \le \lim_{r \to a+} \int_r^b f(x)\, dx.$$

Now let us suppose that R has area. Since $\int_r^b f(x)\, dx$ is the area of a subset of R, it follows that this integral is not greater than the area of R. Since $\int_r^b f(x)\, dx$ is monotone increasing as $r \to a+$, and never is greater than the area of R, it follows that it has a limit as $r \to a+$ and that

$$\lim_{r \to a+} \int_r^b f(x)\, dx \le \text{(area of } R).$$

We have shown that if either member of the two preceding inequalities exists, then the other exists and both inequalities are true statements. When both inequalities are true, they must be equalities.

We shall omit the proof of the next theorem, since it is so similar to the proof of Theorem 3-7.2.

THEOREM 3-7.3. Suppose f is a function that is Riemann integrable on the interval $[a, k]$ if $a \le k < b$. Also suppose that $f(x) \ge 0$ if $a \le x < b$ and that R denotes the region under the graph of f from a to b. Then

$$\lim_{r \to b-} \int_a^r f(x)\, dx = \text{(area of } R),$$

if either member of this equality exists.

When studying the integral of a function f in Section 3-5, we found it convenient to introduce the functions f^+ and f^-, defined by

$$f^+(x) = \tfrac{1}{2}[|f(x)| + f(x)] \quad \text{and} \quad f^-(x) = \tfrac{1}{2}[|f(x)| - f(x)].$$

The student should keep Theorem 3-5.1 in mind during the following discussion.

Suppose f is a function that is not integrable on the interval $[a, b]$ in the sense of Definition 3-4.4, where $a < b$ and a may be $-\infty$ and

b may be $+\infty$. Then we can define the *improper integral*, $\int_a^b f(x)\,dx$, as the area of the region under f^+ from a to b *minus* the area of the region under f^- from a to b, *if both of these regions have area*. However, if f has both positive and negative values, then the limit in Theorem 3-7.2 can exist in cases for which neither f^+ nor f^- define regions that have area [see problem 4 at the end of the section]. For this reason, it is customary to enlarge the preceding concept of improper integral as follows.

If f is bounded on the interval $[a, r]$ for $a \leqq r < b$, but not on the interval $[a, b)$, then the improper integral on $[a, b]$ is defined by

$$\int_a^b f(x)\,dx = \lim_{r \to b-} \int_a^r f(x)\,dx,$$

if this limit exists. Similarly, if f is bounded on the interval $[r, b]$ for $a < r \leqq b$, but not on the interval $(a, b]$, then the improper integral on $[a, b]$ is defined by

$$\int_a^b f(x)\,dx = \lim_{r \to a+} \int_r^b f(x)\,dx,$$

if this limit exists. If f is discontinuous at a point θ between a and b, then we can say that

$$\int_a^b f(x)\,dx = \int_a^\theta f(x)\,dx + \int_\theta^b f(x)\,dx,$$

if the two integrals on the right exist as improper integrals. Clearly, this can be extended to any finite number of points. These need not be infinite discontinuities. For example, they might be points not in the domain of the function. The function $x \ln x$ is not defined when $x = 0$, although $\lim_{x \to 0+} (x \ln x) = 0$. We can define the integral on $[0, 1]$ by

$$\int_0^1 (x \ln x)\,dx = \lim_{r \to 0+} \int_r^1 (x \ln x)\,dx$$

$$= \lim_{r \to 0+} \left[\tfrac{1}{2}x^2 \ln x - \tfrac{1}{4}x^2 \right]_r^1 = -\tfrac{1}{4}.$$

In general, we define improper integrals over unbounded intervals as follows:

$$\int_a^{+\infty} f(x)\, dx = \lim_{s \to +\infty} \int_a^s f(x)\, dx, \quad \text{if this limit exists;}$$

$$\int_{-\infty}^a f(x)\, dx = \lim_{s \to -\infty} \int_s^a f(x)\, dx, \quad \text{if this limit exists;}$$

$$\int_{-\infty}^{+\infty} f(x)\, dx = \int_{-\infty}^a f(x)\, dx + \int_a^{+\infty} f(x)\, dx,$$

if these integrals exist for some number a. In these definitions, $\int_a^s f(x)\, dx$ and $\int_s^a f(x)\, dx$ may themselves be improper integrals.

ILLUSTRATION 2. The *gamma function* is an interesting and important function that is defined by means of an improper integral. This function was first introduced by Leonhard Euler in 1729, and is used a great deal in both pure and applied mathematics. The gamma function is defined for $x > 0$ by the equation

$$\Gamma(x) = \int_0^{+\infty} t^{x-1} e^{-t}\, dt. \qquad (3\text{-}26)$$

However, this definition is not meaningful unless we can show that the integral exists when x is an arbitrary positive number. To do this, we note first that if $1 > x > 0$ then the integrand is not bounded on the interval $(0, 1]$. However,

$$0 < t^{x-1} e^{-t} < t^{x-1} \quad \text{if} \quad 0 < t < 1,$$

so that $\int_0^1 t^{x-1} e^{-t}\, dt$ exists if $\int_0^1 t^{x-1}\, dt$ exists. We have

$$\int_0^1 t^{x-1}\, dt = \lim_{r \to 0+} \int_r^1 t^{x-1}\, dt = \lim_{r \to 0+} \left[\frac{t^x}{x}\right]_r^1 = \lim_{r \to 0+} \left(\frac{1}{x} - \frac{r^x}{x}\right) = \frac{1}{x}.$$

This shows that $\int_0^1 t^{x-1} e^{-t}\, dt$ exists. Now let us consider $\int_1^{+\infty} t^{x-1} e^{-t} dt$ for a particular $x > 0$. To show that this integral exists as an improper integral, it is sufficient to show that $\int_1^s t^{x-1} e^{-t}\, dt$ has an upper bound. Although x may be large, it has a fixed value, and t^{x-1} will be dominated by e^{-t} when t is large enough. Explicitly, let us show that there is a number k such that if $t > k$ then

$$t^{x-1} e^{-t} < t^{-2} \quad \text{or} \quad t^{x+1} e^{-t} < 1.$$

To do this, it is sufficient to show that

$$\lim_{t \to +\infty} \frac{t^{x+1}}{e^t} < 1.$$

This is an easy consequence of L'Hôpital's rule, since the denominator is not changed by differentiation and the exponent in the numerator will eventually become negative or zero. In fact, the limit is actually equal to zero. Now we know that if $s > k$ then

$$\int_1^s t^{x-1} e^{-t}\, dt < \int_1^k t^{x-1} e^{-t}\, dt + \int_k^s \frac{1}{t^2}\, dt < \int_1^k t^{x-1} e^{-t}\, dt + \frac{1}{k}.$$

This gives the upper bound we wanted, and we conclude that $\int_0^{+\infty} t^{x-1} e^{-t}\, dt$ exists. Since $\int_0^1 t^{x-1} e^{-t}\, dt$ and $\int_1^{+\infty} t^{x-1} e^{-t}\, dt$ both exist if $x > 0$, we may conclude that $\Gamma(x)$ exists if $x > 0$. Although for most values of x we cannot evaluate $\Gamma(x)$ explicitly, many interesting properties of this new function are known. We shall derive one of the most surprising of these—namely, that

$$\Gamma(x+1) = x\Gamma(x) \tag{3-27}$$

for all $x > 0$. This is done by integration by parts, as follows:

$$\Gamma(x+1) = \lim_{s \to +\infty} \left\{ \lim_{r \to 0} \int_r^s t^x e^{-t}\, dt \right\}$$

$$= \lim_{s \to +\infty} \left\{ \lim_{r \to 0} \left[-t^x e^{-t} \right]_r^s \right\} + \lim_{s \to +\infty} \left\{ \lim_{r \to 0} \left(x \int_r^s t^{x-1} e^{-t}\, dt \right) \right\}$$

$$= \lim_{s \to +\infty} \left\{ \lim_{r \to 0} (r^x e^{-r} - s^x e^{-s}) \right\} + x \int_0^{+\infty} t^{x-1} e^{-t}\, dt$$

$$= x \int_0^{+\infty} t^{x-1} e^{-t}\, dt = x\Gamma(x).$$

Now that Eq. (3-27) has been proved, it can be used to show that

$$\Gamma(n+1) = n! \tag{3-28}$$

for n any nonnegative integer. This means that the gamma function can be used as a symbol to denote factorials of nonnegative integers. To prove Eq. (3-28) we need only establish the two facts needed for a proof by mathematical induction: (1) *The theorem is true for the first value of n.* That is, $\Gamma(1) = 0!$, or $\int_0^{+\infty} e^{-t} dt = 1$, which is easily verified. (2) *If the theorem is true for one integer, then it is true for the next integer.* If Eq. (3-28) is true for $n = k$, then

$$\Gamma(k+2) = (k+1)\Gamma(k+1) = (k+1) \cdot k! = (k+1)!$$

and (3-28) is true for $n = k+1$.

PROBLEMS

1. For each of the following, determine whether the integral exists as an improper integral and give reasons for your conclusion.

(a) $\displaystyle\int_0^{+\infty} x^{-\frac{1}{2}} dx.$ (c) $\displaystyle\int_0^{+\infty} (1+x^3)^{-1} dx.$ (e) $\displaystyle\int_0^{+\infty} \frac{x}{x^2+1} dx.$

(b) $\displaystyle\int_{-1}^1 x^{-2} dx.$ (d) $\displaystyle\int_0^{+\infty} (x+x^4)^{-\frac{1}{2}} dx.$ (f) $\displaystyle\int_0^{\pi} \frac{\sin x}{x^2} dx.$

2. Prove the following.

(a*) $\displaystyle\Gamma(x) = 2 \int_0^{+\infty} t^{2x-1} e^{-t^2} dt.$ (b) $\displaystyle\Gamma(x) = \int_0^1 (\ln 1/t)^{x-1} dt.$

(c) $\displaystyle\int_0^{+\infty} t^{x-1} e^{-at} dt = \frac{\Gamma(x)}{a^x},$ if $a > 0.$

3. Use an appropriate substitution and prove that, if n is a positive integer and $k > -1$, then

$$\int_0^1 t^k (\ln t)^n dt = \frac{(-1)^n n!}{(k+1)^{n+1}}.$$

4. Prove that the following integrals exist as improper integrals.

(a*) $\displaystyle\int_0^{+\infty} \frac{\sin x}{x} dx.$ (b) $\displaystyle\int_0^1 \left(\sin \frac{1}{x}\right)\left(1 - \frac{1}{x}\right) dx.$

5. (a) Let f be a decreasing function on the interval $(0, 1]$. Show that if $\int_0^1 f(t) dt$ exists, either as an improper integral or as an ordinary integral, then $\lim_{x \to 0+} x \cdot f(x) = 0$.

(b) Let $g(x) = (x \cdot \ln \frac{1}{2}x)^{-1}$ if $x \in (0, 1]$. Show that $\lim_{x \to 0+} x \cdot g(x) = 0$, but that $\int_0^1 g(t) dt$ does not exist.

6. Suppose f is a function for which $\lim_{x\to 0+} f(x) = L$ exists and $\int_r^{+\infty} [f(x)/x]\, dx$ exists for $r > 0$. Show that, for any positive numbers p and q,

(a) $\displaystyle\int_r^{+\infty} \frac{f(px)}{x}\, dx = \int_{pr}^{+\infty} \frac{f(x)}{x}\, dx$;

(b) $\displaystyle\int_0^{+\infty} \frac{f(px)-f(qx)}{x}\, dx = L\cdot\left(\ln \frac{q}{p}\right).$

7. Use problem 6 to prove that

$$\int_0^{+\infty} \frac{e^x - 1}{xe^{2x}}\, dx = \ln 2.$$

8. Suppose that R and S are sets that have area. Prove the following.
(a) $R \cap S$ has area.   (b) $R - S$ has area.   (c) $R \cup S$ has area and

(area of $R \cup S$) = (area of R) + (area of S) − (area of $R \cap S$).

9.* Suppose f is nonnegative on an interval $[a, b]$ and that $\int_a^b f(x)\, dx$ exists, either as an ordinary Riemann integral or as an improper integral. Prove that, for any positive number ε, there is a positive number δ such that

$$\int_D f(x)\, dx < \varepsilon \quad \text{if} \quad D \subset [a, b] \quad \text{and length}\,(D) < \delta.$$

10.* Suppose f and $|f|$ are integrable on $[a, b]$, either as ordinary Riemann integrals or as improper integrals. Prove that fg is integrable on $[a, b]$ if g is continuous on $[a, b]$. Explain why this conclusion might not be valid if f is integrable and $|f|$ is not integrable.

11.* Suppose $\int_a^b |f(x)|\, dx = 0$ or $\int_a^b [f(x)]^2\, dx = 0$. Prove that $\{x: f(x) \neq 0 \text{ and } x \in [a, b]\}$ is of measure zero. [*Hint:* Prove that, for each positive number δ, the set $\{x: |f(x)| > \delta \text{ and } x \in [a, b]\}$ has zero length.]

12.* Suppose $\int_a^b |f(x)|\, dx$ exists and is nonzero, or $\int_a^b [f(x)]^2\, dx$ exists and is nonzero. Prove that there is an interval I of nonzero length with $I \subset [a, b]$ and $f(x) \neq 0$ if $x \in I$.

13.* Suppose both f and g are integrable on $[a, b]$, either as ordinary Riemann integrals or as improper integrals. Prove that $f+g$ is integrable on $[a, b]$.

CONVERGENCE

4-1. LIMITS OF SEQUENCES AND SUMS OF SERIES

A *sequence* was defined as a function whose domain is the set of positive integers [see page 15]. For a sequence f, we usually denote $f(n)$ by a symbol such as a_n. Then a_n is called the nth *term* of the sequence and the sequence is indicated by notation such as

$$\{a_1, a_2, a_3, \cdots, a_n, \cdots\}. \tag{4-1}$$

A *convergent sequence* is a sequence $\{a_1, a_2, \cdots\}$ such that $\lim_{n \to +\infty} a_n$ exists. A *divergent sequence* is a sequence $\{a_1, a_2, \cdots\}$ such that $\lim_{n \to +\infty} a_n$ does not exist. For a convergent sequence, the *limit of the sequence* is the number $\lim_{n \to +\infty} a_n$. Thus, the sequence (4-1) is convergent if and only if there is a number l, the limit of the sequence, such that for each positive number ε there is a number N such that

$$|l - a_n| < \varepsilon \quad \text{if} \quad n > N.$$

We shall now introduce the concept of *infinite series*. If we are concerned with the existence of $\lim_{n \to +\infty} a_n$ for a sequence f with $f(n) = a_n$, we may write the sequence as

$$\{a_1, a_2, a_3, \cdots, a_n, \cdots\}.$$

If we are concerned with determining the existence and value of a *sum* for the terms of the sequence, we may write the sequence as

$$a_1 + a_2 + a_3 + \cdots + a_n + \cdots \quad \text{or} \quad \sum_{n=1}^{+\infty} a_n,$$

168

and call it an *infinite series*.   In the past, we have added only finitely many numbers.   A definition of "sum" for an infinite series will give a new meaning to addition.   In certain cases, we shall be able to "add" infinitely many numbers—not by ordinary addition, but rather by the process of finding a limit.   We can introduce the sequence of *partial sums*, $S_1, S_2, \cdots, S_n, \cdots$, defined as follows:

$$S_1 = a_1,$$

$$S_2 = a_1 + a_2,$$

$$S_3 = a_1 + a_2 + a_3,$$

$$\cdot \quad \cdot \quad \cdot$$

$$S_n = a_1 + a_2 + a_3 + \cdots + a_n = \sum_{k=1}^{n} a_k,$$

$$\cdot \quad \cdot \quad \cdot$$

The nth term, S_n, of this sequence of partial sums is the sum of the first n terms of the infinite series.   If $\lim_{n \to +\infty} S_n$ exists, then the value of this limit is said to be the *sum* of the infinite series.

DEFINITION 4-1.1.   A *convergent infinite series* is an infinite series $a_1 + a_2 + \cdots + a_n + \cdots$ such that $\lim_{n \to +\infty} (a_1 + a_2 + \cdots + a_n)$ exists.   A *divergent infinite series* is an infinite series that is not convergent.   The *sum* of a convergent infinite series is the number S defined by

$$\lim_{n \to +\infty} \sum_{k=1}^{n} a_k = S.$$

A convergent infinite series is said to *converge to* its sum.

For an infinite series

$$a_1 + a_2 + a_3 + \cdots + a_n + \cdots, \tag{4-2}$$

we have the associated sequence of partial sums

$$\{S_1, S_2, S_3, \cdots, S_n, \cdots\}. \tag{4-3}$$

The infinite series has a sum if and only if the sequence of partial sums has a limit.   Conversely, given a sequence denoted by (4-3), we can define the infinite series (4-2) by

$$a_1 = S_1, \quad a_2 = S_2 - S_1, \quad a_3 = S_3 - S_2, \cdots, \quad a_n = S_n - S_{n-1}, \cdots.$$

Then $a_1 + a_2 + a_3 + \cdots + a_n = S_n$ for each n and (4-3) is the sequence of partial sums for (4-2). Therefore, any problem of determining the sum of an infinite series can be replaced by an equivalent problem of determining the limit of a sequence, and any problem of determining the limit of a sequence can be replaced by an equivalent problem of determining the sum of a series.

Infinite decimals provide a simple illustration of this relation between sequences and series. In Section 1-5, we saw that for each sequence of type

$$\{n + 0.d_1, \; n + 0.d_1 d_2, \; n + 0.d_1 d_2 d_3, \; \cdots, \; n + 0.d_1 d_2 \cdots d_n, \; \cdots\}$$

there is a corresponding real number α for which

$$\lim_{k \to +\infty} (n + 0.d_1 d_2 d_3 \cdots d_k) = \alpha.$$

That is, α is the limit of this sequence. Therefore, α also is the sum of the following infinite series:

$$(n + 0.d_1) + (0.0d_2) + (0.00d_3) + \cdots + (0.00 \cdots 0 d_k) + \cdots,$$

which we also denote by $n + 0.d_1 d_2 d_3 \cdots d_n \cdots$.

A *geometric series* is an infinite series of type

$$a + ar + ar^2 + \cdots + ar^{n-1} + \cdots. \qquad (4\text{-}4)$$

It is quite easy to determine whether a given geometric series is convergent and to determine its sum when it is convergent. We know that if S_n is the nth partial sum for (4-4), then

$$S_n = a + ar + ar^2 + \cdots + ar^{n-1} = \frac{a - ar^n}{1 - r} = \frac{a}{1-r} - \frac{a}{1-r} \cdot r^n.$$

Therefore, $\lim_{n \to +\infty} S_n$ exists and equals $a/(1-r)$ if $|r| < 1$, but does not exist if $|r| > 1$ and $a \neq 0$. If $|r| = 1$, it can be verified that $\lim_{n \to +\infty} S_n$ does not exist unless $a = 0$. This means that the geometric series (4-4) is convergent if $|r| < 1$ or if $a = 0$. The sum is equal to $a/(1-r)$ if $|r| < 1$ and equal to zero if $a = 0$. If $a \neq 0$ and $|r| \geq 1$, then the geometric series is divergent.

ILLUSTRATION. By adding the terms of the geometric series in the brackets of the following expression, we obtain the identity

$$\frac{1}{1 + x^2} = [1 - x^2 + x^4 - x^6 + \cdots + (-1)^{n-1} x^{2n-2}] + (-1)^n \frac{x^{2n}}{1 + x^2}.$$

Since $\int_0^1 (1+x^2)^{-1} dx = [\tan^{-1} x]_0^1 = \frac{1}{4}\pi$, it follows that

$$\frac{\pi}{4} = 1 - \frac{1}{3} + \frac{1}{5} - \frac{1}{7} + \cdots + (-1)^{n-1} \frac{1}{2n-1} + E_n,$$

where $|E_n| = \int_0^1 x^{2n}(1+x^2)^{-1} dx < \int_0^1 x^{2n} dx = 1/(2n+1)$. From this, we see that $\lim_{n \to +\infty} E_n = 0$. Therefore,

$$\frac{\pi}{4} = 1 - \frac{1}{3} + \frac{1}{5} - \frac{1}{7} + \cdots + (-1)^{n-1} \frac{1}{2n-1} + \cdots.$$

In the following sections, we shall discuss several methods for determining whether infinite series are convergent. One very simple test for divergence is given by the following theorem.

THEOREM 4-1.1. The infinite series $a_1 + a_2 + a_3 + \cdots + a_n + \cdots$ is divergent if $\lim_{n \to +\infty} a_n$ does not exist, or exists and is not zero.

PROOF. We can restate the theorem in the following equivalent form: "If the infinite series $a_1 + a_2 + a_3 + \cdots + a_n + \cdots$ is convergent, then $\lim_{n \to +\infty} a_n = 0$." If we assume that the infinite series is convergent, then the sequence of partial sums $\{S_1, S_2, \cdots, S_n, \cdots\}$ has a limit. If this limit is S, then for any positive number ε there is a number N such that

$$|S - S_n| < \tfrac{1}{2}\varepsilon \quad \text{if} \quad n > N.$$

If $n > N+1$, then we have

$$|S - S_{n-1}| < \tfrac{1}{2}\varepsilon \quad \text{and} \quad |S - S_n| < \tfrac{1}{2}\varepsilon.$$

Therefore, $|S_n - S_{n-1}| < \varepsilon$, or $|a_n| < \varepsilon$. This shows that $\lim_{n \to +\infty} a_n = 0$ and completes the proof.

This theorem often is very easy to use. For example, the infinite series

$$\frac{1}{2} + \frac{2}{3} + \frac{3}{4} + \cdots + \frac{n}{n+1} + \cdots$$

is divergent, since $n/(n+1)$ approaches 1 instead of 0 as n increases. It is important to realize that the converse of this theorem is not true. That is, it does not follow that an infinite series is convergent just because its nth term approaches zero as n increases. For example,

$$\ln 2 + \ln \left(\frac{3}{2}\right) + \ln \left(\frac{4}{3}\right) + \cdots + \ln \left(\frac{n+1}{n}\right) = \ln (n+1);$$

hence, the series $\sum_1^{+\infty} \ln\left[(n+1)/n\right]$ does not converge, although

$$\lim_{n \to +\infty} a_n = \lim_{n \to +\infty} \ln\left(\frac{n+1}{n}\right) = \ln 1 = 0.$$

PROBLEMS

1. For each of the following sequences, write the infinite series for which the given sequence is the sequence of partial sums. Determine whether the sequence is convergent and determine the limit of the sequence and the sum of the series if the sequence and series are convergent.

(*a*) $1, 2, 3, 4, \cdots, n, \cdots.$

(*c*) $\dfrac{2}{1}, \dfrac{3}{2}, \dfrac{4}{3}, \dfrac{5}{4}, \cdots, \dfrac{n+1}{n}, \cdots.$

(*b*) $\dfrac{1}{2}, \dfrac{2}{3}, \dfrac{3}{4}, \dfrac{4}{5}, \cdots, \dfrac{n}{n+1}, \cdots.$

(*d*) $1, -1, 2, -2, 3, -3, 4, -4, \cdots.$

2. For each of the following infinite series, write the sequence of partial sums in such a form that it can be determined easily whether the sequence converges. Find the sum of the series—i.e., the limit of the sequence—if the series is convergent.

(*a*) $2 + \dfrac{2}{3} + \dfrac{2}{9} + \dfrac{2}{27} + \cdots + \dfrac{2}{3^{n-1}} + \cdots.$

(*d*) $\displaystyle\sum_{n=1}^{+\infty} \dfrac{1}{n(n+1)(n+2)}.$

(*b*) $1 + \displaystyle\sum_{n=2}^{+\infty} \left[\dfrac{x^{n-1}}{(n-1)!} - \dfrac{x^{n-2}}{(n-2)!}\right].$

(*e*) $\displaystyle\sum_{n=1}^{+\infty} (-1)^{n+1} \dfrac{2n+1}{n(n+1)}.$

(*c*) $\displaystyle\sum_{n=1}^{+\infty} \dfrac{1}{n(n+1)} = \sum_{n=1}^{+\infty} \left(\dfrac{1}{n} - \dfrac{1}{n+1}\right).$

(*f*) $\displaystyle\sum_{n=1}^{+\infty} \dfrac{5n+3}{n(n+1)(n+3)}.$

3. For each of the following, determine whether the infinite series is convergent.

(*a*) $\displaystyle\sum_{n=1}^{+\infty} (-1)^{n-1}.$

(*c*) $\displaystyle\sum_{n=1}^{+\infty} \sin n.$

(*b*) $\displaystyle\sum_{n=1}^{+\infty} (-1)^{n-1} \dfrac{n}{n+1}.$

(*d*) $\displaystyle\sum_{n=1}^{+\infty} 2^{-n}.$

(*e*) $\dfrac{1}{4} + \dfrac{3}{16} + \dfrac{9}{64} + \cdots + \dfrac{3^{n-1}}{4^n} + \cdots.$

(*f*) $\dfrac{1}{2} + \dfrac{1}{4} + \dfrac{1}{4} + \dfrac{1}{8} + \dfrac{1}{8} + \dfrac{1}{8} + \dfrac{1}{8} + \dfrac{1}{16} + \dfrac{1}{16} + \cdots + \dfrac{1}{16} + \dfrac{1}{32} + \dfrac{1}{32} + \cdots,$

where for each positive integer n there are 2^{n-1} terms equal to 2^{-n}.

4. Evaluate $\sum_{n=1}^{+\infty} n/2^n$ by showing that the least upper bound of partial sums is the same as for the series

$$\left(\sum_{1}^{+\infty} \frac{1}{2^n}\right) + \left(\sum_{2}^{+\infty} \frac{1}{2^n}\right) + \left(\sum_{3}^{+\infty} \frac{1}{2^n}\right) + \cdots .$$

[Also see problem 4(d) of Section 1-4.]

5. Show that $\frac{1}{4}\pi = \tan^{-1} \frac{1}{2} + \tan^{-1} \frac{1}{3}$. Use this equality to show that

$$\pi = \frac{10}{3} - \frac{4}{3}\left(\frac{1}{2^3} + \frac{1}{3^3}\right) + \frac{4}{5}\left(\frac{1}{2^5} + \frac{1}{3^5}\right) - \frac{4}{7}\left(\frac{1}{2^7} + \frac{1}{3^7}\right) + \cdots .$$

6. Assume that $\pi = 16 \cdot \tan^{-1} \frac{1}{5} - 4 \cdot \tan^{-1} (1/239).$† Use this to show that

$$\pi = \left[\frac{16}{5} - \frac{16}{3 \cdot 5^3} + \frac{16}{5 \cdot 5^5} - \frac{16}{7 \cdot 5^7} + \cdots\right] - 4\left[\frac{1}{239} - \frac{1}{3(239)^3} + \frac{1}{5(239)^5} - \cdots\right].$$

7.* Let $\sum a_n$ be a convergent infinite series. Prove that there is a number M such that $|a_n| \leq M$ for all n.

4-2. POSITIVE SERIES

Theorem 1-4.1 states that, if a sequence $A = \{a_1, a_2, \cdots\}$ has an upper bound and $a_k \leq a_{k+1}$ for each k, then $\lim_{k \to +\infty} a_k$ exists and

$$\lim_{k \to +\infty} a_k = \sup \{a_1, a_2, \cdots\}.$$

The corresponding theorem for infinite series is the following.

THEOREM 4-2.1. An infinite series each of whose terms is positive or zero is convergent if and only if the sequence of partial sums $\{S_1, S_2, \cdots\}$ has an upper bound. If the series is convergent and has sum S, then

$$S = \sup \{S_1, S_2, \cdots, S_n, \cdots\}.$$

PROOF. Since each term of the infinite series is positive or zero, it follows that $S_k \leq S_{k+1}$ for each k. Therefore, if the sequence of partial sums has an upper bound, then it follows from Theorem 1-4.1 that the sequence has a limit S and that

$$S = \sup \{S_1, S_2, \cdots, S_n, \cdots\}.$$

---

† This and some similar equalities are listed by D. H. Lehmer, "On Arccotangent Relations for π," *Amer. Math. Monthly*, **45** (1938), 657–664.

Conversely, if the sequence of partial sums has a limit S, then this limit is an upper bound for this sequence. For if S is not an upper bound, then there is a partial sum S_N with $S_N > S$. This implies that $S_k \geq S_N > S$ for all $k > N$, which is impossible if $\lim_{k \to +\infty} S_k = S$.

For series whose terms are nonnegative, this theorem simplifies the problem of investigating convergence. To establish convergence, it is sufficient to show that the set of partial sums has an upper bound. To establish divergence, it is sufficient to show that the set of partial sums does not have an upper bound. We shall now discuss several specific techniques for doing this. The first of these, the integral test, demonstrates a close relation between convergence of certain types of infinite series and improper integrals.

INTEGRAL TEST. Suppose that for the infinite series $\sum a_n$ there is a positive integer A and a function f that is nonnegative and monotone decreasing for $x \geq A$ and is such that $a_n = f(n)$ if $n \geq A$. Then the series $\sum a_n$ and the integral $\int_A^{+\infty} f(x)\, dx$ are either both convergent or both divergent.

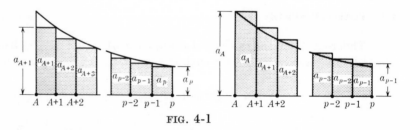

FIG. 4-1

PROOF. Suppose the infinite series $\sum_1^{+\infty} a_n$, the positive integer A, and the function f have the properties that f is nonnegative and monotone decreasing for $x \geq A$ and that $a_n = f(n)$ if $n \geq A$. The proof depends on the inequalities

$$\sum_{A+1}^{p} a_n \leq \int_A^p f(x)\, dx \leq \sum_A^{p-1} a_n.$$

As indicated in Fig. 4-1, these inequalities are consequences of the fact that

$$a_{n+1} \leq \int_n^{n+1} f(x)\, dx \leq a_n \quad \text{if} \quad n \geq A.$$

If the series converges and has sum S, then

$$\int_A^p f(x)\, dx \leq \sum_A^{p-1} a_n \leq \sum_1^{p-1} a_n \leq S$$

for any integer $p > A$. This implies that $\int_A^{+\infty} f(x)\, dx$ exists as an improper integral. Conversely, if $\int_A^{+\infty} f(x)\, dx$ exists as an improper integral, then

$$\sum_1^p a_n = \sum_1^A a_n + \sum_{A+1}^p a_n \leqq \sum_1^A a_n + \int_A^p f(x)\, dx \leqq \sum_1^A a_n + \int_A^{+\infty} f(x)\, dx.$$

Therefore, $\sum_1^A a_n + \int_1^{+\infty} f(x)\, dx$ is an upper bound for the sequence of partial sums. This implies that the series is convergent.

ILLUSTRATION 1. For a positive number p, let us define the function f by stating that $f(x) = 1/x^p$ when $x > 0$. Then f is continuous and decreasing on its entire domain. Also, $f(n) = 1/n^p$ for all positive integers n. Therefore, the infinite series $\sum_{n=1}^{+\infty} 1/n^p$ is convergent if and only if $\int_1^{+\infty} (1/x^p)\, dx$ exists as an improper integral. Since

$$\int_1^k \frac{1}{x^p}\, dx = \left[\frac{x^{1-p}}{1-p}\right]_1^k = \frac{k^{1-p}-1}{1-p}, \quad \text{if} \quad p \neq 1,$$

and $\int_1^k (1/x)\, dx = \ln k$, we see that $\int_1^{+\infty} (1/x^p)\, dx$ exists as an improper integral if and only if $p > 1$. Therefore, the series $\sum_{n=1}^{+\infty} 1/n^p$ converges if $p > 1$ and diverges if $p \leqq 1$. Thus, for example, $\sum_1^{+\infty} 1/n^2$ converges and $\sum_1^{+\infty} 1/n$ diverges.

COMPARISON TEST 1. Consider two infinite series whose terms are nonnegative:

$$a_1 + a_2 + a_3 + \cdots + a_n + \cdots, \qquad b_1 + b_2 + b_3 + \cdots + b_n + \cdots.$$

Suppose there are numbers N and ρ such that $a_n \leqq \rho \cdot b_n$ if $n \geqq N$. Then $\sum a_n$ is convergent if $\sum b_n$ is convergent (or $\sum b_n$ is divergent if $\sum a_n$ is divergent).

PROOF. If $a_n \leqq \rho \cdot b_n$ when $n \geqq N$, then for all positive integers $n \geqq N$ we have

$$\sum_{k=1}^n a_k = \sum_{k=1}^N a_k + \sum_{k=N+1}^n a_k \leqq \sum_{k=1}^N a_k + \rho \cdot \left[\sum_{k=N+1}^n b_k\right]$$

$$\leqq \sum_{k=1}^N a_k + \rho \cdot \left[\sum_{k=1}^n b_k\right]. \tag{4-5}$$

Therefore, the sequence of partial sums for $\sum a_n$ has an upper bound if the sequence of partial sums for $\sum b_n$ has an upper bound; i.e., $\sum a_n$ is convergent if $\sum b_n$ is convergent, and $\sum b_n$ is divergent if $\sum a_n$ is divergent.

ILLUSTRATION 2. For the infinite series $\sum n/(n^2+1)$, we find that

$$\frac{n}{n^2+1} \geq \frac{1}{2n}$$

for all n. Since $\sum 1/n$ diverges, $\sum n/(n^2+1)$ also diverges.

ILLUSTRATION 3. To investigate convergence of the infinite series

$$\frac{8}{1} \cdot 1 + \frac{11}{2} \cdot \frac{1}{2} + \frac{14}{3}\left(\frac{1}{2}\right)^2 + \cdots + \left(\frac{3n+5}{n}\right)\left(\frac{1}{2}\right)^{n-1} + \cdots,$$

we use the convergent series $\sum (\frac{1}{2})^{n-1}$. If $n \geq 5$, we have $(3n+5)/n \leq 4$ and

$$\left(\frac{3n+5}{n}\right)\left(\frac{1}{2}\right)^{n-1} \leq 4 \cdot \left(\frac{1}{2}\right)^{n-1}.$$

Therefore, the given series is convergent.

We can often attempt to guess the behavior of an infinite series by investigating the "order of magnitude" of the nth term. That is, we can try to determine whether a_n approximates the nth term in some familiar series whose convergence (or divergence) is known. The mathematical justification for this type of analysis is given by the following comparison test.

COMPARISON TEST II. Suppose $\sum a_n$ and $\sum b_n$ are two infinite series whose terms are positive and for which $\lim_{n \to +\infty} a_n/b_n$ exists and equals ℓ. Then $\sum a_n$ is convergent if $\sum b_n$ is convergent. If $\ell \neq 0$, then $\sum b_n$ is convergent if $\sum a_n$ is convergent (thus, if $\ell \neq 0$, one series converges if and only if the other does).

PROOF. If $\lim_{n \to +\infty} a_n/b_n = \ell$, then there is a number N such that

$$\left|\ell - \frac{a_n}{b_n}\right| < 1 \quad \text{if} \quad n \geq N.$$

Then

$$\frac{a_n}{b_n} < \ell + 1 \quad \text{if} \quad n \geq N,$$

and it follows from Comparison Test I that $\sum a_n$ is convergent if $\sum b_n$ is convergent.   If $\ell \neq 0$, then $\lim_{n \to +\infty} b_n/a_n = 1/\ell$, and it follows from what we have just proved that $\sum b_n$ is convergent if $\sum a_n$ is convergent.

ILLUSTRATION 4.   Suppose we must determine whether the following infinite series is convergent:

$$1 + \frac{1}{16} + \frac{1}{49} + \cdots + \frac{1}{(3n-2)^2} + \cdots.$$

It is natural to compare this series with the convergent series $\sum 1/n^2$. To do this, we shall consider the following limit:

$$\lim_{n \to +\infty} \frac{1/(3n-2)^2}{1/n^2} = \lim_{n \to +\infty} \left(\frac{n}{3n-2}\right)^2 = \frac{1}{9}.$$

It now follows from Comparison Test II that the given series is convergent.

RATIO TEST I.   Suppose $\sum a_n$ is an infinite series whose terms are nonnegative.   Then $\sum a_n$ is convergent if there is a number $r < 1$ and an integer N such that

$$\frac{a_{n+1}}{a_n} \leq r \quad \text{if} \quad n \geq N. \tag{4-6}$$

The series is divergent if there is an integer N such that

$$\frac{a_{n+1}}{a_n} \geq 1 \quad \text{if} \quad n \geq N. \tag{4-7}$$

PROOF.   We shall suppose first that $a_{n+1}/a_n \leq r < 1$ if $n \geq N$.   (Note that this condition requires implicitly that $a_n \neq 0$ for $n \geq N$, and hence that $r \neq 0$.)   To prove that $\sum a_n$ is convergent, we shall use the convergent series $\sum r^n$.   If $n \geq N$, then

$$a_n \leq r \cdot a_{n-1} \leq r^2 \cdot a_{n-2} \leq \cdots \leq r^{n-N} \cdot a_N.$$

Therefore,

$$a_n \leq \frac{a_N}{r^N} \cdot r^n \quad \text{if} \quad n \geq N.$$

It now follows from Comparison Test I that $\sum a_n$ is convergent.   For the second assertion of the theorem, we shall suppose that $a_{n+1}/a_n \geq 1$

if $n \geq N$. Then $\{a_N, a_{N+1}, \cdots\}$ is a monotone increasing sequence with $a_N \neq 0$, so that $\lim_{n \to +\infty} a_n$ either does not exist or is not zero. Therefore, $\sum a_n$ is divergent.

RATIO TEST II. Suppose $\sum a_n$ is an infinite series whose terms are nonnegative and for which

$$\lim_{n \to +\infty} \frac{a_{n+1}}{a_n} = \ell$$

exists. Then the series converges if $\ell < 1$ and diverges if $\ell > 1$.

PROOF. This test is a direct consequence of Ratio Test I. To show this, we shall suppose that $\lim_{n \to +\infty} a_{n+1}/a_n = \ell$. If $\ell < 1$, then $\ell < \frac{1}{2}(\ell+1) < 1$ and there is an integer N for which (4-6) is true with $r = \frac{1}{2}(\ell+1)$. If $\ell > 1$, then there is an integer N for which (4-7) is true.

ILLUSTRATION 5. For the infinite series $\sum n!/n^n$, we have

$$\frac{a_{n+1}}{a_n} = \frac{(n+1)!}{(n+1)^{n+1}} \frac{n^n}{n!} = \left(\frac{n}{n+1}\right)^n = \left(\frac{1}{1+1/n}\right)^n \to \frac{1}{e} \quad \text{as} \quad n \to +\infty.$$

Since $1/e < 1$, it follows from Ratio Test II that $\sum n!/n^n$ is convergent. Alternatively, we could establish convergence of this series by using Comparison Test I and the convergent series $\sum 1/n^2$, since

$$\frac{n!}{n^n} = \left(\frac{1}{n}\right)\left(\frac{2}{n}\right)\left(\frac{3}{n}\right)\cdots\left(\frac{n}{n}\right) \leq \frac{2}{n^2} \quad \text{for all} \quad n.$$

It is important to note that neither of these ratio tests tells us about convergence of an infinite series $\sum a_n$, when all that is known is that $a_{n+1}/a_n < 1$ if $n \geq A$, or that $\lim_{n \to +\infty} a_{n+1}/a_n = 1$. The reason for this is illustrated by the series $\sum 1/n^p$ with $p > 0$. For this series, we have

$$\frac{a_{n+1}}{a_n} = \left(\frac{n}{n+1}\right)^p.$$

Therefore, $a_{n+1}/a_n < 1$ for all n and $\lim_{n \to +\infty} a_{n+1}/a_n = 1$. However, the series diverges if $p \leq 1$ and converges if $p > 1$ [see Illustration 1]. Ratio Test III gives us methods for testing some series for which the first two ratio tests fail. The part of Ratio Test III that uses the function π usually is called *Raabe's test*.

RATIO TEST III. Suppose $\sum a_n$ is an infinite series whose terms are nonnegative. Let π and q be functions defined when $a_n \neq 0$ by

$$\pi(n) = n\left(1 - \frac{a_{n+1}}{a_n}\right) \quad \text{and} \quad q(n) = n^2\left(\frac{n-1}{n} - \frac{a_{n+1}}{a_n}\right),$$

or by the equivalent equalities

$$\frac{a_{n+1}}{a_n} = 1 - \frac{\pi(n)}{n} \quad \text{and} \quad \frac{a_{n+1}}{a_n} = 1 - \frac{1}{n} - \frac{q(n)}{n^2}.$$

Then $\sum a_n$ is convergent if there is a number $r > 1$ and an integer N such that $\pi(n) > r$ if $n > N$. The series is divergent if there is an integer N such that $\pi(n) \leq 1$ if $n > N$, or if q has an upper bound.

PROOF. We shall use comparisons with series of type $\sum n^{-p}$. First we use the mean value theorem to obtain

$$(1-x)^p = 1^p - x \cdot p(1-\xi)^{p-1},$$

where ξ is between 0 and x. With $x = 1/n$, this gives the inequality

$$\left(1 - \frac{1}{n}\right)^p > 1 - \frac{p}{n} \quad \text{if} \quad p > 1. \tag{4-8}$$

For the series $\sum a_n$, suppose we have $\pi(n) > r > 1$ if $n > N$. The series $1 + \sum_2^{+\infty} b_n$, with $b_n = (n-1)^{-r}$ if $n > 1$, is convergent [see Illustration 1]. Also, using Eq. (4-8) with $p = r$, we have

$$\frac{b_{n+1}}{b_n} = \frac{(n-1)^r}{n^r} = \left(1 - \frac{1}{n}\right)^r > 1 - \frac{r}{n} > 1 - \frac{\pi(n)}{n} = \frac{a_{n+1}}{a_n},$$

if $n > N$. Thus, $b_{n+1}/b_n > a_{n+1}/a_n$ if $n > N$. If we denote a_{N+1}/b_{N+1} by ρ, then $a_{N+1} = \rho b_{N+1}$ and, for $n > N+1$,

$$a_{n+1} < \frac{a_n}{b_n} b_{n+1} \leq \rho b_{n+1} \quad \text{if} \quad a_n \leq \rho b_n.$$

Thus, by mathematical induction, we have $a_n \leq \rho b_n$ if $n > N$. It then follows from Comparison Test I that $\sum a_n$ is convergent. To complete the proof, we must show that $\sum a_n$ is divergent if there is an N such that $\pi(n) \leqq 1$ if $n > N$, or if q has an upper bound. If $\pi(n) \leqq 1$, then it follows from

$$1 - \frac{\pi(n)}{n} = 1 - \frac{1}{n} - \frac{n[\pi(n)-1]}{n^2}$$

that $q(n) = n[\pi(n)-1] \leqq 0$. Thus, the case for which $\pi(n) \leqq 1$ if n is large enough is a special case for which q has an upper bound, so it is sufficient to consider only the case q has an upper bound. Suppose $q(n) \leqq M$ for all n. The series

$$1 + 2 + 3 + \cdots + (k+1) + \sum_{n=k+2}^{+\infty} \frac{1}{n-k-1} \qquad (4\text{-}9)$$

is divergent, since $\sum n^{-1}$ is divergent [see Illustration 1]. If we denote (4-9) by $\sum b_n$, then

$$\frac{b_{n+1}}{b_n} = \frac{n-k-1}{n-k} = 1 - \frac{1}{n-k} = 1 - \frac{1}{n} - \frac{k + k^2(n-k)^{-1}}{n^2} \quad \text{if} \quad n \geqq k+2.$$

With k chosen so that $k \geqq M$, we have

$$\frac{b_{n+1}}{b_n} < 1 - \frac{1}{n} - \frac{M}{n^2} \leqq 1 - \frac{1}{n} - \frac{q(n)}{n^2} = \frac{a_{n+1}}{a_n} \quad \text{if} \quad n \geqq k+2.$$

Now it can be proved by mathematical induction that

$$a_n \geqq \left(\frac{a_{k+2}}{b_{k+2}}\right) b_n \quad \text{if} \quad n \geqq k+2.$$

Then it follows from Comparison Test I that $\sum a_n$ is divergent.

ILLUSTRATION 6. Let us consider the series

$$\frac{1}{r} + \frac{1 \cdot 2}{r(r+1)} + \frac{1 \cdot 2 \cdot 3}{r(r+1)(r+2)} + \cdots + \frac{1 \cdot 2 \cdot 3 \cdots n}{r(r+1) \cdots (r+n-1)} + \cdots .$$

For this series, $a_{n+1}/a_n = (n+1)/(r+n)$ and $\lim_{n \to +\infty} a_{n+1}/a_n = 1$. Thus, the first two ratio tests fail. We have

$$\pi(n) = n\left(1 - \frac{n+1}{r+n}\right) = (r-1)\frac{n}{r+n}.$$

Since $\lim_{n \to +\infty} n/(r+n) = 1$, we conclude from Ratio Test III that the given series converges if $r > 2$. If $0 < r \leqq 2$, then $\pi(n) < 1$ and the series diverges.

PROBLEMS

1. Use the integral test to determine whether the following series are convergent or divergent.

(a) $\displaystyle\sum \frac{1}{\sqrt{n^2+9}}.$

(d) $\displaystyle\sum \frac{1}{n(n+1)(n+2)}.$

(b) $\displaystyle\sum ne^{-n^2}.$

(e) $\displaystyle\sum_{n=2}^{+\infty} \frac{1}{n(\ln n)^p}.$

(c) $\displaystyle\sum \frac{\ln n}{n}.$

(f) $\displaystyle\sum_{n=3}^{+\infty} \frac{1}{n(\ln n)[\ln (\ln n)]^p}.$

2. Use the ratio test to determine whether the following series are convergent or divergent.

(a) $\displaystyle\sum \frac{1}{n!}.$

(c) $\displaystyle\sum \frac{10^{(n^2)}}{n!}.$

(e) $\displaystyle\sum n^5 \left(\frac{2}{3}\right)^n.$

(b) $\displaystyle\sum \frac{10^n}{n!}.$

(d) $\displaystyle\sum \frac{n!}{5^n}.$

(f) $\displaystyle\sum \frac{n(n+3)5^{n+2}}{6^n}.$

3. Let a_n be nonnegative for each n. (a) Show that $\sum a_n$ diverges if for all N there is an $n > N$ such that $\sqrt[n]{a_n} \geqq 1$. (b) Show that $\sum a_n$ converges if there is a number r with $0 < r < 1$ and a number N such that $\sqrt[n]{a_n} < r$ if $n \geqq N$. [These are called nth *root tests*.]

4. For each of the following, determine whether the infinite series is convergent or divergent. Indicate your method.

(a) $\displaystyle\sum \frac{n-3}{n^3+n+2}.$

(e) $\displaystyle\sum \frac{2^n+5n}{3^n-2n}.$

(i) $\displaystyle\sum_{2}^{+\infty} \frac{1}{(\ln n)^n}.$

(b) $\displaystyle\sum \frac{n^2-1}{n^3+2n+5}.$

(f) $\displaystyle\sum \frac{\sin^2 n}{n^2}.$

(j) $\displaystyle\sum \sin \frac{1}{n^2}.$

(c) $\displaystyle\sum \frac{n^4}{(n+1)!}.$

(g) $\displaystyle\sum \frac{1}{(4/3)^n}.$

(k) $\displaystyle\sum \frac{1}{2^{\ln n}}.$

(d) $\displaystyle\sum \frac{1}{\ln (n+1)}.$

(h) $\displaystyle\sum \frac{1}{(1+1/n)^n}.$

(l) $\displaystyle\sum \frac{1}{3^{\ln n}}.$

5. Show that $(\ln n)^{\ln n} = n^{\ln(\ln n)}$ and use this and a similar equality to test the convergence of the following series.

(a) $\displaystyle\sum_{n=2}^{+\infty} \frac{1}{(\ln n)^{\ln n}}.$

(b) $\displaystyle\sum_{n=3}^{+\infty} \frac{1}{[\ln (\ln n)]^{\ln n}}.$

6. Show that

$$\sum_{n=2}^{+\infty} \frac{1}{(\ln n)^{\ln (\ln n)}}$$

is divergent by showing that, if n is sufficiently large, then $(\ln n)^{\ln (\ln n)} < n$.

7. For each of the following, determine whether the infinite series is convergent or divergent. Indicate your method.

(a) $\left(\dfrac{1}{3}\right)^2 + \left(\dfrac{1 \cdot 4}{3 \cdot 6}\right)^2 + \left(\dfrac{1 \cdot 4 \cdot 7}{3 \cdot 6 \cdot 9}\right)^2 + \left(\dfrac{1 \cdot 4 \cdot 7 \cdot 10}{3 \cdot 6 \cdot 9 \cdot 12}\right)^2 + \cdots.$

(b) $\left(\dfrac{1}{2}\right)^2 + \left(\dfrac{1 \cdot 3}{2 \cdot 4}\right)^2 + \left(\dfrac{1 \cdot 3 \cdot 5}{2 \cdot 4 \cdot 6}\right)^2 + \left(\dfrac{1 \cdot 3 \cdot 5 \cdot 7}{2 \cdot 4 \cdot 6 \cdot 8}\right)^2 + \cdots.$

8. In each case, determine the values of the parameters for which the series converges.

(a) $\dfrac{1}{k} + \dfrac{1 \cdot 3}{k(k+2)} + \dfrac{1 \cdot 3 \cdot 5}{k(k+2)(k+4)} + \cdots.$

(b) $\left|\dfrac{x}{1!}\right| + \left|\dfrac{x(x-1)}{2!}\right| + \left|\dfrac{x(x-1)(x-2)}{3!}\right| + \left|\dfrac{x(x-1)(x-2)(x-3)}{4!}\right| + \cdots.$

(c) $\dfrac{\alpha\beta}{\gamma} + \dfrac{\alpha(\alpha+1)\beta(\beta+1)}{2!\,\gamma(\gamma+1)} + \dfrac{\alpha(\alpha+1)(\alpha+2)\beta(\beta+1)(\beta+2)}{3!\,\gamma(\gamma+1)(\gamma+2)} + \cdots.$

9. Suppose that $a_n \geqq a_{n+1} > 0$ for every n. Prove each of the following statements.

(a) $\sum a_n$ converges if and only if $\sum 2^n a_{2^n}$ converges.

(b*) $\lim\limits_{n \to +\infty} n a_n = 0$ if $\sum a_n$ converges.

(c) If $f(n) = n(1 - \sqrt[n]{a_n})$, then $\lim\limits_{n \to +\infty} a_n = 1$ if and only if $\lim\limits_{n \to +\infty} f(n) = 0.$

10. Explain the fallacy in the following arguments.

(a) "Let $S = 1 + 2 + 4 + 8 + 16 + 32 + \cdots$. Then $2S = 2 + 4 + 8 + 16 + 32 + \cdots = S - 1$, so that $S = -1$."

(b) "Let $x = 1 + \frac{1}{3} + \frac{1}{5} + \frac{1}{7} + \cdots$ and $y = \frac{1}{2} + \frac{1}{4} + \frac{1}{6} + \frac{1}{8} + \frac{1}{10} + \cdots$. Then $2y = 1 + \frac{1}{2} + \frac{1}{3} + \frac{1}{4} + \cdots = x + y$, so that $x = y$. However, each term of x is greater than the corresponding term of y, so $x > y$."

11. Let $S_n = 1 + \frac{1}{2} + \frac{1}{3} + \cdots + 1/n$. Show that

(a) $\ln (n+1) < S_n < 1 + \ln n$;   (b) $\lim\limits_{n \to +\infty} S_n/(\ln n) = 1.$

12. Divide the interval $[0, 1]$ into n equal parts and show that

    (a) $\lim\limits_{n \to +\infty} \dfrac{1}{n}\left[\ln\dfrac{1}{n}+\ln\dfrac{2}{n}+\ln\dfrac{3}{n}+\cdots+\ln\dfrac{n}{n}\right] = \displaystyle\int_0^1 \ln x\, dx;$

    (b) $\lim\limits_{n \to +\infty} \sqrt[n]{n!}/n = 1/e.$

[*Note:* This is related to *Stirling's formula*, which states that

$$n! = (n/e)^n\sqrt{2\pi n}\; e^{\theta_n/(12n)}, \quad \text{where} \quad 0 < \theta_n < 1.]$$

13. Show that if $a_n \geq 0$ for each n and $\sum a_n$ is convergent, then $\sum a_n^2$ is convergent.

14. Let $\sum a_n$ be a convergent series whose terms are nonnegative and let $\{b_1, b_2, \cdots\}$ be a sequence of nonnegative numbers with an upper bound. Show that the series $\sum a_n b_n$ is convergent.

4-3. TAYLOR'S THEOREM

There are many situations in which it is convenient to use a polynomial to approximate a function. We shall investigate the possibility of writing, for a particular choice of a,

$$\begin{aligned} f(x) = {}& c_0 + c_1(x-a) + c_2(x-a)^2 + c_3(x-a)^3 \\ & + \cdots + c_n(x-a)^n + R_n(x), \end{aligned} \tag{4-10}$$

and obtaining a useful upper bound for $|R_n(x)|$. We shall choose the coefficients in Eq. (4-10) so that the function f and its first n derivatives have the same values at $x = a$ as the polynomial

$$c_0 + c_1(x-a) + c_2(x-a)^2 + c_3(x-a)^3 + \cdots + c_n(x-a)^n.$$

Then $c_0 = f(a)$, $c_1 = f'(a)$, $c_2 = f''(a)/2!$, $c_3 = f'''(a)/3!$, and, in general,

$$c_r = \frac{f^{[r]}(a)}{r!}.$$

With this choice for the coefficients in Eq. (4-10), we have

$$R_n(x) = f(x) - \left[f(a) + f'(a)(x-a) + \frac{f''(a)}{2!}(x-a)^2 \right.$$
$$\left. + \cdots + \frac{f^{[n]}(a)}{n!}(x-a)^n \right].$$

We have chosen the coefficients of the powers of $x - a$ so that R_n and its first n derivatives are zero when $x = a$. Also,

$$R_n^{[n+1]}(x) = f^{[n+1]}(x)$$

for all x for which $f^{[n+1]}(x)$ exists. We shall assume that $f^{[n+1]}$ is Riemann integrable on the closed interval $[a, x]$. Since we are not using improper integration, this implies the domain of $f^{[n+1]}$ contains the interval $[a, x]$. Then each previous derivative is continuous and the integrals used in the following discussion exist. It is important to realize that the crucial reason for the success of our method is the fact that R_n and its first n derivatives are zero when $x = a$. Our first step is to note that

$$R_n(x) = \int_a^x R_n'(t)\, dt.$$

The student can verify by differentiation that

$$R_n'(t) = -D_t\left[(x-t)R_n'(t) + \frac{(x-t)^2}{2!}R_n''(t) + \frac{(x-t)^3}{3!}R_n'''(t) + \frac{(x-t)^4}{4!}R_n^{[4]}(t)\right.$$

$$\left. + \cdots + \frac{(x-t)^{n-1}}{(n-1)!}R_n^{[n-1]}(t) + \frac{(x-t)^n}{n!}R_n^{[n]}(t)\right] + \frac{(x-t)^n}{n!}R_n^{[n+1]}(t).$$

The expression in brackets is zero when $t = x$ and when $t = a$ since each term is then zero. Therefore, the integral of the derivative of this expression over the interval $[a, x]$ is zero, and we have

$$R_n(x) = \int_a^x R_n'(t)\, dt = \frac{1}{n!}\int_a^x (x-t)^n R_n^{[n+1]}(t)\, dt.$$

Now we can replace $R_n^{[n+1]}$ by $f^{[n+1]}$ to complete the proof of the following theorem.

THEOREM 4-3.1 (TAYLOR'S THEOREM). If f is a function whose $(n+1)$st derivative is Riemann integrable on the interval $[a, x]$, then

$$f(x) = f(a) + f'(a)\cdot(x-a) + \frac{f''(a)}{2!}(x-a)^2 + \frac{f'''(a)}{3!}(x-a)^3$$

$$+ \cdots + \frac{f^{(n)}(a)}{n!}(x-a)^n + R_n(x), \qquad (4\text{-}11)$$

with

$$R_n(x) = \frac{1}{n!}\int_a^x (x-t)^n f^{[n+1]}(t)\, dt. \qquad (4\text{-}12)$$

ILLUSTRATION 1. If $f(x) = \ln(x+1)$ and $a = 0$ in Eqs. (4-11) and (4-12), then

$$\ln(x+1) = x - \frac{x^2}{2} + \frac{x^3}{3} - \frac{x^4}{4} + \cdots + (-1)^{n+1}\frac{x^n}{n} + R_n(x),$$

where

$$R_n(x) = (-1)^n \int_0^x \frac{(x-t)^n}{(t+1)^{n+1}}\, dt.$$

If $0 \leq t \leq x$, then $t+1 \geq 1$. Therefore, we have

$$|R_n(x)| \leq \int_0^x (x-t)^n\, dt = \frac{x^{n+1}}{n+1}, \quad \text{if} \quad x \geq 0. \tag{4-13}$$

Since $x^{n+1}/(n+1) \leq 1/(n+1)$ if $0 \leq x \leq 1$, it follows that $|R_n(x)|$ approaches zero as n increases if $0 \leq x \leq 1$. Now we observe that, if x and t have the same signs and $|t| \leq |x| < 1$, then $|x-t| \leq |x+xt|$, or $|(x-t)/(t+1)| \leq |x|$. Therefore, if $|x| < 1$, then

$$|R_n(x)| = \left| \int_0^x \left(\frac{x-t}{t+1}\right)^n \frac{1}{t+1}\, dt \right| \leq |x|^n \left| \int_0^x \frac{1}{t+1}\, dt \right| = |x|^n |\ln(x+1)|.$$

Since $\lim_{n \to +\infty} |x|^n = 0$ if $|x| < 1$, we can conclude from this and (4-13) that

$$\ln(x+1) = \lim_{n \to +\infty} \left[x - \frac{x^2}{2} + \frac{x^3}{3} - \frac{x^4}{4} + \cdots + (-1)^{n+1}\frac{x^n}{n} \right] \tag{4-14}$$

if $-1 < x \leq 1$, and

$$|R_n(x)| \leq \frac{x^{n+1}}{n+1} \quad \text{if} \quad 0 \leq x \leq 1,$$

$$|R_n(x)| \leq |x|^n |\ln(x+1)| \quad \text{if} \quad -1 < x \leq 0. \tag{4-15}$$

The remainder given by Eq. (4-12) can be changed into other forms that are often more useful.

THEOREM 4-3.2. If f is a function whose $(n+1)$st derivative is continuous on the interval $[a, x]$, then there is a number ξ_1 in (a, x) for which the remainder $R_n(x)$ of Taylor's theorem has the value

$$R_n(x) = \frac{(x-a)^{n+1}}{(n+1)!} f^{[n+1]}(\xi_1). \tag{4-16}$$

This is called *Lagrange's form of the remainder*. There is also a number ξ_2 in (a, x) for which

$$R_n(x) = \frac{(x-\xi_2)^n(x-a)}{n!} f^{[n+1]}(\xi_2). \tag{4-17}$$

This is called *Cauchy's form of the remainder*.

PROOF. Each of these forms of the remainder can be proved by using the second mean value theorem for integrals [Theorem 3-6.5]. For Lagrange's form, we can use Eq. (3-24) with f replaced by $f^{[n+1]}$. Then

$$R_n(x) = \frac{1}{n!} \int_a^x (x-t)^n f^{[n+1]}(t)\, dt = \frac{1}{n!} f^{[n+1]}(\xi_1) \int_a^x (x-t)^n\, dt$$

$$= \frac{(x-a)^{n+1}}{(n+1)!} f^{[n+1]}(\xi_1).$$

For Cauchy's form, we can replace $f(t)$ in (3-24) by $(x-t)^n f^{[n+1]}(t)$ and $h(t)$ by 1, so that

$$R_n(x) = \frac{1}{n!} (x-\xi_2)^n f^{[n+1]}(\xi_2) \int_a^x dt = \frac{(x-\xi_2)^n(x-a)}{n!} f^{[n+1]}(\xi_2).$$

Usually when we apply these forms of the remainder, the only information available about the numbers ξ_1 and ξ_2 is that they are between a and b. One must find an upper bound for the particular form being used, assuming that ξ_1 (or ξ_2) is in the interval (a, x). In general, the Lagrange form is easier to apply and gives good results.

ILLUSTRATION 2. Suppose $f(x) = \sin x$, and that $a = 0$ in Taylor's theorem. Since $f(0) = \sin 0 = 0$, $f'(0) = \cos 0 = 1$, $f''(0) = -\sin 0 = 0$, etc., it follows from Lagrange's form of the remainder that, for any positive integer n, there is a number ξ between 0 and x such that

$$\sin x = x - \frac{x^3}{3!} + \frac{x^5}{5!} - \frac{x^7}{7!} + \cdots + (-1)^{n+1} \frac{x^{2n-1}}{(2n-1)!}$$

$$+ (-1)^{n+2} \frac{x^{2n+1}}{(2n+1)!} \cos \xi.$$

Since $|\cos \xi| \leq 1$, the absolute value of the remainder term is not larger than $|x^{2n+1}|/(2n+1)!$. This approaches zero as n increases. Therefore

$$\sin x = \lim_{n \to +\infty} \left[x - \frac{x^3}{3!} + \frac{x^5}{5!} - \frac{x^7}{7!} + \cdots + (-1)^{n+1} \frac{x^{2n-1}}{(2n-1)!} \right].$$

The error from approximating sin x by the expression in brackets is no larger than the absolute value of the "next term," $x^{2n+1}/(2n+1)!$. Similarly,

$$\cos x = \lim_{n \to +\infty} \left[1 - \frac{x^2}{2!} + \frac{x^4}{4!} - \frac{x^6}{6!} + \cdots + (-1)^{n+1} \frac{x^{2n-2}}{(2n-2)!} \right].$$

Taylor's theorem provides a useful mechanism for determining whether certain series are convergent and for determining their sums if they are convergent. If a is in the domain of each derivative of f, then the infinite series

$$f(a) + f'(a)(x-a) + \frac{f''(a)}{2!}(x-a)^2 + \cdots + \frac{f^{[n]}(a)}{n!}(x-a)^n + \cdots$$

is the *Taylor's series* expansion of the function f about the point a. For each value of x we have an infinite series. For a particular value of x, the difference between $f(x)$ and the sum of the first $n+1$ terms of this infinite series is precisely $R_n(x)$. Therefore, the infinite series converges *and* has the sum $f(x)$ if and only if $\lim_{n \to +\infty} R_n(x) = 0$. It is possible for a Taylor's series expansion of a function to converge even if $\lim_{n \to +\infty} R_n(x)$ is not zero, but in this case the sum of the infinite series is not the corresponding value of the function [see problem 13 at the end of this section].

It follows from Illustration 2 that the Taylor's series about 0 for the sine and cosine converge and, for all x, we have

$$\sin x = x - \frac{x^3}{3!} + \frac{x^5}{5!} - \frac{x^7}{7!} + \cdots + (-1)^{n+1} \frac{x^{2n-1}}{(2n-1)!} + \cdots, \quad (4\text{-}18)$$

$$\cos x = 1 - \frac{x^2}{2!} + \frac{x^4}{4!} - \frac{x^6}{6!} + \cdots + (-1)^{n+1} \frac{x^{2n-2}}{(2n-2)!} + \cdots. \quad (4\text{-}19)$$

PROBLEMS

1. Use Lagrange's form of the remainder to show that

$$e^x = 1 + x + \frac{x^2}{2!} + \frac{x^3}{3!} + \cdots + \frac{x^n}{n!} + R_n(x),$$

where

$$|R_n(x)| < \frac{x^{n+1}}{(n+1)!} e^x \text{ if } x > 0; \quad |R_n(x)| < \frac{|x^{n+1}|}{(n+1)!} \text{ if } x < 0.$$

2. Show that if $|x| < .1$ then

(a) $\sqrt{1+x} = 1+\frac{1}{2}x+E(x)$, where $|E(x)| < .0015$;

(b) $\cos x = 1-\frac{1}{2}x^2+E(x)$, where $|E(x)| < .000,005$;

(c) $\tan x = x+E(x)$, where $|E(x)| < .00035$;

(d) $e^{\sin x} = 1+x+\frac{1}{2}x^2+E(x)$, where $|E(x)| < .00002$;

(e) $\tan x = x+\frac{1}{3}x^3+E(x)$, where $|E(x)| < .000,002$.

3. Prove that $1-\frac{1}{2}x^2+x^4/24 > \cos x > 1-\frac{1}{2}x^2$ if $|x| \leq \frac{1}{2}\pi$.

4. Show that

$$\tan\left(\frac{\pi}{4}-\frac{1}{16}\right) = \frac{7}{8}+E, \quad \text{where} \quad 0 < E < \frac{1}{128}.$$

5. Show that

$$\ln x+\frac{1}{x}-\frac{1}{2x^2} < \ln(x+1) < \ln x+\frac{1}{x} \quad \text{if} \quad x > 0.$$

6. Show that if $f(x)$ is a polynomial of degree n, then

$$f(x) = f(a)+f'(a)\cdot(x-a)+\frac{f''(a)}{2!}(x-a)^2+\cdots+\frac{f^{[n]}(a)}{n!}(x-a)^n$$

for all x.

7. Use Taylor's theorem applied to the function f, where $f(x)$ is equal to $\int_0^x e^{-t}\, dt$ when $x \geq 0$, to show that

(a) $\displaystyle\int_0^{1/2} e^{-t^2}\, dt = \frac{1}{2}+E_1$, where $\quad -\frac{1}{24} < E_1 < 0$;

(b) $\displaystyle\int_0^{1/2} e^{-t^2}\, dt = \frac{11}{24}+E_2$, where $\quad 0 < E_2 < \frac{1}{320}$.

8. For each of the following, prove that for all real-number values of x the infinite series is convergent and has the indicated sum.

(a) $e^x = 1+x+\dfrac{x^2}{2!}+\dfrac{x^3}{3!}+\cdots+\dfrac{x^{n-1}}{(n-1)!}+\cdots$.

(b) $\sinh x = x+\dfrac{x^3}{3!}+\dfrac{x^5}{5!}+\cdots+\dfrac{x^{2n-1}}{(2n-1)!}+\cdots$.

(c) $\cosh x = 1+\dfrac{x^2}{2!}+\dfrac{x^4}{4!}+\cdots+\dfrac{x^{2n-2}}{(2n-2)!}+\cdots$.

(d) $\sqrt{2}\sin\left(x+\frac{1}{4}\pi\right) = 1+x-\dfrac{x^2}{2!}-\dfrac{x^3}{3!}+\dfrac{x^4}{4!}+\dfrac{x^5}{5!}-\dfrac{x^6}{6!}-\dfrac{x^7}{7!}+\cdots$.

9. For each of the following, prove that for the specified values of x the infinite series is convergent and has the indicated sum.

(a) $\ln(1+x) = x - \dfrac{x^2}{2} + \dfrac{x^3}{3} - \dfrac{x^4}{4} + \cdots + (-1)^{n-1}\dfrac{x^n}{n} + \cdots;$

$$-1 < x \leqq 1.$$

(b) $\ln x = 1 + \left(\dfrac{x-e}{e}\right) - \dfrac{1}{2}\left(\dfrac{x-e}{e}\right)^2 + \cdots + (-1)^n \dfrac{1}{n-1}\left(\dfrac{x-e}{e}\right)^{n-1}$

$$+ \cdots; \qquad 0 < x \leqq 2e.$$

10.* Show that if $|x| < 1$ and n is any real number, then

$$(1+x)^n = 1 + nx + \frac{n(n-1)}{2!}x^2 + \cdots$$
$$+ \frac{n(n-1)(n-2)\cdots(n-r+1)}{r!}x^r + \cdots.$$

11. For each of the following, show that the infinite series is convergent and has the indicated sum.

(a) $\ln 2 = 1 - \dfrac{1}{2} + \dfrac{1}{3} - \dfrac{1}{4} + \cdots + (-1)^{n-1}\dfrac{1}{n} + \cdots.$

(b) $\ln 2 = \dfrac{1}{2} + \dfrac{1}{2\cdot2^2} + \dfrac{1}{3\cdot2^3} + \cdots + \dfrac{1}{n\cdot2^n} + \cdots.$

(c) $\sqrt{2} = 1 + \dfrac{1}{2^2} + \dfrac{3}{2!\cdot2^4} + \dfrac{3\cdot5}{3!\cdot2^6} + \dfrac{3\cdot5\cdot7}{4!\cdot2^8} + \dfrac{3\cdot5\cdot7\cdot9}{5!\cdot2^{10}}$

$$+ \frac{3\cdot5\cdot7\cdot9\cdot11}{6!\cdot2^{12}} + \cdots.$$

12. Let $f(x) = (x+1)e^x$ for all x. Show that

(a) $f^{[n]}(0) = n+1$ for all n;

(b) $2e = 1 + 2 + \dfrac{3}{2!} + \dfrac{4}{3!} + \dfrac{5}{4!} + \cdots + \dfrac{n}{(n-1)!} + \cdots.$

13. Let f be the function for which $f(0) = 0$ and $f(x) = e^{-1/x^2}$ if $x \neq 0$. Show that the Taylor's series expansion of f about $x = 0$ converges for all x [because all terms are zero], but that the sum of the series is equal to $f(x)$ only when $x = 0$.

14. (a) Show that Lagrange's form of the remainder in Taylor's theorem can be used to obtain Eq. (4-14) of the text when $-\frac{1}{2} < x \leqq 1$, but not when $-1 < x \leqq -\frac{1}{2}$. (b) Show that Cauchy's form of the remainder can be used to obtain Eq. (4-14) of the text when $-1 < x < 1$. [*Hint:* Show that $|x - \xi|/(1 + \xi) \leqq |x|$ if ξ is between 0 and x.]

15. Let p be a positive integer with $0 \leq p \leq n$. For the remainder $R_n(x)$ of Taylor's theorem, show that there is a number ξ between a and x for which

$$R_n(x) = \frac{(x-a)^{p+1}(x-\xi)^{n-p}}{(p+1)n!} f^{[n+1]}(\xi).$$

16. Let f be a function for which the domain of $f^{[n+1]}$ includes the interval $[a, x]$, for particular numbers a and x. Let K be chosen so that $F(x) = 0$, where F is the function defined by

$$F(t) = f(a) - \left[f(t) + (a-t)f'(t) + \frac{(a-t)^2}{2!} f''(t) \right.$$

$$+ \cdots + \frac{(a-t)^n}{n!} f^{[n]}(t) + \frac{(a-t)^{n+1}}{(n+1)!} K \left. \right].$$

Show that $F(a) = 0$ and use the mean value theorem for derivatives to show that there is a number ξ between a and x for which $K = f^{[n+1]}(\xi)$. Do *not* use Taylor's theorem. [*Note:* This establishes Lagrange's form of the remainder without assuming continuity of $f^{[n+1]}$.]

4-4. REMAINDER OF AN INFINITE SERIES

Series are mainly used when the convergence is known or assumed and we wish to estimate the sum. If S is the sum of a given series, S_n is the sum of the first n terms, and R_n is the sum of the series obtained by deleting the first n terms of the given series, then

$$S = S_n + R_n \quad \text{and} \quad \lim_{n \to +\infty} R_n = 0.$$

Therefore, an upper (or lower) bound for R_n is also an upper (or lower) bound for the error in estimating S by S_n. We shall discuss three methods of obtaining bounds for R_n.

I. *Comparison with an integral.* Suppose that $\sum a_k$ is a convergent infinite series. Also suppose that there is a positive integer N and a function f that is nonnegative and monotone decreasing for $x \geq N$ and for which $a_n = f(n)$ if $n \geq N$. Then, for reasons quite similar to those used to establish the integral test, we have

$$\int_{n=1}^{+\infty} f(x)\,dx < a_{n+1} + a_{n+2} + \cdots < \int_n^{+\infty} f(x)\,dx \quad \text{if} \quad n > N.$$

ILLUSTRATION 1.   For the infinite series $\sum 1/k^2$, we have

$$R_n = \frac{1}{(n+1)^2} + \frac{1}{(n+2)^2} + \cdots,$$

and

$$\int_{n+1}^{+\infty} \frac{1}{x^2}\, dx < R_n < \int_{n}^{+\infty} \frac{1}{x^2}\, dx \quad \text{or} \quad \frac{1}{n+1} < R_n < \frac{1}{n}.$$

We have not only obtained an upper bound for R_n, but also a lower bound. To illustrate the significance of this, let us consider the particular case $n = 10$. The sum of the infinite series differs from

$$1 + \frac{1}{2^2} + \frac{1}{3^2} + \cdots + \frac{1}{10^2} = 1.538+$$

by less than $\frac{1}{10}$. However, since R_{10} is between $\frac{1}{11}$ and $\frac{1}{10}$, it follows that R_{10} differs from $\frac{1}{2}(\frac{1}{10} + \frac{1}{11})$ by less than $\frac{1}{2}(\frac{1}{10} - \frac{1}{11}) = \frac{1}{220}$. Therefore the sum of the series differs from

$$\left(1 + \frac{1}{2^2} + \frac{1}{3^2} + \cdots + \frac{1}{10^2}\right) + \frac{1}{2}\left(\frac{1}{10} + \frac{1}{11}\right) = 1.634- \qquad (4\text{-}20)$$

by less than $\frac{1}{2}(\frac{1}{10} - \frac{1}{11}) = \frac{1}{220}$. If we had used only partial sums to estimate the sum of the series, then the upper bound $1/n$ indicates that 220 terms would have been needed to assure the accuracy given by Eq. (4-20).

II. *Comparison with a geometric series.*   Suppose $\sum a_k$ is an infinite series whose terms are nonnegative. If there are numbers r, s, and N for which

$$0 \leqq r \leqq \frac{a_{n+1}}{a_n} \leqq s < 1 \quad \text{if} \quad n > N,$$

then

$$\frac{a_{N+1}}{1-r} \leqq R_N \leqq \frac{a_{N+1}}{1-s}. \qquad (4\text{-}21)$$

To show this, we note that $a_{n+1} \geqq ra_n$ and $a_{n+1} \leqq sa_n$ if $n > N$, so that for any positive integer p we have

$$a_{N+p} \geqq r \cdot a_{N+p-1} \geqq r^2 \cdot a_{N+p-2} \geqq \cdots \geqq r^{p-1} \cdot a_{N+1},$$

and

$$a_{N+p} \leqq s \cdot a_{N+p-1} \leqq s^2 \cdot a_{N+p-2} \leqq \cdots \leqq s^{p-1} \cdot a_{N+1}.$$

Therefore,

$$a_{N+1}(1+r+r^2+\cdots) \leq \sum_{N+1}^{+\infty} a_k \leq a_{N+1}(1+s+s^2+\cdots),$$

or

$$\frac{a_{N+1}}{1-r} \leq R_N \leq \frac{a_{N+1}}{1-s}.$$

ILLUSTRATION 2. For the infinite series $\sum_{n=1}^{+\infty} x^n/n$ with $x > 0$, we have

$$\frac{a_{n+1}}{a_n} = \left(\frac{n}{n+1}\right)x$$

for all n. Therefore, $a_{n+1}/a_n < x$ for all n. Also, if $k \geq n+1$, then

$$\frac{a_{k+1}}{a_k} \geq \left(\frac{n+1}{n+2}\right)x.$$

It follows from these inequalities and from (4-21) that, if $x < 1$, then

$$\frac{x^{n+1}}{(n+1)\left[1-\left(\dfrac{n+1}{n+2}\right)\cdot x\right]} \leq R_n \leq \frac{x^{n+1}}{(n+1)(1-x)}. \tag{4-22}$$

Often when applying (4-21) to a particular series, it is helpful to repeat essentially the argument used to prove (4-21). For the series $\sum_1^{+\infty} x^n/n$, we would have

$$R_n = \frac{x^{n+1}}{n+1}\left[1+\left(\frac{n+1}{n+2}\right)x+\left(\frac{n+1}{n+3}\right)x^2+\cdots\right]$$

$$< \frac{x^{n+1}}{n+1}(1+x+x^2+\cdots) = \frac{x^{n+1}}{(n+1)(1-x)},$$

and

$$R_n = \frac{x^{n+1}}{n+1}\left[1+\left(\frac{n+1}{n+2}\right)x+\left(\frac{n+1}{n+2}\right)\left(\frac{n+2}{n+3}\right)x^2\right.$$

$$\left. +\left(\frac{n+1}{n+2}\right)\left(\frac{n+2}{n+3}\right)\left(\frac{n+3}{n+4}\right)x^3+\cdots\right]$$

$$> \frac{x^{n+1}}{n+1}\left[1+\left(\frac{n+1}{n+2}x\right)+\left(\frac{n+1}{n+2}x\right)^2+\cdots\right] = \frac{x^{n+1}}{(n+1)\left[1-\left(\dfrac{n+1}{n+2}\right)x\right]}.$$

For the particular case $n = 10$, we see that the sum of the series differs from

$$x + \frac{x^2}{2} + \frac{x^3}{3} + \cdots + \frac{x^{10}}{10}$$

by less than $x^{11}/[11(1-x)]$. In fact, (4-22) becomes

$$\frac{x^{11}}{11(1 - 11x/12)} < R_{10} < \frac{x^{11}}{11(1-x)}.$$

III. *Use of Taylor's theorem.* If an infinite series is the Taylor's series expansion of a function, then Taylor's theorem can be used to estimate the remainder. This can be illustrated by an example.

ILLUSTRATION 3. The Taylor's series expansion of $\ln(1+x)$ about $x = 0$ is given by

$$\ln(1+x) = x - \frac{x^2}{2} + \frac{x^3}{3} - \frac{x^4}{4} + \cdots + (-1)^{n+1} \frac{x^n}{n} + \cdots.$$

From Lagrange's form of the remainder, we see that there is a number ξ between 0 and x for which the remainder after n terms is given by

$$R_n = (-1)^n \frac{x^{n+1}}{(n+1)(1+\xi)^{n+1}}.$$

In particular, when $x = \frac{1}{4}$ and $n = 2$, we have

$$\ln\left(\frac{5}{4}\right) = \frac{1}{4} - \frac{1}{2 \cdot 4^2} + R_2, \quad R_2 = \frac{1}{3 \cdot 4^3 (1+\xi)^3}, \quad 0 < \xi < \frac{1}{4}. \qquad (4\text{-}23)$$

From this, we see that

$$\frac{1}{3 \cdot 5^3} < R_2 < \frac{1}{3 \cdot 4^3}.$$

There are various special techniques that might be used to estimate the remainder of a Taylor's series. We shall not list these, but we can illustrate one by means of an example.

ILLUSTRATION 4. The series of Illustration 3 can be discussed without use of Taylor's theorem as follows. Either by long division or by the usual method for adding finite geometric series, we obtain

$$\frac{1}{1+t} = [1 - t + t^2 - t^3 + \cdots + (-1)^{n-1} t^{n-1}] + (-1)^n \frac{t^n}{1+t}.$$

By integrating each member of this equality between the limits 0 and x, we obtain

$$\ln(1+x) = \left[x - \frac{x^2}{2} + \frac{x^3}{3} - \frac{x^4}{4} + \cdots + (-1)^{n+1}\frac{x^n}{n} \right] + R_n,$$

where

$$R_n = (-1)^n \int_0^x \frac{t^n}{1+t}\,dt \quad \text{or} \quad (-1)^n R_n = \int_0^x \frac{t^n}{1+t}\,dt.$$

If $x > 0$, then

$$\int_0^x \frac{t^n}{1+x}\,dt < (-1)^n R_n < \int_0^x t^n\,dt,$$

or

$$\frac{x^{n+1}}{(1+x)(n+1)} < (-1)^n R_n < \frac{x^{n+1}}{n+1}.$$

In particular, when $x = \frac{1}{4}$ and $n = 2$, we have

$$\frac{4}{5}\left(\frac{1}{3 \cdot 4^3} \right) < R_2 < \frac{1}{3 \cdot 4^3}.$$

Note that this is better than the estimate for R_2 obtained in Illustration 3.

For any sequence, there is a series for which the sequence is the sequence of partial sums; the sequence has a limit if and only if this series has a sum. Also, the remainder after n terms of the series is equal to the difference between the limit of the sequence and the nth term of the sequence. Therefore, bounds for the remainder after n terms of the series are bounds for the error in approximating the limit of the sequence by the nth term. The following example illustrates this use of a series when studying a sequence.

ILLUSTRATION 5. Suppose $s_n = \ln n - (1 + \frac{1}{2} + \frac{1}{3} + \cdots + 1/n)$ for $n \geq 1$. Then the sequence $\{s_1, s_2, \cdots\}$ has the limit L if and only if the series

$$s_1 + (s_2 - s_1) + (s_3 - s_2) + \cdots + (s_n - s_{n-1}) + \cdots$$

converges to the sum L. We note that

$$s_{n+1} - s_n = \ln\left(1 + \frac{1}{n}\right) - \frac{1}{n+1} > \left(\frac{1}{n} - \frac{1}{2n^2}\right) - \frac{1}{n+1} = \frac{n-1}{2n^2(n+1)} \geq 0.$$

To use the integral test, we can define a function f by

$$f(x) = \ln\left(1+\frac{1}{x}\right) - \frac{1}{x+1} \quad \text{for} \quad x > 0,$$

so that $f(n) = s_{n+1} - s_n$ for all n. Since

$$f'(x) = \left(\frac{1}{1+1/x}\right)\left(-\frac{1}{x^2}\right) + \frac{1}{(x+1)^2} = -\frac{1}{x^2+x} + \frac{1}{x^2+2x+1} < 0,$$

the function f is decreasing and the integral test can be used. An antiderivative of f is obtained by integration by parts:

$$\int f(x)\,dx = \int \ln\left(1+\frac{1}{x}\right) dx - \int \frac{1}{x+1}\,dx = x\ln\left(1+\frac{1}{x}\right) + c.$$

It follows from $x\ln(1+1/x) = \ln[(1+1/x)^x]$ that $\lim_{x\to+\infty} x\ln(1+1/x) = 1$, which implies that the series is convergent. Also,

$$\int_n^{+\infty} f(x)\,dx < \sum_n^{+\infty}(s_{k+1}-s_k) < \int_{n-1}^{+\infty} f(x)\,dx,$$

or

$$\left[1 - n\ln\left(1+\frac{1}{n}\right)\right] < L - s_n < \left[1 - (n-1)\ln\left(1+\frac{1}{n-1}\right)\right]. \quad (4\text{-}24)$$

It follows from Taylor's theorem that if $x > -1$ then there is a number ξ in the open interval $(0, x)$ such that

$$\ln(1+x) = x - \frac{x^2}{2} + \frac{x^3}{3(1+\xi)^3}.$$

Hence,

$$x - \frac{x^2}{2} < \ln(1+x) < x - \frac{x^2}{2} + \frac{x^3}{3} \quad \text{if} \quad 0 < x < 1.$$

Therefore,

$$-n\ln\left(1+\frac{1}{n}\right) > -1 + \frac{1}{2n} - \frac{1}{3n^2} = -1 + \frac{3n-2}{6n^2},$$

$$-(n-1)\ln\left(1+\frac{1}{n-1}\right) < -1 + \frac{1}{2(n-1)},$$

and it follows from (4-24) that

$$\frac{3n-2}{6n^2} < L - s_n < \frac{1}{2(n-1)}. \quad (4\text{-}25)$$

For $n = 10$, we have $s_{10} = \ln 10 - (1 + \frac{1}{2} + \frac{1}{3} + \cdots + \frac{1}{10}) = -(.6264-)$ and

$$\frac{7}{150} < L - s_{10} < \frac{1}{18}.$$

Since $\frac{1}{2}(\frac{7}{150} + \frac{1}{18}) = .0511+$ and $\frac{1}{2}(\frac{1}{18} - \frac{7}{150}) = \frac{1}{225}$, it follows that

$$L = -(.6264-) + (.0511+) + E = -(.575+) + E,$$

where $|E| < \frac{1}{225} < .005$. (The number $-L = \gamma$ is called *Euler's constant* and is equal to $0.577216-$; it is not known whether γ is a rational number.)

PROBLEMS

1. For each of the following series, use the method of comparison with an integral to show that the remainder after ten terms satisfies the given inequality.

(a) $\displaystyle\sum_{2}^{+\infty} \frac{1}{n(\ln n)^2}$; $\quad \dfrac{1}{\ln 12} < R_{10} < \dfrac{1}{\ln 11}$.

(b) $\displaystyle\sum_{1}^{+\infty} ne^{-n^2}$; $\quad \frac{1}{2}e^{-121} < R_{10} < \frac{1}{2}e^{-100}$.

(c) $\displaystyle\sum_{1}^{+\infty} \frac{1}{n(n+1)(n+2)}$; $\quad \frac{1}{2}\ln\frac{144}{143} < R_{10} < \frac{1}{2}\ln\frac{121}{120}$.

2. For each of the following series, use the method of comparison with a geometric series to show that the remainder after ten terms satisfies the given inequality.

(a) $\displaystyle\sum_{1}^{+\infty} \frac{1}{n \cdot 2^n}$; $\quad \dfrac{12}{13}\left(\dfrac{1}{11 \cdot 2^{10}}\right) < R_{10} < \dfrac{1}{11 \cdot 2^{10}}$.

(b) $\displaystyle\sum_{1}^{+\infty} n\left(\frac{1}{4}\right)^n$; $\quad \dfrac{4}{3}\left(\dfrac{11}{4^{11}}\right) < R_{10} < \dfrac{11}{8}\left(\dfrac{11}{4^{11}}\right)$.

(c) $\displaystyle\sum_{1}^{+\infty} \frac{1}{n}\left(\frac{9}{10}\right)^n$; $\quad \dfrac{40}{7}\left[\dfrac{1}{11}\left(\dfrac{9}{10}\right)^{11}\right] < R_{10} < 10\left[\dfrac{1}{11}\left(\dfrac{9}{10}\right)^{11}\right]$.

(d) $\displaystyle\sum_{1}^{+\infty} ne^{-n^2}$; $\quad 11 \cdot e^{-121} < R_{10} < (11 \cdot e^{-121})\dfrac{11e^{23}}{11e^{23} - 12}$.

3. For each of the following series, show by any method that the remainder R_n after n terms satisfies the given inequality.

(a) $\displaystyle\sum_{1}^{+\infty} \frac{1}{k^{3/2}};$ $\displaystyle\frac{2}{\sqrt{n+1}} < R_n < \frac{2}{\sqrt{n}}.$

(b) $\displaystyle\sum_{1}^{+\infty} \frac{\sin^2 k}{k^2};$ $0 < R_n < \dfrac{1}{n}.$

(c) $\displaystyle\sum_{1}^{+\infty} \frac{1}{k!};$ $\displaystyle\frac{1}{(n+1)!} < R_n < \frac{n+2}{(n+1)(n+1)!}.$

(d) $\displaystyle\sum_{1}^{+\infty} \frac{1}{k^{\ln k}};$ $0 < R_n < \left[\ln\left(\dfrac{n+1}{e}\right) \cdot n^{+\ln (n+1)/e}\right]^{-1}.$

(e) $\displaystyle\sum_{1}^{+\infty} (-1)^{k+1} \frac{(\frac{1}{5})^{2k-1}}{2k-1};$ $\displaystyle\frac{25}{26} \frac{(\frac{1}{5})^{2n+1}}{2n+1} < (-1)^n R_n < \frac{(\frac{1}{5})^{2n+1}}{2n+1}.$

[*Hint:* Use $(1+t^2)^{-1}$ in the same way that $(1+t)^{-1}$ was used in Illustration 4.]

4. Show that the remainder after n terms of the series $\sum_0^{+\infty} k!/(2k)!$ is between

$$\frac{n!}{(2n)!} \quad \text{and} \quad \frac{n!}{(2n)!} \frac{4n+2}{4n+1}.$$

4-5. ABSOLUTE AND CONDITIONAL CONVERGENCE

Often we have to work with infinite series that have both positive and negative terms. Sometimes we even need to work with series that have some terms which are nonreal complex numbers. We shall show that if we obtain a convergent series when we replace each term of a given series by its absolute value, then the given series is convergent. However, the given series may converge even if the series of absolute values is divergent. The concept of Cauchy sequence will be very useful.

THEOREM 4-5.1. A sequence with terms in R^3 is convergent if and only if it is a Cauchy sequence.

PROOF. We know that a Cauchy sequence in R^3 is convergent [see Theorem 2-10.2]. If the sequence $\{p_n\}$ is convergent and p is its limit, then for each positive number ε there is an integer N such that

$$d(p, p_n) < \tfrac{1}{2}\varepsilon \quad \text{if} \quad n > N.$$

If $m > N$ and $n > N$, then we have

$$d(p_m, p_n) \leqq d(p_m, p) + d(p, p_n) < \tfrac{1}{2}\varepsilon + \tfrac{1}{2}\varepsilon = \varepsilon.$$

Thus, $\{p_n\}$ is a Cauchy sequence.

Analogously to what is meant by a Cauchy sequence in R^3, we define a *Cauchy sequence of complex numbers* to be a sequence of complex numbers $\{S_n\}$ such that, for each positive number ε, there is an integer N for which

$$|S_p - S_q| < \varepsilon \quad \text{if} \quad p > N \text{ and } q > N. \tag{4-26}$$

THEOREM 4-5.2. A sequence of complex numbers is convergent if and only if it is a Cauchy sequence. An infinite series of complex numbers $\sum c_n$ is convergent if and only if, for each positive number ε, there is an integer N such that

$$\left| \sum_{k=m}^{n} c_k \right| < \varepsilon \quad \text{if} \quad N < m \leq n. \tag{4-27}$$

PROOF. When sketching complex numbers, we let the complex number $x + iy$ correspond to the point (x, y). Then, for two complex numbers z_1 and z_2, the distance between the points corresponding to z_1 and z_2 is equal to $|z_1 - z_2|$. Thus, the truth of the first sentence in the statement of Theorem 4-5.2 follows from Theorem 4-5.1. By definition, an infinite series $\sum c_n$ is convergent if and only if the corresponding sequence $\{S_n\}$ of partial sums is convergent and therefore is a Cauchy sequence—i.e. if and only if for each positive number ε there is an integer M such that

$$|S_q - S_p| < \varepsilon \quad \text{if} \quad p > M \quad \text{and} \quad q > M. \tag{4-28}$$

If $m \leq n$, then $|S_n - S_{m-1}| = |\sum_{k=m}^{n} c_k|$. Thus, with $p = m - 1$, and $q = n$, (4-28) becomes

$$\left| \sum_{k=m}^{n} c_k \right| < \varepsilon \quad \text{if} \quad M + 1 < m \leq n.$$

With $M + 1 = N$, this is equivalent to (4-27).

THEOREM 4-5.3. If $\sum c_n$ is an infinite series whose terms are complex numbers, then $\sum c_n$ is convergent if $\sum |c_n|$ is convergent.

PROOF. If $\sum |c_n|$ is convergent, then it follows from Theorem 4-5.1, or Theorem 4-5.2, that for each $\varepsilon > 0$ there is an N for which

$$\sum_{k=m}^{n} |c_k| < \varepsilon \quad \text{if} \quad N < m \leq n.$$

Since $|\sum_{k=m}^{n} c_k| \leq \sum_{k=m}^{n} |c_k|$, we also have

$$\left| \sum_{k=m}^{n} c_k \right| < \varepsilon \quad \text{if} \quad N < m \leq n.$$

Thus, it follows from Theorem 4-5.2 that $\sum c_n$ is convergent.

ILLUSTRATION 1. The series

$$\sum \frac{\cos n + i \sin n}{n^2} = \sum \frac{e^{in}}{n^2}$$

is convergent, since the series $\sum |e^{in}/n^2| = \sum 1/n^2$ is convergent.

THEOREM 4-5.4. Suppose $\sum c_n$ is an infinite series whose terms are complex numbers and that, for each n, the real numbers a_n and b_n are defined by $a_n + ib_n = c_n$. Then $\sum c_n$ is convergent if and only if each of the series $\sum a_n$ and $\sum b_n$ is convergent. If $\sum a_n = A$ and $\sum b_n = B$, then $\sum (a_n + ib_n) = A + iB$.

PROOF. First let us suppose that $\sum a_n$ and $\sum b_n$ are convergent to the sums A and B, respectively. Then we have

$$A + iB = \left(\lim_{n \to +\infty} \sum_{1}^{n} a_k \right) + i \left(\lim_{n \to +\infty} \sum_{1}^{n} b_k \right) = \lim_{n \to +\infty} \sum_{1}^{n} (a_k + ib_k)$$

$$= \lim_{n \to +\infty} \sum_{1}^{n} c_k,$$

so that $\sum c_k$ is convergent to the sum $A + iB$. Now we shall assume that $\sum c_n$ is convergent to the sum C. If $C = A + iB$, where A and B are real numbers, then

$$\lim_{n \to +\infty} \left| (A + iB) - \sum_{1}^{n} (a_k + ib_k) \right| = 0. \tag{4-29}$$

Since

$$\left| (A + iB) - \sum_{1}^{n} (a_k + ib_k) \right| = \left[\left(A - \sum_{1}^{n} a_k \right)^2 + \left(B - \sum_{1}^{n} b_k \right)^2 \right]^{\frac{1}{2}},$$

either member of this equality is at least as large as $|A - \sum_{1}^{n} a_k|$ and at least as large as $|B - \sum_{1}^{n} b_k|$. It follows from this and Eq. (4-29) that $\sum a_n$ and $\sum b_n$ are convergent to the sums A and B, respectively.

ILLUSTRATION 2. The series $\sum (1+in)/n^2$ is divergent. This is seen when we note that this series is convergent if and only if each of the series $\sum 1/n^2$ and $\sum n/n^2$ is convergent, and that the series $\sum n/n^2$ $= \sum 1/n$ is divergent.

DEFINITION 4-5.1. An *absolutely convergent series* is a series, $\sum a_n$, such that $\sum |a_n|$ is convergent. A *conditionally convergent series* is a convergent series that is not absolutely convergent.

For an absolutely convergent series, we might say that the convergence is due to the smallness of the absolute values of the terms. For a conditionally convergent series, the convergence is due not only to the smallness of the terms, but also to cancellation between terms. For a conditionally convergent series, we cannot establish convergence by direct use of the integral test, a comparison test, or a ratio test. The two following special methods can be used for certain series.

DIRICHLET'S TEST. Suppose $\{a_n\}$ is a monotone decreasing sequence with limit zero. If there is a number M such that

$$|b_1+b_2+\cdots+b_n| \leq M \quad \text{for all} \quad n,$$

then the series $\sum a_n b_n$ is convergent and

$$\sum_{k=1}^{+\infty} a_k b_k = \sum_{k=1}^{+\infty} (a_k - a_{k+1})(b_1+b_2+\cdots+b_k).$$

PROOF. The student can check the identity

$$\sum_{k=1}^{n} a_k b_k = (a_1-a_2)b_1+(a_2-a_3)(b_1+b_2)+(a_3-a_4)(b_1+b_2+b_3)+\cdots$$
$$+(a_{n-1}-a_n)(b_1+b_2+\cdots+b_{n-1})+a_n(b_1+b_2+\cdots+b_n).$$

Since $|a_n(b_1+b_2+\cdots+b_n)| \leq |a_n|M$ and $\lim_{n\to+\infty} a_n = 0$, the series $\sum a_n b_n$ and $\sum (a_n - a_{n+1})(b_1+b_2+\cdots+b_n)$ either both converge and have the same sum or they both diverge. The latter series converges, since

$$\sum_{k=1}^{n} |(a_k - a_{k+1})(b_1+b_2+\cdots+b_k)|$$
$$\leq \sum_{k=1}^{n} (|a_k - a_{k+1}| \cdot M) = \sum_{k=1}^{n} [(a_k - a_{k+1}) \cdot M]$$
$$= (a_1 - a_{n+1}) \cdot M \leq a_1 M.$$

ILLUSTRATION 3. If θ is not an even multiple of π, then

$$\left| \sum_{p=1}^{n} e^{p\theta i} \right| = \left| \frac{e^{\theta i} - e^{(n+1)\theta i}}{1 - e^{\theta i}} \right| \leqq \frac{2}{|1 - e^{\theta i}|}.$$

Thus, it follows from Dirichlet's test that $\sum e^{n\theta i}/n$ is convergent if θ is not an even multiple of π. Then it follows from Theorem 4-5.4 that each of the following series is convergent:

$$\frac{\cos \theta}{1} + \frac{\cos 2\theta}{2} + \frac{\cos 3\theta}{3} + \cdots + \frac{\cos n\theta}{n} + \cdots, \quad \theta \neq 2k\pi;$$

$$\frac{\sin \theta}{1} + \frac{\sin 2\theta}{2} + \frac{\sin 3\theta}{3} + \cdots + \frac{\sin n\theta}{n} + \cdots.$$

ALTERNATING SERIES TEST. Suppose $\sum a_n$ is a series whose terms are nonzero real numbers. If each of the following conditions is satisfied, then $\sum a_n$ is convergent and the absolute value of the remainder after n terms is not larger than the absolute value of the $(n+1)$st term:

(i) $a_{n+1} < 0$ if and only if $a_n > 0$;
(ii) $|a_n| \geqq |a_{n+1}|$ for all n;
(iii) $\lim_{n \to +\infty} a_n = 0$.

PROOF. An infinite series $\sum a_n$ that satisfies (i) through (iii) can be written in the form

$$(-1)^r(|a_1| - |a_2| + |a_3| - |a_4| + \cdots),$$

where r is 1 or 2 and the sequence $|a_n|$ is monotone decreasing with limit zero. If we let $b_n = (-1)^{n+r-1}$ for each n, then $b_1 + b_2 + \cdots + b_n$ is ± 1 or 0 according to whether n is odd or even. Therefore, it follows from Dirichlet's test that $\sum |a_n| b_n$ is convergent; i.e., $\sum a_n$ is convergent. Since

$$\sum_{k=1}^{+\infty} a_k = \sum_{k=1}^{n} a_k \pm [|a_{n+1}| - (|a_{n+2}| - |a_{n+3}|) - (|a_{n+4}| - |a_{n+5}|) - \cdots]$$

$$= \sum_{k=1}^{n} a_k \pm [(|a_{n+1}| - |a_{n+2}|) + (|a_{n+3}| - |a_{n+4}|) + \cdots],$$

where each term of type $(|a_{n+p}| - |a_{n+p+1}|)$ is positive, we have

$$|a_{n+1}| - |a_{n+2}| < |R_n| < |a_{n+1}|,$$

where R_n is the remainder after n terms. Therefore, R_n is between 0 and $\pm |a_{n+1}|$, that is, between 0 and a_{n+1} [also see problem 9].

ILLUSTRATION 4. The series $1 - \frac{1}{2} + \frac{1}{3} - \frac{1}{4} + \cdots + (-1)^{n-1} 1/n + \cdots$ is convergent, since $1/(n+1) < 1/n$ for all n and $\lim_{n \to +\infty} 1/n = 0$. The sum differs from 1 by less than $\frac{1}{2}$, from $\frac{1}{2}$ by less than $\frac{1}{3}$, from $\frac{5}{6}$ by less than $\frac{1}{4}$, etc. This series is conditionally convergent, since it is convergent but not absolutely convergent.

The sum of an infinite series $\sum a_n$ was defined as $\lim_{n \to +\infty} (\sum_1^n a_k)$, if this limit exists. This definition makes specific use of the given order of the terms of the series. As yet, we do not know whether a different sum might result if the terms were in a different order, or even whether a convergent series might be made divergent by rearranging the terms. We say that each of the series

$$a_1 + a_2 + a_3 + \cdots + a_n + \cdots \quad \text{and} \quad b_1 + b_2 + b_3 + \cdots + b_n + \cdots$$

is obtainable from the other by *rearranging the terms* if there is a one-to-one correspondence between the terms of one series and the terms of the other series for which corresponding terms are equal. For example,

$$1 + \frac{1}{2^2} + \frac{1}{3^2} + \cdots + \frac{1}{n^2} + \cdots$$

and

$$1 + \frac{1}{2^2} + \frac{1}{4^2} + \frac{1}{3^2} + \frac{1}{5^2} + \frac{1}{7^2} + \frac{1}{6^2} + \frac{1}{8^2} + \cdots$$

are *rearrangements* of each other (the second series is obtained from the first by taking the first odd term, then the first two even terms, then the next three odd terms, then four even terms, five odd terms, etc.). The following theorems show that if a series is absolutely convergent, then the sum is independent of the order of the terms, but that if a series is conditionally convergent, then the order of the terms is important.

THEOREM 4-5.5. If a series is absolutely convergent and has sum S, then any series obtained by rearranging the terms is convergent and has sum S.

PROOF. Suppose $\sum a_n$ is an absolutely convergent series with sum S. Also suppose $\sum b_n$ is obtained by rearranging the terms of $\sum a_n$. Since each term of $\sum b_n$ is a term of $\sum a_n$, we see that $\sum_1^n |b_k| \leq \sum_1^{+\infty} |a_k|$ for all n and that $\sum b_n$ is absolutely convergent. Since $\sum a_n$ is convergent to the sum S and also is absolutely convergent, it follows that for any positive number ε there is an integer N_1 such that

(i)
$$\left| S - \sum_{1}^{n} a_k \right| < \varepsilon \quad \text{if} \quad n \geqq N_1;$$

(ii)
$$\sum_{N_1+1}^{+\infty} |a_k| < \varepsilon.$$

Since each term of $\sum a_n$ is a term of $\sum b_n$, there is an integer N_2 such that each of $a_1, a_2, \cdots, a_{N_1}$ occurs among $b_1, b_2, \cdots, b_{N_2}$. Now if $n \geqq N_2$, then

$$\sum_{1}^{n} b_k = \sum_{1}^{N_1} a_k + E,$$

where E is a sum of terms of $\sum a_k$ each of which occurs after a_{N_1}. It then follows from (ii) that $|E| < \varepsilon$ and then from (i) that

$$\left| S - \sum_{1}^{n} b_k \right| \leqq \left| S - \sum_{1}^{N_1} a_k \right| + |E| < 2\varepsilon \quad \text{if} \quad n \geqq N_2.$$

This implies that $\lim_{n \to +\infty} \sum_{1}^{n} b_k = S$ and completes the proof.

THEOREM 4-5.6. If $\sum a_n$ is a conditionally convergent series of real numbers, then for any real number S the terms of this series can be rearranged in such a way that the new series converges to the sum S. Also, the terms can be rearranged in such a way that the new series is divergent.

PROOF. We shall suppose that $\sum a_n$ is conditionally convergent and let $p_1, p_2, \cdots$ be the positive terms and $-q_1, -q_2, \cdots$ be the negative terms. Since $\sum a_n$ is not absolutely convergent, it is not possible for both $\sum p_n$ and $\sum q_n$ to be convergent. Since $\sum a_n$ is convergent, it is not possible for one of $\sum p_n$ and $\sum q_n$ to be convergent and the other divergent. The only remaining possibility is that both $\sum p_n$ and $\sum q_n$ are divergent. This means that for each of these series the sequence of partial sums does not have an upper bound. It follows from this that if we choose a number S, then there is a first integer m_1 such that

$$\sum_{1}^{m_1} p_k > S.$$

Next we can choose the first integer n_1 such that

$$\sum_1^{m_1} p_k - \sum_1^{n_1} q_k < S,$$

then the first integer m_2 larger than m_1 such that

$$\sum_1^{m_1} p_k - \sum_1^{n_1} q_k + \sum_{m_1+1}^{m_2} p_k > S.$$

Continuing in this way, we obtain a series whose partial sums are sometimes greater than S and sometimes less than S. The original series is convergent, which implies that $\lim_{n \to +\infty} a_n = 0$. Therefore, $\lim_{n \to +\infty} p_n = 0$, $\lim_{n \to +\infty} q_n = 0$, and the oscillation of the partial sums about S takes place between bounds that converge toward S. Therefore, the rearranged series converges to the sum S. Finally, we may observe that there are many ways in which a similar process could produce a divergent series. For example, we could replace S successively by 1, -1, 2, -2, 3, -3, etc., and define m_1, n_1, m_2, n_2, etc., so that

$$\sum_1^{m_1} p_k > 1, \quad \sum_1^{m_1} p_k - \sum_1^{n_1} q_k < -1, \quad \sum_1^{m_1} p_k - \sum_1^{n_1} q_k + \sum_{m_1+1}^{m_2} p_k > 2, \cdots.$$

ILLUSTRATION 5. It follows from the Taylor's series expansion of $\ln(1+x)$ about $x = 0$ that

$$\ln 2 = 1 - \frac{1}{2} + \frac{1}{3} - \frac{1}{4} + \cdots + (-1)^{n+1} \frac{1}{n} + \cdots$$

$$= \lim_{n \to +\infty} \sum_1^{4n} (-1)^{k+1} \frac{1}{k} = \lim_{n \to +\infty} \left[\sum_1^{2n} \frac{1}{2k-1} - \sum_1^{2n} \frac{1}{2k} \right].$$

Also,

$$\tfrac{1}{2} \ln 2 = \tfrac{1}{2} \left[\lim_{n \to +\infty} \sum_1^{2n} (-1)^{k+1} \frac{1}{k} \right] = \lim_{n \to +\infty} \left[\sum_1^{2n} (-1)^{k+1} \frac{1}{2k} \right].$$

Therefore,

$$\tfrac{3}{2} \ln 2 = \lim_{n \to +\infty} \left\{ \sum_1^{2n} \frac{1}{2k-1} + \sum_1^{2n} [(-1)^{k+1} - 1] \frac{1}{2k} \right\}$$

$$= \lim_{n \to +\infty} \left[\sum_1^{2n} \frac{1}{2k-1} - \sum_1^{n} \frac{1}{2k} \right].$$

That is,

$$\tfrac{3}{2}\ln 2 = 1+\tfrac{1}{3}-\tfrac{1}{2}+\tfrac{1}{5}+\tfrac{1}{7}-\tfrac{1}{4}+\tfrac{1}{9}+\tfrac{1}{11}-\tfrac{1}{6}+\cdots.$$

This is a rearrangement of the series for ln 2 (positive terms are taken two at a time and alternated with a single negative term).

PROBLEMS

1. Determine which of the following series are divergent.

   (a) $2-\dfrac{3}{2}+\dfrac{4}{3}-\dfrac{5}{4}+\cdots+(-1)^{n+1}\dfrac{n+1}{n}+\cdots.$

   (b) $1+\tfrac{1}{2}-\tfrac{1}{3}+\tfrac{1}{4}+\tfrac{1}{5}-\tfrac{1}{6}+\tfrac{1}{7}+\tfrac{1}{8}-\tfrac{1}{9}+\cdots.$

   (c) $\sum a_n,$ where $a_{2n} = -\dfrac{1}{2^n}$ and $a_{2n-1} = \dfrac{1}{n}.$

   (d) $\sum (-1)^n \dfrac{10^{2n}}{n!}.$ (e) $\sum (-1)^n \dfrac{n^2+7}{n^3}.$

2. In each case, determine whether the given series is divergent.

   (a) $\sum \dfrac{\cos n}{n^2}.$ (b) $\sum \dfrac{(-1)^n(n)^{3/2}+i}{n^2}.$ (c) $\sum \dfrac{(n+i)^2}{n^4}.$

3. Show that

   (a) $\ln 2 = 1+\tfrac{1}{3}+\tfrac{1}{5}-\tfrac{1}{2}-\tfrac{1}{4}-\tfrac{1}{6}+\tfrac{1}{7}+\tfrac{1}{9}+\tfrac{1}{11}-\tfrac{1}{8}-\tfrac{1}{10}-\tfrac{1}{12}+\cdots;$

   (b) $\tfrac{1}{2}\ln 2 = 1-\tfrac{1}{2}-\tfrac{1}{4}+\tfrac{1}{3}-\tfrac{1}{6}-\tfrac{1}{8}+\tfrac{1}{5}-\tfrac{1}{10}-\tfrac{1}{12}+\tfrac{1}{7}-\cdots.$

4. In each case, determine with reasons whether the given series is convergent.

   (a) $1+\tfrac{1}{2}-\tfrac{1}{3}-\tfrac{1}{4}+\tfrac{1}{5}+\tfrac{1}{6}-\tfrac{1}{7}-\tfrac{1}{8}+\cdots.$

   (b) $1+\tfrac{1}{2}-\tfrac{2}{3}+\tfrac{1}{4}+\tfrac{1}{5}-\tfrac{2}{6}+\tfrac{1}{7}+\tfrac{1}{8}-\tfrac{2}{9}+\cdots.$

   (c) $\dfrac{\sin x}{1}+\dfrac{\sin 2x}{3}-\dfrac{\sin 3x}{2}+\dfrac{\sin 4x}{5}+\dfrac{\sin 5x}{7}-\dfrac{\sin 6x}{4}+\dfrac{\sin 7x}{9}$

   $\qquad\qquad\qquad\qquad\qquad +\dfrac{\sin 8x}{11}-\dfrac{\sin 9x}{6}+\cdots.$

   (d) $\cos x+\dfrac{\cos 3x}{3}+\dfrac{\cos 5x}{5}+\cdots+\dfrac{\cos (2n-1)x}{2n-1}+\cdots,\quad x\neq k\pi.$

   (e) $1+\dfrac{\cos 5x}{2}+\dfrac{\cos 10x}{3}+\cdots+\dfrac{\cos 5(n-1)x}{n}+\cdots,\quad x\neq\tfrac{2}{5}k\pi.$

5. Prove the following, known as *Abel's test*. "$\sum a_n b_n$ is convergent if $\{a_n\}$ is a monotone bounded sequence and $\sum b_n$ is convergent."

6. Show that $\frac{1}{2} + \frac{1}{3} - \frac{1}{4} - \frac{1}{5} - \frac{1}{6} + \frac{1}{7} + \frac{1}{8} + \cdots$ is convergent, where terms with the same sign occur in groups of 2, 3, 4, 5, etc. Use this result and Abel's test [problem 5] to prove that the following series is convergent.

$$\frac{\ln 2}{2 \ln 2} + \frac{\ln 4}{3 \ln 3} - \frac{\ln 6}{4 \ln 4} - \frac{\ln 8}{5 \ln 5} - \frac{\ln 10}{6 \ln 6} + \frac{\ln 12}{7 \ln 7} + \frac{\ln 14}{8 \ln 8} + \cdots.$$

7. Suppose $\sum a_n$ is a convergent series of complex numbers and that the series $\sum (b_n - b_{n+1})$ is absolutely convergent. Prove that $\sum a_n b_n$ is convergent.

8. Let $\sum a_n$ be a conditionally convergent series of complex numbers. Show that the terms can be rearranged so that the new series is divergent.

9. Explain how problem 5, page 30, could be used in the proof of the *alternating series test*.

10. Show that $\sum a_n b_n$ is absolutely convergent if $\sum |a_n|^2$ is convergent and $\sum |b_n|^2$ is convergent.

11. (a) Show that $\sum a_n^2$ is absolutely convergent if $\sum a_n$ is absolutely convergent. (b) Give an example of a convergent series $\sum a_n$ for which $\sum a_n^2$ is divergent.

12. Let $\sum a_n$ be a convergent series of positive numbers for which $a_n \geqq a_{n+1}$ for each n. Show that $\lim_{n \to +\infty} n a_n = 0$.

4-6. ALGEBRAIC OPERATIONS WITH SERIES AND POWER SERIES

Suppose that $\sum a_n$ is a convergent infinite series. Then for any number c it is clear that

$$c \lim_{n \to +\infty} \sum_1^n a_k = \lim_{n \to +\infty} \sum_1^n c a_k.$$

That is, if we multiply each term of a convergent infinite series by the same number c, the new series is convergent and its sum is the product of c and the sum of the given series. The following theorem gives a similar fact about the "sum" of two series.

THEOREM 4-6.1. If $\sum a_n$ and $\sum b_n$ are two convergent infinite series with sums A and B, then the series $\sum (a_n + b_n)$ is convergent to the sum $A + B$.

PROOF. Since $A = \sum a_n$ and $B = \sum b_n$, we have

$$A = \lim_{n \to +\infty} \sum_1^n a_k, \quad \text{and} \quad B = \lim_{n \to +\infty} \sum_1^n b_k.$$

Therefore,

$$A + B = \left(\lim_{n \to +\infty} \sum_1^n a_k \right) + \left(\lim_{n \to +\infty} \sum_1^n b_k \right)$$

$$= \lim_{n \to +\infty} \left(\sum_1^n a_k + \sum_1^n b_k \right) = \lim_{n \to +\infty} \sum_1^n (a_k + b_k).$$

ILLUSTRATION 1. We know that if $-1 < x \leq 1$ then

$$\ln(1+x) = x - \frac{x^2}{2} + \frac{x^3}{3} - \frac{x^4}{4} + \cdots + (-1)^{n-1} \frac{x^n}{n} + \cdots \qquad (4\text{-}30)$$

[see Illustration 1, page 185]. If we replace x by $-x$ and multiply by -1, we obtain

$$-\ln(1-x) = x + \frac{x^2}{2} + \frac{x^3}{3} + \frac{x^4}{4} + \cdots + \frac{x^n}{n} + \cdots. \qquad (4\text{-}31)$$

Now we add corresponding members of (4-30) and (4-31) to obtain

$$\ln \frac{1+x}{1-x} = 2 \left[x + \frac{x^3}{3} + \frac{x^5}{5} + \cdots + \frac{x^{2n-1}}{2n-1} + \cdots \right].$$

The substitution $x = (2y+1)^{-1}$ changes $\ln(1+x)/(1-x)$ into $\ln(1+y) - \ln y$ and we have the following useful equality, valid for all positive y:

$$\ln(1+y) = \ln y + \frac{2}{2y+1} + \frac{2}{3(2y+1)^3} + \frac{2}{5(2y+1)^5}$$

$$+ \cdots + \frac{2}{(2n-1)(2y+1)^{2n-1}} + \cdots. \qquad (4\text{-}32)$$

Multiplication of series is much more complicated than addition of series. However, we may begin the discussion with the simple observation that it is natural to feel that the product of two infinite series should include all products of a term of one series by a term of the other series. Thus, the product of the series $\sum a_n$ and the series $\sum b_n$ should include all terms in either of the identical arrays in Fig. 4-2.

There are two methods indicated in Fig. 4-2 for arranging such an array as a series. For the first array, starting with the term a_1b_1, then the remaining terms in the corner 2-by-2 array, then the remaining terms in the corner 3-by-3 array, etc., the indicated polygonal path determines the following series:

$$a_1b_1 + a_1b_2 + a_2b_2 + a_2b_1 + a_3b_1 + a_3b_2 + a_3b_3 + a_2b_3 + \cdots . \qquad (4\text{-}33)$$

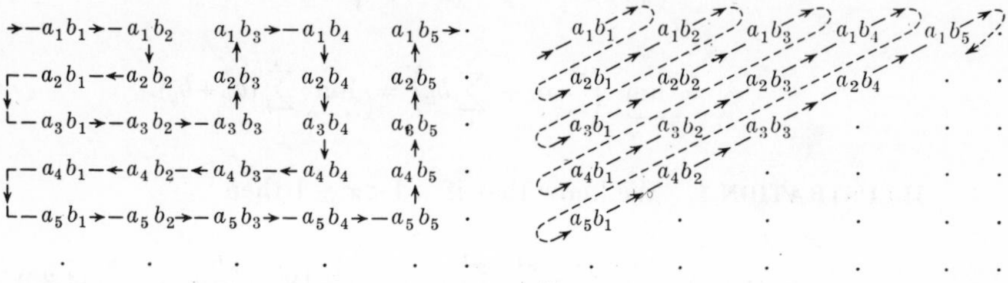

FIG. 4-2

The sum of the absolute values of the first n^2 of these terms is equal to $(\sum_1^n |a_k|)(\sum_1^n |b_k|)$. If $\sum a_n$ and $\sum b_n$ are absolutely convergent and c_n denotes the nth term of series (4-33), then we have

$$\sum_1^{n^2} |c_k| = \left(\sum_1^n |a_k| \right) \left(\sum_1^n |b_k| \right) \le \left(\sum_1^{+\infty} |a_k| \right) \left(\sum_1^{+\infty} |b_k| \right) ,$$

and it follows that series (4-33) is absolutely convergent. Therefore, its terms can be rearranged arbitrarily without affecting the sum. If we still use the arrangement of terms in (4-33), it follows that the sum of this series is equal to

$$\lim_{n \to +\infty} \left(\sum_1^n a_k \right) \left(\sum_1^n b_k \right) = \left[\lim_{n \to +\infty} \left(\sum_1^n a_k \right) \right] \left[\lim_{n \to +\infty} \left(\sum_1^n b_k \right) \right] = AB,$$

where A and B are the sums of the given series. Often it is convenient to arrange the terms in the product as indicated in the second of the previous arrays, listing in succession the terms in successive diagonals. We can also group together the terms in the same diagonal. This gives the following infinite series, called the *Cauchy product* of $\sum a_n$ and $\sum b_n$:

$$a_1b_1 + (a_2b_1 + a_1b_2) + (a_3b_1 + a_2b_2 + a_1b_3)$$
$$+ \cdots + (a_nb_1 + a_{n-1}b_2 + \cdots + a_1b_n) + \cdots . \qquad (4\text{-}34)$$

THEOREM 4-6.2. If $\sum a_n$ and $\sum b_n$ are absolutely convergent series with sums A and B, then the Cauchy product of these series is absolutely convergent to the sum AB.

PROOF. We have seen that if $\sum a_n$ and $\sum b_n$ are absolutely convergent to sums A and B, respectively, then the infinite series indicated by (4-33) is an absolutely convergent series with sum AB. Therefore, it follows from Theorem 4-5.5 that series (4-34) with the parentheses omitted is absolutely convergent and has sum AB. Since all partial sums for (4-34) are partial sums when the parentheses are removed, the Cauchy product (4-34) converges absolutely to the sum AB.

Theorem 4-6.2 followed easily from the absolute convergence of the two given series. With a little more effort, we can prove the following theorem, using absolute convergence of only one of the given series. Another theorem related to Theorem 4-6.2 will be proved later [Theorem 4-7.5].

THEOREM 4-6.3. Suppose $\sum a_n$ and $\sum b_n$ are convergent series with sums A and B and that one of these series is absolutely convergent. Then the Cauchy product of these series is convergent to the sum AB.

PROOF. For $n > N$, we shall use the equality

$$
\begin{aligned}
AB &= \sum_{k=1}^{+\infty} a_k B = \sum_{k=1}^{n} a_k B + \sum_{k=n+1}^{+\infty} a_k B \\
&= \left[a_1\left(\sum_{1}^{n} b_k \right) + a_2\left(\sum_{1}^{n-1} b_k \right) + \cdots + a_N\left(\sum_{1}^{n-N+1} b_k \right) + \cdots + a_n\left(\sum_{1}^{1} b_k \right) \right] \\
&\quad + \left[a_1\left(\sum_{n+1}^{+\infty} b_k \right) + a_2\left(\sum_{n}^{+\infty} b_k \right) + \cdots + a_N\left(\sum_{n-N+2}^{+\infty} b_k \right) \right] \\
&\quad + \left[a_{N+1}\left(\sum_{n-N+1}^{+\infty} b_k \right) + \cdots + a_n\left(\sum_{2}^{+\infty} b_k \right) \right] + \left[\sum_{n+1}^{+\infty} a_k \right] B. \quad (4\text{-}35)
\end{aligned}
$$

If $\sum b_n$ is convergent, there is a number Ω such that $\left| \sum_{n}^{+\infty} b_k \right| < \Omega$ for all n [see problem 12]. Assuming $\sum a_n$ is absolutely convergent and $\sum b_n$ is convergent, for an arbitrary positive number ε, there is an integer N such that

$$
\left| \sum_{n}^{+\infty} b_k \right| < \frac{\frac{1}{3}\varepsilon}{\sum |a_i|} \quad \text{if} \quad n > N, \quad (4\text{-}36)
$$

$$
\sum_{N+1}^{+\infty} |a_k| < \frac{\frac{1}{3}\varepsilon}{\Omega + B}. \quad (4\text{-}37)
$$

If $n > 2N$, then $n - N + 2 > N$, and it follows from (4-36) that

$$\left| a_1\left(\sum_{n+1}^{+\infty} b_k\right) + a_2\left(\sum_n^{+\infty} b_k\right) + \cdots + a_N\left(\sum_{n-N+2}^{+\infty}\right)b_k \right| < \tfrac{1}{3}\varepsilon. \quad (4\text{-}38)$$

If $n > N$, then it follows from (4-37) that

$$\left| a_{N+1}\left(\sum_{n-N+1}^{+\infty} b_k\right) + \cdots + a_n\left(\sum_2^{+\infty} b_k\right) \right| \leq \left(\sum_{N+1}^{+\infty} |a_k|\right)\Omega < \tfrac{1}{3}\varepsilon, \quad (4\text{-}39)$$

and

$$\left| \left(\sum_{n+1}^{+\infty} a_k\right)B \right| \leq \left(\sum_{N+1}^{+\infty} |a_k|\right)B < \tfrac{1}{3}\varepsilon. \quad (4\text{-}40)$$

Now let S_n be the nth partial sum for the Cauchy product of $\sum a_n$ and $\sum b_n$; that is, S_n is the first bracketed expression in the last member of (4-35). If $n > 2N$, then it follows from (4-38), (4-39), and (4-40) that

$$|AB - S_n| < \tfrac{1}{3}\varepsilon + \tfrac{1}{3}\varepsilon + \tfrac{1}{3}\varepsilon = \varepsilon.$$

Thus, the Cauchy product is convergent and its sum is AB.

The principal use of multiplication of infinite series is in the theory of power series. A series of the form

$$c_0 + c_1(z-a) + c_2(z-a)^2 + \cdots + c_n(z-a)^n + \cdots$$

is a *power series* in $(z-a)$. In this section, we shall consistently let $a = 0$ and leave it to the student to generalize the results. For two power series

$$\sum_0^{+\infty} a_n z^n \quad \text{and} \quad \sum_0^{+\infty} b_n z^n, \quad (4\text{-}41)$$

the Cauchy product is the infinite series $\sum_0^{+\infty} c_n z^n$, where

$$c_n = a_0 b_n + a_1 b_{n-1} + a_2 b_{n-2} + \cdots + a_n b_0.$$

The fact that the nth term of the Cauchy product [(4-34)] is the sum of all products $a_i b_j$ for which $i + j = n + 1$ implies that the nth term of the Cauchy product of the two power series of (4-41) is the sum of all products $a_i b_j z^i z^j$ for which $i + j = n - 1$. To use Theorems 4-6.2 or 4-6.3 with power series, it is convenient to have the following theorem.

THEOREM 4-6.4. If $\sum_0^{+\infty} a_n z^n$ is a power series, then either this series converges absolutely for all z or there is a real number R such that the series is absolutely convergent if $|z| < R$ and the series is divergent if $|z| > R$.

PROOF. We let r denote a real number and R be the least upper bound of the set

$$\left\{ r: \sum_0^{+\infty} a_n z^n \text{ converges absolutely if } |z| < r \right\}. \quad (4\text{-}42)$$

Since this set contains all nonpositive numbers, it follows that $R \geq 0$. If $R = +\infty$, then $\sum_0^{+\infty} |a_n z^n|$ converges for all z. Now let us suppose that R is a (finite) real number. We shall demonstrate first that $\sum_0^{+\infty} a_n z^n$ is divergent if $|z| > R$. We can do this by showing that if $\sum_0^{+\infty} a_n z^n$ converges for a particular value w of z, then the series converges absolutely for any z with $|z| < |w|$, which implies that $|w|$ belongs to set (4-42) and $R \geq |w|$. We may suppose that w is a number for which $\sum_0^{+\infty} a_n w^n$ is convergent. However, the only result of convergence of this series which we need to use is that there is a number M such that $|a_n w^n| \leq M$ for all n [see problem 7 of Section 4-1]. For such a number M, we have

$$|a_n z^n| = |a_n w^n| \cdot \left| \frac{z}{w} \right|^n \leq M \left| \frac{z}{w} \right|^n.$$

If $|z| < |w|$, then $|z/w| < 1$, the series $\sum_0^{+\infty} (M|z/w|^n)$ is convergent, and it follows from Comparison Test I that $\sum_0^{+\infty} |a_n z^n|$ is convergent. This shows that $\sum_0^{+\infty} a_n z^n$ is divergent if $|z| > R$. To complete the proof of the theorem, we need to show that $\sum_0^{+\infty} a_n z^n$ is absolutely convergent if $|z| < R$. Let us suppose that z_0 is a particular number with $|z_0| < R$. Because of the definition of R, there is a number r greater than $|z_0|$ such that $\sum_0^{+\infty} a_n z^n$ converges absolutely whenever $|z| < r$; in particular, $\sum_0^{+\infty} a_n z_0^n$ converges absolutely.

For a nonnegative real number R, the set of all complex numbers z for which $|z| < R$ is the interior of a circle of radius R with center at the origin. Therefore, Theorem 4-6.4 can be interpreted as stating that, for any power series $\sum_0^{+\infty} a_n z^n$, either the series converges for all z or there is a circle with center at the origin for which the series converges absolutely at all points inside the circle and diverges at all points outside the circle. Nothing can be said in general about points on the circle [see problem 9]. This circle is called the *circle of convergence* of the power series and its radius is the *radius of convergence*.

For power series, it follows from Theorems 4-6.2 and 4-6.4 that the Cauchy product of two power series converges absolutely at any point inside the smaller circle of convergence. That is, the circle of convergence for the Cauchy product is at least as large as the smaller of the circles of convergence for the two given series.

ILLUSTRATION 2. We know from Taylor's theorem that

$$\sin x = x - \frac{x^3}{3!} + \frac{x^5}{5!} - \frac{x^7}{7!} + \cdots$$

for all x. Since $1/(1-x) = (\sum_1^n x^{k-1}) + x^n/(1-x)$, it follows that

$$\frac{1}{1-x} = 1 + x + x^2 + x^3 + x^4 + \cdots \quad \text{if } |x| < 1.$$

Clearly, this series diverges if $|x| \geqq 1$. We can multiply these series and obtain

$$\frac{\sin x}{1-x} = x + x^2 + \left(1 - \frac{1}{3!}\right)x^3 + \left(1 - \frac{1}{3!}\right)x^4 + \left(1 - \frac{1}{3!} + \frac{1}{5!}\right)x^5$$

$$+ \left(1 - \frac{1}{3!} + \frac{1}{5!}\right)x^6 + \left(1 - \frac{1}{3!} + \frac{1}{5!} - \frac{1}{7!}\right)x^7 + \cdots.$$

From our theorems, it follows that this equality is valid if $|x| < 1$. It can be shown that it is not valid if $|x| \geqq 1$.

The product of two polynomials is a polynomial. We have generalized this and can now say that the product of two power series is a power series. Clearly the quotient of two polynomials need not be a polynomial. However, any polynomial can be thought of as being a power series with lots of zero coefficients; hence, any definition of quotient for power series automatically gives a definition of quotient for polynomials.

It is customary to define the *quotient* of two power series $\sum_0^{+\infty} a_n z^n$ and $\sum_0^{+\infty} b_n z^n$ as the power series $\sum_0^{+\infty} q_n z^n$ for which

$$\left(\sum_0^{+\infty} b_n z^n\right)\left(\sum_0^{+\infty} q_n z^n\right) = \sum_0^{+\infty} a_n z^n,$$

where the product is the Cauchy product of the two series. This implies that

$$a_0 = b_0 q_0,$$
$$a_1 = b_1 q_0 + b_0 q_1,$$
$$a_2 = b_2 q_0 + b_1 q_1 + b_0 q_2,$$
$$a_3 = b_3 q_0 + b_2 q_1 + b_1 q_2 + b_0 q_3, \quad \text{etc.}$$

If $b_0 \neq 0$, then we can find q_0 from the first of these equations, q_1 from the second equation, q_2 from the third, and so forth. However, if this procedure is to be useful, we need a criterion for determining the circle of convergence of the quotient series. It can be shown that the quotient series converges, and that its sum is the quotient of the sums of $\sum_0^{+\infty} a_n z^n$ and $\sum_0^{+\infty} b_n z^n$, if z is inside the largest circle which has the properties that (1) it does not contain a point for which $\sum_0^{+\infty} b_n z^n = 0$ and (2) it is contained in each of the circles of convergence of the two given series. We shall not prove this theorem, since the facts by which it is most easily proved stem from the theory of functions of a complex variable which we have not discussed.

PROBLEMS

1. (a) Show by comparison with a geometric series that the remainder after the term $2/[(2n-1)(2y+1)^{2n-1}]$ in Eq. (4-32) is less than

$$\frac{4y+3}{(2n+1)(2y+1)^{2n+2}} \quad \text{if} \quad y > \sqrt{\tfrac{1}{2}}.$$

(b) Given that $\ln 10 = 2.3025851-$, use $n = 2$ in Eq. (4-32) and show that $\ln 11 = (2.3978952-)+E$, where $0 < E < 2 \cdot 10^{-7}$.

2. Use the fact that $e^{iy} = \cos y + i \sin y$ if y is a real number to show that

$$e^{iy} = \sum_0^{+\infty} \frac{(iy)^n}{n!}.$$

3. Show that the series $\sum_1^{+\infty} (-1)^{n-1} n^{-\frac{1}{2}}$ is convergent, but that the Cauchy product $\sum c_n$ of this series with itself is divergent because c_n does not approach zero as n increases.

4. By multiplying suitable series, find the first four nonzero terms in power series expansions of each of the following functions.

   (**a**) $x^2 \sin x$.   (**b**) $e^x \sin x$.   (**c**) $e^x \ln (1+x)$.

5. Show that the Cauchy product of $\sum_0^{+\infty} z^n$ and $\sum_0^{+\infty} (-z)^n$ is equal to $\sum_0^{+\infty} z^{2n}$. Determine the sum of the given series and of the Cauchy product.

6. Obtain the first three nonzero terms of the power series for $\tan x$ by dividing the Taylor's series expansion about zero of $\sin x$ and $\cos x$.

7. Show that the Cauchy product of $\sum_0^{+\infty} u^n/n!$ and $\sum_0^{+\infty} v^n/n!$ is the series $\sum_0^{+\infty} (u+v)^n/n!$ and that each of these series converges absolutely for all u and v.

8. Use problems 2 and 7 and show that $e^z = \sum_0^{+\infty} z^n/n!$ if z is any complex number.

9. (a) Show that $\sum_1^{+\infty} z^n/n^2$ converges if $|z| \leq 1$ and diverges if $|z| > 1$.
(b) Show that $\sum_0^{+\infty} z^n$ converges if $|z| < 1$ and diverges if $|z| \geq 1$.
(c) Show that $\sum_1^{+\infty} z^n/n$ converges if $|z| \leq 1$ and $z \neq 1$ and diverges if $|z| > 1$ or $z = 1$.

10. Find the circle of convergence of each of the following: the Taylor's series expansion about $x = 0$ of $(1-x)^{-2}$; the Taylor's series expansion about $x = 0$ of $(1-x)^2$; the Cauchy product of these two series.

11. Let $\sum_0^{+\infty} a_n z^n$ be the series for which $a_0 = 1$, $a_1 = -1$, $a_2 = 1$, and $a_n = 0$ if $n > 2$. Find the Cauchy product of $\sum_0^{+\infty} a_n z^n$ and the series

$$1 - z^2 - z^3 + z^5 + z^6 - z^8 - z^9 + z^{11} + z^{12} - z^{14} - z^{15} + \cdots.$$

12. Show that if $\sum a_n$ is convergent, then there is a number Ω such that $\left| \sum_{k=n}^{+\infty} a_k \right| < \Omega$ for all n.

4-7. UNIFORM CONVERGENCE

Suppose that for each positive integer n we are given a function S_n. There are many ways to define $\lim_{n \to +\infty} S_n$. The definition we shall use depends directly and simply on the theory we have developed.

DEFINITION 4-7.1. The *limit* of a sequence of functions $\{S_1, S_2, \cdots\}$ is the function S defined by

$$S(z) = \lim_{n \to +\infty} S_n(z).$$

The domain of S is the set of all numbers z in the intersection of the domains of the functions $S_1, S_2, \cdots$ which have the property that this limit exists.

Sometimes the functions in the sequence are known, but the limit function is not. In trying to find information about the limit, it is important to know how to determine the integral or derivative of the limit, when given the integral or derivative of each term of the sequence. For this purpose, the concept of uniform convergence given in the following definition is helpful.

DEFINITION 4-7.2. A sequence of functions *uniformly convergent on a set* D is a sequence $\{S_1, S_2, \cdots\}$ with the following properties:
(i) The domain of S contains D, where S is $\lim_{n \to +\infty} S_n$.
(ii) For any positive number ε there is a number N such that

$$|S(z) - S_n(z)| < \varepsilon \quad \text{if} \quad n \geq N \quad \text{and} \quad z \in D.$$

Expressed less formally, this definition states that $\{S_1, S_2, \cdots\}$ converges uniformly on D to the limit S if for any positive number ε the value of $S_n(z)$ approximates $S(z)$ with an error less than ε *everywhere on D*, provided only that n is chosen large enough. The important thing to understand is that the choice of n does not depend on the value of z.

We know that any sequence determines an infinite series for which the sequence is the sequence of partial sums. If in Definition 4-7.2 we think of $S_n(z)$ as being the nth partial sum and $S(z)$ as the sum of an infinite series, then this definition becomes a definition of *uniform convergence for an infinite series*: If we use the symbol R_n for the remainder, we can say that an infinite series is uniformly convergent on a set D if for any positive number ε there is a number N such that $|R_n(z)| < \varepsilon$ if $n \geq N$ and $z \in D$. To establish uniform convergence of an infinite series, we need to show that the remainder can be made small *independently of z*. For example,

$$\frac{1}{1-z} = 1 + z + z^2 + \cdots + z^{n-1} + R_n(z),$$

where $R_n(z) = z^n/(1-z)$ if $z \neq 1$. If $|z| \leq r$, where $r < 1$, then

$$|R_n(z)| \leq \frac{|z|^n}{1-|z|} \leq \frac{r^n}{1-r}.$$

Given a positive number ε, we can choose N large enough so that $r^n/(1-r) < \varepsilon$ if $n \geq N$. Then for all z in the circle $|z| \leq r$, we have

$$|R_n(z)| \leq \frac{r^n}{1-r} < \varepsilon \quad \text{if} \quad n \geq N.$$

Each of the tests that were used to obtain upper bounds for the remainder of an infinite series can provide a test for uniform convergence. The following is one such test.

WEIERSTRASS' TEST FOR UNIFORM CONVERGENCE: Suppose that $\sum M_n$ is a convergent series of nonnegative numbers and that $\{u_1, u_2, \cdots\}$ is a sequence of functions for which $|u_n(z)| \leq M_n$ for each positive integer n and each z in a set D. Then $\sum u_n$ converges absolutely at each point of D and converges uniformly on D.

PROOF. Since $\sum M_n$ is convergent, it follows from Comparison Test I and the inequalities $|u_n(z)| \leq M_n$ for $n = 1, 2, 3, 4, \cdots$, that $\sum u_n(z)$ is absolutely convergent if $z \in D$. Also, for any positive number ε there is an integer N such that the remainder of $\sum M_n$ after n terms is less than ε if $n \geq N$, that is, $\sum_n^{+\infty} M_k < \varepsilon$ if $n > N$. Then

$$\left| \sum_n^{+\infty} u_k(z) \right| \leq \sum_n^{+\infty} |u_k(z)| \leq \sum_n^{+\infty} M_k < \varepsilon$$

if $z \in D$ and $n > N$. This shows that $\sum u_n$ is uniformly convergent on D.

ILLUSTRATION 1. For the series $\sum_1^{+\infty} (\sin nx)/n^2$, we have

$$\left| \frac{\sin nx}{n^2} \right| \leq \frac{1}{n^2}$$

for all n and all real numbers x. Since $\sum 1/n^2$ is convergent, the series $\sum (\sin nx)/n^2$ is absolutely convergent for all x and uniformly convergent on the set of real numbers.

One of the simplest and most useful applications of Weierstrass' test is the following theorem about power series.

THEOREM 4-7.1. A power series is *uniformly convergent* on any circle (and its interior) concentric with and smaller than the circle of convergence.

PROOF. Suppose we let $\sum_0^{+\infty} a_n z^n$ be a power series and R be its radius of convergence (possibly $R = +\infty$). Also suppose we let r be a nonnegative number less than R. Since the series $\sum_0^{+\infty} a_n r^n$ is convergent and

$$|a_n z^n| \leq |a_n r^n| \quad \text{if} \quad |z| \leq r,$$

it follows from Weierstrass' test that $\sum_0^{+\infty} a_n z^n$ is uniformly convergent on the set of all z for which $|z| \leq r$.

The next test is related closely to Dirichlet's test [page 200]. It is often very useful.

DIRICHLET'S TEST FOR UNIFORM CONVERGENCE. Suppose $\{a_n\}$ is a sequence of functions for which $a_n(x) \geq a_{n+1}(x)$ and $a_n(x) \to 0$ uniformly on a set S. If $\{f_n\}$ is a sequence of functions for which there is a number M such that

$$|f_1(x) + f_2(x) + \cdots + f_n(x)| \leq M \quad \text{if} \quad n \geq 1 \quad \text{and} \quad x \in S,$$

then the series $\sum a_n(x) f_n(x)$ converges uniformly on S.

PROOF. It follows from Dirichlet's test [page 200] that $\sum a_n(x)f_n(x)$ converges if $x \in S$. The following formal identity is similar to an identity used in the proof of Dirichlet's test:

$$[a_n(x) - a_{n+1}(x)]f_n(x) + [a_{n+1}(x) - a_{n+2}(x)][f_n(x) + f_{n+1}(x)]$$
$$+ \cdots + [a_{p-1}(x) - a_p(x)][f_n(x) + \cdots + f_{p-1}(x)]$$
$$+ a_p(x)[f_n(x) + \cdots + f_p(x)] = \sum_{k=n}^{p} a_k(x)f_k(x).$$

Since $|\sum_{k=n}^{q} f_k(x)| \leqq 2M$ if $q > n$, we can conclude that

$$\left| \sum_{k=n}^{p} a_k(x)f_k(x) \right| \leqq 2Ma_n(x) \quad \text{if} \quad n \geqq 1 \quad \text{and} \quad x \in S.$$

Therefore, $|\sum_{k=n}^{+\infty} a_k(x)f_k(x)| \leqq 2Ma_n(x)$. This and the fact that $a_n \to 0$ uniformly imply that $\sum a_n(x)f_n(x)$ converges uniformly on S.

Given a uniformly convergent sequence $\{S_1, S_2, \cdots\}$ of integrable functions, it is not reasonable to attempt to determine an integral of the limit function S before it is shown that S is integrable. One method of doing this is by proving that a uniformly convergent sequence of continuous functions has a continuous limit function. This theorem assumes more than is necessary and has a stronger conclusion than is needed, since a function need not be continuous to be integrable. However, its simplicity and wide applicability make it valuable.

THEOREM 4-7.2. If the sequence $\{S_1, S_2, \cdots\}$ is uniformly convergent to S in some neighborhood of a point z_0 and S_n is continuous at z_0 for each n, then S is continuous at z_0.

PROOF. We suppose that $\{S_1, S_2, \cdots\}$ is a uniformly convergent sequence with limit S and that S_n is continuous at z_0 for each n. We must show that for any positive number ε there is a positive number δ for which

$$|S(z) - S(z_0)| < \varepsilon \quad \text{if} \quad |z - z_0| < \delta. \tag{4-43}$$

We shall use the following inequality:

$$|S(z) - S(z_0)| = |[S(z) - S_n(z)] + [S_n(z) - S_n(z_0)] + [S_n(z_0) - S(z_0)]|$$
$$\leqq |S(z) - S_n(z)| + |S_n(z) - S_n(z_0)| + |S_n(z_0) - S(z_0)|. \tag{4-44}$$

We shall show that there is an integer n and a positive number δ such that each term in the right member of (4-44) is less than $\frac{1}{3}\varepsilon$, if $|z - z_0| < \delta$. Since there is a neighborhood W of z_0 on which the given sequence is uniformly convergent, there is a positive integer n such that $|S(z) - S_n(z)| < \frac{1}{3}\varepsilon$ for all z in W. For this n, the first and last terms in the right member of (4-44) are each less than $\frac{1}{3}\varepsilon$. Because of continuity of S_n and the fact that W contains a circular neighborhood of z_0, there is a positive number δ such that (1) $z \in W$ if $|z - z_0| < \delta$, and (2)

$$|S_n(z) - S_n(z_0)| < \tfrac{1}{3}\varepsilon \quad \text{if} \quad |z - z_0| < \delta.$$

Now we see that the sum of the terms in the right member of (4-44) is less than ε if $|z - z_0| < \delta$. This completes the proof.

It can easily be shown that the limit of a sequence of continuous functions need not be continuous if the convergence is not uniform. For example, suppose that

$$S_n(x) = (\sin x)^n \quad \text{if} \quad 0 \leqq x \leqq \pi.$$

If $S(x) = \lim_{n \to +\infty} S_n(x)$, then $S(x)$ equals 1 if $x = \frac{1}{2}\pi$, and equals 0 if $0 \leqq x \leqq \pi$ and $x \neq \frac{1}{2}\pi$; hence, S is discontinuous at $\frac{1}{2}\pi$.

If each term of an infinite series is continuous, then each partial sum is continuous. Therefore it follows from Theorem 4-7.2 that the sum of a uniformly convergent series is continuous at a point z_0 if each term of the series is continuous at z_0. Since a power series is uniformly convergent on any circle smaller than its circle of convergence, it follows that the sum of a power series is continuous at all points inside its circle of convergence. An immediate application of this fact is illustrated by the following problem.

ILLUSTRATION 2. Suppose we wish to evaluate

$$\lim_{x \to 0} \frac{\cosh x - (1 + x^2)^{1/2}}{\sin^4 x}.$$

We can use Taylor's series for the various functions involved and write this as

$$\lim_{x \to 0} \frac{\left(1 + \dfrac{x^2}{2!} + \dfrac{x^4}{4!} + \dfrac{x^6}{6!} + \cdots\right) - \left(1 + \dfrac{1}{2}x^2 - \dfrac{1}{8}x^4 + \dfrac{1}{16}x^6 + \cdots\right)}{\left(x - \dfrac{x^3}{3!} + \dfrac{x^5}{5!} - \cdots\right)^4}$$

$$= \lim_{x \to 0} \frac{\dfrac{1}{6}x^4 - \dfrac{11}{180}x^6 + \cdots}{x^4 - \dfrac{2}{3}x^6 + \dfrac{1}{5}x^8 - \cdots} = \lim_{x \to 0} \frac{\dfrac{1}{6} - \dfrac{11}{180}x^2 + \cdots}{1 - \dfrac{2}{3}x^2 + \dfrac{1}{5}x^4 - \cdots}.$$

Now we may argue that the numerator and denominator of the last fraction are continuous at $x = 0$, so the fraction is continuous and the limit can be evaluated by letting $x = 0$. Therefore, the answer is $\frac{1}{6}$.

The converse of Theorem 4-7.2 is false, since the limit of a sequence can be continuous even if the convergence is not uniform [see problem 7]. However, the following theorem of Ulisse Dini (1845–1918) describes a situation for which the convergence must be uniform. We use the convention that a *monotone increasing sequence of functions* on D is a sequence of functions such that, for each x in D, the sequence of values of the functions at x is monotone increasing. A *monotone decreasing sequence of functions* and a *monotone sequence* of functions are defined in the natural way.

THEOREM 4-7.3 (DINI). Let $\{S_n\}$ be a monotone sequence of real-valued continuous functions that converges to S on a compact set D. Then $\{S_n\}$ converges uniformly to S on D if S is continuous on D.

PROOF. Let ε be an arbitrary positive number. Then for a particular point p in D, there is an N_p for which

$$|S(p) - S_{N_p}(p)| < \tfrac{1}{3}\varepsilon.$$

Since S and S_{N_p} are continuous, there is an open neighborhood U_p of p such that

$$|S(r) - S(p)| < \tfrac{1}{3}\varepsilon \quad \text{and} \quad |S_{N_p}(r) - S_{N_p}(p)| < \tfrac{1}{3}\varepsilon, \quad \text{if } r \in U_p.$$

Then

$$|S(r) - S_{N_p}(r)| \leq |S(r) - S(p)| + |S(p) - S_{N_p}(p)| + |S_{N_p}(p) - S_{N_p}(r)| < \varepsilon,$$

if $r \in U_p$. Since the sequence $\{S_n\}$ is monotone, we then have

$$|S(r) - S_n(r)| < \varepsilon \quad \text{if} \quad r \in U_p \quad \text{and} \quad n \geq N_p.$$

We now use the cover of D whose members consist of one such open set U_p for each p in D. This cover can be reduced to a finite cover [see Definition 2-3.1]. We let N be the largest of all N_p's corresponding to members of this finite cover. Then

$$|S(r) - S_n(r)| < \varepsilon \quad \text{if} \quad n \geq N.$$

Thus, $\{S_n\}$ is uniformly convergent on D.

We know that the sum of a uniformly convergent series of continuous functions is continuous. For power series, the next theorem gives a useful extension of this theorem.

THEOREM 4-7.4 (ABEL'S LIMIT THEOREM). If $\sum_0^{+\infty} b_k$ is convergent, then

$$\lim_{t \to 1-} \sum_0^{+\infty} b_k t^k = \sum_0^{+\infty} b_k.$$

PROOF. It follows from Theorem 4-6.4 that $\sum_0^{+\infty} b_k t^k$ is convergent if $|t| < 1$. We need to show that, for any $\varepsilon > 0$, there is a $\delta > 0$ such that

$$\left| \sum_0^{+\infty} b_k t^k - \sum_0^{+\infty} b_k \right| < \varepsilon \quad \text{if} \quad 1 - \delta < t < 1. \tag{4-45}$$

Since $\sum b_n$ is convergent, it follows from Theorem 4-5.2 that there is an N such that

$$\left| \sum_N^{N+p} b_k \right| < \tfrac{1}{3}\varepsilon \quad \text{for all integers} \quad p \geq 0. \tag{4-46}$$

Then $\left| \sum_N^{+\infty} b_k \right| \leq \tfrac{1}{3}\varepsilon$ and, since we can choose δ small enough that

$$\left| \sum_0^{N-1} b_k t^k - \sum_0^{N-1} b_k \right| < \tfrac{1}{3}\varepsilon \quad \text{if} \quad 1 - \delta < t < 1,$$

we can complete the proof of (4-45) by showing that $\left| \sum_N^{+\infty} b_k t^k \right| < \tfrac{1}{3}\varepsilon$. We can use the identity

$$\sum_N^{N+p} b_k t^k = t^N [(1-t)b_N + (t-t^2)(b_N + b_{N+1}) + (t^2 - t^3)(b_N + b_{N+1} + b_{N+2})$$

$$+ \cdots + (t^{p-1} - t^p)(b_N + b_{N+1} + \cdots + b_{N+p-1})$$

$$+ t^p(b_N + b_{N+1} + \cdots + b_{N+p})]$$

to obtain, when $|t| < 1$,

$$\sum_N^{+\infty} b_k t^k = t^N [(1-t)b_N + (t-t^2)(b_N + b_{N+1})$$

$$+ (t^2 - t^3)(b_N + b_{N+1} + b_{N+2}) + \cdots]$$

$$= t^N (1-t)[b_N + t(b_N + b_{N+1}) + t^2(b_N + b_{N+1} + b_{N+2}) + \cdots].$$

It follows from this and (4-46) that, if $0 < t < 1$, then

$$\left| \sum_{N}^{+\infty} b_k t^k \right| \leq (1-t)(\tfrac{1}{3}\varepsilon) \sum_{0}^{+\infty} t^k = \tfrac{1}{3}\varepsilon.$$

Abel's limit theorem has several applications among the problems of the next section. Also, it provides the machinery for proving the next theorem.

THEOREM 4-7.5. If $\sum a_n$ and $\sum b_n$ are convergent series with sums A and B, then if the Cauchy product of these series is convergent its sum is AB.

PROOF. If $\sum a_n$ and $\sum b_n$ are convergent, then it follows from Theorem 4-6.4 that $\sum a_n t^n$ and $\sum b_n t^n$ converge absolutely if $|t| < 1$. Then it follows from Theorem 4-6.2 that

$$\sum c_n t^n = (\sum a_n t^n)(\sum b_n t^n), \quad \text{if} \quad |t| < 1,$$

where $\sum c_n$ is the Cauchy product of $\sum a_n$ and $\sum b_n$. If $\sum c_n$ is convergent, it follows from Abel's limit theorem that we can let $t \to 1-$ and obtain $\sum c_n = AB$.

PROBLEMS

1. For each of the following, show that the given sequence converges uniformly on the interval stated.

(a) $S_n = x^n$; $[-\tfrac{3}{4}, \tfrac{3}{4}]$.   (b) $S_n = \dfrac{x}{1+nx}$; $[0, 1]$.

2. For each of the following, show that the series converges uniformly on the interval stated.

(a) $1-x+x^2-x^3+\cdots$; $[-\tfrac{1}{2}, \tfrac{1}{2}]$.   (b) $\displaystyle\sum_{1}^{+\infty} \dfrac{x^2}{n^2+x^2}$; $[-10, 10]$.

3. For each of the following, show that the given sequence converges on the interval stated. Find the limit and show that the convergence is not uniform.

(a) $S_n = \dfrac{n^2 x^2}{1+n^2 x^2}$; $[-1, 1]$.   (b) $S_n = \dfrac{x^{2n}}{1+x^{2n}}$; $[-2, 2]$.

(c) $S_n = (\tanh x)^{1/n}$; $[0, 1]$.

4. For each of the following, show that the given series converges in the interval stated, but does not converge uniformly.

(a) $1 - x + x^2 - x^3 + \cdots$; [0, 1). (b) $\displaystyle\sum_{1}^{+\infty} \frac{x^2}{n^2 + x^2}$; all x.

5. For each of the following, determine whether the sequence converges uniformly on the interval stated. Give reasons.

(a) $S_n = \dfrac{nx}{1 + n^2 x^2}$; $[-1, 1]$.

(c) $S_n = \sin^n x$; $[0, \pi]$.

(b) $S_n = \dfrac{x^n}{n}$; $[-1, 1]$.

(d) $S_n = \tanh^n x$; all x.

6. For each of the following, determine whether the infinite series converges uniformly on the interval stated. Give reasons.

(a) $1 - \dfrac{x}{2} + \dfrac{x^2}{3} - \dfrac{x^3}{4} + \cdots$; [0, 1].

(d) $\displaystyle\sum_{1}^{+\infty} \frac{\sqrt{x^{2n} - 1}}{3^n}$; [1, 2].

(b) $\displaystyle\sum_{1}^{+\infty} \left(\frac{\sin nx}{n} \right)^2$; all x.

(e) $\displaystyle\sum_{0}^{+\infty} \frac{x^2}{(1 + x^2)^n}$; all x.

(c) $\displaystyle\sum_{1}^{+\infty} e^{-nx}$; $x > 0$.

(f*) $\displaystyle\sum_{n=1}^{+\infty} n^k e^{-nx}$; $0 < \theta \le x$.

7. Let $S_n(x) = e^{-(x-n)^2}$ for all real numbers x. Show that the sequence $\{ S_1, S_2, \cdots \}$ has a limit which is continuous for all x, but that the convergence is not uniform.

8. Use power series to find the limits of the following expressions as $x \to 0$.

(a) $\dfrac{e^x - \cos x}{\sin x}$.

(c) $\dfrac{e^{(x^2)} - 1 - \sin x^2}{x^4}$.

(b) $\dfrac{\tan x - \sin x}{\sin^2 x}$.

(d) $\dfrac{(1 - x^2)^{1/3} - \cos x}{\sin^2 x}$.

9.* (a) Prove that if x is not an even multiple of π then

$$\sum_{k=0}^{n} e^{ikx} = \frac{1 - e^{i(n+1)x}}{1 - e^{ix}} = \frac{\sin \frac{1}{2}(n+1)x}{\sin \frac{1}{2}x} e^{inx/2},$$

$$\sum_{k=1}^{n} \sin kx = \frac{\sin \frac{1}{2}nx \sin \frac{1}{2}(n+1)x}{\sin \frac{1}{2}x},$$

$$\sum_{k=0}^{n} \cos kx = \frac{\cos \frac{1}{2}nx \sin \frac{1}{2}(n+1)x}{\sin \frac{1}{2}x} = \frac{\sin (n + \frac{1}{2})x}{2 \sin \frac{1}{2}x} + \frac{1}{2}.$$

(b) Use the identities of part (a) and prove that $\sum_{1}^{+\infty} e^{inx}/n$, $\sum_{1}^{+\infty} (\sin nx)/n$, and $\sum_{1}^{+\infty} (\cos nx)/n$ are uniformly convergent on any closed interval that does not contain an even multiple of π.

10.* (a) Prove that if x is not an even multiple of π then

$$\sum_{k=1}^{n} e^{i(2k-1)x} = \frac{\sin nx}{\sin x} e^{inx},$$

$$\sum_{k=1}^{n} \cos (2k-1)x = \frac{\sin 2nx}{2 \sin x},$$

$$\sum_{k=1}^{n} \sin (2k-1)x = \frac{\sin^2 nx}{\sin x}.$$

(b) Use the identities of part (a) and the conclusions of problem 9 and prove that $\sum c_n/n$ converges uniformly on any closed interval not containing a multiple of π, if $c_n = \sin (2n-1)\,x$, $c_n = \cos (2n-1)x$, $c_n = \sin 2nx$, or $c_n = \cos 2nx$.

11. Suppose $0 < r < s < \pi$. Determine in each case whether the given series converges uniformly on $[r, s]$.

(a) $\displaystyle\sum_{1}^{+\infty} \frac{\sin nx}{\ln n}.$ (c) $\displaystyle\sum_{1}^{+\infty} e^{-nx} \sin nx.$

(b) $\displaystyle\sum_{1}^{+\infty} \frac{\sin nx}{\ln nx}.$ (d) $\displaystyle\sum_{1}^{+\infty} \sin \frac{x}{n^{1/2}} \cos nx.$

12. Let the rational numbers of the interval $[0, 1]$ be put in one-to-one correspondence with the positive integers, so that they can be listed as the terms of a sequence $\{r_1, r_2, \cdots\}$. For each positive integer n, define a function S_n by $S_n(x) = 1$ if x is one of the numbers $r_1, r_2, \cdots, r_n$; and $S_n(x) = 0$ if x is not one of the numbers $r_1, r_2, \cdots, r_n$. Show that $\lim_{n \to +\infty} S_n(x) = S(x)$ exists for each x in the interval $[0, 1]$, but that S_n does not converge uniformly to S. Also show that S is discontinuous at each point of $[0, 1]$ and that $\int_0^1 S(x)\, dx$ does not exist, although $\int_0^1 S_n(x)\, dx = 0$ for all n.

13. Suppose f_n is Riemann integrable on $[a, b]$ for $n = 1, 2, \cdots$. Prove that f is Riemann integrable if $\{f_n\}$ converges uniformly to f on $[a, b]$. Discuss the possibility of using improper integration.

4-8. DIFFERENTIATION AND INTEGRATION OF SEQUENCES AND SERIES

Since it is beyond the scope of this text to discuss the theory of differentiation and integration of functions with respect to variables whose values are in regions of the complex plane, it will be understood in this section that each variable may have only real-number values.

THEOREM 4-8.1. If the sequence $\{S_n\}$ is uniformly convergent to the sum S on the interval $[a, b]$ and S_n is continuous on $[a, b]$ for each n, then

$$\int_a^b S(t)\, dt = \lim_{n \to +\infty} \int_a^b S_n(t)\, dt. \tag{4-47}$$

Also, $\lim_{n \to +\infty} \int_a^x S_n(t)\, dt = \int_a^x S(t)\, dt$ for all x in $[a, b]$ and the convergence to the limit is uniform on $[a, b]$.

PROOF. It follows from Theorem 4-7.2 that S is continuous on $[a, b]$ and therefore integrable. We shall let $R_n = S - S_n$, so that

$$\int_a^x S(t)\, dt = \int_a^x S_n(t)\, dt + \int_a^x R_n(t)\, dt \quad \text{if} \quad x \in [a, b]. \tag{4-48}$$

Since the given sequence is uniformly convergent on $[a, b]$, for any positive number ε there is an integer N such that $|R_n(x)|$ is less than ε for all x in $[a, b]$ if $n \geqq N$. Then

$$\left| \int_a^x R_n(t)\, dt \right| \leqq \left| \int_a^x |R_n(t)|\, dt \right| \leqq \varepsilon \left| \int_a^x dt \right| \leqq \varepsilon |b - a|,$$

which implies that $\lim_{n \to +\infty} \left| \int_a^x R_n(x)\, dx \right| = 0$ and that this limit is approached uniformly on $[a, b]$. From this and (4-48) we can see that $\int_a^x S_n(t)\, dt$ converges uniformly on $[a, b]$ to the limit $\int_a^x S(t)\, dt$.

It follows from Theorem 4-8.1 that a sequence uniformly convergent on an interval $[a, b]$ can be integrated repeatedly between limits in that interval. Any sequence obtained by integration using limits a and x, with x in $[a, b]$, converges uniformly on $[a, b]$.

ILLUSTRATION 1. Since $|\sin x/n| \leqq |x/n|$ for all x, the sequence whose nth term is $\sin x/n$ converges uniformly to zero on any finite interval. Therefore,

$$\int_0^x \sin \frac{t}{n}\, dt = n - n \cos \frac{x}{n}$$

converges uniformly to zero on any finite interval;

$$\int_0^x \left(n - n \cos \frac{t}{n} \right) dt = nx - n^2 \sin \frac{x}{n}$$

converges uniformly to zero on any finite interval; and so forth. This example shows that it is important to use definite integrals rather than antiderivatives when stating Theorem 4-8.1, since an antiderivative of $\sin x/n$ is $-n \cos x/n$ and $\lim_{n \to +\infty} n \cos x/n$ does not exist for any x.

To adapt Theorem 4-8.1 to series, we must use the fact that the integral of a finite sum is the sum of the integrals of individual terms, and the fact that a finite sum is continuous at any point for which each term is continuous. Explicitly, suppose we let $\sum u_n$ be an infinite series with the nth partial sum denoted by S_n. Then

$$\int_a^b S_n(x)\,dx = \int_a^b \left[\sum_1^n u_k(x) \right] dx = \sum_1^n \left[\int_a^b u_k(x)\,dx \right].$$

If the series is uniformly convergent on an interval $[a, b]$ and each u_n is continuous on $[a, b]$, then from Theorem 4-8.1 we have

$$\int_a^b S(x)\,dx = \lim_{n \to +\infty} \sum_1^n \int_a^b u_k(x)\,dx = \sum_1^{+\infty} \int_a^b u_k(x)\,dx.$$

ILLUSTRATION 2. Since

$$\left| \frac{\cos nx}{n^2} \right| \leqq \frac{1}{n^2}$$

for all real x and all n, it follows from Weierstrass' test that the infinite series $\sum_1^{+\infty} (\cos nx)/n^2$ is uniformly convergent on the set of real numbers. If S is the sum of this series, then for any number x we have

$$\int_0^x S(t)\,dt = \sum_1^{+\infty} \left[\int_0^x \frac{\cos nt}{n^2}\,dt \right] = \sum_1^{+\infty} \frac{\sin nx}{n^3}.$$

Theorem 4-8.1 is a theorem about integration of sequences. Because of the fundamental theorem of calculus, it seems reasonable that a theorem about integration should yield a theorem about differentiation. The following is such a theorem.

THEOREM 4-8.2. Suppose $\{S_n\}$ is a sequence of functions with derivatives continuous at each point of an interval $[a, b]$. If the sequence $\{S_n(x)\}$ is convergent for at least one x in $[a, b]$ and if the sequence $\{S_n'\}$ is uniformly convergent on $[a, b]$, then $\{S_n\}$ is uniformly convergent on $[a, b]$ to a limit S for which

$$S'(x) = \lim_{n \to +\infty} S_n'(x) \quad \text{if} \quad x \in [a, b].$$

PROOF. Suppose that $f(x) = \lim_{n \to +\infty} S_n'(x)$ for x in $[a, b]$ and that x_0 is a number in $[a, b]$ for which $\lim_{n \to +\infty} S_n(x_0)$ exists. Since $\{S_n'\}$ is uniformly convergent on $[x_0, x]$ for all x in $[a, b]$, it follows from Theorem 4-8.1 that

$$\int_{x_0}^{x} f(t) \, dt = \lim_{n \to +\infty} \left[\int_{x_0}^{x} S_n'(t) \, dt \right] = \lim_{n \to +\infty} [S_n(x) - S_n(x_0)] \quad (4\text{-}49)$$

and that the convergence is uniform on $[a, b]$. Since $\lim_{n \to +\infty} S_n(x_0)$ exists, we can write

$$\lim_{n \to +\infty} [S_n(x) - S_n(x_0)] + \lim_{n \to +\infty} S_n(x_0) = \lim_{n \to +\infty} S_n(x),$$

and conclude that $\lim_{n \to +\infty} S_n(x)$ exists. Now if we let

$$S(x) = \lim_{n \to +\infty} S_n(x),$$

we can deduce from (4-49) that

$$S(x) = \lim_{n \to +\infty} S_n(x_0) + \int_{x_0}^{x} f(t) \, dt,$$

where the convergence is uniform on $[a, b]$. Since f is the limit of a uniformly convergent sequence of functions continuous on $[a, b]$, f is continuous on $[a, b]$, and it follows from the fundamental theorem of calculus that the right member of this equality is differentiable at x and has the derivative $f(x)$. Therefore, S is differentiable at x and

$$S'(x) = f(x) = \lim_{n \to +\infty} S_n'(x).$$

We now know that a sequence (or series) can be integrated term-by-term or differentiated term-by-term and the result will be a sequence (or series) whose limit (or sum) is the integral or derivative of the limit (or sum) of the given sequence (or series), provided certain conditions are satisfied. A power series converges uniformly on any circle smaller than its circle of convergence [Theorem 4-7.1]. Therefore, a power series can be integrated term-by-term between limits each of which is inside the circle of convergence. We shall show in the next theorem that the series obtained by term-by-term differentiation of a power series has the same radius of convergence as the given series. Therefore, a power series can be differentiated term-by-term at any point inside its circle of convergence.

THEOREM 4-8.3. If R is the radius of convergence of the power series $\sum_0^{+\infty} a_n x^n$, then each of the following power series, obtained by term-by-term differentiation and term-by-term integration, respectively, has radius of convergence equal to R:

$$\sum_{1}^{+\infty} na_n x^{n-1}, \qquad \sum_{0}^{+\infty} \frac{a_n}{n+1} x^{n+1}.$$

PROOF. Suppose $\sum_{0}^{+\infty} a_n x^n$ is a power series with radius of convergence R. If $0 < r < R$, then $\sum_{0}^{+\infty} |a_n r^n|$ is convergent. Also,

$$\lim_{n \to +\infty} \frac{na_n x^{n-1}}{a_n r^n} = \lim_{n \to +\infty} \frac{n}{r} \left(\frac{x}{r}\right)^{n-1} = 0 \quad \text{if} \quad |x| < r,$$

$$\lim_{n \to +\infty} \frac{[a_n/(n+1)]x^{n+1}}{a_n r^n} = \lim_{n \to +\infty} \frac{x}{n+1} \left(\frac{x}{r}\right)^{n} = 0 \quad \text{if} \quad |x| < r;$$

hence, it follows from Comparison Test II that each of the series $\sum_{1}^{+\infty} na_n x^{n-1}$ and $\sum_{0}^{+\infty} [a_n/(n+1)]x^{n+1}$ converges if $|x| < r$. Since this is true if r is any number less than R, each series has radius of convergence at least as large as R. That is, neither differentiation nor integration of a power series can decrease the radius of convergence. Therefore, neither can increase the radius of convergence, and thus our proof is complete.

ILLUSTRATION 3. We know that $e^x = \sum_{1}^{+\infty} x^n/n!$ for all x. Therefore,

$$xe^x = x + x^2 + \frac{x^3}{2!} + \frac{x^4}{3!} + \cdots,$$

and by differentiation we obtain

$$xe^x + e^x = 1 + 2x + \frac{3x^2}{2!} + \frac{4x^3}{3!} + \cdots.$$

In particular, when $x = 1$ we have

$$2e = 1 + \frac{2}{1!} + \frac{3}{2!} + \frac{4}{3!} + \cdots + \frac{n}{(n-1)!} + \cdots.$$

ILLUSTRATION 4. We know that

$$(1-x)^{-1} = 1 + x + x^2 + x^3 + \cdots + x^{n-1} + \cdots \quad \text{if} \quad |x| < 1. \quad (4\text{-}50)$$

By differentiation, we obtain

$$(1-x)^{-2} = 1 + 2x + 3x^2 + 4x^3 + \cdots + nx^{n-1} + \cdots$$

and

$$2(1-x)^{-3} = 2+2\cdot 3x+3\cdot 4x^2+4\cdot 5x^3+\cdots+n(n+1)x^{n-1}+\cdots,$$

both of which converge when $|x|<1$ [also see problem 10, page 189]. Now suppose we replace x in (4-50) by t and integrate with respect to t between the limits 0 and x, where $|x|<1$. Then we have

$$-\ln(1-x) = x+\frac{x^2}{2}+\frac{x^3}{3}+\frac{x^4}{4}+\cdots+\frac{x^n}{n}+\cdots.$$

Successive application of this process gives the following equalities:

$$(1-x)\ln(1-x)+x = \frac{x^2}{1\cdot 2}+\frac{x^3}{2\cdot 3}+\frac{x^4}{3\cdot 4}+\frac{x^5}{4\cdot 5}+\cdots+\frac{x^{n+1}}{n(n+1)}+\cdots,$$

$$(4\text{-}51)$$

$$-\frac{(1-x)^2}{2}\ln(1-x)-\frac{x}{2}+\frac{3x^2}{4}$$

$$= \frac{x^3}{1\cdot 2\cdot 3}+\frac{x^4}{2\cdot 3\cdot 4}+\cdots+\frac{x^{n+2}}{n(n+1)(n+2)}+\cdots.$$

The left member of (4-51) is continuous at $x=1$, if we define the value at $x=1$ to be $+1$. Since the right member converges at $x=1$, we can use Abel's limit theorem [Theorem 4-7.4] to obtain

$$1 = \frac{1}{1\cdot 2}+\frac{1}{2\cdot 3}+\frac{1}{3\cdot 4}+\frac{1}{4\cdot 5}+\cdots+\frac{1}{n(n+1)}+\cdots.$$

Often term-by-term integration of a sequence or a series is valid without uniform convergence or continuity of the terms or of the limit. The following theorem is considerably more general than Theorem 4.8.1. It might be called the *bounded convergence theorem* for Riemann integration [see Theorem 12-4.2].

THEOREM 4-8.4. Let $\{S_n\}$ be a sequence of functions and S be a function for which $\lim_{n\to+\infty} S_n(x) = S(x)$ for all x in $[a,b]$ except for points in a set of measure zero. Also, assume that there is a number M such that $|S_n(x)| \leq M$ for all n and for all x in $[a,b]$. If S and each S_n are Riemann integrable on $[a,b]$, then

$$\lim_{n\to+\infty}\int_a^b S_n(x)\,dx = \int_a^b S(x)\,dx. \qquad (4\text{-}52)$$

PROOF. We shall use a proof by contradiction. Assuming that (4-52) is false, there is a positive number ε such that, for infinitely many values of n,

$$\left| \int_a^b [S(x) - S_n(x)]\, dx \right| > \varepsilon. \tag{4-53}$$

Since S is integrable, S is bounded on $[a, b]$ and there is a number M' such that, for all n,

$$|S(x) - S_n(x)| \leq M' \quad \text{if} \quad x \in [a, b].$$

For an n that satisfies (4-53), $\int_a^b |S(x) - S_n(x)|\, dx > \varepsilon$ [see problem 4, page 151] and there is a partition of $[a, b]$ that determines an inner sum s_* greater than ε for the region under the graph of $|S - S_n|$. Then the sum of the widths of rectangles with altitudes greater than $\frac{1}{2}\varepsilon/(b-a)$ is greater than $\frac{1}{2}\varepsilon/M'$, since otherwise we could consider rectangles with altitudes greater than $\frac{1}{2}\varepsilon/(b-a)$, and those with altitudes not greater than $\frac{1}{2}\varepsilon/(b-a)$, to obtain

$$s_* \leq M' \frac{\frac{1}{2}\varepsilon}{M'} + \frac{\frac{1}{2}\varepsilon}{b-a}(b-a) = \varepsilon.$$

The union of the bases of the rectangles with altitudes greater than $\frac{1}{2}\varepsilon/(b-a)$ is a subset J_n of $[a, b]$ with the following properties:
   (i) J_n is the union of a finite number of intervals;
   (ii) the length of J_n is greater than $\frac{1}{2}\varepsilon/M'$;
   (iii) $|S(x) - S_n(x)| > \frac{1}{2}\varepsilon/(b-a)$ if $x \in J_n$.
It follows from (i) and (ii) that the set of points belonging to infinitely many of the sets J_n is not of measure zero [see problem 14]. This contradicts the hypothesis that $\lim S_n(x) = S(x)$ except on a set of measure zero, since if x satisfies (iii) for infinitely many values of n then it is not true that $\lim S_n(x) = S(x)$.

PROBLEMS

1. For each of the following, expand the integrand as a power series and integrate to obtain an infinite series whose sum is equal to the given integral.

(a) $\int_0^1 e^{-x^2}\, dx$.

(d) $\int_0^{1/2} (1 - x^4)^{1/2}\, dx$.

(b) $\int_0^1 \frac{\ln(1+x)}{x}\, dx$.

(e) $\int_0^1 \frac{\sin x}{x}\, dx$.

(c) $\int_0^1 \cos \sqrt{x}\, dx$.

(f) $\int_0^{1/2} \frac{1}{1 - x^2}\, dx$.

2. Use a power series formula for $(1-x^2)^{-\frac{1}{2}}$ to obtain a power series for $\sin^{-1} x$.

3. Use integration of a power series to show that

$$\sinh^{-1} x = x - \left(\frac{1}{2}\right)\frac{x^3}{3} + \left(\frac{1\cdot3}{2\cdot4}\right)\frac{x^5}{5} - \left(\frac{1\cdot3\cdot5}{2\cdot4\cdot6}\right)\frac{x^7}{7} + \cdots.$$

4. Verify directly that term-by-term differentiation of the binomial series for $2(1+x)^{\frac{1}{2}}$ gives the binomial series for $(1+x)^{-\frac{1}{2}}$.

5. Let $S(x) = \sum_1^{+\infty} n^{-x}$, where $x > 1$. Evaluate $S'(x)$ and $\int_2^x S(t)\, dt$ and justify the procedure used.

6. Integrate suitable series to evaluate the following.

(a) $\displaystyle\sum_1^{+\infty} \frac{1}{n(n+1)(n+2)}.$

(b) $\displaystyle\sum_1^{+\infty} \frac{1}{n(n+1)(n+2)(n+3)}.$

(c) $\displaystyle\sum_0^{+\infty} (-1)^n \frac{1}{2n+1}.$

(d) $\displaystyle\frac{1}{1\cdot2} - \frac{1}{2\cdot3} + \frac{1}{3\cdot4} - \frac{1}{4\cdot5} + \cdots.$

(e) $\displaystyle\frac{1}{1\cdot2} - \frac{1}{3\cdot4} + \frac{1}{5\cdot6} - \frac{1}{7\cdot8} + \cdots.$

(f) $\displaystyle\frac{1}{1\cdot2} + \frac{1}{3\cdot4} + \frac{1}{5\cdot6} + \frac{1}{7\cdot8} + \cdots.$

7. Evaluate the following.

(a) $\displaystyle\sum_0^{+\infty} \frac{(n+1)^2}{n!}.$

(b) $\displaystyle\sum_0^{+\infty} \frac{(n+1)(n+2)}{n!}.$

(c) $\displaystyle\sum_1^{+\infty} \frac{n(n+1)}{2^n}.$

(d) $\displaystyle\sum_1^{+\infty} \frac{n^2(n+1)^2}{2^n}.$

8. Explain the fallacy in the following "application" of Theorem 4-8.2. "Let $S_n(x) = x + (-1)^n$. Then $S_n'(x) = 1$ for all x, so $S'(x) = 1$ and there is a number c such that $S(x) = x + c$ and

$$\lim_{n\to+\infty} x + (-1)^n = x + c.$$

For the number $\frac{1}{2}$, there is a number n such that

$$|(x+c) - [x + (-1)^n]| < \tfrac{1}{2} \quad \text{and} \quad |(x+c) - [x + (-1)^{n+1}]| < \tfrac{1}{2}.$$

Now we obtain $|(-1)^{n+1} - (-1)^n| < 1$, or $2 < 1$, by subtracting the expressions inside the absolute value signs."

9. For each of the following, determine whether differentiation of each S_n at a point of the interval stated gives a sequence that converges to the derivative of the limit of the given sequence.

(a) $S_n(x) = \sum_1^n \dfrac{\cos kx}{k^2}$; $[\frac{1}{6}\pi, \frac{1}{2}\pi]$. (b) $S_n(x) = \dfrac{\sin nx}{\sqrt{n}}$; $[0, 1]$.

10. In each case, show that the sequence $\{S_1, S_2, \cdots\}$ does not converge uniformly on the interval $[-1, 1]$, but that

$$\int_{-1}^1 \left[\lim_{n \to +\infty} S_n(x)\, dx \right] = \lim_{n \to +\infty} \int_{-1}^1 S_n(x)\, dx.$$

[*Note:* This shows that term-by-term integration may yield a correct result even if the given sequence is not uniformly convergent.]

(a) $S_n(x) = (1-x^2)^n$. (b) $S_n(x) = n^2 x^2/(1+n^2 x^2)$.

11. Let $S_n(x) = n^2(x^{n-1} - x^n)$. Show that for each x in $[0, 1]$ there is a number $S(x)$ for which $\lim_{n \to +\infty} S_n(x) = S(x)$. Also show that the function S is continuous on $[0, 1]$, but that $\lim_{n \to +\infty} \int_0^1 S_n(x)\, dx \neq \int_0^1 S(x)\, dx$. [*Note:* This shows that to justify term-by-term integration one must assume more than existence and continuity of the limit function.]

12. Show that there are polynomials H_n of degree n (called *Hermite polynomials*) such that

$$e^{-t^2 + 2xt} = \sum_0^{+\infty} \frac{H_n(x)}{n!}\, t^n$$

for all real x and t. [*Hint:* Multiply the series for e^{-t^2} and e^{2xt}.]

13. For the Hermite polynomials of problem 12 show that

(a) $H_n' = 2nH_{n-1}$ for all n;

(b) $H_{n+1}(x) - 2xH_n(x) + 2nH_{n-1}(x) = 0$ for all n and x;

(c) H_n is a solution of the differential equation $y'' - 2xy' + 2ny = 0$;

(d) $D_x[e^{-x^2}H_n'(x)] = -2nH_n(x)e^{-x^2}$;

(e) $2mn \int_{-\infty}^{+\infty} H_m(x)H_n(x)e^{-x^2}\, dx = m \int_{-\infty}^{+\infty} H_m'(x)H_n'(x)e^{-x^2}\, dx$
$$= n \int_{-\infty}^{+\infty} H_m'(x)H_n'(x)e^{-x^2}\, dx;$$

(f) $\int_{-\infty}^{+\infty} H_m(x)H_n(x)e^{-x^2}\, dx = 0$ if $m \neq n$.

14. Suppose I is an interval and $\{U_n\}$ is a sequence of sets such that each U_n is the union of a finite number of intervals contained in I. Also suppose that $\varepsilon > 0$ and that $\ell(U_n) > \varepsilon$ for all n, where $\ell(U_n)$ is the length of U_n. Then $\sup \{\ell(\bigcup_{k=n}^p U_k): p > n\}$ is monotone decreasing in n and if θ is defined by

$$\theta = \lim_{n \to +\infty} \sup \left\{ \ell\left(\bigcup_{k=n}^p U_k \right): p > n \right\},$$

then $\theta \geq \varepsilon$. For sequences of positive numbers $\{\varepsilon_n\}$ and $\{\delta_n\}$, choose an increasing sequence of integers $\{m_i\}$ and a sequence of sets $\{V_i\}$ inductively so that

$$\sup\left\{\ell\left(\bigcup_{k=m_1}^{p} U_k\right): p > m_1\right\} < \theta + \varepsilon_1,$$

$$\ell(V_1) > \theta - \delta_1, \quad V_1 = \bigcup_{k=m_1}^{m_2} U_k;$$

$$\sup\left\{\ell\left(\bigcup_{k=m_3}^{p} U_k\right): p > m_3\right\} < \theta + \varepsilon_2,$$

$$\ell(V_2) > \theta - \delta_2, \quad V_2 = \bigcup_{k=m_3}^{m_4} U_k;$$

. . .

$$\sup\left\{\ell\left(\bigcup_{k=m_{2n-1}}^{p} U_k\right): p > m_{2n-1}\right\} < \theta + \varepsilon_n,$$

$$\ell(V_n) > \theta - \delta_n, \quad V_n = \bigcup_{k=m_{2n-1}}^{m_{2n}} U_k;$$

Prove each of the following.

(a) $V_1 - (\bigcap_1^{+\infty} V_n) \subset (V_1 - V_2) \cup (V_2 - V_3) \cup (V_3 - V_4) \cup \cdots$.

(b) $\ell(V_n - V_{n+1}) < \varepsilon_n + \delta_{n+1}$ for all n.

(c) If each W_n is a union of open intervals and $V_1 \subset \bigcup_1^{+\infty} W_n$, then $\sum_1^{+\infty} \ell(W_n) \geq \theta - \delta_1$. [*Hint:* Use the Heine-Borel theorem.]

(d) $\bigcap_1^{+\infty} V_n$ is not of measure zero if $\sum_1^{+\infty} (\varepsilon_n + \delta_{n+1}) < \theta - \delta_1$.

(e) Each member of $\bigcap_1^{+\infty} V_n$ belongs to infinitely many of the sets U_n.

4-9. CHANGE OF ORDER OF LIMITS AND DIFFERENTIATION OR INTEGRATION

The nth term $S_n(x)$ of a sequence can be thought of as being the value at the point (x, n) of a function f for which $f(x, n) = S_n(x)$ for all x and n. The domain of f is restricted to points (x, n) for which x is in some given set D and n is a positive integer. We now wish to consider functions whose domains need not be of this type. For limits of type $\lim_{n \to +\infty} S_n(x)$, a *stage* is the set of all positive integers larger than some designated number α. In this section, we shall use general systems of stages and specify the nature of the stages when dealing with specific examples. We shall also understand that the second variable in a functional symbol denotes members of a stage. For example, for a particular value of x we shall use $\lim_S f(x, t)$ to denote a limit relative to the system of stages S, with t used to denote members of a specific stage. The definition of uniform convergence for sequences can be generalized in the following way.

DEFINITION 4-9.1. A function of two variables *uniformly convergent on a set* D with respect to a system of stages S is a function f with the following properties.

(i) $\lim_S f(x, t) = L(x)$ exists for all x in D.

(ii) For any positive number ε, there is a stage A such that

$$|L(x) - f(x, t)| < \varepsilon \quad \text{if} \quad t \in A \quad \text{and} \quad x \in D.$$

ILLUSTRATION 1. Suppose $f(x, t) = (\sin tx)/t$ if $t \neq 0$. For this illustration, we use the system of stages consisting of deleted neighborhoods of 0. It follows from Taylor's theorem that there is a number ξ between 0 and tx such that

$$\sin tx = tx - \frac{(tx)^3}{3!} \cos \xi.$$

Therefore,

$$\left| x - \frac{\sin tx}{t} \right| \leqq \frac{t^2 |x|^3}{3!},$$

and $\lim_{t \to 0} f(x, t) = x$ for all x. If $|x| \leq M$, then

$$\left| x - \frac{\sin tx}{t} \right| \leqq \frac{t^2 M^3}{3!}.$$

This implies that the convergence is uniform on the set $D = \{x \colon |x| \leqq M\}$.

The theorems of the last two sections dealing with continuity, integration, and differentiation of sequences and series can be generalized as follows.

THEOREM 4-9.1. Suppose f is a function of two variables and S is a system of stages with respect to which $f \to L$ uniformly on some neighborhood of x_0. Also suppose that there is a stage A such that for each t in A the function of one variable whose value at x is $f(x, t)$ is continuous at x_0. Then L is continuous at x_0.

THEOREM 4-9.2. Suppose f is a function of two variables and S is a system of stages with respect to which $f \to L$ uniformly on an interval $[a, b]$. Also suppose that there is a stage A such that for each t

in A the function of one variable whose value at x is $f(x, t)$ is continuous at each point of $[a, b]$. Then

$$\lim_S \int_a^b f(x, t)\, dx = \int_a^b L(x)\, dx.$$

Also, $\lim_S \int_a^x f(u, t)\, du = \int_a^x L(u)\, du$ for all x in $[a, b]$ and the convergence to the limit is uniform on $[a, b]$.

THEOREM 4-9.3. Suppose f is a function of two variables and S is a system of stages for which there is a stage A such that for each t in A the function of one variable whose value at x is $\partial f(x, t)/\partial x$ is continuous at each point of an interval $[a, b]$. Also suppose that there is a number x_0 in $[a, b]$ such that $\lim_S f(x_0, t)$ exists and that, for this system of stages, $\partial f/\partial x$ converges uniformly on $[a, b]$ to a limit l. Then f converges uniformly on $[a, b]$ to a limit L for which

$$L'(x) = \lim_S \frac{\partial f(x, t)}{\partial x} \quad \text{if} \quad x \in [a, b].$$

Theorems 4-9.2 and 4-9.3 are summarized in Fig. 4-3, which may help the student test understanding of these theorems. In this figure, the conclusions of the theorems are in boldface type, the hypotheses in ordinary type.

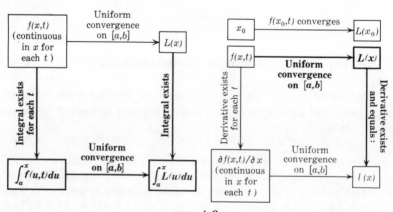

FIG. 4-3

The proofs of these theorems are analogous to the proofs of the corresponding theorems for sequences. We shall give one proof to illustrate the analogy, and leave the other to the student.

PROOF OF THEOREM 4-9.2. Let us suppose that f is a function of two variables for which $f \to L$ uniformly on an interval $[a, b]$ with respect to a system of stages S, and that for each t in some stage A the function of one variable whose value at x is $f(x, t)$ is continuous at each point of $[a, b]$. Then it follows from Theorem 4-9.1 that L is continuous on $[a, b]$, so that $\int_a^b L(x)\, dx$ exists. Since $f \to L$ uniformly on the interval $[a, b]$ with respect to the system of stages S, for any positive number ε_1 there is a stage A such that if $t \in A$ then

$$|L(x) - f(x, t)| < \varepsilon_1 \quad \text{for all } x \text{ in } [a, b].$$

Then

$$\left| \int_a^x L(u)\, du - \int_a^x f(u, t)\, du \right| \leq \left| \int_a^x |L(u) - f(u, t)|\, du \right| \leq \varepsilon_1 |b - a|.$$

Now for a positive number ε, we can choose the number ε_1 so that $\varepsilon_1 |b - a| < \varepsilon$. Then the stage A has the property that

$$\left| \int_a^x L(u)\, du - \int_a^x f(u, t)\, du \right| < \varepsilon \quad \text{if} \quad t \in A.$$

That is, $\lim_S \int_a^x f(u, t)\, du = \int_a^x L(u)\, du$ and this limit is approached uniformly on $[a, b]$. This completes the proof.

ILLUSTRATION 2. Suppose $f(x, t) = (\sin tx)/t$ if $t \neq 0$. Then f converges uniformly on any finite interval to the function whose value at x is x [see Illustration 1]. Therefore, for the interval $[0, 1]$ we can use Theorem 4-9.2 and obtain

$$\lim_{t \to 0} \int_0^1 \frac{\sin tx}{t}\, dx = \int_0^1 x\, dx = \frac{1}{2}, \quad \text{or} \quad \lim_{t \to 0} \frac{1 - \cos t}{t^2} = \frac{1}{2}.$$

PROBLEMS

1. For each of the following, show either that the limit is uniform on the interval stated or that the limit is not uniform.

(a) $\displaystyle\lim_{t \to +\infty} \frac{1}{1 + tx}$; $[0, 2]$.

(b) $\displaystyle\lim_{t \to \pi} \sin(tx)$; $[0, 10]$.

(c) $\displaystyle\lim_{t \to +\infty} e^{-tx}$; $x > 0$.

(d) $\displaystyle\lim_{t \to 0} \frac{\sin tx}{x^2}$; $(0, \pi]$.

(e) $\displaystyle\lim_{t \to 0} \frac{\sin tx}{t}$; $x \geq 0$.

(f) $\displaystyle\lim_{t \to 3} \frac{t + x}{1 + tx}$; $[0, 1]$.

2. For each of the following, show that the limit is uniform on the interval $[0, 1]$ and verify directly that $\lim_{t \to 0} \int_0^1 f(x, t) \, dx = \int_0^1 [\lim_{t \to 0} f(x, t)] \, dx$.

(a) $f(x, t) = \dfrac{\sin tx}{t}$.

(c) $f(x, t) = \left(\dfrac{e^{tx} - (1 + tx)}{t^2} \right) e^x$.

(b) $f(x, t) = \dfrac{\sin tx}{t} e^x$.

(d) $f(x, t) = \dfrac{\ln (1 + tx)}{t}$.

3. For each of the following, show that the convergence is uniform on the interval $[1, 2]$ and verify directly that $\lim_{t \to +\infty} \int_1^2 f(x, t) \, dx = \int_1^2 [\lim_{t \to +\infty} f(x, t)] \, dx$.

(a) $f(x, t) = \dfrac{\sin tx}{t}$.

(b) $f(x, t) = e^{-tx}$.

4. Explain why the following is not a true statement, but is not a contradiction to Theorem 4-9.3

$$D_x \left[\lim_{t \to 0} \frac{\cos tx}{t} \right] = \lim_{t \to 0} D_x \left[\frac{\cos tx}{t} \right] = 0.$$

5

MULTIPLE
INTEGRATION

5-1. VOLUME

The concept of area is intimately related to the concept of definite integral. In much the same way, the concept of volume is intimately related to the concept of double integral. Therefore, it is natural to discuss volume before discussing double integrals. This will be done sketchily, with those proofs omitted that are similar to those for the corresponding theorems about area.

DEFINITION 5-1.1. Suppose B is a set of points and $\{R_1, R_2, \cdots, R_n\}$ is a set of rectangular parallelepipeds, no two of which overlap and each of which is contained in B. Also suppose a_i, b_i, and c_i are the lengths of three adjacent edges of R_i. Then $\sum_{i=1}^{n} a_i b_i c_i$ is a 3-D *inner sum* for the set B.

DEFINITION 5-1.2. Suppose B is a set of points and $\{R_1, R_2, \cdots, R_n\}$ is a set of rectangular parallelepipeds whose union contains B. Also suppose a_i, b_i, and c_i are the lengths of three adjacent edges of R_i. Then $\sum_{i=1}^{n} a_i b_i c_i$ is a 3-D *outer sum* for the set B.

DEFINITION 5-1.3. A *set of points that has volume* is a set of points for which there exists at least one 3-D outer sum and

$$\sup \text{(inner sums)} = \inf \text{(outer sums)}.$$

The *volume* (or 3-D *content*) of a set having volume is the common value of [sup (inner sums)] and [inf (outer sums)].

For the facts about length and area, there are corresponding facts about volume that can be proved by similar methods. These facts make up I, II, and Theorem 5-1.1.

I. If B is a bounded set of points in R^3 and s_* and s^* are inner and outer sums for B, then $s_* \leqq s^*$.

II. If A and B are sets that have volume, then $A \cap B$, $B - A$, and $A \cup B$ have volume. If $A \cap B = \Phi$, then the volume of $A \cup B$ is the sum of the volumes of A and B.

The conditions for a set to have area all have analogous statements for volume that can be proved by similar methods. These are listed in the following theorem. For this theorem, we need to extend the definitions of system of rectangles and partition of a plane set. A *system of rectangular parallelepipeds* with *mesh* σ is a set of rectangular parallelepipeds formed by three families of parallel planes that divide R^3 into rectangular parallelepipeds for which σ is the least upper bound of the lengths of edges of these parallelepipeds and there is a positive lower bound for these lengths. For a set T that has volume, a *partition* of T is a set $\{T_1, T_2, \cdots, T_n\}$ whose members are subsets of T that have volume, whose union is T, and for which $T_i \cap T_j$ has zero volume if $i \neq j$. The *fineness* of a partition is the number

$$\sup \{d(p, q): p \text{ and } q \text{ in the same set of the partition}\}.$$

For a set B, the *inner sum determined by a partition* of a set T that contains B is the sum of the volumes of all members of the partition that are contained in B, and the *outer sum determined by a partition* of a set T that contains B is the sum of the volumes of all members of the partition that contain points of B.

THEOREM 5-1.1. For a bounded set B in R^3, each of the following is a necessary and sufficient condition for B to have volume.

(i) For each positive number ε, there exist inner and outer sums s_* and s^* for B such that $s^* - s_* < \varepsilon$.

(ii) For each positive number ε, there is a positive number δ such that, if s_* and s^* are the inner and outer sums determined by a system of rectangular parallelepipeds with mesh less than δ, then $s^* - s_* < \varepsilon$.

(iii) For each positive number ε, there are sets A and C that have volume and for which $A \subset B \subset C$ and the volume of $C - A$ is less than ε.

(iv) For each positive number ε, there is a positive number δ such that $s^* - s_* < \varepsilon$ if s_* and s^* are the inner and outer sums determined by a partition with fineness less than δ of a set containing B.

There are many ways in which definite integrals can be used to evaluate volumes. The next theorem provides a simple method that often is useful.

THEOREM 5-1.2.   Suppose W is a set that has volume. Also suppose L is a directed line and that the symbol t denotes distances of points along this line from some fixed point on the line. If the plane perpendicular to L at t intersects W in a set that has area equal to $A(t)$, then

$$\text{(volume of } W) = \int_a^b A(t)\, dt,$$

where the numbers a and b are any two numbers for which W is between the plane perpendicular to L at a and the plane perpendicular to L at b.

PROOF.   All we need to show is that, for any positive number ε, there is a positive number Δ such that, for any partition of $[a, b]$ of fineness less than Δ, we have

$$|\text{(volume of } W) - \sum_i A(\tau_i)\, \Delta_i t| < \varepsilon. \tag{5-1}$$

This can be accomplished by choosing Δ small enough that if s_* and s^* are the 3-D inner and outer sums determined by a system of rectangular parallelepipeds whose mesh is less than Δ, then $s^* - s_* < \varepsilon$. To show this, we shall choose a partition of $[a, b]$ that determines subintervals of length less than Δ. We shall use planes perpendicular to L at the

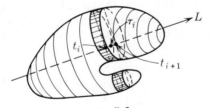

FIG. 5-1

division points of this partition and other planes perpendicular to these planes to form a system of rectangular parallelepipeds whose mesh is less than Δ. Now we can use this system of rectangular parallelepipeds to determine 3-D inner and outer sums s_{i*} and s_i^* for the slab bounded by planes through t_i and t_{i+1} [see Fig. 5-1]. Then, since $s_{i*}/\Delta_i t$ and $s_i^*/\Delta_i t$ are inner and outer sums for $A(\tau_i)$, we have

$$s_{i*} \leqq A(\tau_i)\, \Delta_i t \leqq s_i^*,$$

if $\tau_i \in [t_i, t_{i+1}]$. When we add these for each slab, we obtain

$$s_* \leqq \sum_i A(\tau_i) \Delta_i t \leqq s^*.$$

Since $s^* - s_* < \varepsilon$, and both $\sum_i A(\tau_i) \Delta_i t$ and the volume of W are in the interval $[s_*, s^*]$, inequality (5-1) must be true.

ILLUSTRATION 1. A solid W has a base that is a circle of radius r and one diameter of this circle has the property that the intersection of W and a plane perpendicular to this diameter is a square.

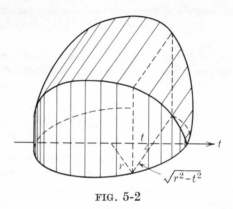

FIG. 5-2

We can choose coordinates on the line that contains this diameter, with the origin at the center of the circle [see Fig. 5-2]. The side of the square in the plane perpendicular to the t-axis at the point t is of length $2(r^2 - t^2)^{1/2}$ and the area of this square is $4(r^2 - t^2)$. Therefore, the volume of W is

$$\int_{-r}^{r} 4(r^2 - t^2)\, dt = \left[4(r^2 t - \tfrac{1}{3} t^3) \right]_{-r}^{r} = \frac{16r^3}{3}.$$

ILLUSTRATION 2. A solid W is generated by rotating the region bounded by a circle of radius r about a line T at distance a from the center of the circle. We can choose coordinates on T so that the plane perpendicular to T at the origin passes through the center of the circle, as shown in Fig. 5-3. The intersection of W and a plane perpendicular to T is the region between two concentric circles whose radii are $a + (r^2 - t^2)^{1/2}$ and $a - (r^2 - t^2)^{1/2}$. Therefore, the area of this region is

$$\pi[a + (r^2 - t^2)^{1/2}]^2 - \pi[a - (r^2 - t^2)^{1/2}]^2 = 4\pi a(r^2 - t^2)^{1/2},$$

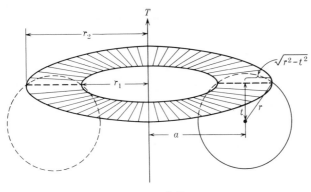

FIG. 5-3

and we can compute the volume of W as

$$\int_{-r}^{+r} 4\pi a(r^2 - t^2)^{1/2}\, dt = 2\pi^2 r^2 a.$$

In these examples we have not shown that the set involved actually has volume. In the next section, we shall prove theorems that could be used to establish the existence of volume in all these cases [Theorems 5-2.1 and 5-2.3]. For the next illustration, we shall continue to assume that the given set has volume.

ILLUSTRATION 3. Suppose W is the region in the first octant that is inside the cylinder whose equation is $x^2 + y^2 = 4$ and under the surface whose equation is $z = 2xy$ [see Fig. 5-4]. Then a plane

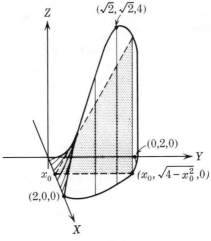

FIG. 5-4

perpendicular to the x-axis at the point $(x_0, 0, 0)$ cuts a section from W whose area is

$$A(x_0) = \int_0^{\sqrt{4-x_0^2}} (2x_0 y)\, dy = \left[x_0 y^2 \right]_0^{\sqrt{4-x_0^2}} = 4x_0 - x_0^3.$$

Therefore, the volume of W is equal to

$$\int_0^2 (4x - x^3)\, dx = \left[2x^2 - \frac{1}{4} x^4 \right]_0^2 = 4.$$

PROBLEMS

1. Derive the usual formula for the volume of a cone.

2. For each of the following, compute the volume of the solid generated by rotating about the x-axis the region between the graphs of f and g.
   (**a**) $f(x) = 3x, g(x) = 0, 0 \leqq x \leqq 2$.
   (**b**) $f(x) = x^2, g(x) = 1, 0 \leqq x \leqq 1$.

3. A plane perpendicular to the x-axis at a point between $(0, 0)$ and $(1, 0)$ intersects a solid W in a circular disk that has a diameter that is in the first quadrant of the (x, y)-plane and joins points of the graphs of $y = x^2$ and $y^2 = x$. Find the volume of the solid.

4. The sections of a solid in planes perpendicular to the x-axis are circles with diameters that extend from the graph of $y = x^2$ to the graph of $y = 8 - x^2$. The solid lies between the two planes perpendicular to the x-axis which contain the points of intersection of these curves. Find the volume of the solid.

5. Let R be the region bounded by the x-axis and the arc of the graph of $y = \sin x$ that joins the points $(0, 0)$ and $(\pi, 0)$. Find the volume of the solid that is generated by rotating R about (**a**) the x-axis; (**b**) the line $y = -1$.

6. Let W be the ellipsoid that is the set of all points (x, y, z) for which

$$\frac{x^2}{a^2} + \frac{y^2}{b^2} + \frac{z^2}{c^2} = 1.$$

Show that the volume of the region bounded by W is $\frac{4}{3}\pi abc$. [Assume that the area of an ellipse is πab if the semi-axes are a and b.]

7. For each of the following, assume that the set described has volume and find the volume.
   (**a**) $\{(x, y, z): (x^2 + y^2 \leqq 9) \text{ and } (0 \leqq z \leqq 7 - 2x)\}$.

(**b**) The set of all points that are under the graph of $z = 2x + y^2$, above the (x, y)-plane, and inside the cylinder bounded by the planes whose equations are $y = 0$, $y = x$, and $x + 2y = 2$.

8. Show that a bounded plane set has volume and that the volume is zero, whether or not the set has area.

9. Prove that a bounded set in R^3 has volume if and only if the boundary of the set has volume and the volume is zero. [See problem 5, page 126, and problem 11, page 133.]

10.* Explain why a set is bounded if it has volume.

11. Prove the following theorem: "Suppose W is a plane set that has area. Also suppose L is a directed line in the plane and that the symbol t denotes distances of points along this line from some fixed point on the line. If the line perpendicular to L at t intersects W in a set that has length equal to $\ell(t)$, then the area of W is $\int_a^b \ell(t)\, dt$, where the numbers a and b are any two numbers for which W is between the line perpendicular to L at a and the line perpendicular to L at b."

5-2. DOUBLE INTEGRALS

We shall now introduce the double integral and show its close relation to volume and to Theorem 5-1.2. The theory of double integrals is similar to the theory of definite integrals in many respects. The student can benefit greatly from comparing the following discussion with that of definite integrals in Section 3-4.

In Section 3-2, we defined a partition of a plane set R with area to be a set $\{\Delta_1 R, \Delta_2 R, \cdots, \Delta_n R\}$ whose members are subsets of R that have area and whose union is R, and for which $(\Delta_i R) \cap (\Delta_j R)$ has zero area if $i \neq j$. A *partition with selection* is an ordered pair

$$s = (\{\Delta_1 R, \Delta_2 R, \cdots, \Delta_n R\}, \ \{p_1, p_2, \cdots, p_n\}), \tag{5-2}$$

whose first member is a partition $\{\Delta_1 R, \Delta_2 R, \cdots, \Delta_n R\}$ of R and whose second member is an ordered set $\{p_1, p_2, \cdots, p_n\}$ with the property that, for each i, the point p_i is in the set $\Delta_i R$.

Suppose we denote the area of $\Delta_i R$ by $\Delta_i A$. For a function f whose domain includes R, we define a function F by

$$F(s) = \sum_{i=1}^{n} f(p_i)\, \Delta_i A,$$

so that the domain of F is the set of all partitions with selection. This sum is called a *Riemann sum*.

The *fineness* of a partition $\{\Delta_1 R, \Delta_2 R, \cdots, \Delta_n R\}$ is the number

$$\sup \{d(p, q): p \text{ and } q \text{ in the same set of the partition}\}.$$

For s a partition with selection, we shall let $\delta(s)$ denote the fineness of the partition that is the first member of s. Now we shall let S be the system of stages for which A is a stage if there is a positive number Δ for which $A = \{s: \delta(s) < \Delta\}$. Then we define $\lim_{\delta \to 0} \sum_{i=1}^{n} f(p_i) \, \Delta_i A = l$, or $\lim_{\delta \to 0} F(s) = l$, to mean that $\lim_S F = l$.

DEFINITION 5-2.1. A *Riemann integrable function* on a plane set R is a function f such that $\lim_{\delta \to 0} \sum_{i=1}^{n} f(p_i) \, \Delta_i A$ exists. For an integrable function f, the value of this limit is the *double integral* of f over R and is denoted by the symbol

$$\int_R f(p) \, dA.$$

Suppose we let f be a function for which $f(p) \geqq 0$ if p is in R. Then suppose we form a Riemann sum using a partition of R. If $\Delta_i A$ is the area of a region $\Delta_i R$, then the term $f(p_i) \, \Delta_i A$ is the volume of a rectangular parallelepiped if $\Delta_i R$ is a rectangle [see Fig. 5-5]. It is the

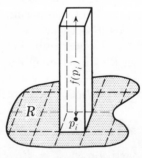

FIG. 5-5

volume of a cylindrical solid if $\Delta_i R$ is not a rectangle [see problem 7]. As in the proof of Theorem 3-4.1, if

$$m_i = \inf \{f(p): p \in \Delta_i R\}, \quad M_i = \sup \{f(p): p \in \Delta_i R\}, \quad (5\text{-}3)$$

then the two numbers $m_i \, \Delta_i A$ and $M_i \, \Delta_i A$ are, respectively, terms of a 3-D inner and a 3-D outer sum for the region between R and the graph of f. This suggests a proof of the following theorem.

THEOREM 5-2.1. Suppose R is a plane set with area and suppose f is a function such that $f(p) \geqq 0$ if $p \in R$. Then f is Riemann integrable on R if and only if the region between R and the graph of f has volume.

PROOF. We shall assume first that f is Riemann integrable on R. Then, for any positive number ε, there is a partition of R (such as indicated in Fig. 5-5), for which

$$\left| \int_R f(p)\, dA - \sum f(p_i)\, \Delta_i A \right| < \tfrac{1}{3}\varepsilon,$$

for any points p_i in the respective subsets $\Delta_i R$ with area $\Delta_i A$. We shall leave it to the student to show that $|f|$ is bounded on R [problem 8]. It then follows that the numbers m_i and M_i of (5-3) exist. Also,

$$\left| \int_R f(p)\, dA - \sum m_i\, \Delta_i A \right| \leqq \tfrac{1}{3}\varepsilon, \qquad \left| \int_R f(p)\, dA - \sum M_i\, \Delta_i A \right| \leqq \tfrac{1}{3}\varepsilon.$$

It follows from these inequalities that $\sum M_i\, \Delta_i A - \sum m_i\, \Delta_i A < \varepsilon$. The numbers $\sum m_i\, \Delta_i A$ and $\sum M_i\, \Delta_i A$ are volumes of sets A and C, respectively, for which $A \subset B \subset C$ and the volume of $C - A$ is less than ε. Therefore, it follows from Theorem 5-1.1(iii) that W has volume.

Now let us assume that W has volume. For an arbitrary positive number ε, let δ be a positive number such that $s^* - s_* < \varepsilon$ if s_* and s^* are the 3-D inner and outer sums for W determined by a partition with fineness less than δ of a set containing W [see Theorem 5-1.1(iv)]. Let $\{\Delta_1 R, \Delta_2 R, \cdots, \Delta_n R\}$ be a partition of R with fineness less than $\delta/\sqrt{2}$. Since W is bounded [see problem 10, page 243], there is a plane Π parallel to the plane of R such that W is contained in the cylinder with base R and top in the plane Π. Now we form a partition of this cylinder by dividing all cylinders with sets $\Delta_i R$ as bases into pieces by planes that are parallel to Π with the distance between successive planes less than $\delta/\sqrt{2}$. This partition has fineness less than δ, so $s^* - s_* < \varepsilon$ if s_* and s^* are the 3-D inner and outer sums determined for W. Also,

$$s_* \leqq \sum f(p_i)\, \Delta_i A \leqq s^*$$

for any points $\{p_i\}$ in the respective sets $\{\Delta_i R\}$. Since

$$s_* \leqq (\text{volume of } W) \leqq s^*,$$

we then have $|(\text{volume of } W) - \sum f(p_i)\, \Delta_i A| < \varepsilon$. Therefore, $\int_R f(p)\, dA$ exists and is the volume of W.

We shall now state several properties of double integrals. These properties and their proofs are similar to the corresponding properties discussed in Section 3-5 for definite integrals.

(i) For any number c, $\int_R cf(p)\, dA = c \int_R f(p)\, dA$ if f is integrable on R.

(ii) $\int_R [f(p) + g(p)]\, dA = \int_R f(p)\, dA + \int_R g(p)\, dA$ if f and g are integrable on R.

(iii) $\int_{R_1} f(p)\, dA + \int_{R_2} f(p)\, dA = \int_{R_1 \cup R_2} f(p)\, dA$ if the area of the set $R_1 \cap R_2$ is zero and the first two integrals exist.

(iv) $\int_R |f(p)|\, dA$ exists if $\int_R f(p)\, dA$ exists.

If a function is not known to be positive everywhere on a set R, then we can define f^+ and f^- as in Section 3-5 and obtain a theorem similar to Theorem 3-5.1. The changes we need to make in the proof of Theorem 3-5.1 to give a proof of Theorem 5-2.2 are so natural that we shall leave the details to the student.

THEOREM 5-2.2. Suppose R is a plane set with area and that f is a function whose domain contains R. Each of the following is a necessary and sufficient condition for f to be integrable on R:
 (i) f^+ and f^- are integrable on R;
 (ii) the region W between R and the graph of f has volume.
If f is integrable on R, then $\int_R f(p)\, dA$ is equal to the volume of the region between R and the graph of f^+ *minus* the volume of the region between R and the graph of f^-, that is, the volume of the part of W on the positive side of the plane containing R *minus* the volume of the part of W on the negative side of this plane.

The next theorem and its proof are very similar to Theorem 3-3.1(ii) and its proof.

THEOREM 5-2.3. Suppose R is a compact plane set with area. If f is continuous on R, then f is integrable on R.

PROOF. Because of Theorem 5-2.2, it is sufficient to treat only the case for which $f(p) \geq 0$ if $p \in R$. Let ε be an arbitrary positive number. Since R is compact and f is continuous on R, we know that f is uniformly continuous on R [Theorem 2-3.3]. Therefore, there is a positive number δ such that, if p and q are in R, then

$$|f(p) - f(q)| < \frac{\varepsilon}{\text{area of } R} \quad \text{if} \quad d(p, q) < \delta. \tag{5-4}$$

Now choose a partition $\{\Delta_1 R, \cdots, \Delta_n R\}$ of R with fineness less than δ. Since $|f|$ is bounded on R [Theorem 2-8.2], the following numbers exist:

$$m_i = \inf\{f(p) : p \in \Delta_i R\}, \qquad M_i = \sup\{f(p) : p \in \Delta_i R\}.$$

Also, it follows from (5-4) that $M_i - m_i \leq \varepsilon/(\text{area of } R)$. Therefore,

$$\sum M_i \, \Delta_i A - \sum m_i \, \Delta_i A \leq \frac{\varepsilon}{\text{area of } R} \sum \Delta_i A = \varepsilon.$$

Since $\sum m_i \, \Delta_i A$ and $\sum M_i \, \Delta_i A$ are volumes of sets A and C with $A \subset W \subset C$, it follows from (iii) of Theorem 5-1.1 that W has volume. Then it follows from Theorem 5-2.1 that f is integrable on R.

Theorem 5-2.3 is a special case of the next theorem. It was stated and proved to demonstrate the effectiveness of uniform continuity in proving integrability for continuous functions. As was done in the proof of Theorem 3-3.3, the use of uniform continuity can be replaced by direct use of the Heine-Borel theorem when proving Theorem 5-2.4. We shall not prove Theorem 5-2.4, since such a proof would be essentially a translation of the arguments used to obtain Theorem 3-5.2. To establish Theorem 3-5.2, we first proved Theorems 3-3.2 and 3-3.3. These were then used to prove Theorem 3-3.4, which easily gave Theorem 3-5.2. Using the following definition, it is easy to retrace these steps and prove Theorem 5-2.4.† Note that the definition of oscillation of a function [Definition 3-3.2] applies to functions whose domains are plane sets.

DEFINITION 5-2.2. A plane set of 2-D *measure zero* is a plane set B such that for each positive number ε there is a sequence of rectangles R_n such that $B \subset \cup R_n$ and $\sum_{n=1}^{+\infty} (\text{area of } R_n)$ is less than ε.

THEOREM 5-2.4. Suppose R is a plane set that has area and that f is a function whose domain contains R. If f is bounded on R, then f is Riemann integrable on R if and only if the set of discontinuities of f in R is of 2-D measure zero.

---

† The Heine-Borel theorem was used in proving Theorems 3-3.3 and 3-3.4. Since R in Theorem 5-2.4 need not be closed, some adjustment must be made before the Heine-Borel theorem can be used as it was in proving Theorems 3-3.3 and 3-3.4. One technique is to introduce a function ϕ defined by $\phi(x, y) = f(x, y)$ if $(x, y) \in R$ and $\phi(x, y) = 0$ if $(x, y) \notin R$. Then it is easy to show that f is integrable on R if and only if ϕ is integrable on any set that contains R and has area, and that the set of discontinuities of f in R is of 2-D measure zero if and only if the set of discontinuities of ϕ is of 2-D measure zero [see problem 12]. Thus, it is sufficient to prove Theorem 5-2.4 for R closed—in fact, R a cube, if we wish.

To evaluate a double integral, one usually uses two definite integrals evaluated in succession, a process described and justified by the following theorem. In stating this theorem, we have used the convention that $\int f(x, y) \, dx$ is to be evaluated for a constant value of y and, for this value y_0, is equal to the integral of $f(x, y_0)$ over the intersection of R and the line $y = y_0$ in the (x, y)-plane [see Definition 3-5.1]. Now, if we define a function F by

$$F(y) = \int f(x, y) \, dx,$$

then $F(y_0)$ is the difference of the areas of the regions in the plane $y = y_0$ which are above and below the (x, y)-plane, respectively, and between the (x, y)-plane and the graph of $z = f(x, y)$ [see Fig. 5-6].

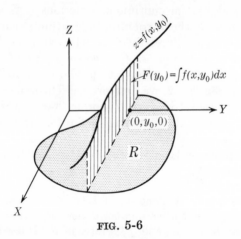

FIG. 5-6

With c and d numbers such that R is between the lines $y = c$ and $y = d$ in the (x, y)-plane, we use

$$\int \left[\int f(x, y) \, dx \right] dy \quad \text{or} \quad \int \int f(x, y) \, dx \, dy$$

to denote $\int_c^d F(y) \, dy$. This notation is inadequate by itself and must be supplemented by suitable information about the nature of R.

THEOREM 5-2.5. Suppose R is a set in the (x, y)-plane that has area and that the intersection of R and any line parallel to the x-axis is a set that has length. Also suppose that f is bounded and integrable on

R, and that, for any y_0, the function whose value at x is $f(x, y_0)$ is integrable on the intersection of R and the line $y = y_0$. Then

$$\int_R f(p) \, dA = \int \left[\int f(x, y) \, dx \right] dy. \qquad (5\text{-}5)$$

PROOF. We shall use the functions f^+ and f^- that have been useful so often. Since f^+ is continuous wherever f is continuous, it follows from Theorems 5-2.4 and 5-2.1 that $\int_R f^+(p) \, dA$ exists and is equal to the volume of the region W^+ between R and the graph of f^+. Similarly, the function with value $f^+(x, y_0)$ at (x, y_0), when $(x, y_0) \in R$, is integrable on the set R_{y_0} that is the intersection of R and the line $y = y_0$ in the (x, y)-plane. Also, $\int_{R_{y_0}} f^+(x, y_0) \, dx$ is the area of the intersection of W^+ and the plane $y = y_0$. Therefore, if R_y denotes the set of points in R with ordinates y, and if we choose numbers c and d such that R is between the lines $y = c$ and $y = d$ in the (x, y)-plane, then it follows from Theorem 5-1.2 that

$$\int_R f^+(p) \, dA = \int_c^d \left[\int_{R_y} f^+(x, y) \, dx \right] dy.$$

Similarly,

$$\int_R f^-(p) \, dA = \int_c^d \left[\int_{R_y} f^-(x, y) \, dx \right] dy.$$

Now we can obtain (5-5) by subtracting the first members and subtracting the last members of these equalities.

ILLUSTRATION 1. The solid of Fig. 5-7 has vertical sides, its top is in the plane whose equation is $z = 2y - x + 2$, and its base is the triangle bounded by the x- and y-axes and the line whose equation is $x + y = 2$. For any x between 0 and 2, y varies between 0 and $2 - x$. Therefore, the volume is

$$\int_0^2 \left[\int_0^{2-x} (2y - x + 2) \, dy \right] dx = \int_0^2 [(2-x)^2 - x(2-x) + 2(2-x)] \, dx$$

$$= \int_0^2 (2x^2 - 8x + 8) \, dx = \frac{16}{3}.$$

ILLUSTRATION 2. Suppose we wish to evaluate $\int_R (2y - x) \, dA$, where R is the region illustrated in Fig. 5-8. For a particular value of x, y varies from x^2 to $x + 2$. Therefore, we can write the given double integral as

$$\int_{-1}^2 \left[\int_{x^2}^{x+2} (2y - x) \, dy \right] dx.$$

Since

$$\int_{x^2}^{x+2} (2y-x)\, dy = \left[y^2-xy\right]_{y=x^2}^{y=x+2} = [(x+2)^2 - x(x+2)] - [x^4 - x^3]$$

$$= -x^4 + x^3 + 2x + 4,$$

the given integral is equal to

$$\int_{-1}^{2} (-x^4 + x^3 + 2x + 4)\, dx = 12.15.$$

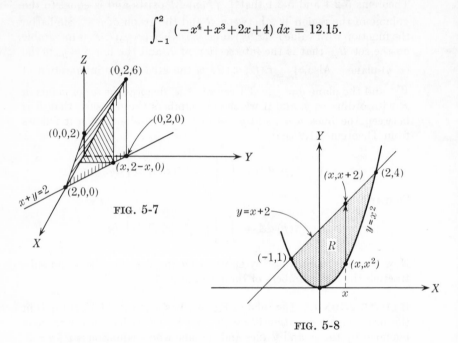

FIG. 5-7

FIG. 5-8

PROBLEMS

1. For each of the following, evaluate the double integral of the given function over the region indicated. (*a*) $x^{1/2} + y - 3x^2y$; R bounded by the graphs of $x = 0$, $x = 1$, $y = 1$, and $y = 3$. (*b*) $y + 2x$; R bounded by the graphs of $y^2 = x$ and $y^2 = 4 - x$. (*c*) $4 - x^2 - 4y^2$; R bounded by the graphs of $x = 0$, $y = 0$, and $x + 2y = 2$.

2. For each of the following, determine the volume of W. (*a*) W is the set of points under the graph of $z = x + 2$ and above the region in the (x, y)-plane bounded by the graphs of $y = x$ and $x^2 = y + 2$. (*b*) W is in the first octant and bounded above by the graph of $z = 16 - x^2 - 4y^2$ and below by the (x, y)-plane. (*c*) W is the piece of the solid cylinder $x^2 + y^2 \leqq a^2$ which is bounded below by the (x, y)-plane and above by the graph of $z = 3x^2 + y^2$.

3. Evaluate the following "iterated" integrals.

(a) $\displaystyle\int_0^3 \int_0^y y\, dx\, dy.$

(b) $\displaystyle\int_{-2}^2 \int_{-\sqrt{4-y^2}}^{\sqrt{4-y^2}} 3\, dx\, dy.$

(c) $\displaystyle\int_{-2}^2 \int_{x^2}^4 (x+2y)\, dy\, dx.$

4. Express each iterated integral of problem 3 as an equivalent iterated integral with dx and dy interchanged. Evaluate each.

5. Express the following as a single iterated integral with dx and dy interchanged and evaluate the integral.

$$\int_0^1 \int_{-y^{1/2}}^{y^{1/2}} (1+x)\, dx\, dy + \int_1^4 \int_{y-2}^{y^{1/2}} (1+x)\, dx\, dy.$$

6. Change the order of integration and evaluate

$$\int_{-1}^1 \int_{|y|}^1 (x+2y)\, dx\, dy.$$

7. Let $f(p) = c$ for all p. Prove that f is integrable on any set R that has area and that $\int_R f(p)\, dA = c \cdot (\text{area of } R)$.

8. Prove that $|f|$ is bounded on R if f is integrable on R.

9. Let m and M be two numbers for which $m \leq f(p) \leq M$ if $p \in R$. Show that if $\int_R f(p)\, dA$ exists, then

$$m(\text{area of } R) \leq \int_R f(p)\, dA \leq M(\text{area of } R).$$

10. Let f be a function that is continuous at a point p_0 in the (x, y)-plane. Explain why f^+ and f^- are continuous at p_0.

11. Let $W = W_1 \cup W_2$, where

$W_1 = \{(x, y, z)\colon x \text{ is rational, } 0 \leq x \leq 1, 0 \leq y \leq 1, \text{ and } 0 \leq z \leq 1\};$

$W_2 = \{(x, y, z)\colon x \text{ is irrational, } 0 \leq x \leq 1,$

$$-1 \leq y \leq 0, \text{ and } 0 \leq z \leq 1\}.$$

(a) Describe a function f and a rectangle R in the (x, y)-plane such that the set W is the region between R and the graph of f. (b) Show that $\int f(x, y)\, dy = 1$ if $0 \leq x \leq 1$ and f is the function of part (a), and that $\int \int f(x, y)\, dy\, dx = 1$, but that $\int_R f(p)\, dA$ does not exist.

12. Suppose the domain D of f is a set that has area. Let $\phi(x, y)$ $= f(x, y)$ if $(x, y) \in D$ and $\phi(x, y) = 0$ if $(x, y) \notin D$. Let A and B be the sets of discontinuities of f and ϕ, respectively, and prove (a) the set of numbers that are discontinuities of ϕ and not of f has area zero; (b) A is of 2-D measure zero if and only if B is of 2-D measure zero. [See problem 12, page 151.]

5-3. IMPROPER DOUBLE INTEGRALS

We can extend the concept of volume to unbounded sets much as we extended the concept of area in Section 3-7.

DEFINITION 5-3.1. An *unbounded set with volume* is an unbounded set R that has the two properties:
(i) $R \cap S$ has volume if S is a bounded set that has volume.
(ii) The following set has an upper bound:

$$\{(\text{volume of } R \cap S): S \text{ a bounded set with volume}\}.$$

When R has volume, the least upper bound of this set is the *volume* of R.

As for area, when we wish to determine whether a set has volume and when we wish to determine the volume of a set, we need methods that do not demand consideration of the intersection with R of all bounded sets that have volume. This is given by the following theorem.

THEOREM 5-3.1. Suppose that R is an unbounded set and that $\{S_1, S_2, \cdots\}$ is a sequence of bounded sets with volume such that $S_k \cap R$ has volume and $S_k \subset S_{k+1}$ for all k. Also suppose that, for any bounded set S, there is a k such that $(S \cap R) \subset (S_k \cap R)$. Then

$$(\text{volume of } R) = \lim_{k \to +\infty} (\text{volume of } S_k \cap R), \qquad (5\text{-}6)$$

where one member of this equality exists if and only if the other exists.

PROOF. We shall let V_k denote the volume of $S_k \cap R$. Since $\{V_k\}$ is a monotone increasing sequence, $\lim_{k \to +\infty} V_k$ exists if and only if the sequence $\{V_k\}$ has an upper bound. Also, for any bounded set S with volume, there is a k such that $S \cap R$ is a subset of $S_k \cap R$. Since $S_k \cap R$ and S each have volume, and $S \cap R = S \cap (S_k \cap R)$, it follows

that $S \cap R$ has volume.   Therefore, (i) of Definition 5-3.1 is satisfied.
Also, when $S \cap R$ is a subset of $S_k \cap R$, we have

$$(\text{volume of } S \cap R) \leq V_k.$$

Therefore, (ii) of Definition 5-3.1 is satisfied if and only if $\lim_{k \to +\infty} V_k$
exists.   This is the same as saying that one member of (5-6) exists if
and only if the other exists.   If $\lim_{k \to +\infty} V_k = l$, then l is the least
upper bound of the set $\{V_k\}$ and is therefore the least upper bound of
the volumes of sets of type $S \cap R$, where S has volume.   This
completes the proof.

ILLUSTRATION 1.   Suppose that $f(x, y) = y^2/(x^2+1)^3$ at points of the
unbounded wedge W of Fig. 5-9, and that R is the region between the

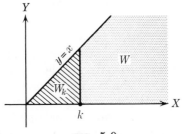

FIG. 5-9

graph of f and the wedge W.   We shall let W_k denote the triangle cut
from W by the line $x = k$ and let V_k denote the volume of the region
between the graph of f and the triangle W_k.   Then

$$V_k = \int_{W_k} \frac{y^2}{(x^2+1)^3} \, dA$$

$$= \int_0^k \int_0^x \frac{y^2}{(x^2+1)^3} \, dy \, dx = \frac{1}{3} \int_0^k \frac{x^3}{(x^2+1)^3} \, dx.$$

With $x^2+1 = t$, this integral becomes

$$\frac{1}{6} \int_1^{k^2+1} \left(\frac{t-1}{t^3} \right) dt = \frac{1}{6} \left[-\frac{1}{t} + \frac{1}{2t^2} \right]_1^{k^2+1}$$

$$= \frac{1}{12} - \frac{1}{6} \left[\frac{1}{k^2+1} - \frac{1}{2(k^2+1)^2} \right].$$

This approaches $\frac{1}{12}$ as k increases and we can conclude that the volume
of R is $\frac{1}{12}$.

A double integral, $\int_W f(p)\,dA$, may fail to exist if f is not continuous. It does fail to exist if f is not bounded on W, or if W is not a bounded set. As in Section 3-7, it is convenient to use "positive and negative parts" of a function to define improper double integrals. For a function f whose domain is a set in the (x, y)-plane, the functions f^+ and f^- are defined by the following familiar rules: If $f(x, y) \geqq 0$, then $f^+(x, y) = f(x, y)$ and $f^-(x, y) = 0$. If $f(x, y) \leqq 0$, then $f^+(x, y) = 0$ and $f^-(x, y) = -f(x, y)$.

DEFINITION 5-3.2. Suppose that f is a function whose domain includes all of a set W of the (x, y)-plane except for a set of zero area. Also suppose that f is not integrable over W. Then the *improper integral*, $\int_W f(p)\,dA$, is equal to the volume of the region between W and the graph of f^+ *minus* the volume of the region between W and the graph of f^-, if both of these regions have volume.

This definition is practical to use along with Theorem 5-3.1 to determine whether improper integrals exist over unbounded sets. For bounded sets, it is convenient to use the following theorem. This theorem and its proof are similar to Theorem 3-7.2 and its proof. In the statement of the theorem and the illustrative examples that follow, the symbol c denotes an ordinary real number. It is not difficult to change the theorem and its proof so as to apply to limits on the left, and also for $c = +\infty$ with r a positive integer.

THEOREM 5-3.2. Suppose W is a set in the (x, y)-plane that has area and D_r is a collection of sets with area. Also let us suppose that W is a bounded set and f has no negative values on W, f is integrable on $W - D_r$ for each $r > c$, $D_s \subset D_t$ if $c < s < t$, and

$$\lim_{r \to c+} (\text{area of } D_r) = 0.$$

Then

$$\int_W f(p)\,dA = \lim_{r \to c+} \int_{W - D_r} f(p)\,dA,$$

if either member of this equality exists.

PROOF. Since f has no negative values, we know that $\int_W f(p)\,dA$ exists if and only if the region R between W and the graph of f has volume. Let us choose a rectangle that contains W, and for each positive integer

k let S_k be a rectangular parallelepiped with this rectangle as its bottom face and the top face in the plane $z = k$. If $R_k = S_k \cap R$, then R_k has volume.†   Also, since (volume of R_k) $\leq k$(area of D_r)$+\int_{W-D_r} f(p)\, dA$, we have

$$\text{(volume of } R_k) \leq \lim_{r \to c+} \int_{W-D_r} f(p)\, dA,$$

if this limit exists. Therefore, if this limit exists then it follows from Theorem 5-3.1 that R has volume and that the volume of R is the least upper bound of the volumes of all R_k's, so that

$$\text{(volume of } R) \leq \lim_{r \to c+} \int_{W-D_r} f(p)\, dA.$$

Now let us suppose that R has volume. Since $\int_{W-D_r} f(p)\, dA$ is the volume of a subset of R, it follows that this integral is not greater than the volume of R. If $s < t,$ then $D_s \subset D_t$ and $W - D_s \supset W - D_t$. Therefore, $\int_{W-D_r} f(p)\, dA$ is monotone increasing as $r \to c+$, as well as never being greater than the volume of R. This implies that the limit of the integral exists and

$$\lim_{r \to c+} \int_{W-D_r} f(p)\, dA \leq \text{(volume of } R).$$

We have shown that if either member of the two preceding inequalities exists, then the other exists and both inequalities are true statements. When both inequalities are true, they must be equalities.

ILLUSTRATION 2.   Suppose $f(x, y) = 1/x$ for (x, y) in the triangle T of Fig. 5-10. The only point of discontinuity is at $(0, 0)$. If we let D_r denote the hatched part of T in the first diagram, then

$$\int_{T-D_r} \frac{1}{x}\, dA = \int_r^1 \int_0^x \frac{1}{x}\, dy\, dx = \int_r^1 dx = 1-r.$$

---

† This can be shown as follows. If $R_{k,r}$ is the part of R_k between $W - D_r$ and the graph of f, then $R_{k,r}$ has volume because it is the intersection of S_k and the region between the graph of the integrable function f and the set $W - D_r$. Also, $R_k - R_{k,r}$ is contained in a set whose volume is k(area of D_r). That R_k has volume now follows from (iii) of Theorem 5-1.1, with $A = R_{k,r}$ and C the union of $R_{k,r}$ and this set with volume k(area of D_r).

Since $\lim_{r \to 0} (1 - r) = 1$, we may conclude that $\int_T x^{-1} \, dA = 1$. Similarly, if D_r is the hatched region in the second diagram of Fig. 5-10, then

$$\int_{T - D_r} \frac{1}{x} \, dA = \int_r^1 \int_r^x \frac{1}{x} \, dy \, dx = \int_r^1 \left(1 - \frac{r}{x}\right) dx = 1 - r + r \ln r,$$

which again approaches 1 as r approaches zero.

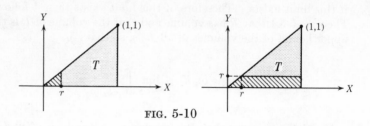

FIG. 5-10

ILLUSTRATION 3. Suppose $f(x, y) = |x - y|^{-\frac{1}{2}}$ for (x, y) in the square S in the (x, y)-plane of Fig. 5-11. We can let D_r be the strip between the lines whose equations are $y = x \pm r$. Then

$$\int_{S - D_r} |x - y|^{-\frac{1}{2}} \, dA = 2 \int_r^1 \int_0^{x - r} (x - y)^{-\frac{1}{2}} \, dy \, dx$$

$$= 4 \int_r^1 \left[-(x - y)^{\frac{1}{2}} \right]_0^{x - r} dx = 4 \int_r^1 (x^{\frac{1}{2}} - r^{\frac{1}{2}}) \, dx$$

$$= 4 \left[\frac{2}{3} x^{\frac{3}{2}} - r^{\frac{1}{2}} x \right]_r^1 = \frac{8}{3} - 4 r^{\frac{1}{2}} + \frac{4}{3} r^{\frac{3}{2}}.$$

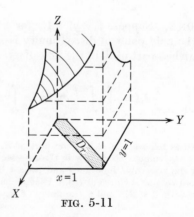

FIG. 5-11

Since this approaches $\frac{8}{3}$ as r approaches zero, we can conclude that

$$\int_S |x-y|^{-\frac{1}{2}} \, dA = \tfrac{8}{3}.$$

Sometimes an iterated integral can have the order of integration changed without changing the value of the integral. However, caution must be used. The next theorem describes a situation for which caution is not needed, i.e., when the double integral of f exists.

THEOREM 5-3.3. Suppose R is a set (possibly unbounded) in the (x, y)-plane that has area, and that the intersection of R and any line parallel to the x-axis is a set (possibly unbounded) that has length. Also suppose that either f is integrable on R or the improper integral of f over R exists, and that, for any y_0, the function whose value at x is $f(x, y_0)$ either is integrable on the intersection of R and the line $y = y_0$ or its improper integral exists over this set. Then

$$\int_R f(p) \, dA = \int \left[\int f(x, y) \, dx \right] dy.$$

PROOF. If f is integrable over R or if the improper integral of f over R exists, then this integral is equal to the volume of the region between R and the graph of f^+ *minus* the volume of the region between R and the graph of f^- [see Definition 5-3.2]. Suppose f is zero at all points not in R, and let S_{mn} be the rectangle $\{(x, y): |x| \leqq m \text{ and } |y| \leqq n\}$. Also, let f_k^+ be defined for $k > 0$ by

$$f_k^+(p) = \text{minimum } \{f^+(p), \, k\}.$$

Now we can use Theorem 5-3.1 to obtain

$$\int_R f^+(p) \, dA = \sup_{(m,n,k)} \int_{-n}^{+n} \left[\int_{-m}^{+m} f_k^+(p) \, dx \right] dy.$$

Since, for any function f of three variables,

$$\sup \{f(n, m, k): (n, m, k)\} = \sup_n \left\{ \sup_m \left[\sup_k f\left(n, m, k\right) \right] \right\},$$

we can use Theorem 3-7.1 to replace f_k^+ by f^+ and then let $m \to +\infty$ and $n \to +\infty$ to obtain

$$\int_R f^+(p) \, dA = \sup_{(m,n)} \int_{-n}^{+n} \left[\int_{-m}^{+m} f^+(p) \, dx \right] dy = \int_{-\infty}^{+\infty} \left[\int_{-\infty}^{+\infty} f^+(p) \, dx \right] dy.$$

Now this equality for f^+ and a similar one for f^- can be combined to complete the proof.

ILLUSTRATION 4. Let R be the "rectangle" containing all points (x, y) with $x \geq 0$ and $0 \leq y \leq 1$. Since $|e^{-x} \sin xy| \leq e^{-x}$ and e^{-x} is integrable on R, we know that $e^{-x} \sin xy$ is integrable on R. We also have

$$\int_0^{+\infty} \left[\int_0^1 e^{-x} \sin xy \, dy \right] dx = \int_0^{+\infty} \frac{e^{-x}(1 - \cos x)}{x} \, dx,$$

and

$$\int_0^1 \left[\int_0^{+\infty} e^{-x} \sin xy \, dx \right] dy = \int_0^1 \left[\frac{-e^{-x} \sin xy - y e^{-x} \cos xy}{1 + y^2} \right]_0^{+\infty} dy$$

$$= \int_0^1 \frac{y}{1 + y^2} \, dy = \tfrac{1}{2} \ln 2.$$

Therefore,

$$\int_0^{+\infty} \frac{e^{-x}(1 - \cos x)}{x} \, dx = \tfrac{1}{2} \ln 2.$$

PROBLEMS

1. Let R be the region in the (x, y)-plane which is to the right of the line $x = 1$ and between the x-axis and the graph of $y = x^{-2/3}$. (a) Does R have area? Why? (b) Show that the set generated by rotating R about the x-axis has volume and the volume is 3π.

2. Evaluate the following double integrals.

    (a) $\qquad\qquad\qquad\qquad \int_R x^{-1/2} \, dA;$

$R = \{(x, y): 0 \leq x \leq 1 \text{ and } 0 \leq y \leq 1\}.$

    (b) $\qquad\qquad\qquad\qquad \int_R xy \cdot e^{-(x^2 + y^2)} \, dA;$

R the region in the first quadrant between the graphs of $y = 0$ and $y = 1$.

    (c) $\qquad\qquad\qquad\qquad \int_R \left(\frac{1}{x^2(1 - x)} \right) dA;$

R the region between the graphs of $y = x$ and $y = -x + 2$ which is to the right of the point $(1, 1)$.

3. For each of the following, let R be the region in the (x, y)-plane between the x-axis and the line $y = 1$. Determine whether the region between R and the graph of the given function has volume.

(a) $(x^2 + 1)^{-4}$.   (b) $x^{-\frac{1}{2}}$.   (c) $(x^2 + y^2)^{-\frac{1}{2}}$.   (d) x^{-2}.

4. Let $f(x, y) = 1/x$ if $x \neq 0$ and $f(0, y) = 0$. Also, let T be the triangle in the (x, y)-plane whose vertices are $(0, 0)$, $(1, 1)$, and $(-1, 1)$. Determine whether $\int_T f(x, y)\, dA$ exists.

5. Let $R = \{(x, y)\colon x \geq 1 \text{ and } y \geq 1\}$. (a) Prove that $\int_R x^{-2} y^{-2}\, dA = 1$. (b) Use part (a) and show that $\sum_{m, n = 1}^{+\infty} m^{-2} n^{-2}$ is convergent, whatever order is used for the terms.

6.* Suppose $\int_W f(p)\, dA$ exists, either as an ordinary double integral or as an improper double integral. Prove that, for any positive number ε, there is a positive number δ such that

$$\int_D f(p)\, dA < \varepsilon \text{ if } D \subset W \text{ and area}(D) < \delta.$$

[Also see problem 9, page 167.]

7. Let $R = \{(x, y)\colon x \geq 0 \text{ and } 1 \leq y \leq k\}$. By integrating e^{-xy} over R in two different ways, prove that

$$\int_0^{+\infty} \frac{e^{-x} - e^{-kx}}{x}\, dx = \ln k \text{ if } k > 0.$$

[Also see problem 7, page 167.]

8.* Let $R = \{(x, y)\colon 0 \leq x \leq n\pi \text{ and } y \geq 0\}$. By integrating $(\sin x)e^{-xy}$ in two different ways, prove that

$$\int_0^{n\pi} \frac{\sin x}{x}\, dx = \int_0^{+\infty} \frac{1 - (-1)^n e^{-n\pi y}}{1 + y^2}\, dy, \qquad \int_0^{+\infty} \frac{\sin x}{x}\, dx = \frac{\pi}{2}.$$

5-4.   TRIPLE INTEGRALS

The definition and theory of triple integrals are similar to that for double integrals. Therefore, we shall omit many of the details.

For a three-dimensional set R that has volume, a *partition* of R is a set $\{\Delta_1 R, \Delta_2 R, \cdots, \Delta_n R\}$ whose members are subsets of R that have volume, whose union is R, and for which $(\Delta_i R) \cap (\Delta_j R)$ has zero volume if $i \neq j$. A *partition with selection* is an ordered pair

$$s = (\{\Delta_1 R, \Delta_2 R, \cdots, \Delta_n R\}, \{p_1, p_2, \cdots, p_n\})$$

whose first member is a partition $\{\Delta_1 R, \Delta_2 R, \cdots, \Delta_n R\}$ of R and whose second member is an ordered set $\{p_1, p_2, \cdots, p_n\}$ with the property that, for each i, the point p_i is in the set $\Delta_i R$.

Let us denote the volume of $\Delta_i R$ by $\Delta_i V$. For a function f whose domain includes R, we shall define a function F by

$$F(s) = \sum_{i=1}^{n} f(p_i) \Delta_i V,$$

so that the domain of F is the set of all partitions with selection. This sum is called a *Riemann sum*.

The *fineness* of a partition $\{\Delta_1 R, \Delta_2 R, \cdots, \Delta_n R\}$ is the number

$$\sup \{d(p, q): p \text{ and } q \text{ in the same set of the partition}\}.$$

For s a partition with selection, we shall let $\delta(s)$ denote the fineness of the partition that is the first member of s. Now we can let S be the system of stages for which A is a stage if there is a positive number Δ such that $A = \{s: \delta(s) < \Delta\}$. Then we can define $\lim_{\delta \to 0} \sum_{i=1}^{n} f(p_i) \Delta_i V = l$, or $\lim_{\delta \to 0} F(s) = l$, to mean that $\lim_S F = l$.

DEFINITION 5-4.1. $\forall$ *Riemann integrable function* on a three-dimensional set R is a function f such that $\lim_{\delta \to 0} \sum_{i=1}^{n} f(p_i) \Delta_i V$ exists. For an integrable function f, the value of this limit is the *triple integral* of f over R and is denoted by the symbol $\int_R f(p) \, dV$.

Four-dimensional volume can be defined analogously to three-dimensional volume and two-dimensional area. Then Theorem 5-2.1 can be generalized to triple integrals, and it can be shown that the triple integral of a function that is nonnegative on a three-dimensional set R that has volume exists if and only if the region between R and the graph of f has four-dimensional volume, and that if this triple integral exists it is equal to this four-dimensional volume. Also, Theorem 5-2.4 can be generalized to show that, if R is a three-dimensional set with volume, then a bounded function f whose domain contains R is Riemann integrable on R if and only if the set of discontinuities of f in R is of 3-D measure zero. We shall leave it to the student to provide a definition of "set of 3-D measure zero" and the missing details of this argument if he wishes.

To evaluate a triple integral, three definite integrals evaluated in succession are generally used. This process is justified by the following theorem. When the details of the foregoing discussion are known, a proof of this theorem can be given that is very similar to the proof of Theorem 5-2.5. We shall omit the proof, but the student if he wishes may satisfy his curiosity by reading the proof of Theorem 5-2.5 carefully.

THEOREM 5-4.1. Suppose R is a set that has volume and that the intersection of R and any plane perpendicular to the z-axis has area. Also suppose that $|f|$ is bounded and integrable on R and that, for any z_0, the function whose value at (x, y) is $f(x, y, z_0)$ is integrable on the intersection of R and the plane $z = z_0$. Then

$$\int_R f(p) \, dV = \int \left[\int\!\!\int_{z \text{ constant}} f(x, y, z) \, dA \right] dz. \tag{5-7}$$

If it is also true that each line parallel to the x-axis intersects R in a set that has length and that, for any (y_0, z_0), the function whose value at x is $f(x, y_0, z_0)$ is integrable on the intersection of R and the line, $y = y_0$, $z = z_0$, then

$$\int_R f(p) \, dV = \int \left\{ \int \left[\int f(x, y, z) \, dx \right] dy \right\} dz. \tag{5-8}$$

The notation used in this theorem needs some explanation. The double integral in Eq. (5-7), $\int_{z \text{ constant}} f(x, y, z) \, dA$, is to be evaluated for a constant value z_0 of z and, for this value of z, is equal to the double integral of $f(x, y, z_0)$ over the intersection of R and the plane $z = z_0$. We could define a function F by

$$F(z) = \int_{z \text{ constant}} f(x, y, z) \, dA.$$

If a and b are numbers such that R is entirely between the planes $z = a$ and $z = b$, then we can write

$$\int_a^b F(z) \, dz \quad \text{as} \quad \int \left[\int\!\!\int_{z \text{ constant}} f(x, y, z) \, dA \right] dz.$$

This notation is inadequate by itself and must be supplemented by suitable information about the nature of R. Equation (5-8) can be derived from Eq. (5-7) by evaluating the double integral in (5-7) as two successive definite integrals, as described in Section 5-2. Then

$$\int_{z \text{ constant}} f(x, y, z) \, dA = \int \left[\int f(x, y, z) \, dx \right] dy = \int \left[\int f(x, y, z) \, dy \right] dx.$$

ILLUSTRATION 1. The plane whose equation is $2x+4y+3z=12$ cuts from the first octant a region R. The volume of this region is $\int_R dV$. If we write this triple integral as $\int \left[\int \int_{z\ \text{constant}} dA \right] dz$, then the double integral is simply the area of the triangle indicated in Fig. 5-12. This area is equal to $\frac{1}{2}(6-\frac{3}{2}z)(3-\frac{3}{4}z)$, so that the volume is equal to

$$\int_0^4 \frac{1}{2}(6-\tfrac{3}{2}z)(3-\tfrac{3}{4}z)\,dz = \frac{9}{16}\int_0^4 (4-z)^2\,dz = 12.$$

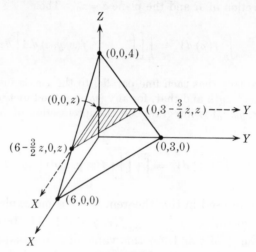

FIG. 5-12

Alternatively, we could determine the area of the triangle by double integration. In the plane $z=z_0$ and with respect to x- and y-axes introduced in this plane, the triangle is bounded by the x-axis, the y-axis, and the line whose equation is $2x+4y+3z_0=12$. Therefore, the area is given by

$$\int_0^{3-\frac{3}{4}z_0} \left[\int_0^{6-2y-\frac{3}{2}z_0} dx \right] dy,$$

and the volume of the given region R is

$$\int_0^4 \int_0^{3-\frac{3}{4}z} \int_0^{6-2y-\frac{3}{2}z} dx\,dy\,dz = \int_0^4 \int_0^{3-\frac{3}{4}z} (6-2y-\tfrac{3}{2}z)\,dy\,dz$$

$$= \int_0^4 [6y-y^2-\tfrac{3}{2}yz]_0^{3-\frac{3}{4}z}\,dz$$

$$= \int_0^4 (3-\tfrac{3}{4}z)^2\,dz = 12.$$

ILLUSTRATION 2. Suppose we wish to determine the mass of the region R bounded by the paraboloid whose equation is $z = x^2 + 4y^2$, and the plane whose equation is $2y + 5z = 6$, given that the density is equal to $10|x|$. This means that the mass of R is equal to the triple integral, $\int_R 10|x| \, dV$. In this case, it is not convenient to intersect R with planes perpendicular to the z-axis, since such intersections are sometimes bounded by a curve in the paraboloid and sometimes by curves partly in the paraboloid and partly in the plane. There is also a complication if we use planes perpendicular to the x-axis, since the point of R with the largest x-coordinate is not in the (x, z)-plane. Therefore, we shall use planes perpendicular to the y-axis and write

$$\int_R 10|x| \, dV = \int_{-3/5}^{1/2} \left[\int\!\!\!\int_{y \text{ constant}} 10|x| \, dA \right] dy.$$

The intersection of a plane $y = y_0$ and the region R is indicated in Fig. 5-13. If we imagine x- and z-axes in this plane, then the boundary of this intersection consists of pieces of the straight line and the parabola whose equations are

$$2y_0 + 5z = 6 \quad \text{and} \quad z = x^2 + 4y_0^2. \tag{5-9}$$

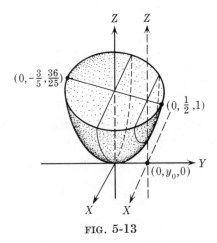

FIG. 5-13

The double integral over this intersection is equal to

$$\int_{4y_0^2}^{(6-2y_0)/5} \left[\int_{-\sqrt{z - 4y_0^2}}^{\sqrt{z - 4y_0^2}} 10|x| \, dx \right] dz, \tag{5-10}$$

where the limits on the inner integral are determined from the equation $z = x^2 + 4y_0^2$, and the limits on the outer integral are determined by putting $x = 0$ in the equations in (5-9). This double integral can be interpreted as being the mass of the intersection of R and the plane $y = y_0$, with the two-dimensional density at points of this plane region equal to $10|x|$. Also, the inner integral of (5-10) can be interpreted as being the mass of a vertical line segment extending from the paraboloid to the plane, with the linear density at points of this segment equal to $10|x|$. Since both the intersection of R with the plane $y = y_0$ and the density are symmetric about the (y, z)-plane, it suffices to integrate over only the half of the region for which x is positive, provided we double the result. By doing this, we can eliminate the absolute value signs and obtain the following expression for the mass of R:

$$2 \int_{-3/5}^{1/2} \int_{4y^2}^{(6-2y)/5} \int_{0}^{(z-4y^2)^{1/2}} 10x \, dx \, dz \, dy$$

$$= 2 \int_{-3/5}^{1/2} \int_{4y^2}^{(6-2y)/5} (5z - 20y^2) \, dz \, dy$$

$$= \tfrac{4}{5} \int_{-3/5}^{1/2} (9 - 6y - 59y^2 + 20y^3 + 100y^4) \, dy = 4.2947 - .$$

PROBLEMS

1. Let R be the tetrahedron with vertices $(1, 1, 0)$, $(1, 3, 0)$, $(2, 3, 0)$, $(1, 3, 3)$. For each of the following, evaluate the triple integral over R of the given function. Choose a convenient order of integration.

   (**a**) 5.   (**b**) y^2.   (**c**) z.   (**d**) $2z - 3y$.

2. Evaluate $\iiint |xyz| \, dx \, dy \, dz$ over the region bounded by the ellipsoid whose equation is $\tfrac{1}{2}x^2 + \tfrac{1}{3}y^2 + \tfrac{1}{4}z^2 = 1$.

3. Determine the mass of the ellipsoid whose equation is

$$\frac{x^2}{a^2} + \frac{y^2}{b^2} + \frac{z^2}{c^2} = 1,$$

if the density is equal to $16|x|$ at all points.

4.* Determine the four-dimensional volume of a four-dimensional sphere of radius r.

5. Evaluate the following triple integral by writing it as an integral with respect to x of a double integral evaluated over a region in a plane $x = $ constant:

$$\int_{-2}^{2} \int_{-\sqrt{4-y^2}}^{\sqrt{4-y^2}} \int_{y^2+z^2}^{4} dx \, dz \, dy.$$

6. Use a triple integral to determine the volume of the region bounded by the elliptic paraboloids whose equations are $z = x^2 + 3y^2$ and $z = 18 - x^2 - 3y^2$.

7. Use a triple integral to determine the volume of the region bounded by the elliptic paraboloids whose equations are $z = 8 - x^2 - y^2$ and $z = x^2 + 3y^2$.

8. Determine the volume of the region that is inside the elliptic cylinder with equation $x^2 + 2y^2 = 4$ and between the graphs of $x + z = 2$ and $x + 2y + z + 6 = 0$.

9. For each of the following, express the given triple integral as a triple integral such that the successive integrals are in the order indicated and evaluate the integral.

(a) $\displaystyle\int_0^1 \int_0^2 \int_0^{2-x} z^4 \, dz \, dx \, dy$ in the order y, x, z.

(b) $\displaystyle\int_0^1 \int_0^{3z} \int_{2+\frac{2}{3}y-2z}^2 x^2 \, dx \, dy \, dz$ in the order y, z, x.

(c) $\displaystyle\int_{-2}^2 \int_{\frac{1}{2}y-3}^{1-y} \int_{-\sqrt{4-y^2}}^{\sqrt{4-y^2}} |x|^5 \, dx \, dz \, dy$ in the order z, y, x.

10. Express the following triple integral as a triple integral with integrals in the order y, z, x:

$$\int_{-3}^1 \int_{z^2}^{3-2z} \int_{-\sqrt{y-z^2}}^{\sqrt{y-z^2}} f(x, y, z) \, dx \, dy \, dz.$$

11. Let f be a function that is continuous on a neighborhood of the point $P_0 = (x_0, y_0, z_0)$. For each positive number ε, let R be a set that has nonzero volume $|R|$ and is contained in the ε-neighborhood of P_0. Show that

$$\lim_{\varepsilon \to 0} \frac{1}{|R|} \int_R f(x, y, z) \, dV = f(x_0, y_0, z_0).$$

5-5. SOME APPLICATIONS OF INTEGRATION

There are many uses of definite integration for which the definition of definite integral given in Section 3-4 is not directly applicable. In this section we shall study a useful generalization of this definition, which first we shall illustrate with a discussion of the problem of determining the volume of a solid of revolution by the *cylindrical shell method*. We know that the volume of a set W can be expressed as $\int_a^b A(t) \, dt$, where a plane perpendicular to the t-axis at t intersects W in a set with area $A(t)$, and W is between the planes perpendicular to the t-axis at a and b, respectively [Theorem 5-1.2]. Often the area of a section of a solid of revolution in a plane perpendicular to the axis of rotation can be determined easily. However, there are many examples for which the cylindrical shell method is more practical.

Suppose a cylindrical shell is generated by rotating about the y-axis a rectangle of width Δx and altitude h, as shown in Fig. 5-14(a). If ξ is the distance from the y-axis to the center of the rectangle, then the area of the base of the cylindrical shell (i.e., the area of a horizontal section) is equal to

$$\pi(\xi + \tfrac{1}{2}\,\Delta x)^2 - \pi(\xi - \tfrac{1}{2}\,\Delta x)^2 \;=\; (2\pi\xi)\,\Delta x.$$

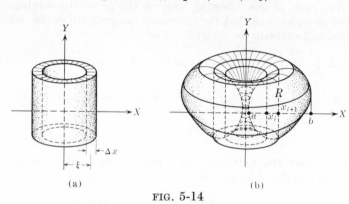

(a)   (b)

FIG. 5-14

The volume is the product of the area of the base and the altitude. Now let us suppose that a solid is generated by rotating about the y-axis a region R of the (x, y)-plane lying entirely between two lines, $x = a$ and $x = b$, where neither a nor b is negative. Also suppose that the vertical line through $(x, 0)$ interests the region R in a line segment of length $h(x)$, where h is a continuous function. If R is divided into strips parallel to the y-axis, then a typical strip between $x = x_i$ and $x = x_{i+1}$ generates a cylindrical shell [see Fig. 5-14(b)]. The volume of this shell is not smaller than the product of the area of a horizontal section and the smallest value of h in the interval, and is not larger than the product of the area of a horizontal section and the largest value of h in the interval. Therefore, there is a number ξ_i in the interval $[x_i, x_{i+1}]$ such that, if η_i is the midpoint of the interval, then the volume of the cylindrical shell is equal to

$$h(\xi_i)(2\pi\eta_i)\,\Delta_i x, \quad \text{where} \quad \Delta_i x = x_{i+1} - x_i.$$

Therefore, if Δ is the largest of the numbers $\Delta_i x$ and if

$$\lim_{\Delta \to 0} \sum h(\xi_i)(2\pi\eta_i)\,\Delta_i x \tag{5-11}$$

exists, independently of the choice of ξ_i and η_i in the interval $[x_i, x_{i+1}]$, then this limit is the volume of the solid of revolution.   As a matter of fact, this limit does exist and equals

$$\int_a^b h(x)(2\pi x)\, dx.$$

However, unlike the usual sum whose limit defines a definite integral, the sum in (5-11) uses two points, ξ_i and η_i, in each interval, rather than a single point ξ_i.   Thus, the fact that a continuous function is integrable cannot be used directly.   Fortunately, this causes little trouble, since the following theorem shows that integrability of continuous functions can be generalized to situations such as that just discussed.

For simplicity, we shall state this theorem for a function of three variables, leaving it to the student to convince himself that this can be generalized to functions of arbitrarily many variables.   This theorem can also be generalized to multiple integrals.   However, since the statement and proof are so similar to those for single integrals, we shall omit both the statement and proof, but use the theorem whenever it is needed.

THEOREM 5-5.1.   If f is a function of three variables which is continuous at all points (x, y, z) such that $x = y = z$ and x is in the interval $[a, b]$, then the function of one variable whose value at t is $f(t, t, t)$ is integrable on $[a, b]$ and

$$\int_a^b f(t, t, t)\, dt = \lim_{\Delta \to 0} \sum_{i=1}^n f(\xi_i, \eta_i, \zeta_i)\, \Delta_i t,$$

where Δ is the fineness of the partition $\{a = t_1, t_2, \cdots, t_{n+1} = b\}$ of the interval $[a, b]$, $\Delta_i t = t_{i+1} - t_i$, and ξ_i, η_i, and ζ_i are arbitrary numbers in the interval $[t_i, t_{i+1}]$.

PROOF.   Let ε be an arbitrary positive number.   For each t in $[a, b]$, use continuity of f at (t, t, t) to choose a positive number δ_t such that

$$|f(x, y, z) - f(t, t, t)| < \tfrac{1}{2}\varepsilon \quad \text{if} \quad d[(x, y, z), (t, t, t)] < \delta_t. \quad (5\text{-}12)$$

For each t, let U_t be the open ball of radius $\tfrac{1}{2}\delta_t$ with center at (t, t, t). These sets U_t constitute a cover of the closed segment from (a, a, a) to (b, b, b) by open sets.   By the Heine-Borel theorem, this cover can be reduced to a finite cover.   Let δ be the radius of the smallest ball used in this finite cover.   Since $f(t, t, t)$ is continuous on the interval $[a, b]$, this function is integrable on $[a, b]$ and there is a number $\Delta < \delta/\sqrt{3}$

such that, if the fineness of the partition $\{a = t_1, t_2, \cdots, t_{n+1} = b\}$ is less than Δ, then

$$\left| \int_a^b f(t, t, t)\, dt - \sum_{i=1}^n f(\tau_i, \tau_i, \tau_i) \Delta_i t \right| < \varepsilon. \tag{5-13}$$

Suppose we choose a partition with fineness less than Δ and for each i let (ξ_i, η_i, ζ_i) be a point such that $\xi_i, \eta_i,$ and ζ_i are numbers in the ith interval. If τ_i is any number in the ith interval, then each of $\xi_i, \eta_i,$ and ζ_i differ from τ_i by less than Δ and we have

$$[(\xi_i - \tau_i)^2 + (\eta_i - \tau_i)^2 + (\zeta_i - \tau_i)^2]^{1/2} < \sqrt{3}\,\Delta < \delta.$$

Thus, if (τ_i, τ_i, τ_i) is in the ball U_t, then both (τ_i, τ_i, τ_i) and (ξ_i, η_i, ζ_i) are in the open ball with center at (t, t, t) and radius δ_t. From (5-12), we then have

$$|f(\xi_i, \eta_i, \zeta_i) - f(\tau_i, \tau_i, \tau_i)| < \varepsilon,$$

and then it follows from (5-13) that

$$\left| \int_a^b f(t, t, t)\, dt - \sum_{i=1}^n f(\xi_i, \eta_i, \zeta_i) \Delta_i t \right|$$

$$< \varepsilon + \left| \sum_{i=1}^n [f(\xi_i, \eta_i, \zeta_i) - f(\tau_i, \tau_i, \tau_i)] \Delta_i t \right|$$

$$< \varepsilon + \varepsilon \left| \sum_{i=1}^n \Delta_i t \right| = \varepsilon(1 + |b - a|).$$

Since ε was an arbitrary positive number, this completes the proof of the theorem.

ILLUSTRATION 1. Suppose a solid right circular cone has altitude 10 and the radius of the base is 5. Also suppose that the density is proportional to the vertical distance from the vertex, so that, if coordinate axes are placed as shown in Fig. 5-15, then the density is equal to $c(10 - y)$ for some constant c. If we choose a partition of the interval $[0, 10]$ on the y-axis, then for each i there is a number η_i in the ith interval such that, if $\Delta_i y$ denotes $y_{i+1} - y_i$, then $\pi(5 - \frac{1}{2}\eta_i)^2 \Delta_i y$ is the volume of the slice of the cone between planes perpendicular to the y-axis at the end points y_i and y_{i+1} of the ith interval. There is another number ζ_i in the ith interval such that $c(10 - \zeta_i)$ is the average density of this slice. Then the mass of the cone is exactly equal to

$$\sum c(10 - \zeta_i)\pi(5 - \tfrac{1}{2}\eta_i)^2 \Delta_i y.$$

Therefore, if independently of the choice of η_i and ζ_i in the ith interval the limit of this sum exists as the fineness of the partition approaches zero, then the limit is the mass of the cone. It follows from Theorem 5-5.1 that this limit does exist and is equal to

$$\int_0^{10} \pi c(10-y)(5-\tfrac{1}{2}y)^2 \, dy = \frac{\pi c}{4} \int_0^{10} (10-y)^3 \, dy = 625\pi c.$$

The preceding illustrative example was discussed much more formally than is necessary once the use of Theorem 5-5.1 is understood. It usually is possible to write the integral directly.

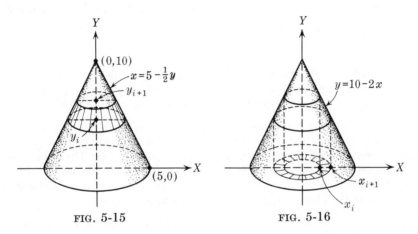

FIG. 5-15   FIG. 5-16

ILLUSTRATION 2. Suppose the solid right circular cone of Fig. 5-16 has density proportional to the distance from the y-axis, so that there is a number c such that the density is equal to cr if r is the distance from the y-axis. In this case, we can use the cylindrical shell method and determine the mass as

$$\int_0^5 cx(2\pi x)(10-2x) \, dx = 4\pi c \int_0^5 (5x^2 - x^3) \, dx = \frac{625\pi c}{3}.$$

We can justify this as follows. A typical term of the sum whose limit is the integral is

$$c\xi_i(2\pi\eta_i)(10-2\zeta_i) \, \Delta_i x, \qquad (5\text{-}14)$$

where ξ_i, η_i, and ζ_i are arbitrary numbers in the ith interval. We can choose η_i so that $2\pi\eta_i \, \Delta_i x$ is the area of the base of the corresponding cylindrical shell. Then we can choose ζ_i so that $10-2\zeta_i$ is the number between the largest and smallest values of y in the ith interval for which expression (5-14) without the factor $c\xi_i$ is the volume of the cylindrical shell. Finally, we can choose ξ_i so that (5-14) is precisely the mass of the cylindrical shell.

PROBLEMS

1. For each of the following, use the cylindrical shell method and determine the volume of the region generated by rotating the indicated plane region about the line described. (**a**) The triangle with vertices at $(0, 0)$, $(2, 0)$, and $(0, 2)$ is rotated about the x-axis. (**b**) The region bounded by the graphs of $y^2 + x = 2y$ and $x = 0$ is rotated about the x-axis. (**c**) The region bounded by the graph of $y = 6 \sin 2x$ $(0 \leq x \leq \frac{1}{2}\pi)$ is rotated about the y-axis. (**d**) The region bounded by the graphs of $x = \sqrt{y}$, $y = 1$, and $x = 0$ is rotated about the line $x = 1$. (**e**) The region bounded by the graphs of $x^2 + \ln y = 0$ $(0 \leq x \leq 1)$ and $y = (e^{-1} - 1)x + 1$ is rotated about the y-axis.

2. (**a**) Determine the volume of the torus generated by rotating a circle of radius r about a line L in the plane of the circle and at distance d from the center of the circle $(d > r)$. (**b**) Determine the mass of the torus of part (a) if the density is equal to the distance from the line L.

3. In each of the following, for the given density function ρ, determine the mass of the three-dimensional region generated by rotating the indicated plane region about the line described. (**a**) The triangle with vertices $(0, 0)$, $(1, 0)$, and $(1, 2)$ is rotated about the x-axis; ρ is the distance from the x-axis. (**b**) Same as (a), except that ρ is the distance from the plane perpendicular to the x-axis at $(1, 0)$.

4. The region bounded by the graphs of $2y = x^2$ and $2y = x + 2$ generates various three-dimensional regions when rotated about the following lines. Determine the volume in each case.

(**a**) The x-axis.   (**c**) The line $y = 2$.

(**b**) The line $x = 2$.   (d) The line $y = 1$.

5. The region bounded by the curves whose equations are $2y = x^2$ and $2y = x + 2$ is rotated about the line $x = -1$. Determine the mass of the solid generated, given that ρ is the distance from the axis of rotation.

6. The base of a certain solid is the circle whose equation is $x^2 + y^2 = r^2$. Each section cut from the solid by a plane perpendicular to the x-axis is a square with one edge in the base of the solid. The density is constant in planes perpendicular to the x-axis and is equal to $r - |x_0|$ if the plane cuts the x-axis at $(x_0, 0)$. Determine the mass of the solid.

7. Discuss how Theorem 5-5.1 might be proved with the hypothesis weakened so that f is assumed to be bounded on the intersection of a cylinder (with axis on the line $x = y = z$) and the cube of points (x, y, z) with x, y, and z in the interval $[a, b]$, and f is assumed to be continuous at points (t, t, t) with $a \leq t \leq b$ *except for a set of 1-D measure zero.*

6

PARTIAL
DIFFERENTIATION

6-1. DIFFERENTIALS

The use of differentials goes back to Leibniz and his notation for derivatives. Differential notation suggests a great many relations among derivatives, most of which happen to be true. Early mathematicians arrived intuitively at many results with the aid of differentials, as still do present-day workers when attempting mathematical formulations of physical problems. However, the previous definitions of differentials were so confusing, what with talk of "infinitely small quantities," "ultimate ratios," "infinitesimals," "differentials," etc., that it is small wonder Bishop Berkeley derisively described them as "ghosts of departed quantities." We shall give a more defensible definition, first for functions of one variable.

DEFINITION 6-1.1. The *differential* of a function f is the function whose domain is the set of all pairs of numbers (x, t) such that $f'(x)$ exists and whose value at (x, t) is $f'(x) \cdot t$. We shall denote the differential of f by df.

If I is the function defined by $I(x) = x$ for all x, then $I'(x) = 1$ and the value of dI at (x, t) is equal to t for all numbers x and t. Therefore, the quotient of the values of df and dI is equal to $f'(x)$, if $t \neq 0$ and $f'(x)$ exists. That is,

$$\left[\frac{df}{dI}\right]_{(x,t)} = f'(x),$$

where df/dI is the function that is the quotient of the functions df and dI. Just as we sometimes denote the function I by the symbol x, we might also denote dI by dx. Then we would write

$$\left[\frac{df}{dx}\right]_{(x,t)} = f'(x).$$

Although the domain of df/dx is the set of all points (x, t) such that $t \neq 0$ and $f'(x)$ exists, the value of df/dx is independent of t. Thus, it is customary to write $df/dx = f'$.

The meaning of differentials may be clearer if one understands the way in which a differential closely approximates the corresponding change in function value when the change in the independent variable is sufficiently small. To describe the nature of this approximation, let us suppose that the graph of $y = f(x)$ has a nonvertical tangent line at a point (x_0, y_0). Then the slope of this tangent line is $f'(x_0)$ and $f'(x_0) \Delta x$ is the difference between the ordinates of the points *on the tangent line* whose abscissas are $x_0 + \Delta x$ and x_0 [see Fig. 6-1]. The values of dx and dy at the point $(x_0, \Delta x)$ are

$$[dx]_{(x_0,\Delta x)} = \Delta x \quad \text{and} \quad [dy]_{(x_0,\Delta x)} = f'(x_0) \Delta x.$$

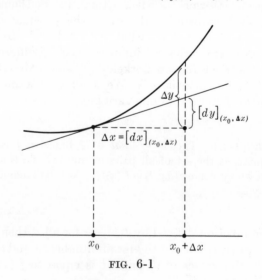

FIG. 6-1

Therefore, the slope of the tangent line is

$$f'(x_0) = \frac{[dy]_{(x_0,\Delta x)}}{[dx]_{(x_0,\Delta x)}} = \left[\frac{dy}{dx}\right]_{x_0}.$$

Now suppose Δy is the difference between the ordinates of the points *on the graph of* $y = f(x)$ whose abscissas are $x_0 + \Delta x$ and x_0. Then

$$\lim_{\Delta x \to 0} \frac{\Delta y - [dy]_{(x_0, \Delta x)}}{\Delta x} = \lim_{\Delta x \to 0} \left[\frac{\Delta y}{\Delta x} - f'(x_0) \right] = 0. \qquad (6\text{-}1)$$

Before defining differentials of functions of more than one variable, it is useful to discuss the meaning of continuity for such functions. Let us recall that a function f being continuous at a point p_0 of its domain means that whenever V is a neighborhood of $f(p_0)$, the inverse image of V is a neighborhood of p in the domain of f. If the range of f is a set of numbers, this is equivalent to requiring that, whenever ε is a positive number, there is a positive number δ such that, if p is in the domain of f, then

$$|f(p) - f(p_0)| < \varepsilon \quad \text{if} \quad d(p, p_0) < \delta. \qquad (6\text{-}2)$$

ILLUSTRATION 1. Suppose $f(x, y) = 3x + 5y$ for all (x, y). To prove that f is continuous at all points of the plane, we shall prove continuity at a point (x_0, y_0) for which no restriction has been placed on the values of x_0 and y_0. We note first that, for any (x, y),

$$\begin{aligned}
|f(x, y) - f(x_0, y_0)| &= |(3x + 5y) - (3x_0 + 5y_0)| \\
&\leq 3|x - x_0| + 5|y - y_0|.
\end{aligned}$$

Since neither $|x - x_0|$ nor $|y - y_0|$ is larger than the distance between (x_0, y_0) and (x, y), it follows that

$$|f(x, y) - f(x_0, y_0)| \leq 8 \cdot d[(x_0, y_0), (x, y)]. \qquad (6\text{-}3)$$

Now we let ε be a positive number and let $\delta = \tfrac{1}{8}\varepsilon$. Then it follows from (6-3) that

$$|f(x, y) - f(x_0, y_0)| < \varepsilon \quad \text{if} \quad d[(x_0, y_0), (x, y)] < \delta.$$

This completes the proof.

Direct use of the definition of continuity as in the preceding illustration can be very difficult if f is not so simple a function. However, we know that for any number c the functions cf, $f + g$, and fg are continuous at a point p if f and g are continuous at p. Also, f/g is continuous at any point p at which both f and g are continuous and $g(p) \neq 0$. These facts, as well as the continuity of specific functions such as the trigonometric, logarithmic, and exponential functions, and Theorem 2-6.6 about continuity of a "function of a function," can be used to establish continuity of specific functions. For example, suppose that the method of the preceding illustration was used to prove that all constant functions are continuous and that the functions f and g for which $f(x, y) = x$ and $g(x, y) = y$ are continuous. Then it follows that $2x + 3y$ and $x^2 + 5xy$ are continuous. Now using the fact that sine is continuous and that the quotient of two continuous functions is continuous, we have [sin $(2x + 3y)]/(x^2 + 5xy)$ continuous at all points of the (x, y)-plane except points not in the domain of this function, i.e., points for which $x^2 + 5xy = 0$.

ILLUSTRATION 2. If $f(x, y) = xy/(x^2 + y^2)$ when $x^2 + y^2 \neq 0$, then f is continuous at all points of the (x, y)-plane except $(0, 0)$. The point $(0, 0)$ is not in the domain of f. Whatever value may be given $f(0, 0)$, the resulting function is discontinuous at $(0, 0)$. To show this, we observe that

$$f(x, 0) = 0 \quad \text{if} \quad x \neq 0 \quad \text{and} \quad f(x, x) = \tfrac{1}{2} \quad \text{if} \quad x \neq 0.$$

Now suppose we let the point p_0 of (6-2) be the point $(0, 0)$. Since there are points arbitrarily close to $(0, 0)$ at which f has the value zero, and others at which f has the value $\tfrac{1}{2}$, we can see that (6-2) is not true when $\varepsilon < \tfrac{1}{4}$, whatever the value of δ and no matter how we define $f(0, 0)$.

The meaning of partial differentiation is very simple: a partial derivative of a function of several variables is an ordinary derivative with all but one of the variables replaced by constants. If f is a function of three variables, then the partial derivative with respect to the first variable, evaluated at the point (x_0, y_0, z_0), is

$$\lim_{h \to 0} \frac{f(x_0 + h, y_0, z_0) - f(x_0, y_0, z_0)}{h}.$$

Some of the symbols used to denote this partial derivative are

$$f_1(x_0, y_0, z_0), \quad f_x(x_0, y_0, z_0), \quad [D_x f]_{(x_0, y_0, z_0)},$$

$$D_x f, \quad \left[\frac{\partial f}{\partial x}\right]_{(x_0, y_0, z_0)}, \quad \text{and} \quad \frac{\partial f}{\partial x}.$$

We know that a function whose domain is a set of real numbers is continuous at any point where it is differentiable. However, the existence of partial derivatives does not imply continuity. The function of Illustration 2 can be used to show this. If we define $f(0, 0)$ as zero, then $f(x, 0) = 0$ for all x and $f(0, y) = 0$ for all y. Therefore, both $f_1(0, 0)$ and $f_2(0, 0)$ are defined, each being equal to zero. However, we know that f is not continuous at $(0, 0)$.

In the rest of this section, we shall generalize the concept of differentiability to functions of more than one variable in such a way that a function must be continuous at each point at which it is differentiable. To simplify notation, we shall discuss a function f of three variables. Since the generalization to functions of more than three variables is very similar, it will be left for the student. We shall first consider the difference between values of f at points (x_0, y_0, z_0) and $(x_0 + \Delta x, y_0 + \Delta y, z_0 + \Delta z)$:

$$\Delta f = f(x_0 + \Delta x, y_0 + \Delta y, z_0 + \Delta z) - f(x_0, y_0, z_0).$$

This difference can be written as follows:

$$\Delta f = [f(x_0 + \Delta x, y_0 + \Delta y, z_0 + \Delta z) - f(x_0, y_0 + \Delta y, z_0 + \Delta z)]$$
$$+ [f(x_0, y_0 + \Delta y, z_0 + \Delta z) - f(x_0, y_0, z_0 + \Delta z)]$$
$$+ [f(x_0, y_0, z_0 + \Delta z) - f(x_0, y_0, z_0)]. \tag{6-4}$$

In order to apply results about functions of a single variable to the difference in the first brackets, we shall introduce the function g defined by

$$g(t) = f(t, y_0 + \Delta y, z_0 + \Delta z).$$

Then the difference in the first brackets becomes $g(x_0 + \Delta x) - g(x_0)$, which, by the mean value theorem, is equal to $g'(\xi) \Delta x$ for some number ξ between x_0 and $x_0 + \Delta x$. This number ξ is equal to $x_0 + \theta \Delta x$, where θ is a suitable number between 0 and 1, and

$$g'(\xi) = g'(x_0 + \theta \Delta x) = f_1(x_0 + \theta \Delta x, y_0 + \Delta y, z_0 + \Delta z).$$

If the domains of the three first-order partial derivatives of f contain a sphere about the point (x_0, y_0, z_0), and if this sphere contains the point $(x_0 + \Delta x, y_0 + \Delta y, z_0 + \Delta z)$, then this use of the mean value theorem is valid. Similar procedures can be used for each of the other brackets in Eq. (6-4). Therefore, there are numbers θ_1, θ_2, and θ_3, between 0 and 1, such that

$$\Delta f = f_1(x_0 + \theta_1 \Delta x, y_0 + \Delta y, z_0 + \Delta z) \Delta x + f_2(x_0, y_0 + \theta_2 \Delta y, z_0 + \Delta z) \Delta y$$
$$+ f_3(x_0, y_0, z_0 + \theta_3 \Delta z) \Delta z. \tag{6-5}$$

Now suppose we define the numbers ε_1, ε_2, and ε_3 by the equations

$$\begin{cases} f_1(x_0 + \theta_1\,\Delta x,\, y_0 + \Delta y,\, z_0 + \Delta z) - f_1(x_0,\, y_0,\, z_0) = \varepsilon_1, \\ f_2(x_0, \qquad y_0 + \theta_2\,\Delta y,\, z_0 + \Delta z) - f_2(x_0,\, y_0,\, z_0) = \varepsilon_2, \\ f_3(x_0, \qquad y_0, \qquad z_0 + \theta_3\,\Delta z) - f_3(x_0,\, y_0,\, z_0) = \varepsilon_3. \end{cases}$$

Then

$$\Delta f = f_1(x_0,\, y_0,\, z_0)\,\Delta x + f_2(x_0,\, y_0,\, z_0)\,\Delta y$$
$$+ f_3(x_0,\, y_0,\, z_0)\,\Delta z + \varepsilon_1\,\Delta x + \varepsilon_2\,\Delta y + \varepsilon_3\,\Delta z. \qquad (6\text{-}6)$$

If f_1, f_2, and f_3 have domains whose intersection contains a neighborhood of (x_0, y_0, z_0), and if these partial derivatives are continuous at (x_0, y_0, z_0), then each of the numbers ε_1, ε_2, and ε_3 approaches zero as $[(\Delta x)^2 + (\Delta y)^2 + (\Delta z)^2]^{\frac{1}{2}}$ approaches zero. Since $[(\Delta x)^2 + (\Delta y)^2 + (\Delta z)^2]^{\frac{1}{2}}$ is at least as large as the largest of $|\Delta x|$, $|\Delta y|$, and $|\Delta z|$, it follows that the number ε defined by

$$\varepsilon_1\,\Delta x + \varepsilon_2\,\Delta y + \varepsilon_3\,\Delta z = \varepsilon[(\Delta x)^2 + (\Delta y)^2 + (\Delta z)^2]^{\frac{1}{2}}$$

also approaches zero as $[(\Delta x)^2 + (\Delta y)^2 + (\Delta z)^2]^{\frac{1}{2}}$ approaches zero. This suggests that we write

$$\Delta f = f_1(x_0,\, y_0,\, z_0)\,\Delta x + f_2(x_0,\, y_0,\, z_0)\,\Delta y + f_3(x_0,\, y_0,\, z_0)\,\Delta z$$
$$+ \varepsilon[(\Delta x)^2 + (\Delta y)^2 + (\Delta z)^2]^{\frac{1}{2}}. \qquad (6\text{-}7)$$

Since each term in the right member of Eq. (6-7) approaches zero as the point (x, y, z) approaches the point (x_0, y_0, z_0), it follows that f is continuous at (x_0, y_0, z_0). Thus, we have shown that a function is continuous at a point P_0 if P_0 has a neighborhood contained in the intersection of the domains of the first-order partial derivatives and these partial derivatives are continuous at P_0.

For a function of one variable, Eq. (6-1) might be said to state that the differential is a "good estimate" for the increment y. This is a property of differentials we wish to preserve for differentials of functions of more than one variable. Unfortunately, the mere existence of partial derivatives is not enough. However, we can overcome this difficulty simply by requiring that equality (6-8) in the following definition be satisfied. This definition is given for a function of three variables, with generalizations left for the student.

DEFINITION 6-1.2. Suppose (x_0, y_0, z_0) is an interior point of the domain of f and belongs to the domains of the first-order partial derivatives of f, and let

$$[\Delta f]_{(r,s,t)} = f(x_0 + r, y_0 + s, z_0 + t) - f(x_0, y_0, z_0).$$

Then f is said to be *differentiable* at (x_0, y_0, z_0), and the function df, defined by

$$[df]_{(r,s,t)} = f_1(x_0, y_0, z_0) \cdot r + f_2(x_0, y_0, z_0) \cdot s + f_3(x_0, y_0, z_0) \cdot t,$$

is said to be the *differential* of f at the point (x_0, y_0, z_0), if and only if

$$\lim_{(r,s,t) \to (0,0,0)} \left(\frac{\Delta f - df}{(r^2 + s^2 + t^2)^{1/2}} \right) = 0. \tag{6-8}$$

The next theorem is proved when it is observed that ε in Eq. (6-7) approaches zero as $[(\Delta x)^2 + (\Delta y)^2 + (\Delta z)^2]^{1/2}$ approaches zero, if the function f satisfies the hypotheses of the theorem.

THEOREM 6-1.1. A function f is differentiable at a point P_0 if the intersection of the domains of the first-order partial derivatives of f contains a neighborhood of P_0 and these partial derivatives are continuous at P_0.

It follows from Eq. (6-8) and the fact that $df \to 0$ as $[(\Delta x)^2 + (\Delta y)^2 + (\Delta z)^2]^{1/2} \to 0$, that $\Delta f \to 0$. *Therefore a function is continuous at all points at which it is differentiable.* Illustration 2, with $f(0, 0)$ defined as zero, provides an example of a function which is not continuous at $(0, 0)$, even though $(0, 0)$ is in the domain of each partial derivative. Since this function is not continuous at $(0, 0)$, it is not differentiable at $(0, 0)$. [Problem 9 provides an example of a function that is continuous at a point in the domains of the first-order partial derivatives, but is not differentiable at this point.]

For a function f of two variables, differentiability can be given geometric meaning by showing that the function is differentiable at a point P if and only if the graph of $z = f(x, y)$ has a tangent plane at P that is not parallel to the z-axis. This is a generalization of the fact that a function of one variable is differentiable at a point P if and only if the graph of $y = f(x)$ has a tangent line at P that is not parallel to the y-axis. In Section 7-7, we shall show that the graph of an equation $f(x, y, z) = 0$ has a tangent plane at any point at which f is differentiable and not all first-order partial derivatives of f are zero.

DEFINITION 6-1.3. Suppose that S is the graph of an equation of type $z = f(x, y)$ or, more generally, $F(x, y, z) = 0$, and that P_0 is a point of S. A *tangent plane* to S at P_0 is a plane II that contains P_0 and has the property that, for points P of S, the angle θ between the line $P_0 P$ and the plane II approaches zero as the distance between P_0 and P approaches zero.

THEOREM 6-1.2. A function f of two variables is differentiable at an interior point (x_0, y_0) of its domain if and only if the graph of the equation $z = f(x, y)$ has a tangent plane at the point (x_0, y_0, z_0), where $z_0 = f(x_0, y_0)$, and this tangent plane is not parallel to the z-axis. The equation of the tangent plane is

$$z - z_0 = f_1(x_0, y_0)(x - x_0) + f_2(x_0, y_0)(y - y_0). \qquad (6\text{-}9)$$

If a tangent plane at P_0, (x_0, y_0, z_0), is not parallel to the z-axis, its equation can be written in the form

$$z - z_0 = A(x - x_0) + B(y - y_0). \qquad (6\text{-}10)$$

The line L of intersection of this plane with the plane $x = x_0$ has the equations $x = x_0$, $z - z_0 = B(y - y_0)$, and this line is tangent to the curve of intersection of the plane $x = x_0$ with the graph of $z = f(x, y)$ [see Fig. 6-2]. Therefore, the slope of L in the plane $x = x_0$ is $B = f_2(x_0, y_0)$.

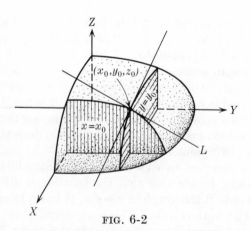

FIG. 6-2

Similarly, $A = f_1(x_0, y_0)$. This shows that if there is a nonvertical tangent plane at P_0, then Eq. (6-9) is an equation of this plane. We know the graph of (6-9) is a tangent plane if and only if the angle θ between $P_0 P$ and this plane approaches zero as $P \to P_0$, where P is a point on the graph of $z = f(x, y)$. The distance D from (x, y, z) to the plane can be computed by putting Eq. (6-9) in normal form.† This gives

$$D = \left| \frac{(z - z_0) - f_1(x_0, y_0)(x - x_0) - f_2(x_0, y_0)(y - y_0)}{[f_1(x_0, y_0)^2 + f_2(x_0, y_0)^2 + 1]^{1/2}} \right|.$$

Therefore, with $\Delta x = x - x_0$, $\Delta y = y - y_0$, and $\Delta z = z - z_0$, we have

$$\sin \theta = \frac{|\Delta z - f_1(x_0, y_0)\, \Delta x - f_2(x_0, y_0)\, \Delta y|}{[f_1(x_0, y_0)^2 + f_2(x_0, y_0)^2 + 1]^{1/2}[(\Delta x)^2 + (\Delta y)^2 + (\Delta z)^2]^{1/2}}. \quad (6\text{-}11)$$

By definition, f is differentiable at P_0 if and only if

$$\lim_{[(\Delta x)^2 + (\Delta y)^2]^{1/2} \to 0} \frac{|\Delta z - f_1(x_0, y_0)\, \Delta x - f_2(x_0, y_0)\, \Delta y|}{[(\Delta x)^2 + (\Delta y)^2]^{1/2}} = 0. \quad (6\text{-}12)$$

If f is differentiable, we can replace the denominator in the right member of Eq. (6-11) by $[(\Delta x)^2 + (\Delta y)^2]^{1/2}$ without decreasing, but possibly increasing, its value. Then we can conclude from (6-12) that $\sin \theta \to 0$ as $[(\Delta x)^2 + (\Delta y)^2 + (\Delta z)^2]^{1/2} \to 0$. Now suppose that $\sin \theta \to 0$ as $[(\Delta x)^2 + (\Delta y)^2 + (\Delta z)^2]^{1/2} \to 0$, so that Eq. (6-9) is the equation of a nonvertical tangent plane. Then (6-12) can be false only if

$$\frac{[(\Delta x)^2 + (\Delta y)^2 + (\Delta z)^2]^{1/2}}{[(\Delta x)^2 + (\Delta y)^2]^{1/2}} = \left[1 + \left(\frac{\Delta z}{[(\Delta x)^2 + (\Delta y)^2]^{1/2}} \right)^2 \right]^{1/2}$$

is not bounded for P near P_0. However, $\Delta z / [(\Delta x)^2 + (\Delta y)^2]^{1/2}$ is the tangent of the angle between $P_0 P$ and the horizontal and must be bounded if the angle between $P_0 P$ and the tangent plane approaches zero as $P \to P_0$ and the tangent plane is not parallel to the z-axis.

ILLUSTRATION 3. The graph of

$$z = 2 - \left(\frac{x^2}{4} + \frac{y^2}{9} \right)$$

is the paraboloid shown in Fig. 6-3. By giving z a constant value z_0, we see that a plane perpendicular to the z-axis intersects the surface in an ellipse if $z_0 < 2$, the single point $(0, 0, 2)$ if $z_0 = 2$, and in the null

---

† If the student is not familiar with use of the normal form of the equation of a plane for determining the distance from a point to the plane, he can look ahead to problem 9, page 308, and Eq. (7-26) of Section 7-2.

set if $z_0 > 2$. If we give x or y a constant value, we see that a plane parallel to the (y, z)-plane, or parallel to the (x, z)-plane, intersects the surface in a parabola. The partial derivatives,

$$\frac{\partial z}{\partial x} = -\tfrac{1}{2}x \quad \text{and} \quad \frac{\partial z}{\partial y} = -\tfrac{2}{9}y,$$

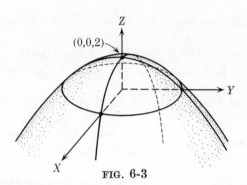

FIG. 6-3

have the values $-\tfrac{1}{2}x_0$ and $-2y_0/9$ at the point (x_0, y_0) and an equation of the plane tangent to the paraboloid at the point (x_0, y_0, z_0) is

$$z - z_0 = -\tfrac{1}{2}x_0(x - x_0) - \tfrac{2}{9}y_0(y - y_0).$$

In particular, the tangent plane at the point $(4, 3, -3)$ has the equation

$$(z + 3) = -2(x - 4) - \tfrac{2}{3}(y - 3) \quad \text{or} \quad 6x + 2y + 3z = 21.$$

PROBLEMS

1. Let

$$f(x, y) = \frac{x^2 - y^2}{x^2 + y^2} \quad \text{if} \quad x^2 + y^2 \neq 0.$$

Show that f has a discontinuity at $(0, 0)$, whatever value may be given $f(0, 0)$.

2. For each of the following, determine the points of the (x, y)-plane at which the function f is not continuous and determine which of these points become points of continuity if f is given a suitable value at the point.

(**a**) $f(x, y) = \dfrac{1}{x - y}.$ (**b**) $f(x, y) = \dfrac{x^3 + y^2}{x^2 + y}.$

(**c**) $f(0, 0) = 0$ and $f(x, y) = (\sin xy)(x^2 + y^2)^{-\frac{1}{2}}$ if $x^2 + y^2 \neq 0$.
[*Hint:* Show that $|f(x, y)|$ is not larger than the larger of $|x|$ and $|y|$.]

3. Let f be defined by $f(0, 0) = 0$ and $f(x, y) = (3x+4y) \ln (x^2+y^2)$ if $x^2+y^2 \neq 0$. Show that f is continuous at all points of the (x, y)-plane.

4. For each of the following, compute $\Delta u - du$ at the point indicated and use the result to show that u is differentiable at this point.

   (a) $u(x, y, z) = 2x+3y+5z$; $(2, -3, 7)$.

   (b) $u(x, y) = \dfrac{x-y}{x+y}$; $(1, 1)$.

   (c) $u(x, y, z) = xyz$; $(1, -1, 2)$.

5. For each of the following, find an equation of the tangent plane at the point indicated.

   (a) $z = xy$; $(3, -2, -6)$.   (c) $z = 3x+y^2$; $(0, 2, 4)$.

   (b) $z = x^3+y^3+3xy$; $(1, -1, -3)$.   (d) $z = e^{x^2+y^2}$; $(0, 0, 1)$.

6. Let u be a differentiable function of x, y, and z. Prove that

$$d(\cos u) = -(\sin u) \, du.$$

7. Let f be defined by $f(x, y) = x^2 \sin (1/x)+y$ if $x \neq 0$ and $f(0, y) = y$ for all y. (a) Show that $f_1(x, y)$ has a value at $(0, 0)$ but is discontinuous at $(0, 0)$. (b) Determine whether f is differentiable at $(0, 0)$.

8. Let f be defined by $f(x, y) = y^3/x$ if $x \neq 0$ and $f(0, y) = 0$ for all y. (a) Show that f is discontinuous at $(0, 0)$. (b) Show that each plane through the z-axis intersects the graph of $z = f(x, y)$ in a curve that is tangent to a line in the (x, y)-plane. (c) Show that the graph of $z = f(x, y)$ does not have a tangent plane at $(0, 0, 0)$.

9. Let f be defined by $f(x, y) = xy(x^2+y^2)^{-\frac{1}{2}}$ if x and y are positive and $f(x, y) = 0$ if x or y is negative or zero. Show that f is continuous at $(0, 0)$ and that $f_1(0, 0) = 0$ and $f_2(0, 0) = 0$, but that the graph of $z = f(x, y)$ does not have a tangent plane at $(0, 0)$. Why does this not contradict the fact that the graph of a differentiable function has a tangent plane?

6-2. THE CHAIN RULE

The *chain rule for functions of one variable* can be stated as the following theorem.

THEOREM 6–2.1 Let f and u be two functions of one variable and let F be the function defined by

$$F(x) = f[u(x)],$$

for all x in the domain of u such that $u(x)$ is in the domain of f. If u is differentiable at the particular number x, f is differentiable at $u(x)$, and each deleted neighborhood of x contains numbers in the domain of F, then F is differentiable at x and the value at x of the derivative of F is $f'[u(x)] \cdot u'(x)$. This can be abbreviated as

$$D_x F = (D_u f)(D_x u) \quad \text{or} \quad F'(x) = f'[u(x)] \cdot u'(x).$$

PROOF. For $\Delta x \neq 0$ with $x + \Delta x$ in the domain of u and $u(x + \Delta x)$ in the domain of f, let $\Delta u = u(x + \Delta x) - u(x)$ and $\Delta F = f[u(x + \Delta x)] - f[u(x)]$. Then

$$\frac{\Delta F}{\Delta x} = f'[u(x)] \frac{\Delta u}{\Delta x} + \{f[u(x+\Delta x)] - f[u(x)] - f'[u(x)] \cdot \Delta u\} \frac{1}{\Delta x}$$

$$= f'[u(x)] \frac{\Delta u}{\Delta x} + \phi(\Delta x) \frac{\Delta u}{\Delta x},$$

with ϕ defined by $\phi(\Delta x) = 0$ if $\Delta u = 0$ and

$$\phi(\Delta x) = \frac{f[u(x+\Delta x)] - f[u(x)]}{\Delta u} - f'[u(x)] \quad \text{if} \quad \Delta u \neq 0. \quad (6\text{-}13)$$

Since $\lim_{\Delta x \to 0} \Delta u / \Delta x = u'(x)$, to prove that

$$\lim_{\Delta x \to 0} \frac{\Delta F}{\Delta x} = f'[u(x)] \cdot u'(x)$$

we need only prove that $\lim_{\Delta x \to 0} \phi(\Delta x) = 0$. Since f is differentiable at $u(x)$, for an arbitrary $\varepsilon > 0$ there is a $\delta_1 > 0$ such that

$$\left| \frac{f[u(x)+r] - f[u(x)]}{r} - f'[u(x)] \right| < \varepsilon \quad \text{if} \quad 0 < |r| < \delta_1 \quad (6\text{-}14)$$

and $u(x) + r$ is in the domain of f. Since u is differentiable at x and therefore is continuous at x, there is a $\delta_2 < 0$ such that $|\Delta u| < \delta_1$ if $|\Delta x| < \delta_2$ and $x + \Delta x$ is in the domain of u. Now suppose that $|\Delta x| < \delta_2$, $x + \Delta x$ is in the domain of u, and $u(x + \Delta x)$ is in the domain of f. Then $|\Delta u| < \delta_1$ and $|\phi(\Delta x)| < \varepsilon$, since $\phi(\Delta x) = 0$ if $\Delta u = 0$ and $|\phi(\Delta x)| < \varepsilon$ follows from (6-14) with $r = \Delta u$ if $\Delta u \neq 0$. Thus,

$$\lim_{\Delta x \to 0} \phi(\Delta x) = 0.$$

If f is a function of more than one variable, then the fact that in Eq. (6-4) differences such as $f(x_0, y_0 + \Delta y, z_0 + \Delta z) - f(x_0, y_0, z_0 + \Delta z)$ need to be considered, where neither term is the value of f at (x_0, y_0, z_0), makes direct generalization of Theorem 6-2.1 impossible. Because of this, when discussing chain rules for functions of several variables, we shall make more severe hypotheses than those of Theorem 6-2.1.

Suppose that f is a function of three variables and that x, y, and z are functions of a single variable t. Then f can be considered to be a function of t. Explicitly, we could define a function F by

$$F(t) = f[x(t), y(t), z(t)]. \qquad (6\text{-}15)$$

Now let us assume that, for a particular number t, each of the functions x, y, and z is differentiable at t, each of their domains contains a neighborhood of t, and that f is differentiable at $[x(t), y(t)\, z(t)]$. Then, for a nonzero number Δt, we let

$$\Delta x = x(t+\Delta t) - x(t), \quad \Delta y = y(t+\Delta t) - y(t), \quad \Delta z = z(t+\Delta t) - z(t),$$

and

$$\Delta F = F(t+\Delta t) - F(t) = f[x(t)+\Delta x, y(t)+\Delta y, z(t)+\Delta z]$$
$$-f[x(t), y(t), z(t)].$$

We have $\lim_{(\Delta x, \Delta y, \Delta z) \to (0,0,0)} (\Delta f - df)[(\Delta x)^2 + (\Delta y)^2 + (\Delta z)^2]^{-\frac{1}{2}} = 0$, since f is differentiable. Therefore $\varepsilon \to 0$ as $(\Delta x, \Delta y, \Delta z) \to (0, 0, 0)$, if ε is defined so that $\Delta f - df$ is equal to $\varepsilon[(\Delta x)^2 + (\Delta y)^2 + (\Delta z)^2]^{\frac{1}{2}}$. Then,

$$\frac{\Delta F}{\Delta t} = f_1[x(t), y(t), z(t)]\frac{\Delta x}{\Delta t} + f_2[x(t), y(t), z(t)]\frac{\Delta y}{\Delta t}$$
$$+ f_3[x(t), y(t), z(t)]\frac{\Delta z}{\Delta t} \pm \varepsilon\left[\left(\frac{\Delta x}{\Delta t}\right)^2 + \left(\frac{\Delta y}{\Delta t}\right)^2 + \left(\frac{\Delta z}{\Delta t}\right)^2\right]^{\frac{1}{2}}, \qquad (6\text{-}16)$$

where the upper sign is used if Δt is positive and the negative sign is used if Δt is negative. By taking limits of each member of Eq. (6-16), we obtain the *chain rule*

$$F'(t) = f_1[x(t), y(t), z(t)] \cdot x'(t) + f_2[x(t), y(t), z(t)] \cdot y'(t)$$
$$+ f_3[x(t), y(t), z(t)] \cdot z'(t). \qquad (6\text{-}17)$$

This formula can be written in the following forms, which are abbreviated but perhaps more suggestive:

$$\frac{dF}{dt} = f_1(x, y, z)\frac{dx}{dt} + f_2(x, y, z)\frac{dy}{dt} + f_3(x, y, z)\frac{dz}{dt};$$
$$\frac{df}{dt} = \frac{\partial f}{\partial x}\frac{dx}{dt} + \frac{\partial f}{\partial y}\frac{dy}{dt} + \frac{\partial f}{\partial z}\frac{dz}{dt}. \qquad (6\text{-}18)$$

ILLUSTRATION 1. Suppose that $f(x, y, z) = 2x^3 + y^2 + 7z$, where $x = t^2 + 3t$, $y = 5t + 7$, and $z = t^5$. If F is defined by Eq. (6-15), then

$$F'(t) = (6x^2) \cdot x'(t) + (2y) \cdot y'(t) + (7) \cdot z'(t)$$
$$= 6(t^2 + 3t)^2 \cdot (2t + 3) + 2(5t + 7) \cdot 5 + 7 \cdot 5t^4.$$

The same result could be obtained by using the chain rule for functions of one variable and the equation

$$F(t) = 2(t^2 + 3t)^3 + (5t + 7)^2 + 7t^5.$$

ILLUSTRATION 2. Suppose $f(x, y) = x^y$, where x and y are differentiable functions of t. Also suppose the function F is defined by

$$F(t) = f[x(t), y(t)].$$

Then

$$F'(t) = [yx^{y-1}]x'(t) + [x^y \ln x]y'(t).$$

If $x(t) = t$ and $y(t) = t$ for all t, this becomes

$$D(t^t) = t^t + t^t \cdot \ln t.$$

It will be recalled that without the chain rule we could have obtained the last equality by letting $w = t^t$ and $\ln w = t \ln t$. Then

$$\frac{1}{w} D(w) = 1 + \ln t \quad \text{or} \quad D(t^t) = t^t(1 + \ln t).$$

Now suppose that f is a function of three variables and that x, y, and z are functions of two variables. Also assume that the domains of the partial derivatives of x, y, and z contain the point (u_0, v_0), the domains of x, y, and z contain a neighborhood of (u_0, v_0), and that f is differentiable at $[x(u_0, v_0), y(u_0, v_0), z(u_0, v_0)]$. The partial derivatives, $\partial x/\partial u$, $\partial y/\partial u$, and $\partial z/\partial u$, are evaluated by giving v the value v_0 and then differentiating x, y, and z with respect to u. Therefore, the chain rule of (6-18) can be used to obtain

$$\frac{\partial f}{\partial u} = f_1(x, y, z) \frac{\partial x}{\partial u} + f_2(x, y, z) \frac{\partial y}{\partial u} + f_3(x, y, z) \frac{\partial z}{\partial u}, \qquad (6\text{-}19)$$

with a similar equation for differentiation with respect to v. The student should note that we have formulas for determining $\partial f/\partial u$ and $\partial f/\partial v$. But we have not yet shown that a differentiable function of differentiable functions is differentiable [Theorem 6-2.2]. We do know that (6-19) is valid at (u_0, v_0) when $\partial x/\partial u$, $\partial y/\partial u$, and $\partial z/\partial u$ have values at (u_0, v_0) and (u_0, v_0) is an interior point of the domains of x, y, and z, provided f is differentiable at the point (x, y, z). Thus, if f is differentiable at $[x(u_0, v_0), y(u_0, v_0), z(u_0, v_0)]$ and x, y, and z are differentiable at (u_0, v_0), then the partial derivatives of F can be evaluated by using (6-19), if we define F by

$$F(u, v) = f[x(u, v), y(u, v), z(u, v)]. \tag{6-20}$$

ILLUSTRATION 3. Suppose we have $w(x, y) = x^2 + 3xy - 2y$, where $x = r \cos \theta$ and $y = r \sin \theta$, and that $W(r, \theta)$ denotes $w(r \cos \theta, r \sin \theta)$. Then

$$\frac{\partial W}{\partial r} = (2x + 3y) \cos \theta + (3x - 2) \sin \theta,$$

$$\frac{\partial W}{\partial \theta} = (2x + 3y)(-r \sin \theta) + (3x - 2)r \cos \theta.$$

More generally, if $F(r, \theta) = f(r \cos \theta, r \sin \theta) = f(x, y)$, then

$$\frac{\partial F}{\partial r} = f_1(x, y)(\cos \theta) + f_2(x, y)(\sin \theta) = \frac{\partial f}{\partial x} \cos \theta + \frac{\partial f}{\partial y} \sin \theta,$$

$$\frac{\partial F}{\partial \theta} = f_1(x, y)(-r \sin \theta) + f_2(x, y)(r \cos \theta)$$

$$= \frac{\partial f}{\partial x} (-r \sin \theta) + \frac{\partial f}{\partial y} (r \cos \theta).$$

These two equations can be regarded as simultaneous linear equations in $\partial f/\partial x$ and $\partial f/\partial y$. The solutions are

$$\frac{\partial f}{\partial x} = \cos \theta \frac{\partial F}{\partial r} - \frac{\sin \theta}{r} \frac{\partial F}{\partial \theta}, \qquad \frac{\partial f}{\partial y} = \sin \theta \frac{\partial F}{\partial r} + \frac{\cos \theta}{r} \frac{\partial F}{\partial \theta},$$

from which it follows that

$$\left(\frac{\partial f}{\partial x}\right)^2 + \left(\frac{\partial f}{\partial y}\right)^2 = \left(\frac{\partial F}{\partial r}\right)^2 + \frac{1}{r^2} \left(\frac{\partial F}{\partial \theta}\right)^2.$$

This expresses the effect on the expression $(\partial f/\partial x)^2 + (\partial f/\partial y)^2$ when rectangular coordinates are replaced by polar coordinates. Such information is often very useful.

To obtain simplicity in notation, we have written the chain rule for the special case of a function f of three variables and functions

x, y, and z of one variable [Eq. (6-18)], and for the case when x, y, and z are functions of two variables [Eq. (6-19)]. Similarly, the discussion of differentials to follow will be restricted to special cases in order to avoid complicated notation. The extensions of these results to other cases are similar and are left for the student.

The differential of a function f at a point (x_0, y_0, z_0) is a function df of three variables [see Definition 6-1.2]. If these variables are denoted by r, s, and t, then

$$[df]_{(r,s,t)} = f_1(x_0, y_0, z_0) \cdot r + f_2(x_0, y_0, z_0) \cdot s + f_3(x_0, y_0, z_0) \cdot t. \qquad (6\text{-}21)$$

For the three functions I, J, and K defined for all (x, y, z) by

$$I(x, y, z) = x, \quad J(x, y, z) = y, \quad K(x, y, z) = z,$$

we have

$$[dI]_{(r,s,t)} = r, \quad [dJ]_{(r,s,t)} = s, \quad [dK]_{(r,s,t)} = t.$$

Similarly to the way in which we used the symbol dx for dI in Section 6-1, we shall denote the functions dI, dJ, and dK by dx, dy, and dz, respectively. Then Eq. (6-21) can be written as

$$df = f_1(x, y, z)\, dx + f_2(x, y, z)\, dy + f_3(x, y, z)\, dz. \qquad (6\text{-}22)$$

This discussion is based on the assumption that f is a function of independent variables x, y, and z. The equality analogous to (6-22) for a function y of a single variable x is $dy = y'(x)\, dx$. Because of the chain rule for functions of one variable, $dy = y'(x)\, dx$ even if x is not the independent variable. To show this, let us assume that x is a function of the variable t. Then $dy/dt = y'(x)x'(t)$ and $dx = x'(t)\, dt$, so that

$$dy = y'(x)x'(t)\, dt = y'(x)\, dx.$$

We shall show that (6-22) is valid if x, y, and z are functions of two variables u and v and leave further generalizations to the student. To do this, we must show that df can be evaluated formally by use of (6-22) when f is considered to be a function of u and v. But we must also show that f is differentiable as a function of u and v; that is, we must establish the equality analogous to (6-8) for this case. We shall evaluate df formally now and complete the argument in the proof of Theorem 6-2.2. Let us define F by

$$F(u, v) = f[x(u, v), y(u, v), z(u, v)]. \qquad (6\text{-}23)$$

Then

$$dF = F_1(u, v)\, du + F_2(u, v)\, dv.$$

Now we can use the chain rule to evaluate $F_1(u, v)$ and $F_2(u, v)$, giving

$$dF = \left[f_1(x, y, z)\frac{\partial x}{\partial u} + f_2(x, y, z)\frac{\partial y}{\partial u} + f_3(x, y, z)\frac{\partial z}{\partial u} \right] du$$

$$+ \left[f_1(x, y, z)\frac{\partial x}{\partial v} + f_2(x, y, z)\frac{\partial y}{\partial v} + f_3(x, y, z)\frac{\partial z}{\partial v} \right] dv.$$

Next we rearrange the right member of this equality to obtain

$$dF = f_1(x, y, z)\left[\frac{\partial x}{\partial u}\, du + \frac{\partial x}{\partial v}\, dv\right] + f_2(x, y, z)\left[\frac{\partial y}{\partial u}\, du + \frac{\partial y}{\partial v}\, dv\right]$$

$$+ f_3(x, y, z)\left[\frac{\partial z}{\partial u}\, du + \frac{\partial z}{\partial v}\, dv\right],$$

or

$$dF = f_1(x, y, z)\cdot dx + f_2(x, y, z)\cdot dy + f_3(x, y, z)\cdot dz. \qquad (6\text{-}24)$$

THEOREM 6-2.2. A differentiable function of differentiable functions is differentiable.

PROOF. To avoid excessive notation, we shall give a proof for the case represented by (6-23). The student should be able to see that essentially the same argument can be used in general. We shall use the abbreviated notation whereby x_0, y_0, z_0 denote $x(u_0, v_0)$, $y(u_0, v_0)$, $z(u_0, v_0)$ and $x_0 + \Delta x$, $y_0 + \Delta y$, $z_0 + \Delta z$ denote $x(u_0 + \theta, v_0 + \phi)$, $y(u_0 + \theta, v_0 + \phi)$, $z(u_0 + \theta, v_0 + \phi)$. We are to assume that x, y, and z are differentiable at (u_0, v_0) and that f is differentiable at x_0, y_0, z_0. We must then prove F as defined by (6-23) is differentiable at (u_0, v_0). We have seen that dF can be evaluated formally by use of (6-24), so we need only prove that

$$\lim_{(\theta, \phi) \to (0, 0)} \frac{\Delta F - dF}{(\theta^2 + \phi^2)^{\frac{1}{2}}} = 0.$$

Since f is differentiable at (x_0, y_0, z_0), we know that

$$\frac{[f(x_0 + r,\ y_0 + s,\ z_0 + t) - f(x_0, y_0, z_0)]}{(r^2 + s^2 + t^2)^{\frac{1}{2}}}$$

$$- \frac{[f_1(x_0, y_0, z_0)\cdot r + f_2(x_0, y_0, z_0)\cdot s + f_3(x_0, y_0, z_0)\cdot t]}{(r^2 + s^2 + t^2)^{\frac{1}{2}}}$$

approaches zero as $(r, s, t) \to (0, 0, 0)$. Therefore,

$$\lim_{(r,s,t)\to(0,0,0)} h(r, s, t) = 0,$$

if we define h so that $h(0, 0, 0) = 0$ and, if $(r, s, t) \neq (0, 0, 0)$,

$$(r^2 + s^2 + t^2)^{1/2} h(r, s, t) = [f(x_0 + r, y_0 + s, z_0 + t) - f(x_0, y_0, z_0)]$$
$$- [f_1(x_0, y_0, z_0) \cdot r + f_2(x_0, y_0, z_0) \cdot s$$
$$+ f_3(x_0, y_0, z_0) \cdot t].$$

The last equality is valid whether or not $(r, s, t) = (0, 0, 0)$. Also, $(\Delta F - dF)/(\theta^2 + \phi^2)^{1/2}$ is equal to

$$\frac{[f(x_0 + \Delta x, y_0 + \Delta y, z_0 + \Delta z) - f(x_0, y_0, z_0)]}{(\theta^2 + \phi^2)^{1/2}}$$

$$- \frac{[f_1(x_0, y_0, z_0)\, dx + f_2(x_0, y_0, z_0)\, dy + f_3(x_0, y_0, z_0)\, dz]}{(\theta^2 + \phi^2)^{1/2}}$$

$$= h(\Delta x, \Delta y, \Delta z) \left[\frac{(\Delta x)^2 + (\Delta y)^2 + (\Delta z)^2}{\theta^2 + \phi^2} \right]^{1/2}$$

$$+ f_1(x_0, y_0, z_0) \frac{\Delta x - dx}{(\theta^2 + \phi^2)^{1/2}}$$

$$+ f_2(x_0, y_0, z_0) \frac{\Delta y - dy}{(\theta^2 + \phi^2)^{1/2}}$$

$$+ f_3(x_0, y_0, z_0) \frac{\Delta z - dz}{(\theta^2 + \phi^2)^{1/2}}.$$

The last three terms approach zero as $(\theta, \phi) \to (0, 0)$, since x, y, and z are differentiable at (u_0, v_0). Since x, y, and z are differentiable at (u_0, v_0), each of Δx, Δy, and Δz, and therefore also $h(\Delta x, \Delta y, \Delta z)$, approaches zero as $(\theta, \phi) \to (0, 0)$. Therefore, to complete the proof, it is sufficient to show that

$$\frac{(\Delta x)^2 + (\Delta y)^2 + (\Delta z)^2}{\theta^2 + \phi^2} \quad \text{or} \quad \left[\frac{\Delta x}{(\theta^2 + \phi^2)^{1/2}} \right]^2 + \left[\frac{\Delta y}{(\theta^2 + \phi^2)^{1/2}} \right]^2 + \left[\frac{\Delta z}{(\theta^2 + \phi^2)^{1/2}} \right]^2$$

is bounded on some neighborhood of $(0, 0)$. By choosing α so that $\theta = (\theta^2 + \phi^2)^{1/2} \cos \alpha$ and $\phi = (\theta^2 + \phi^2)^{1/2} \sin \alpha$, we see that

$$\left| \frac{dx}{(\theta^2 + \phi^2)^{1/2}} \right| = \left| \frac{x_1(u_0, v_0) \cdot \theta + x_2(u_0, v_0) \cdot \phi}{(\theta^2 + \phi^2)^{1/2}} \right| \leq |x_1(u_0, v_0)| + |x_2(u_0, v_0)|.$$

It then follows that $|\Delta x/(\theta^2+\phi^2)^{1/2}| < |x_1(u_0, v_0)| + |x_2(u_0, v_0)| + 1$, if the distance between (θ, ϕ) and $(0, 0)$ is small enough that $(\Delta x - dx)/(\theta^2+\phi^2)^{1/2} < 1$. Similarly, there are neighborhoods of $(0, 0)$ in which

$$|\Delta y/(\theta^2+\phi^2)^{1/2}| \quad \text{and} \quad |\Delta z/(\theta^2+\phi^2)^{1/2}|$$

are bounded.

PROBLEMS

1. Use the chain rule for partial derivatives to evaluate the following derivatives.

(a) $D_t(x^y)$, where $x = \sin t$ and $y = \cos t$.

(b) $D_t(e^{x+y})$, where $x = 3t$ and $y = 5t^2$.

(c) $D_t(xy)$, where $x = 2t+1$ and $y = (t+1)^{1/2}$.

(d) $D_t x^{(y^z)}$, where $x = 3t, y = 4t, z = 5t$.

2. In each of the following, f is a function of u, v, and w, and u, v, and w are functions of x and y. Evaluate $\partial F/\partial x$ and $\partial F/\partial y$ at the points indicated, where $F(x, y) = f(u, v, w)$, without first explicitly computing F as a function of x and y.

(a) $f(u, v, w) = uvw; u = 3x+xy, v = x, w = y;$ (0, 1).

(b) $f(u, v, w) = 3+uvw; u = 7x-xy, v = y, w = x;$ (1, -1).

(c) $f(u, v, w) = u^2+uv-v^2;$ $u = 2x+y, v = x-3y,$ $w = x^2+y^2;$ (2, 1).

(d) $f(u, v, w) = (u-v)/(1+uvw); u = x^2-y^2, v = x^2+y^2, w = xy;$ (1, 0).

3. (a) For x, y, and z positive, the equation $x^2+y^2+z^2 = 4$ can be regarded as defining x as a function of y and z, or y as a function of x and z, or z as a function of x and y. Show that

$$\frac{\partial x}{\partial y} \frac{\partial y}{\partial z} \frac{\partial z}{\partial x} = -1.$$

(b) Assume that the equation $f(x, y, z) = 0$ defines x as a differentiable function of y and z, y as a differentiable function of x and z, and z as a differentiable function of x and y. Show that $(\partial x/\partial y)(\partial y/\partial z)(\partial z/\partial x) = -1$ wherever $f_1 f_2 f_3 \neq 0$ and f is differentiable.

4. Let rectangular axes in a plane be rotated through the angle θ. Then new coordinates ξ, η for a point are related to the old coordinates

by the equations $x = \xi \cos\theta - \eta \sin\theta$, and $y = \xi \sin\theta + \eta \cos\theta$. Let $F(\xi, \eta) = f(x, y)$ for all (x, y). Show that

$$\left(\frac{\partial F}{\partial \xi}\right)^2 + \left(\frac{\partial F}{\partial \eta}\right)^2 = \left(\frac{\partial f}{\partial x}\right)^2 + \left(\frac{\partial f}{\partial y}\right)^2.$$

5. Let $w(x, y) = f(x^2 - y^2)$ for all (x, y). Show that

$$y\frac{\partial w}{\partial x} + x\frac{\partial w}{\partial y} = 0.$$

6. Let

$$w(x, y) = f\left(\frac{x}{y}, \frac{x-y}{x}\right)$$

if $xy \neq 0$. Show that

$$x\frac{\partial w}{\partial x} + y\frac{\partial w}{\partial y} = 0.$$

7. In each case, express df at the point for which $r = 1$ and $s = 0$ in terms of dx, dy, dz, and in terms of dr and ds. Do not express f explicitly as a function of r and s.

   (a) $f(x, y, z) = xy/z$, $x = rs$, $y = 2r + 3s$, $z = 3r - 5s$.

   (b) $f(x, y) = 3x + 5y$, $x = 2r - 7s$, $y = r + 2s$.

   (c) $f(x, y) = e^{2x + y} \cos(\pi xy)$, $x = r^2 - s$, $y = r + s^3$.

8. Let f be a function of three variables which has continuous first-order partial derivatives and is *homogeneous of degree n* in the sense that

$$f(tx, ty, tz) = t^n f(x, y, z)$$

for all x, y, and z, and t.

   (a) Show that

   $$xf_1(tx, ty, tz) + yf_2(tx, ty, tz) + zf_3(tx, ty, tz) = nt^{n-1}f(x, y, z).$$

   (b) Show that

   $$xf_1(x, y, z) + yf_2(x, y, z) + zf_3(x, y, z) = nf(x, y, z).$$

[*Note:* This is *Euler's theorem* about homogeneous functions.]

9. Use the definition of problem 8 and verify that $x^3 + 7x^2y + 5yz^2 - 3y^2z$ is homogeneous of degree three. Verify that the conclusion of problem 8(b) is true for this function.

10. Let f, g, and h be functions such that

$$f(x, y) = x^2 g\left(\frac{x}{y}\right) + xy \cdot h\left(\frac{x}{x+y}, \frac{x^2}{y^2}\right).$$

Verify that f is homogeneous of degree two and that

$$xf_1(x, y) + yf_2(x, y) = 2f(x, y).$$

11. Let f be the function for which $f(0, 0) = 0$ and

$$f(u, v) = \frac{u^2 v^2}{(u^2 + v^2)^{3/2}}$$

when $u^2 + v^2 \neq 0$. (a) Show that $f_1(u, v)$ and $f_2(u, v)$ are defined for all (u, v). (b) Does $D_t f(u, v)$ exist for $t = 0$ when $u(t) = t$ and $v(t) = t$? (c) Why does the result of part (b) not contradict the chain rule?

6-3. DIFFERENTIATION OF INTEGRALS

Suppose that f is a continuous function of two variables and that the function F is defined by the equation

$$F(x) = \int_a^b f(x, t) \, dt. \tag{6-25}$$

Natural questions to ask are whether F is differentiable and whether F' can be determined without first evaluating the integral. These questions are answered by the following theorem, for the case that f_1 is continuous.

THEOREM 6-3.1. Suppose F is defined by Eq. (6-25) in an interval containing x_0. Also suppose that f_1 is continuous in a rectangle R which is the set of those points (x, t) such that $t \in [a, b]$ and $x \in I$, where I is a compact interval in the domain of F that contains x_0 (as an interior point if possible). Then

$$F'(x_0) = \int_a^b f_1(x_0, t) \, dt.$$

PROOF. We form the difference quotient whose limit (if it exists) is $F'(x_0)$:

$$\frac{F(x_0 + h) - F(x_0)}{h} = \int_a^b \left[\frac{f(x_0 + h, t) - f(x_0, t)}{h} \right] dt.$$

It follows from the mean value theorem that there is a number θ, depending on h and t, which is between 0 and 1 and is such that

$$\frac{f(x_0 + h, t) - f(x_0, t)}{h} = f_1(x_0 + \theta h, t).$$

For h fixed, it can be shown that θ need not be a continuous function of t. However, it does follow from the fact that the left member of this equality is an integrable function of t that $f_1(x_0 + \theta h, t)$ is integrable. Now we note that

$$\left| \frac{F(x_0 + h) - F(x_0)}{h} - \int_a^b f_1(x_0, t)\, dt \right|$$

$$= \left| \int_a^b [f_1(x_0 + \theta h, t) - f_1(x_0, t)]\, dt \right|. \quad (6\text{-}26)$$

Since f_1 is continuous in the rectangle described in the statement of the theorem, it follows that f_1 is uniformly continuous in this rectangle and that, for any positive number ε, there is a positive number δ such that, if (x_1, t_1) and (x_2, t_2) are in this rectangle, then

$$|f_1(x_1, t_1) - f_1(x_2, t_2)| < \varepsilon \quad \text{if} \quad [(x_1 - x_2)^2 + (t_1 - t_2)^2]^{\frac{1}{2}} < \delta.$$

It is true in particular that, if $t \in [a, b]$, then

$$|f_1(x, t) - f_1(x_0, t)| < \varepsilon \quad \text{if} \quad |x - x_0| < \delta.$$

If $|h| < \delta$, then the right member of Eq. (6-26) is not larger than $\varepsilon(b - a)$. Therefore, it follows from (6-26) that

$$F'(x_0) = \lim_{h \to 0} \left[\frac{F(x_0 + h) - F(x_0)}{h} \right] = \int_a^b f_1(x_0, t)\, dt.$$

ILLUSTRATION 1. Suppose that

$$F(x) = \int_0^1 \frac{\sin xt}{t}\, dt.$$

Since $\partial[(\sin xt)/t]/\partial x = \cos xt$ and $\cos xt$ is continuous for all (x, t), it follows from Theorem 6-3.1 that

$$F'(x) = \int_0^1 \cos xt\, dt = \left[\frac{\sin xt}{x} \right]_0^1 = \frac{\sin x}{x}.$$

[If in the integral that defines $F(x)$ we make the substitution $xt = s$, we obtain $\int_0^x (\sin s)/s\, ds$, from which we can obtain $F'(x) = (\sin x)/x$ by using the fundamental theorem of calculus.]

By using the chain rule, we can extend Theorem 6-3.1 to the case for which the limits of integration are functions of x. If we wish to find $F'(x)$, where f and f_1 are continuous and F is defined by

$$F(x) = \int_{u(x)}^{v(x)} f(x, t)\, dt,$$

we may consider the expression $\int_u^v f(x, t)\, dt = \Phi(u, v, x)$. Formal use of the chain rule gives

$$F'(x) = \frac{\partial \Phi}{\partial u}\frac{du}{dx} + \frac{\partial \Phi}{\partial v}\frac{dv}{dx} + \frac{\partial \Phi}{\partial x}.$$

From Theorem 6-3.1 and the fundamental theorem of calculus, we obtain

$$\frac{\partial \Phi}{\partial x} = \int_u^v f_1(x, t)\, dt, \quad \frac{\partial \Phi}{\partial u} = \frac{\partial}{\partial u}\int_v^u -f(x, t)\, dt = -f(x, u),$$

$$\frac{\partial \Phi}{\partial v} = f(x, v).$$

Continuity of $\partial \Phi / \partial x$ in the region R described in Theorem 6-3.1 can be established by using uniform continuity of f_1, much as it was used in the proof of Theorem 6-3.1. Continuity of $\partial \Phi / \partial u$ and $\partial \Phi / \partial v$ follows from continuity of f. Thus, use of the chain rule was valid. If we substitute for the partial derivatives of Φ in $F'(x)$, we obtain

$$F'(x) = \int_{u(x)}^{v(x)} f_1(x, t)\, dt - f[x, u(x)]u'(x) + f[x, v(x)]v'(x). \quad (6\text{-}27)$$

ILLUSTRATION 2. Suppose that

$$F(x) = \int_{1/x}^{x} t^{-1}e^{xt}\, dt.$$

Then

$$F'(x) = \int_{1/x}^{x} e^{xt}\, dt - (x^{-1})^{-1}e^{xx^{-1}}(-x^{-2}) + x^{-1}e^{x^2}$$

$$= [x^{-1}e^{xt}]_{1/x}^{x} + x^{-1}e + x^{-1}e^{x^2} = 2x^{-1}e^{x^2}.$$

Often it is useful to differentiate an improper integral with respect to a parameter underneath the integral sign. The following theorem describes a situation for which this leads to a valid conclusion. Note that x_0 may be an end point of I.

THEOREM 6-3.2. Suppose $F(x) = \int_c^{+\infty} f(x, t)\, dt$ for x in an interval containing x_0 and that f_1 is continuous on the set of all (x, t) for which $x \in I$ and $t \geq c$, where I is a compact interval in the domain of F that contains x_0 (as an interior point if possible). Suppose also that

$\int_c^\tau f_1(x, t)\, dt$ converges uniformly to $\int_c^{+\infty} f_1(x, t)\, dt$ on I as $\tau \to +\infty$. Then

$$F'(x_0) = \int_c^{+\infty} f_1(x_0, t)\, dt.$$

PROOF. The proof is similar to that of Theorem 6-3.1. We can derive the following equation exactly as Eq. (6-26) was derived:

$$\left| \frac{F(x_0+h) - F(x_0)}{h} - \int_c^{+\infty} f_1(x_0, t)\, dt \right|$$

$$= \left| \int_c^{+\infty} [f_1(x_0 + \theta h, t) - f_1(x_0, t)]\, dt \right|. \qquad (6\text{-}28)$$

Since $\int_c^\tau f_1(x, t)\, dt$ approaches $\int_c^{+\infty} f_1(x, t)\, dt$ uniformly on I as $\tau \to +\infty$, for any positive number ε there is a number T such that

$$\left| \int_T^{+\infty} f_1(x, t)\, dt \right| < \tfrac{1}{4}\varepsilon \quad \text{if} \quad x \in I.$$

Then the right member of Eq. (6-28) differs from

$$\left| \int_c^T [f_1(x_0 + \theta h, t) - f_1(x_0, t)]\, dt \right| \qquad (6\text{-}29)$$

by less than $\tfrac{1}{2}\varepsilon$. Just as in the proof of Theorem 6-3.1, we could show that expression (6-29) approaches zero as $h \to 0$. Then the right member of (6-28) is less than ε if $|h|$ is small enough that expression (6-29) is less than $\tfrac{1}{2}\varepsilon$. Therefore, both members of Eq. (6-28) approach zero as $h \to 0$, and

$$F'(x_0) = \lim_{h \to 0} \frac{F(x_0+h) - F(x_0)}{h} = \int_c^{+\infty} f_1(x_0, t)\, dt.$$

ILLUSTRATION 3. Let us evaluate $\int_c^{+\infty} (\sin t)/t\, dt$, which we know exists as an improper integral [see problem 4(a), page 166, and problem 8, page 259]. We shall use the function F defined for $x > 0$ by

$$F(x) = \int_0^{+\infty} \frac{\sin t}{t}\, e^{-xt}\, dt. \qquad (6\text{-}30)$$

If we differentiate (6-30) and then integrate, we obtain

$$F'(x) = -\int_0^{+\infty} \sin t\, e^{-xt}\, dt = \frac{-1}{1+x^2}. \qquad (6\text{-}31)$$

For $x \geq r > 0$, we have

$$\left| \int_T^{+\infty} \sin t \, e^{-xt} \, dt \right| \leq \int_T^{+\infty} e^{-xt} \, dt = \frac{e^{-xT}}{x} \leq \frac{e^{-rT}}{r}.$$

Since $e^{-rT}/r \to 0$ as $T \to +\infty$, it follows that $\int_0^\tau \sin t \, e^{-xt} \, dt$ approaches $\int_0^{+\infty} \sin t \, e^{-xt} \, dt$ uniformly on $\{x : x \geq r\}$. Thus, the differentiation was valid for $x > 0$, and it follows from Eq. (6-31) that there is a number c such that

$$F(x) = c - \tan^{-1} x \quad \text{if} \quad x > 0.$$

Since $|\sin t| \leq |t|$, we have $|F(x)| \leq \int_0^{+\infty} e^{-xt} \, dt = 1/x$ and $\lim_{x \to +\infty} F(x) = 0$. Thus, $c = \frac{1}{2}\pi$ and

$$F(x) = \tfrac{1}{2}\pi - \tan^{-1} x \quad \text{if} \quad x > 0. \tag{6-32}$$

To obtain our final conclusions, we shall show that

$$\lim_{x \to 0} \left| \int_0^{+\infty} \frac{\sin t}{t} \, dt - F(x) \right| = \lim_{x \to 0} \left| \int_0^{+\infty} \frac{\sin t}{t} \, dt - \int_0^{+\infty} \frac{\sin t}{t} e^{-xt} \, dt \right| = 0.$$

To do this, we write

$$\int_0^{+\infty} \frac{\sin t}{t} (1 - e^{-xt}) \, dt = \sum_{n=1}^{+\infty} a_n, \qquad a_n = \int_{(n-1)\pi}^{n\pi} \frac{\sin t}{t} (1 - e^{-xt}) \, dt.$$

Since $e^\theta > 1 + \theta$ if $\theta > 0$, we have

$$\frac{d[(1 - e^{-xt})/t]}{dt} = \frac{1 + tx - e^{xt}}{t^2 \, e^{xt}} < 0 \quad \text{if} \quad x > 0 \quad \text{and} \quad t > 0.$$

Therefore, $(1 - e^{-xt})/t$ is a decreasing function of t for $t > 0$, so that $|a_n| > |a_{n+1}|$ for all n. Since $\sum a_n$ is an alternating series, this implies that the absolute value of the sum is less than $|a_1|$ [see the *alternating series test*, page 201]. Thus,

$$\left| \int_0^{+\infty} \frac{\sin t}{t} (1 - e^{-xt}) \, dt \right|$$
$$< \int_0^\pi \sin t \, \frac{1 - e^{-xt}}{t} \, dt < x \int_0^\pi \sin t \, dt = 2x.$$

Finally, we have

$$\int_0^{+\infty} \frac{\sin t}{t} \, dt = \lim_{x \to 0} F(x) = \tfrac{1}{2}\pi. \tag{6-33}$$

PROBLEMS

1. For each of the following, let $f(x)$ be equal to the given expression. Evaluate $f'(x)$ by differentiating, without integrating first. Check by integrating and then differentiating.

(a) $\int_1^{\sqrt{x}} t \, dt.$

(c) $\int_0^x \sin^{-1} \dfrac{t}{x} \, dt.$

(b) $\int_{x^2}^{x^3} (t+t^2) \, dt.$

(d) $\int_0^{3x} \cos(x+t) \, dt.$

2. Evaluate the following derivatives.

(a) $D_x \int_1^2 \dfrac{\cos xt}{t} \, dt.$

(c) $D_x \int_0^{1/x} \dfrac{\sin xt}{t} \, dt.$

(b) $D_x \int_{x^2}^3 \ln(1+t^2) \, dt.$

(d) $D_x \int_{x^2}^{x^3} \dfrac{\sin xt}{t} \, dt.$

3. Use the fact that $\int_0^1 t^k \, dt = 1/(k+1)$ if $k > 0$ to evaluate $\int_0^1 t^k (\ln t)^2 \, dt$ for $k > 0$, where k is an arbitrary positive number.

4. Evaluate each of the following integrals by first evaluating the derivatives with respect to x and then integrating and evaluating the constant of integration.

(a) $\int_0^1 f(x, t) \, dt$, where $f(x, 1) = x$, $f(x, 0) = 0$, and $f(x, t) = (t^x - 1)/(\ln t)$ if $0 < t < 1$.

(b) $\int_0^{x - 1/2} \ln(1 + xt^2) \, dt, \quad x > 0.$

5. Use the results of problem 4 to evaluate the following.

(a) $\int_0^1 \dfrac{t-1}{\ln t} \, dt.$

(b) $\int_0^1 \ln(1+t^2) \, dt.$

6. Evaluate $\int_0^{+\infty} e^{-xt} \, dt$ for $x > 0$ and use the result to prove that, for any positive integer n,

$$\int_0^{+\infty} t^n e^{-xt} \, dt = \frac{n!}{x^{n+1}} \quad \text{if} \quad x > 0.$$

7. Evaluate $\int_0^{+\infty} (\sin^2 xt)/t^2 \, dt$ by using integration by parts.

8. (a) Evaluate the derivative of $\int_0^{+\infty} (e^{-xt} - e^{-kt}) t^{-1} \, dt$ for k a positive constant and $x > 0$. (b) Use the result of part (a) to show that

$$\int_0^{+\infty} \frac{e^{-t} - e^{-kt}}{t} \, dt = \ln k \quad \text{if} \quad k > 0.$$

9. Given $F(x) = \int_0^{+\infty} e^{-t^2} \cos tx \, dt$, use differentiation and integration by parts to prove that $F'(x) = -\frac{1}{2}xF(x)$ and that

$$\int_0^{+\infty} e^{-t^2} \cos tx \, dt = e^{-x^2/4} \int_0^{+\infty} e^{-t^2} \, dt \text{ for all } x.$$

[In Illustration 3 of Section 8-2, we shall see that $\int_0^{+\infty} e^{-t^2} \, dt = \frac{1}{2}\sqrt{\pi}$.]

10. Suppose that

$$F(x) = \int_0^x \frac{(x-t)^{n-1}}{(n-1)!} f(t) \, dt.$$

Show that (a) $F^{(n)}(x) = f(x)$; (b) $F(x)$ can be obtained from f by integrating n times between the limits 0 and x.

11. Recall that $\Gamma(n+1) = n!$ [Illustration 2, page 164], which suggests we might define the function F of problem 10 by

$$F(x) = \int_0^x \frac{(x-t)^{n-1}}{\Gamma(n)} f(t) \, dt,$$

for n any positive number. Let F be called the nth *integral* of f between the limits 0 and x. [*Note:* Any expression obtained by n successive antidifferentiations of f differs from F by a polynomial of degree $n-1$.] (**a**) Evaluate the "one-half integral" of f, where $f(x) = x$ for all x. (**b**) Evaluate the "one-half integral" of g, where

$$g(x) = \frac{4}{3\Gamma(\frac{1}{2})} x^{3/2} \text{ for all } x.$$

12. For the nth integral as defined in problem 11, show that the mth integral of the nth integral of a continuous function f is equal to the $(m+n)$th integral of f, whether or not m and n are integers. Assume the following equality [see problem 9 of Section 8-2]:

$$\int_s^x (x-t)^{m-1}(t-s)^{n-1} \, dt = (x-s)^{m+n-1} \frac{\Gamma(m)\Gamma(n)}{\Gamma(m+n)}.$$

6-4. MIXED PARTIAL DERIVATIVES

As with ordinary differentiation, one can take partial derivatives of partial derivatives to obtain partial derivatives of higher order. The use of subscripts and of the symbol ∂ in denoting such derivatives is indicated by the following example. Suppose f is the function defined by

$$f(x, y) = \sin xy + x^3 y^5.$$

Then

$$\frac{\partial f}{\partial x} = f_1(x, y) = y \cos xy + 3x^2 y^5, \quad \frac{\partial f}{\partial y} = f_2(x, y) = x \cos xy + 5x^3 y^4.$$

The second-order partial derivatives are

$$\frac{\partial^2 f}{\partial x^2} = f_{11}(x, y) = -y^2 \sin xy + 6xy^5,$$

$$\frac{\partial^2 f}{\partial y^2} = f_{22}(x, y) = -x^2 \sin xy + 20x^3 y^3,$$

$$\frac{\partial}{\partial y}\left(\frac{\partial f}{\partial x}\right) = \frac{\partial^2 f}{\partial y \, \partial x} = f_{12}(x, y) = \cos xy - xy \sin xy + 15x^2 y^4,$$

$$\frac{\partial}{\partial x}\left(\frac{\partial f}{\partial y}\right) = \frac{\partial^2 f}{\partial x \, \partial y} = f_{21}(x, y) = \cos xy - xy \sin xy + 15x^2 y^4.$$

When differentiations are performed with respect to several variables, questions arise as to the importance of the order in which these differentiations occur. There is at least a formal difference between the meaning of f_{12} and f_{21}, but in the above example these are equal. We now wish to prove a rather general theorem about commutativity of partial differentiation.

THEOREM 6-4.1. Suppose f is a function of two variables such that f_{21} is continuous at all points of a neighborhood of the point (x_0, y_0), and (x_0, y_0) is in the domain of f_1. Then (x_0, y_0) is in the domain of f_{12} and

$$f_{12}(x_0, y_0) = f_{21}(x_0, y_0).\dagger$$

PROOF. Since f_{21} is continuous in a neighborhood U of (x_0, y_0), there is a neighborhood V of (x_0, y_0) which is the interior of a square and in which f_{21} is continuous [see Fig. 6-4]. Then for any (x, y) in this square

---

† By another method, this conclusion can be shown to follow from the following assumptions: the domain of f_{21} contains a neighborhood of (x_0, y_0); f_{21} is continuous *at* (x_0, y_0), and the domain of f_1 contains a neighborhood of (x_0, y_0). See *Differential and Integral Calculus* by R. Courant (New York: Interscience Publishers, Inc., 1936), II, p. 56, footnote.

the following double integral exists [see Theorem 5-2.3] and can be evaluated as an iterated integral [Theorem 5-2.5]:

$$\int_R f_{21} \, dA = \int_{y_0}^y \int_{x_0}^x f_{21}(s, t) \, ds \, dt$$

$$= \int_{y_0}^y [f_2(x, t) - f_2(x_0, t)] \, dt. \qquad (6\text{-}34)$$

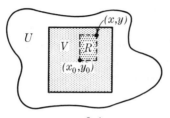

FIG. 6-4

Although we do not know that the integrand in the right member of this equality is continuous, we can conclude from our manipulations that the integral exists. The rest of the proof uses only the existence of the last integral in Eq. (6-34) and makes no further use of the double integral. The integrand has an antiderivative—namely, $f(x, t) - f(x_0, t)$—and it follows from the second form of the fundamental theorem of calculus [Theorem 3-6.2] that the integral is equal to

$$f(x, y) - f(x_0, y) - f(x, y_0) + f(x_0, y_0).$$

Therefore,

$$f(x, y) = \int_{y_0}^y [f_2(x, t) - f_2(x_0, t)] \, dt + f(x_0, y) + f(x, y_0) - f(x_0, y_0). \quad (6\text{-}35)$$

Since f_{21} is continuous, we can evaluate the partial derivative with respect to x of the integral in this equality by differentiating under the integral sign. The only other term in the right member which involves x is $f(x, y_0)$ and $f_1(x_0, y_0)$ is assumed to exist. Therefore, $f_1(x_0, y)$ exists for y near y_0 and

$$f_1(x_0, y) = \int_{y_0}^y f_{21}(x_0, t) \, dt + f_1(x_0, y_0).$$

Since f_{21} is continuous, we can use the first form of the fundamental theorem of calculus [Theorem 3-6.1] to obtain $f_{12}(x_0, y_0) = f_{21}(x_0, y_0)$.

This theorem about commutativity of partial differentiation implies that the number of distinct derivatives of the second and higher orders is much smaller than might have been expected. For example, if f is a function of three variables and all the derivatives formed are continuous, then

$$f_{112} = f_{121} = f_{211},$$

$$f_{1223} = f_{1232} = f_{1322} = f_{3122} = f_{3212} = f_{2312}$$

$$= f_{2132} = f_{2123} = f_{2213} = f_{2231} = f_{2321} = f_{3221}.$$

In these equalities, each partial derivative is obtained from the preceding one by interchanging adjacent subscripts. This method can be used to show that *in the repeated differentiation of a function of several variables the order of differentiation may be changed at will, provided only that all partial derivatives of that order are defined and continuous* [see problem 7].

PROBLEMS

1. For each of the following, verify by direct evaluation that $f_{12} = f_{21}$.
   (a) $f(x, y) = e^{2x} \sinh 3y + \sin (5x - 7y)$.
   (b) $f(x, y, z) = xy^2 + x^2y^3z + x^5y^2z^3$.

2. By direct evaluation, verify that $f_{123} = f_{312}$, where

$$f(x, y, z) = xy^4 \cos (2x - y - 2z) + 7x - 9y.$$

3. Let $f(x, y) = x + F(x - y^2)$. Show that

$$2y^2 \frac{\partial^2 f}{\partial x^2} - y \frac{\partial^2 f}{\partial x \, \partial y} - \frac{\partial^2 f}{\partial y^2} - 2 \frac{\partial f}{\partial x} = -2.$$

4. Let $f(x, y) = x \cdot F(3x + 2y)$. Show that

$$4x \frac{\partial^2 f}{\partial x^2} - 9x \frac{\partial^2 f}{\partial y^2} - 12 \frac{\partial f}{\partial y} = 0.$$

5. Let $u(x, y) = f(2x + 3y) + g(3x - 2y) = f(r) + g(s) = v(r, s)$. Show that

   (a) $\dfrac{\partial^2 u}{\partial x^2} = 4f''(2x + 3y) + 9g''(3x - 2y)$;

   (b) $\dfrac{\partial^2 u}{\partial x \, \partial y} = 6f''(2x + 3y) - 6g''(3x - 2y)$;

   (c) $\dfrac{\partial^2 u}{\partial y^2} = 9f''(2x + 3y) + 4g''(3x - 2y)$;

   (d) $\dfrac{\partial^2 u}{\partial x^2} + \dfrac{\partial^2 u}{\partial y^2} = 13 \left[\dfrac{\partial^2 v}{\partial r^2} + \dfrac{\partial^2 v}{\partial s^2} \right].$

6. Let $u(x, y) = f(3x+2y)+g(x-2y) = f(r)+g(s) = v(r, s)$. Show that

(a) $\dfrac{\partial^2 u}{\partial x^2} = 9f''(3x+2y)+g''(x-2y)$;

(b) $\dfrac{\partial^2 u}{\partial x\,\partial y} = 6f''(3x+2y)-2g''(x-2y)$;

(c) $\dfrac{\partial^2 u}{\partial y^2} = 4f''(3x+2y)+4g''(x-2y)$;

(d) $4\dfrac{\partial^2 u}{\partial x^2}-4\dfrac{\partial^2 u}{\partial x\,\partial y}-3\dfrac{\partial^2 u}{\partial y^2} = 0$, $\dfrac{\partial^2 v}{\partial r\,\partial s} = 0$.

7.* Let f be a function of k variables, all of whose partial derivatives of order n are continuous at a point P. Explain why all partial derivatives of order less than n are continuous at P.

8. Let $f(x, y) = x^2 y^3 + y^2 \sin(1/y) + x^2 \sin(1/x)$ if neither x nor y is zero, $f(0, y) = y^2 \sin(1/y)$ if $y \neq 0$, $f(x, 0) = x^2 \sin(1/x)$ if $x \neq 0$, and $f(0, 0) = 0$. (a) Show that the conditions of Theorem 6-4.1 are satisfied and that $f_{12}(x, y) = f_{21}(x, y)$ for all (x, y). (b) Show that neither f_1 nor f_2 is continuous at $(0, 0)$. [*Note:* The second and third terms in the expression for $f(x, y)$ correspond to the terms $f(x_0, y)$ and $f(x, y_0)$ in Eq. (6-35), whose partial derivatives may be discontinuous.]

9. Let f be defined by $f(0, 0) = 0$ and $f(x, y) = xy(x^2-y^2)(x^2+y^2)^{-1}$ if $x^2+y^2 \neq 0$. Prove that $\partial^2 f/\partial x\partial y$ and $\partial^2 f/\partial y\partial x$ exist and are not equal at the point $(0, 0)$. Explain why this does not contradict Theorem 6-4.1.

10. Let r and θ be functions of x and y for which $x = r\cos\theta$ and $y = r\sin\theta$. Show that

$$\frac{\partial r}{\partial x} = \cos\theta, \quad \frac{\partial\theta}{\partial x} = -\frac{\sin\theta}{r}, \quad \frac{\partial r}{\partial y} = \sin\theta, \quad \frac{\partial\theta}{\partial y} = \frac{\cos\theta}{r}.$$

[*Hint:* Differentiate each of the given equations with respect to x and with respect to y.]

11. Let $u(x, y) = u(r\cos\theta, r\sin\theta) = v(r, \theta)$. Use the results of problem 10 and show that

(a) $\left(\dfrac{\partial u}{\partial x}\right)^2 + \left(\dfrac{\partial u}{\partial y}\right)^2 = \left(\dfrac{\partial v}{\partial r}\right)^2 + \dfrac{1}{r^2}\left(\dfrac{\partial v}{\partial\theta}\right)^2$;

(b*) $\dfrac{\partial^2 u}{\partial x^2} + \dfrac{\partial^2 u}{\partial y^2} = \dfrac{\partial^2 v}{\partial r^2} + \dfrac{1}{r}\left(\dfrac{\partial v}{\partial r}\right) + \dfrac{1}{r^2}\dfrac{\partial^2 v}{\partial\theta^2}$.

6-5. TAYLOR'S THEOREM AND MAXIMA AND MINIMA

There is a simple method by which Taylor's theorem can be extended to a function of more than one variable. We shall discuss this only for a function of two variables, but the student should be able to write analogous formulas for functions of more than two variables. For a function f of two variables and points (a, b) and (x, y), we let $h = x - a$ and $k = y - b$, and define a function F by

$$F(t) = f(a + th, b + tk). \tag{6-36}$$

Then $F(1) = f(x, y)$ and $F(0) = f(a, b)$. If we apply Taylor's theorem with Lagrange's form of the remainder, we obtain

$$F(1) = F(0) + F'(0) + \frac{1}{2!} F''(0) + \frac{1}{3!} F'''(0)$$

$$+ \cdots + \frac{1}{n!} F^{(n)}(0) + \frac{1}{(n+1)!} F^{(n+1)}(\theta), \tag{6-37}$$

where θ is a number between 0 and 1. The chain rule for partial differentiation is needed for evaluating the derivatives of F. For F', we have

$$F'(t) = h \cdot f_1(a + th, b + tk) + k \cdot f_2(a + th, b + tk).$$

If we let D_1 and D_2 indicate differentiation with respect to the first and second variables, respectively, then we can write $F'(t)$ as

$$F'(t) = [(hD_1 + kD_2)f]_{(a + th, b + tk)}.$$

For any function of two variables whose first variable is replaced by $a + th$ and second variable by $b + tk$, the derivative with respect to t can be found by applying the operator $hD_1 + kD_2$, as we have done for the function F. Therefore, to find $F''(t)$, we shall use this operator again. Since $D_1 D_2 = D_2 D_1$ and

$$D_1(hD_1 + kD_2) = hD_1^2 + kD_1D_2, \quad D_2(hD_1 + kD_2) = hD_2D_1 + kD_2^2,$$

it follows that

$$[hD_1 + kD_2][(hD_1 + kD_2)f] = (h^2 D_1^2 + 2hk D_1 D_2 + k^2 D_2^2)f,$$

and

$$\begin{aligned} F''(t) &= [(hD_1 + kD_2)^2 f]_{(a + th, b + tk)} \\ &= [(h^2 D_1^2 + 2hk \cdot D_1 D_2 + k^2 D_2^2)f]_{(a + th, b + tk)} \\ &= h^2 f_{11}(a + th, b + tk) + 2hk \cdot f_{12}(a + th, b + tk) \\ &\quad + k^2 f_{22}(a + th, b + tk). \end{aligned}$$

In general, we have

$$F^{(n)}(t) = [(hD_1 + kD_2)^n f]_{(a+th,\,b+tk)}.$$

where $(hD_1 + kD_2)^n$ is expanded as if h and k were constants.

Now for the number θ of Eq. (6-37), we let $(a + \theta h, b + \theta k) = (\xi, \eta)$ and write (6-37) as the following equality, called *Taylor's theorem for a function of two variables*:

$$f(x, y) = f(a, b) + [h \cdot f_1(a, b) + k \cdot f_2(a, b)]$$

$$+ \frac{1}{2!} [h^2 f_{11}(a, b) + 2hk \cdot f_{12}(a, b) + k^2 f_{22}(a, b)]$$

$$+ \cdots + \frac{1}{n!} [(hD_1 + kD_2)^n f]_{(a,b)}$$

$$+ \frac{1}{(n+1)!} [(hD_1 + kD_2)^{n+1} f]_{(\xi,\eta)}, \qquad (6\text{-}38)$$

where (ξ, η) is a point on the line segment joining (a, b) and (x, y). To justify use of the chain rule and to justify changes in the order of partial differentiation, we shall assume that all partial derivatives in (6-38) are continuous in a neighborhood of (a, b). This will be the case if all partial derivatives of order $n + 1$ are continuous in a neighborhood of (a, b) [see problem 7 of Section 6-4].

ILLUSTRATION 1.   If $f(x, y) = \sin (x + \ln y)$, then

$$f_1(x, y) = \cos (x + \ln y), \qquad f_2(x, y) = \frac{1}{y} \cos (x + \ln y),$$

$$f_{11}(x, y) = -\sin (x + \ln y), \quad f_{12}(x, y) = \frac{-\sin (x + \ln y)}{y},$$

and

$$f_{22}(x, y) = \frac{-\sin (x + \ln y) - \cos (x + \ln y)}{y^2}.$$

Using $(a, b) = (0, 1)$ and $n = 2$ in Eq. (6-38), we have

$$f(x, y) = x + (y-1) - \tfrac{1}{2}(y-1)^2 + \tfrac{1}{6}\{[xD_1 + (y-1)D_2]^3 f\}_{(\xi,\eta)}, \quad (6\text{-}39)$$

where we understand that D_1 and D_2 in $[xD_1 + (y-1)D_2]^3$ behave as if the x and y in the bracketed expression were constants.

Also, (ξ, η) is a point on the line joining $(0, 1)$ and (x, y). The last term in Eq. (6-39) is the error in approximating $\sin(x+\ln y)$ by $x+(y-1)-\frac{1}{2}(y-1)^2$. Although the values of ξ and η are not known and the error terms cannot be determined precisely by using this expression, we can obtain an upper bound for the error. For example, if we assume that $y > 1$, so that $1/\eta < 1$, then $|f_{111}|$, $|f_{112}|$, $|f_{122}|$, and $|f_{222}|$ have upper bounds of 1, 1, 2, and 4, respectively, and it follows that the error is not larger than

$$\tfrac{1}{6}[|x|^3 + 3x^2(y-1) + 6|x|(y-1)^2 + 4(y-1)^3].$$

If in particular $x = .1$ and $y = 1.1$, then the error is not larger than

$$\tfrac{1}{6}[.001 + .003 + .006 + .004] < .0024.$$

Therefore, $\sin(.1 + \ln 1.1) = .195 + E$, where $|E| < .0024$.

Taylor's theorem can be used to establish tests for maxima and minima of functions of two variables. At present, we know only that if a function f has a relative maximum or a relative minimum at a point (a, b) and the domains of f_1 and f_2 contain a neighborhood of (a, b), then

$$f_1(a, b) = f_2(a, b) = 0.$$

If we assume because of mathematical or physical considerations that f *has* a maximum (or minimum) at some point with a neighborhood in the domains of f_1 and f_2, then this maximum (or minimum) is one of the points at which both f_1 and f_2 have zero values. However, a point at which both f_1 and f_2 have zero values is not necessarily a maximum point or a minimum point. We shall establish the following rule for determining whether such a point is a maximum point or a minimum point.

Suppose f is a function whose second-order partial derivatives are continuous at all points of a neighborhood of a point (a, b), and that

$$f_1(a, b) = f_2(a, b) = 0. \tag{6-40}$$

If $(f_{12})^2 - f_{11}f_{22}$ is negative at (a, b), then f has an extreme value at (a, b); this is a relative maximum if $f_{11}(a, b) < 0$ [and consequently $f_{22}(a, b) < 0$], and a relative minimum if $f_{11}(a, b) > 0$.

If $(f_{12})^2 - f_{11}f_{22}$ is positive at (a, b), then f has neither a relative maximum nor a relative minimum at (a, b), but has a saddle point.

The fact that $[f_{12}(a, b)]^2 - f_{11}(a, b)f_{22}(a, b) = 0$ is not sufficient information to determine whether f has a relative maximum or minimum, or neither a relative maximum nor a relative minimum.

The equalities in (6-40) are necessary conditions for a relative maximum or a relative minimum. These conditions are equivalent to the geometric condition that the tangent plane to the surface whose equation is $z = f(x, y)$ be horizontal. A proof that f has a relative maximum at (a, b) can be interpreted as showing that for points (x, y) near (a, b) the surface is not above the tangent plane. A proof that f has a relative minimum at (a, b) can be interpreted as showing that for points near (a, b) the surface is not below the tangent plane.

Because of conditions (6-40), it follows from Taylor's theorem that

$$f(x, y) = f(a, b) + \tfrac{1}{2}[f_{11}(\xi, \eta) \cdot h^2 + 2f_{12}(\xi, \eta) \cdot hk + f_{22}(\xi, \eta) \cdot k^2]. \quad (6\text{-}41)$$

Now, if we let $A = f_{11}(\xi, \eta)$, $B = f_{12}(\xi, \eta)$, and $C = f_{22}(\xi, \eta)$, then the expression in brackets in Eq. (6-41) is equal to

$$Ah^2 + 2Bhk + Ck^2. \quad (6\text{-}42)$$

This can be changed into an expression with no mixed-product term by a rotation of axes. Explicitly, there is a number α which has the property that, if

$$h = h^* \cos \alpha - k^* \sin \alpha \quad \text{and} \quad k = h^* \sin \alpha + k^* \cos \alpha,$$

then there are numbers A^* and C^* for which (6-42) is equal to

$$A^*(h^*)^2 + C^*(k^*)^2, \quad (6\text{-}43)$$

and

$$(2B)^2 - 4AC = -4A^*C^*, \quad A + C = A^* + C^*. \quad (6\text{-}44)$$

Now suppose that $(f_{12})^2 - f_{11}f_{22}$ is negative at (a, b). Then neither $f_{11}(a, b)$ nor $f_{22}(a, b)$ is zero. Since f_{11}, f_{12}, and f_{22} are continuous, there is a neighborhood U of (a, b) such that, if $(x, y) \in U$, then $B^2 - AC < 0$ for the numbers A, B, and C in (6-42). Since f_{11} is continuous and $f_{11}(a, b) \neq 0$, we can choose the neighborhood U so that it is also true that A has the same sign as $f_{11}(a, b)$. It now follows from $B^2 - AC < 0$ and the equations in (6-44) that A and C are both positive or both negative; A^* and C^* are both positive or both negative; and finally that A, C, A^*, and C^* are all positive or all negative. If $f_{11}(a, b) > 0$, then A^* and C^* are positive, so that (6-43) is positive, making (6-42) positive, from which it follows via (6-41) that $f(x, y) > f(a, b)$. Therefore, f has a relative minimum at (a, b) if $f_{11}(a, b) > 0$, Similarly, f has a relative maximum at (a, b) if $f_{11}(a, b) < 0$.

Now suppose that $(f_{12})^2 - f_{11}f_{22}$ is positive at (a, b). The line in the (x, y)-plane which passes through the point (a, b) and has slope m has parametric equations $x = a + t$ and $y = b + mt$. We can define a function F by $F(t) = f(a + t, b + mt)$. Then

$$F'(0) = f_1(a, b) + mf_2(a, b) = 0,$$

and F has a relative maximum or a relative minimum at $t = 0$ according to whether $F''(0) < 0$ or $F''(0) > 0$. Suppose g is the function defined by

$$F''(0) = f_{11}(a, b) + 2mf_{12}(a, b) + m^2 f_{22}(a, b) = g(m).$$

If $f_{22}(a, b) \neq 0$, then the graph of g is a parabola. Since the discriminant of this quadratic equation is positive, $g(m)$ has two zeros. If $f_{22}(a, b) = 0$, then the linear equation $g(m) = 0$ has one solution. In either case, there are two lines [one of which is parallel to the y-axis if $f_{22}(a, b) = 0$] separating those lines for which $F''(0) < 0$ and those for which $F''(0) > 0$. If $F''(0) < 0$ for a certain value of m, then there is a relative maximum at (a, b) for the set of points (x, y, z) for which $z = f(x, y)$ and (x, y) is on the line through (a, b) with slope m; if $F''(0) > 0$, there is a relative minimum at (a, b). This means that the surface has a *saddle point* at (a, b) in the sense that there are two lines through (a, b) that separate (1) those lines through (a, b) which have the property that for sufficiently small segments about (a, b) corresponding points on the surface are *above* the tangent plane, and (2) those lines for which the corresponding points on the surface are *below* the tangent plane. In Fig. 6-5, these separating lines are the lines L_1 and L_2.

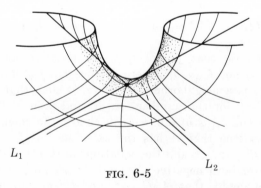

L_1 L_2

FIG. 6-5

If $(f_{12})^2 - f_{11}f_{22}$ is zero at (a, b), then more information must be known before it can be determined whether f has an extreme value at (a, b) [see problems 3(e), 6, 7]. However, in this case f *does not* have a saddle point at (a, b).

PROBLEMS

1. For each of the following, use (a, b) as the given point and find the terms given by Taylor's theorem involving derivatives of second or lower orders.

(*a*) e^{2x+3y}; $(0, 0)$.

(*b*) $(\sin x)(\cos y)$; $(0, 0)$.

(*c*) $\cos (x^y)$; $(\pi, 1)$.

(*d*) $8/(2-3x+5y)$; $(0, 0)$.

(*e*) $(x+1)^{(x+1)(y+1)}$; $(0, 0)$.

(*f*) $x^{\sin y}$; $(1, 0)$.

2. Use Taylor's theorem to write f as a polynomial in $x-1$, $y+2$, and $z-3$, where f is defined by $f(x, y, z) = 3z - 4y + 2x^2 + yz + x^2y$.

3. For each of the following, determine all maximum points, minimum points, and saddle points.

(*a*) $x^2 + 4xy$.

(*b*) $3xy - 3x^2 - y^2 - 12x + 7y + 5$.

(*c*) $x^4 + 2y^4 + 32x - y + 17$.

(*d*) $x^2 + 4xy + 2y^2 - 2y$.

(*e*) $(x-1)^4 + (y-1)^4$.

(*f*) $x^2 + 3y^4 - 4y^3 - 12y^2$.

(*g*) $(2x+5y-10)(x-7)(y-1)$,

(*h*) $(2x-3y+4)(3x+y-5)$.

4. Let $f(x, y) = 2x + 4y - kx^2y^4$, where $k \neq 0$. Show that f has a saddle point, but no points of relative maximum or minimum.

5. Find the shortest distance from $(2, 0, -1)$ to a point of the graph of $y^2 = x + z$. [This surface is a parabolic cylinder whose elements are parallel to the line having equations $x + z = 0$, $y = 0$.]

6. Let $f(x, y) = x^2 + 4y^2 - x^2y^2$. (a) Show that f has one extreme point and this is a relative minimum at $(0, 0)$. (b) Show that there are saddle points at $(2, 1)$, $(2, -1)$, $(-2, 1)$, and $(-2, -1)$. [*Hint:* Use Taylor's theorem with $n = 2$.]

7. Let $f(x, y) = [x^2 + (y-1)^2 - 1][x^2 + (y-3)^2 - 9]$. (a) For each factor, describe the region of the (x, y)-plane for which that factor is positive and for which it is negative. Describe the region of the plane for which f is positive and for which f is negative. (b) Show that both first-order partial derivatives of f are zero at $(0, 0)$, but that f does not have a relative maximum, relative minimum, or saddlepoint at $(0, 0)$. (c) Let L be a straight line through the origin. Show that for the values of f at points of L there is a relative minimum at $(0, 0)$.

8. (*a*) Find the dimensions of the rectangular parallelepiped of greatest volume which has three faces in the coordinate planes and one vertex in the plane $15x + 10y + 6z = 90$. (*b*) Find the volume of the rectangular parallelepiped of greatest volume which can be inscribed in the ellipsoid

$$\frac{x^2}{a^2} + \frac{y^2}{b^2} + \frac{z^2}{c^2} = 1.$$

(*c*) Find the dimensions of the rectangular box, without a top, of greatest volume whose surface area is 108 square feet. (d) Find the greatest and least distances from the origin to a point of the curve $5x^2 + 6xy + 5y^2 = 8$.

9. The equation $Ax + By + Cz + D = 0$ is the equation of a plane if $A^2 + B^2 + C^2 \neq 0$. Prove that the distance from the point (x_0, y_0, z_0) to this plane is

$$\left| \frac{Ax_0 + By_0 + Cz_0 + D}{(A^2 + B^2 + C^2)^{1/2}} \right|.$$

7

VECTORS AND
CURVES

7-1. VECTORS AND PARAMETRIC EQUATIONS

It is common to say that a *vector* is a quantity having magnitude
and direction. This suggests such physical concepts as displacement,
velocity, acceleration, force, and momentum. Given a line, it is easy
to define a positive direction for the line (e.g., by choosing two points
and designating one as "first" and the other as "second"). A natural
definition for "direction" is to define a *direction* to be a directed line.
The term "magnitude" indicates the choice of a number. This number
might be represented as the length of a line segment. Thus, the terms
"magnitude" and "direction" might suggest a directed line segment.
We call a directed line segment an *arrow*; hence, an arrow consists of
a point designated as the *initial point*, a point designated as the *terminal
point*, and the line segment joining these points. The two points may
be the same and the line segment of length zero. Two *equivalent
arrows* are two arrows that are either of zero length or have the same
length and the same direction. Having the same direction means
they are parallel and directed in the same sense.

An arrow is determined if its initial point and its terminal point are
specified. If the initial point is $P_1 = (x_1, y_1, z_1)$ and the terminal point
is $P_2 = (x_2, y_2, z_2)$ [see Fig. 7-1] then the number $|x_2 - x_1|$ is the distance
between two planes perpendicular to the x-axis, one passing through
P_1 and the other through P_2. If the points of intersection of these
planes with the x-axis are P_1^* and P_2^*, then the number $x_2 - x_1$ is the
signed distance from P_1^* to P_2^*. Similar descriptions can be given for
the numbers $y_2 - y_1$ and $z_2 - z_1$. These three numbers are called the
components of the arrow. Clearly, two arrows are equivalent if and
only if they have the same components.

The set of all arrows that are equivalent to a given arrow is an equivalence class [see Definition 1-2.4]. Since all vectors in the same equivalence class have the same components, the equivalence class can be described by specifying these components. We shall define a vector as an ordered set of three numbers called components. Then each vector determines an equivalence class of arrows—the set of all arrows whose components are the three components of the vector.

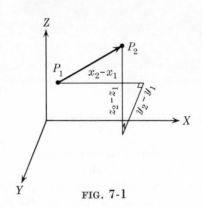

FIG. 7-1

DEFINITION 7-1.1 A *three-dimensional vector* is a set of three numbers arranged in order. The numbers are called *components* of the vector. The vector with components u_1, u_2, and u_3, in this order, is denoted by (u_1, u_2, u_3), or **u**. The equality

$$(u_1, u_2, u_3) = (v_1, v_2, v_3)$$

is equivalent to the three equalities, $u_1 = v_1$, $u_2 = v_2$, $u_3 = v_3$. The *zero vector* is the vector $(0, 0, 0)$ and is denoted by **0**.

One can define vectors of any number of dimensions. For example, one-dimensional vectors have only one component and two-dimensional vectors have two components. We often identify the set of two-dimensional vectors with the set of three-dimensional vectors whose third components are zero. Vectors of higher dimension can be defined by simply increasing the number of components.

When the three coordinate axes have been located, we can represent the vector (u_1, u_2, u_3) by any arrow whose initial point (x_1, y_1, z_1) and terminal point (x_2, y_2, z_2) are such that $x_2 - x_1 = u_1, y_2 - y_1 = u_2,$ and $z_2 - z_1 = u_3$. The choice of the initial point is arbitrary, so there are many arrows that can be used to represent a given vector. We shall see that many facts about vectors have geometric interpretations in terms of arrows. Because of this, it is natural to use the same symbol to designate an arrow as for the corresponding vector. In this book, we shall use boldface type to symbolize vectors.

If the arrow that represents a vector $\mathbf{u} = (u_1, u_2, u_3)$ has its initial point at the origin, then the terminal point has coordinates u_1, u_2, and u_3. The arrow is then said to be the *position arrow* for the point (u_1, u_2, u_3). The symbol (u_1, u_2, u_3) is used both for a point with coordinates u_1, u_2, and u_3 and for a vector with components u_1, u_2, and u_3. There is no reason for making a sharp distinction between vectors and points, since a position arrow can be regarded as determining either a point or a vector. However, for certain concepts and certain operations of "addition" and "multiplication," we shall call the symbol (u_1, u_2, u_3) a vector rather than a point. Some of these concepts and operations will be discussed in this section, others in later sections.

DEFINITION 7-1.2. The *length* of the vector $\mathbf{u} = (u_1, u_2, u_3)$ is denoted by $|\mathbf{u}|$ and is given by the formula

$$|\mathbf{u}| = (u_1^2 + u_2^2 + u_3^2)^{1/2}. \tag{7-1}$$

If $P_1 = (x_1, y_1, z_1)$ and $P_2 = (x_2, y_2, z_2)$ are the initial and terminal points of an arrow for which $u_1 = x_2 - x_1$, $u_2 = y_2 - y_1$, and $u_3 = z_2 - z_1$, then two applications of the Pythagorean theorem [see Fig. 7-2] show that $|\mathbf{u}|$ is the distance between P_1 and P_2. That is, the length of a vector is equal to the length of any arrow that represents the vector. In terms of the points P_1 and P_2, Eq. (7-1) becomes

$$d(P_1, P_2) = [(x_2 - x_1)^2 + (y_2 - y_1)^2 + (z_2 - z_1)^2]^{1/2}. \tag{7-2}$$

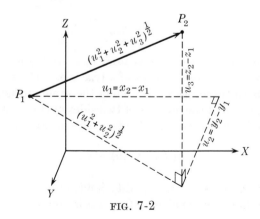

FIG. 7-2

In particular, if P_1 is the origin, then $|\mathbf{u}|$ is the distance from the origin to the point (u_1, u_2, u_3).

DEFINITION 7-1.3. The *sum* of vectors (u_1, u_2, u_3) and (v_1, v_2, v_3) is defined by the formula

$$(u_1, u_2, u_3) + (v_1, v_2, v_3) = (u_1 + v_1, u_2 + v_2, u_3 + v_3). \qquad (7\text{-}3)$$

If for two vectors $\mathbf{u}$ and $\mathbf{v}$ we let $\mathbf{u}$ be represented by an arrow and let $\mathbf{v}$ be represented by an arrow whose initial point is at the terminal point of $\mathbf{u}$, then $\mathbf{u} + \mathbf{v}$ is represented by the arrow whose initial point is the initial point of $\mathbf{u}$ and whose terminal point is the terminal point of $\mathbf{v}$. The truth of this statement is indicated by Fig. 7-3 and can be demonstrated by showing that one can get from the initial point of $\mathbf{u} + \mathbf{v}$ to the terminal point by either of two equivalent paths: (1) moving a distance $u_1 + v_1$ in the direction of the x-axis, then a distance $u_2 + v_2$ in the direction of the y-axis, and then a distance $u_3 + v_3$ in the direction of the z-axis; (2) moving distances u_1, u_2, and u_3 in the directions of the respective axes, then following with similar moves of distances v_1, v_2, and v_3.

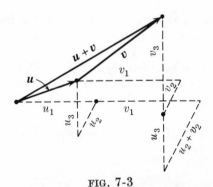

FIG. 7-3

This discussion shows that vectors $\mathbf{u}$, $\mathbf{v}$, and $\mathbf{u} + \mathbf{v}$ can be represented by arrows that are the sides of a triangle. The triangle may be collapsed, with all three sides lying along the same straight line. But, in any case, the sum of the lengths of two sides of the triangle is at least as large as the length of the third side. This means that

$$|\mathbf{u} + \mathbf{v}| \leq |\mathbf{u}| + |\mathbf{v}|, \qquad (7\text{-}4)$$

for any vectors $\mathbf{u}$ and $\mathbf{v}$. The equality holds only when the triangle is collapsed, and then only when $\mathbf{u}$ and $\mathbf{v}$ point in the same direction or one is of zero length. Inequality (7-4) is called the *triangle inequality*. It can also be proved, without using geometric representations of the vectors, by a method that can be generalized to vectors with more than three components. First we use the definition of length and the definition of sum of two vectors to state inequality (7-4) in the form

$$[(u_1 + v_1)^2 + (u_2 + v_2)^2 + (u_3 + v_3)^2]^{\frac{1}{2}}$$
$$\leq (u_1^2 + u_2^2 + u_3^2)^{\frac{1}{2}} + (v_1^2 + v_2^2 + v_3^2)^{\frac{1}{2}}. \qquad (7\text{-}5)$$

After squaring both members of (7-5) and dropping the terms that appear in both members, we see that (7-5) is equivalent to

$$u_1 v_1 + u_2 v_2 + u_3 v_3 \leq (u_1^2 + u_2^2 + u_3^2)^{\frac{1}{2}} (v_1^2 + v_2^2 + v_3^2)^{\frac{1}{2}}. \qquad (7\text{-}6)$$

For any particular vectors (u_1, u_2, u_3) and (v_1, v_2, v_3) we know that (7-5) is true if and only if (7-6) is true. Also, we want (7-6) to be true for all vectors. In particular, if the left member is negative, we wish (7-6) to be true if we replace (u_1, u_2, u_3) by $(-u_1, -u_2, -u_3)$. That is, we wish to prove that

$$|u_1 v_1 + u_2 v_2 + u_3 v_3| \leq (u_1^2 + u_2^2 + u_3^2)^{\frac{1}{2}} (v_1^2 + v_2^2 + v_3^2)^{\frac{1}{2}}. \qquad (7\text{-}7)$$

If (7-7) is true, then clearly (7-6) is true, and therefore (7-5) is true. To prove (7-7), we square both members and then see that (7-7) is equivalent to

$$2u_1 u_2 v_1 v_2 + 2u_2 u_3 v_2 v_3 + 2u_3 u_1 v_3 v_1$$
$$\leq (u_1^2 v_2^2 + u_2^2 v_1^2) + (u_2^2 v_3^2 + u_3^2 v_2^2) + (u_3^2 v_1^2 + u_1^2 v_3^2).$$

If each term of the left member is put with the corresponding term of the right member, this inequality can be written as

$$0 \leq (u_1 v_2 - u_2 v_1)^2 + (u_2 v_3 - u_3 v_2)^2 + (u_3 v_1 - u_1 v_3)^2. \qquad (7\text{-}8)$$

Since (7-8) is equivalent to (7-7), and (7-8) is true whatever the vectors **u** and **v**, the proof is complete.

DEFINITION 7-1.4. The *product* of a number a and a vector (u_1, u_2, u_3) is the vector given by the formula

$$a \cdot (u_1, u_2, u_3) = (au_1, au_2, au_3). \qquad (7\text{-}9)$$

If we let **u** be represented by an arrow with initial point at the origin, then it follows from the similarity of certain triangles in Fig. 7-4 that $a\mathbf{u}$ can be represented by the arrow along the line containing **u** which has length $|a| \cdot |\mathbf{u}|$. This arrow points in the same direction as **u** if a is positive, and in the opposite direction if a is negative.

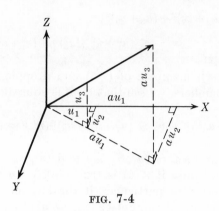

FIG. 7-4

DEFINITION 7-1.5. Two *parallel vectors* are two vectors **u** and **v** for which there are two numbers r and s not both zero such that $r\mathbf{u} = s\mathbf{v}$.

It is easy to see that **u** and **v** are parallel if and only if they can be represented by arrows that lie along parallel lines. Also, **u** and **v** are parallel if and only if one of the vectors is a scalar multiple of the other.

The vectors (1, 0, 0), (0, 1, 0), and (0, 0, 1) are denoted by **i**, **j**, and **k**. It follows from Definitions 7-1.3 and 7-1.4 that

$$(u_1, u_2, u_3) = u_1(1, 0, 0) + u_2(0, 1, 0) + u_3(0, 0, 1)$$

$$= u_1\mathbf{i} + u_2\mathbf{j} + u_3\mathbf{k}.$$

The vectors **i**, **j**, and **k** can be represented by arrows of unit length in the directions of the coordinate axes. They are called *unit vectors*.

We shall now use our knowledge of vectors to determine parametric equations for lines and planes. Note first that a line is determined if two points on the line are given. We let L be a line and (x_1, y_1, z_1) and (x_2, y_2, z_2) be points on L. We also let

$$\mathbf{p} = x_1\mathbf{i} + y_1\mathbf{j} + z_1\mathbf{k} \quad \text{and} \quad \mathbf{d} = (x_2 - x_1)\mathbf{i} + (y_2 - y_1)\mathbf{j} + (z_2 - z_1)\mathbf{k}.$$

For any number t, we have

$$\mathbf{p} + t\mathbf{d} = [x_1 + t(x_2 - x_1)]\mathbf{i} + [y_1 + t(y_2 - y_1)]\mathbf{j} + [z_1 + t(z_2 - z_1)]\mathbf{k}.$$

The sum of **p** and t**d** can be determined geometrically by placing **p** as indicated in Fig. 7-5, and then putting the initial point of t**d** at the terminal point (x_1, y_1, z_1) of **p**. Since t**d** and **d** are parallel, this implies that the vector $\mathbf{p} + t\mathbf{d}$ can be represented by an arrow whose initial point is at the origin and whose terminal point is on the line L. The terminal point of $\mathbf{p} + t\mathbf{d}$ has coordinates (x, y, z), where

$$\begin{cases} x = x_1 + (x_2 - x_1)t, \\ y = y_1 + (y_2 - y_1)t, \\ z = z_1 + (z_2 - z_1)t. \end{cases} \tag{7-10}$$

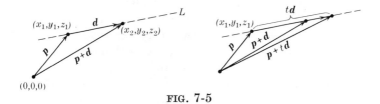

FIG. 7-5

These are *parametric equations* for L. The symbol t is the parameter. Now let us reverse this discussion, starting with any three equations such as

$$\begin{cases} x = x_0 + at, \\ y = y_0 + bt, \\ z = z_0 + ct, \end{cases} \tag{7-11}$$

where not all of a, b, and c are zero. We let (x_1, y_1, z_1) and (x_2, y_2, z_2) of the discussion leading to the equations in (7-10) be the points (x_0, y_0, z_0) and $(x_0 + a, y_0 + b, z_0 + c)$, respectively. Then the equations in (7-10) become the equations in (7-11), so we can conclude that the equations in (7-11) are parametric equations of a line. Of course, this line is the line through any two points whose coordinates can be obtained from (7-11) by giving specific values to t.

Note that if $z_0 = 0$ and $c = 0$, then the equations in (7-11) are parametric equations for a line in the (x, y)-plane. Also, suppose we let P_1 denote (x_1, y_1, z_1), P_2 denote (x_2, y_2, z_2), and P_t denote the point given by the equations in (7-10). Then P_t is the point on the line through P_1 and P_2 for which the directed distance from P_1 to P_t is t times the directed distance from P_1 to P_2.

ILLUSTRATION 1. Given the two points $P_1 = (0, 4, 3)$ and $P_2 = (2, -2, 4)$, we use (7-10) to find the following parametric equations for the line through P_1 and P_2:

$$x = 2t, \quad y = 4 - 6t, \quad z = 3 + t.$$

These equations give the point P_1 when $t = 0$, and the point P_2 when $t = 1$. We can obtain the midpoint between P_1 and P_2 by letting $t = \frac{1}{2}$. This midpoint is $(1, 1, \frac{7}{2})$. If we let $t = -1$, we obtain the point $(-2, 10, 2)$. The point P_1 is the midpoint of the line segment whose end points are $(-2, 10, 2)$ and P_2.

We shall now generalize the development of parametric equations for lines to obtain parametric equations for planes. Suppose (x_0, y_0, z_0) is a point in a plane Π and suppose **a** and **b** are any two nonparallel vectors. Also suppose **p** denotes the vector $x_0\mathbf{i} + y_0\mathbf{j} + z_0\mathbf{k}$. Then for any two numbers, u and v, the vector $\mathbf{p} + u\mathbf{a} + v\mathbf{b}$ determines a point in the plane Π. This point is the terminal point of $\mathbf{p} + u\mathbf{a} + v\mathbf{b}$, when the vector **p** is represented by an arrow with its initial point at the origin and the additions are performed geometrically in the usual way. That is, we can move first from the origin to the terminal point of **p** to arrive at the point (x_0, y_0, z_0) in the plane Π; then we can move along $u\mathbf{a}$ (in Π); and finally we can move along $v\mathbf{b}$ (in Π). If we let $\mathbf{a} = (a_1, a_2, a_3)$ and $\mathbf{b} = (b_1, b_2, b_3)$, then the terminal point of $\mathbf{p} + u\mathbf{a} + v\mathbf{b}$ is given by the following equations:

$$\begin{cases} x = x_0 + a_1 u + b_1 v, \\ y = y_0 + a_2 u + b_2 v, \\ z = z_0 + a_3 u + b_3 v. \end{cases} \tag{7-12}$$

The vectors **a** and **b** can be any two nonparallel vectors that can be represented by arrows in the plane. If we are given any three non-collinear points in a plane, then any two arrows that join different pairs of these points can be used to determine **a** and **b**. Thus,

$$\begin{cases} x = x_1 + (x_2 - x_1)u + (x_3 - x_1)v, \\ y = y_1 + (y_2 - y_1)u + (y_3 - y_1)v, \\ z = z_1 + (z_2 - z_1)u + (z_3 - z_1)v \end{cases} \tag{7-13}$$

are *parametric equations* for the plane that is determined by the three points (x_1, y_1, z_1), (x_2, y_2, z_2), and (x_3, y_3, z_3).

ILLUSTRATION 2. Suppose we wish to determine the point of intersection of the line and plane that have the following parametric equations:

$$\begin{cases} x = -1+t, \\ y = 2-t, \\ z = 4-3t; \end{cases} \qquad \begin{cases} x = 5+u-v \\ y = -1-4u-v, \\ z = 1+9u+2v. \end{cases}$$

This means that we want to find values of u, v, and t such that u and v give the same point on the plane that t gives on the line. Thus, we must have

$$\begin{cases} -1+t = 5+u-v, \\ 2-t = -1-4u-v, \\ 4-3t = 1+9u+2v; \end{cases} \quad \text{or} \quad \begin{cases} t-u+v = 6, \\ t-4u-v = 3, \\ 3t+9u+2v = 3. \end{cases}$$

By successive elimination of variables, we can determine that $t = 2$, $u = -1$, and $v = 3$. The value 2 of the parameter t gives the point $(1, 0, -2)$ on the line, and the values -1 and 3 for the parameters u and v give the same point on the plane.

PROBLEMS

1. Explain why $|\mathbf{u}| \leq |\mathbf{u}+\mathbf{v}| + |\mathbf{v}|$ for any vectors $\mathbf{u}$ and $\mathbf{v}$.

2. Prove each of the following. In each case, draw a diagram and explain the meaning of the given equality for arrows.

   (a) $\mathbf{u}+\mathbf{v} = \mathbf{v}+\mathbf{u}$ for any vectors $\mathbf{u}$ and $\mathbf{v}$.

   (b) $\mathbf{u}+(\mathbf{v}+\mathbf{w}) = (\mathbf{u}+\mathbf{v})+\mathbf{w}$ for any vectors $\mathbf{u}$, $\mathbf{v}$, and $\mathbf{w}$.

   (c) $a(\mathbf{u}+\mathbf{v}) = a\mathbf{u}+a\mathbf{v}$ for any number a and vectors $\mathbf{u}$ and $\mathbf{v}$.

3. Show that $|\mathbf{u}+\mathbf{v}|^2 + |\mathbf{u}-\mathbf{v}|^2 = 2(|\mathbf{u}|^2 + |\mathbf{v}|^2)$ for any vectors $\mathbf{u}$ and $\mathbf{v}$.

4. For each of the following, find parametric equations of the line determined by the two given points. Also, find the midpoint of the line segment whose end points are the given points.

   (*a*) $(-2, 4, 1)$; $(6, 0, 1)$.   (*c*) $(5, 7, 0)$; $(-1, 3, 0)$.

   (b) $(0, 0, 4)$; $(1, 2, 4)$.   (d) $(1, -1, 3)$; $(3, -3, 7)$.

5. For each of the following, find parametric equations of the plane determined by the three given points.

   (*a*) $(1, 2, 4)$; $(2, 0, 1)$; $(4, 0, 0)$.   (*c*) $(0, 0, 0)$; $(2, 0, 3)$; $(3, 0, 2)$.

   (b) $(2, 1, 0)$; $(3, 3, 3)$; $(4, 0, 2)$.   (d) $(0, 0, 2)$; $(2, 0, 1)$; $(3, 1, 2)$.

6. Find parametric equations of the plane that contains the points $(1, 2, -1)$ and $(3, 0, 5)$ and is parallel to the line whose parametric equations are $x = 2t$, $y = 1-t$, $z = 1+t$.

7. Find parametric equations of the plane that contains the point $(2, 3, -1)$ and is parallel to each of the two lines whose parametric equations are

$$\begin{cases} x = t, \\ y = 1-t, \\ z = 2+3t; \end{cases} \qquad \begin{cases} x = 1-s, \\ y = 2+3s, \\ z = -1+s. \end{cases}$$

8. For each of the following, the two lines that have the given parametric equations have a point of intersection. Determine parametric equations of the plane that contains both lines.

(a) $\begin{cases} x = 1+t, \\ y = 2t, \\ z = t; \end{cases} \qquad \begin{cases} x = 2-s, \\ y = 1-s, \\ z = -2+2s. \end{cases}$

(b) $\begin{cases} x = 2-t, \\ y = -1+t, \\ z = 3-t; \end{cases} \qquad \begin{cases} x = 3-t, \\ y = 2-t, \\ z = 8-3t. \end{cases}$

9. For each of the following, find a point of intersection of the line and the plane that have the given parametric equations, or show that they do not intersect.

(a) $\begin{cases} x = 3-t, \\ y = 2t-2, \\ z = 1+t; \end{cases} \qquad \begin{cases} x = 2-2u-v, \\ y = u+v, \\ z = 1+u+v. \end{cases}$

(b) $\begin{cases} x = 3+t, \\ y = t, \\ z = 7+3t; \end{cases} \qquad \begin{cases} x = 1+u-v, \\ y = 2-u+3v, \\ z = 3+2u-v. \end{cases}$

(c) $\begin{cases} x = 1+2t, \\ y = 2+3t, \\ z = 3+t; \end{cases} \qquad \begin{cases} x = 2-u+3v, \\ y = u+2v, \\ z = 1+2u-v. \end{cases}$

(d) $\begin{cases} x = 3-t, \\ y = 1-t, \\ z = 1-t; \end{cases} \qquad \begin{cases} x = 1-u-v, \\ y = -5+u-v, \\ z = 1+u+v. \end{cases}$

10. Find the distance between the point $(1, 3, -2)$ and the line whose parametric equations are $x = 3+t$, $y = 3-2t$, $z = 2+3t$.

11. Let $P_1 = (x_1, y_1, z_1)$ and $P_2 = (x_2, y_2, z_2)$ be two distinct points on a line L that does not pass through the origin. Show that the point

$$(ax_1 + bx_2, \ ay_1 + by_2, \ az_1 + bz_2)$$

is a point on L if and only if $a + b = 1$, and that this point is on L and between P_1 and P_2 if and only if a and b are positive and $a + b = 1$.

12. Let (x_1, y_1, z_1), (x_2, y_2, z_2) and (x_3, y_3, z_3) be any three points that are not collinear. Then these three points determine a plane Π. Prove that Π contains all those points

$$(ax_1 + bx_2 + cx_3, \ ay_1 + by_2 + cy_3, \ az_1 + bz_2 + cz_3)$$

for which $a + b + c = 1$, and no other points.

13. Let $\mathbf{u}$, $\mathbf{v}$, and $\mathbf{w}$ be three vectors represented by arrows with their initial points at the origin. Suppose that the initial point of $\frac{1}{3}(\mathbf{u} + \mathbf{v} + \mathbf{w})$ is placed at the origin. Prove that the terminal point is the point of intersection of the medians of the triangle whose vertices are the terminal points of $\mathbf{u}$, $\mathbf{v}$, and $\mathbf{w}$.

7-2. SCALAR PRODUCT

There are two ways of combining vectors to give what is called a product. Because of the notation customarily used, these will be called the *scalar product* and the *cross product*. The scalar product of two vectors is a number, while the cross product is a vector. In each case, we shall see that there is a distributive law that uses that type of multiplication and the method for combining vectors which we have called addition. It is not necessary to call a method for combining vectors addition or multiplication, but a distributive law suggests strongly which might be called addition and which multiplication if these labels are to be used.

DEFINITION 7-2.1. Suppose $\mathbf{u} = u_1\mathbf{i} + u_2\mathbf{j} + u_3\mathbf{k}$ and $\mathbf{v} = v_1\mathbf{i} + v_2\mathbf{j} + v_3\mathbf{k}$. Then the *scalar product*† of $\mathbf{u}$ and $\mathbf{v}$ is the number defined by

$$\mathbf{u} \cdot \mathbf{v} = u_1 v_1 + u_2 v_2 + u_3 v_3.$$

If the components of vectors $\mathbf{u}$, $\mathbf{v}$, and $\mathbf{w}$ are denoted in the usual way, then

$$\mathbf{u} \cdot (\mathbf{v} + \mathbf{w}) = \mathbf{u} \cdot [(v_1 + w_1)\mathbf{i} + (v_2 + w_2)\mathbf{j} + (v_3 + w_3)\mathbf{k}]$$
$$= u_1(v_1 + w_1) + u_2(v_2 + w_2) + u_3(v_3 + w_3)$$
$$= (u_1 v_1 + u_2 v_2 + u_3 v_3) + (u_1 w_1 + u_2 w_2 + u_3 w_3),$$

---

† The scalar product is often called the *dot product* or the *inner product*.

and

$$\mathbf{u} \cdot (\mathbf{v} + \mathbf{w}) = \mathbf{u} \cdot \mathbf{v} + \mathbf{u} \cdot \mathbf{w}. \tag{7-14}$$

This is the distributive law that was promised for the scalar product. There are several other properties of the scalar product that can be proved easily. For any vectors $\mathbf{u}$ and $\mathbf{v}$ and any number t,

$$\mathbf{u} \cdot \mathbf{v} = \mathbf{v} \cdot \mathbf{u}, \tag{7-15}$$

$$t(\mathbf{u} \cdot \mathbf{v}) = (t\mathbf{u}) \cdot \mathbf{v} = \mathbf{u} \cdot (t\mathbf{v}), \tag{7-16}$$

$$\mathbf{u} \cdot \mathbf{u} = |\mathbf{u}|^2, \tag{7-17}$$

and

$$|\mathbf{u} \cdot \mathbf{v}| \leqq |\mathbf{u}| \, |\mathbf{v}| \qquad \text{[Schwarz's inequality]}. \tag{7-18}$$

The proofs of Eqs. (7-15) through (7-17) will be left as problems for the student. We proved inequality (7-18) in the proof of the triangle inequality. [In fact, (7-7) of Section 7-1 is the same as Schwarz's inequality and was proved to be equivalent to the true statement (7-8) of Section 7-1.]

For vectors $\mathbf{u}$ and $\mathbf{v}$ of nonzero length, we can write (7-18) as

$$-1 \leqq \frac{\mathbf{u} \cdot \mathbf{v}}{|\mathbf{u}| \, |\mathbf{v}|} \leqq 1.$$

There is then exactly one angle θ such that $0 \leqq \theta \leqq \pi$ and

$$\cos \theta = \frac{\mathbf{u} \cdot \mathbf{v}}{|\mathbf{u}| \, |\mathbf{v}|}. \tag{7-19}$$

We shall now show that this angle is the angle between arrows representing $\mathbf{u}$ and $\mathbf{v}$. Note first that, for arrows $\mathbf{u}$ and $\mathbf{v}$ with initial points at the origin, there is exactly one angle θ between $\mathbf{u}$ and $\mathbf{v}$ for which $0 \leqq \theta \leqq \pi$. Moreover, all other angles with $\mathbf{u}$ and $\mathbf{v}$ as sides are expressible as $\pm\,\theta + 2k\pi$ for k a positive integer and all have the same cosine as θ. We have not oriented the plane of $\mathbf{u}$ and $\mathbf{v}$, so we shall not consider negative angles between $\mathbf{u}$ and $\mathbf{v}$. Now we can apply the law of cosines to the triangle indicated in Fig. 7-6, to obtain

$$|\mathbf{v} - \mathbf{u}|^2 = |\mathbf{u}|^2 + |\mathbf{v}|^2 - 2|\mathbf{u}| \, |\mathbf{v}| \cos \theta.$$

This can be written as

$$(x_2 - x_1)^2 + (y_2 - y_1)^2 + (z_2 - z_1)^2$$
$$= (x_1^2 + y_1^2 + z_1^2) + (x_2^2 + y_2^2 + z_2^2) - 2|\mathbf{u}|\,|\mathbf{v}|\,\cos\,\theta,$$

or

$$x_1 x_2 + y_1 y_2 + z_1 z_2 = |\mathbf{u}|\,|\mathbf{v}|\,\cos\,\theta. \qquad (7\text{-}20)$$

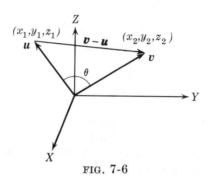

FIG. 7-6

The left member of this equality is $\mathbf{u} \cdot \mathbf{v}$. Let us now define an *angle between two vectors* as an angle between any two arrows that represent the vectors and have the same initial points. Then (7-20) gives us the following theorem.

THEOREM 7-2.1. For any two nonzero vectors $\mathbf{u}$ and $\mathbf{v}$,

$$\mathbf{u} \cdot \mathbf{v} = |\mathbf{u}|\,|\mathbf{v}|\cos\,\theta, \qquad (7\text{-}21)$$

where θ is any angle between $\mathbf{u}$ and $\mathbf{v}$.

Suppose $\mathbf{u} = u_1\mathbf{i} + u_2\mathbf{j} + u_3\mathbf{k}$ and $\mathbf{v} = v_1\mathbf{i} + v_2\mathbf{j} + v_3\mathbf{k}$ are arrows of nonzero length. Then $\mathbf{u}$ and $\mathbf{v}$ are perpendicular if and only if $\cos\,\theta = 0$, where θ is an angle between the arrows. It follows from this and Theorem 7-2.1 that $\mathbf{u}$ and $\mathbf{v}$ are perpendicular if and only if

$$u_1 v_1 + u_2 v_2 + u_3 v_3 = 0.$$

We know that this must be equivalent for nonvertical lines in the (x, y)-plane to the familiar perpendicularity condition, $m_1 m_2 = -1$, where m_1 and m_2 are the slopes of the lines. But let us verify this directly. If the lines contain the arrows $\mathbf{u}$ and $\mathbf{v}$, then $u_3 = v_3 = 0$

[see Fig. 7-7]. Also, the slopes of the lines are u_2/u_1 and v_2/v_1. Then $m_1m_2 = -1$ becomes

$$\left(\frac{u_2}{u_1}\right)\left(\frac{v_2}{v_1}\right) = -1 \quad \text{or} \quad u_1v_1 + u_2v_2 = 0.$$

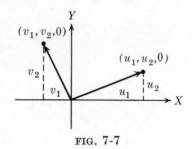

FIG. 7-7

Perpendicularity of arrows can be used to define perpendicularity of vectors. We shall give a definition of orthogonal vectors, which allows one or both of two orthogonal vectors to be **0**; in fact, the vector **0** is orthogonal to all vectors.

DEFINITION 7-2.2. For any two vectors, $\mathbf{u} = u_1\mathbf{i} + u_2\mathbf{j} + u_3\mathbf{k}$ and $\mathbf{v} = v_1\mathbf{i} + v_2\mathbf{j} + v_3\mathbf{k}$, the statement that $\mathbf{u}$ is orthogonal to $\mathbf{v}$ is equivalent to the statement

$$u_1v_1 + u_2v_2 + u_3v_3 = 0.$$

The scalar product of vectors is a very effective tool to use in deriving nonparametric equations for a line in a plane or for a plane in space. We shall first discuss a line in the (x, y)-plane. Given a line L, suppose we choose an arrow of nonzero length that is also in the plane, is perpendicular to L, and has its initial point (x_0, y_0) on L [see Fig. 7-8]. We shall let a and b be the components of this arrow. Then a point (x, y), other than (x_0, y_0), is a point of L if and only if the arrow that joins (x_0, y_0) to (x, y) is perpendicular to the arrow $a\mathbf{i} + b\mathbf{j}$, that is, if and only if

$$[a\mathbf{i} + b\mathbf{j}] \cdot [(x - x_0)\mathbf{i} + (y - y_0)\mathbf{j}] = 0.$$

This equation is also satisfied by the coordinates of the point (x_0, y_0) and is an equation of the line L. It can be written as

$$a(x - x_0) + b(y - y_0) = 0 \quad \text{or} \quad ax + by + c = 0, \qquad (7\text{-}22)$$

where $c = -(ax_0 + by_0)$. We have shown that, for any arrow $a\mathbf{i} + b\mathbf{j}$ that is perpendicular to a line L, L has an equation of type (7-22).

Now suppose, conversely, that L is the graph of the equation $ax + by + c = 0$ and that $a^2 + b^2 \neq 0$. We shall show that L is a line that is perpendicular to the arrow $a\mathbf{i} + b\mathbf{j}$. Since a and b are not both zero, there are numbers x_0 and y_0 for which $-c = ax_0 + by_0$. Then $ax + by + c = 0$ can be written as

$$a(x - x_0) + b(y - y_0) = 0.$$

This means that, for any point (x, y) in the graph, other than (x_0, y_0), the arrow $(x - x_0)\mathbf{i} + (y - y_0)\mathbf{j}$ is perpendicular to the arrow $a\mathbf{i} + b\mathbf{j}$. Therefore, the graph is the line through (x_0, y_0) that is perpendicular to the arrow $a\mathbf{i} + b\mathbf{j}$.

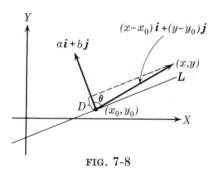

FIG. 7-8

We shall now investigate the problem of determining the distance between a point and a line. Suppose θ is the angle shown in Fig. 7-8 and D is the distance between (x, y) and the line L. Then

$$D = |(x - x_0)\mathbf{i} + (y - y_0)\mathbf{j}| \cos \theta,$$

if we use the convention that D is positive or negative according to whether (x, y) is on the same side of L as the terminal point of $a\mathbf{i} + b\mathbf{j}$ or on the opposite side. That is, D is positive if (x, y) is on the side of the line toward which the arrow $a\mathbf{i} + b\mathbf{j}$ points. We now divide both members of the equality

$$[a\mathbf{i} + b\mathbf{j}] \cdot [(x - x_0)\mathbf{i} + (y - y_0)\mathbf{j}] = |a\mathbf{i} + b\mathbf{j}| \, |(x - x_0)\mathbf{i} + (y - y_0)\mathbf{j}| \cos \theta$$

by the length of $a\mathbf{i} + b\mathbf{j}$ and obtain

$$\frac{a(x - x_0) + b(y - y_0)}{(a^2 + b^2)^{1/2}} = D \quad \text{or} \quad \frac{ax + by + c}{(a^2 + b^2)^{1/2}} = D. \qquad (7\text{-}23)$$

If $l = a/(a^2+b^2)^{1/2}$, $m = b/(a^2+b^2)^{1/2}$, and d_0 is the distance from the line to the origin, then $l^2+m^2 = 1$ and (7-23) becomes $lx+my+d_0 = D$. Since (x, y) is a point of L if and only if $D = 0$, an equation for the line is

$$lx+my+d_0 = 0. \tag{7-24}$$

Any equation such as (7-24) with $l^2+m^2 = 1$ is said to be in *normal form*. Substitution of the coordinates of a point into the left member of such an equation gives the distance between the point and the line, positive for points on one side of the line and negative for points on the other side.

The scalar product of vectors can be used to obtain an equation for a plane by essentially the same method that was used for a line in the (x, y)-plane. Given a plane Π, let us choose an arrow that is perpendicular to Π and has its initial point (x_0, y_0, z_0) in Π. We shall let a, b, and c be the components of this arrow. Then a point (x, y, z), other than (x_0, y_0, z_0), is a point of Π if and only if the arrows $a\mathbf{i}+b\mathbf{j}+c\mathbf{k}$ and $(x-x_0)\mathbf{i}+(y-y_0)\mathbf{j}+(z-z_0)\mathbf{k}$ are perpendicular, that is,

$$[a\mathbf{i}+b\mathbf{j}+c\mathbf{k}]\cdot[(x-x_0)\mathbf{i}+(y-y_0)\mathbf{j}+(z-z_0)\mathbf{k}] = 0.$$

This equation is also satisfied by the coordinates of the point (x_0, y_0, z_0), so it is an equation of the plane Π. This equation can be written as

$$a(x-x_0)+b(y-y_0)+c(z-z_0) = 0 \quad \text{or} \quad ax+by+cz+d = 0, \tag{7-25}$$

where $d = -(ax_0+by_0+cz_0)$. We have shown that, for any arrow $a\mathbf{i}+b\mathbf{j}+c\mathbf{k}$ perpendicular to Π, Π has an equation of type (7-25). Now let us assume, conversely, that Π is the graph of the second of the equations in (7-25) and that $a^2+b^2+c^2 \neq 0$. Then since a, b, and c are not all zero, there are numbers x_0, y_0, and z_0 for which $-d = ax_0 + by_0+cz_0$ and the equation of Π can be written as

$$a(x-x_0)+b(y-y_0)+c(z-z_0) = 0.$$

This means that for any point (x, y, z) in the graph of Π, other than (x_0, y_0, z_0), the arrow $(x-x_0)\mathbf{i}+(y-y_0)\mathbf{j}+(z-z_0)\mathbf{k}$ is perpendicular to the arrow $a\mathbf{i}+b\mathbf{j}+c\mathbf{k}$. Therefore, Π is the plane through (x_0, y_0, z_0) that is perpendicular to the arrow $a\mathbf{i}+b\mathbf{j}+c\mathbf{k}$.

Just as Eq. (7-23) gives the distance from a point to a line, the distance between the point (x, y, z) and the plane with equation $ax+by+cz+d = 0$ is given by

$$\frac{ax+by+cz+d}{(a^2+b^2+c^2)^{1/2}} = D, \tag{7-26}$$

where D is positive if and only if the point (x, y, z) is on the same side of the plane as the terminal point of the arrow $a\mathbf{i}+b\mathbf{j}+c\mathbf{k}$ when the initial point of this arrow is in the plane.

Now suppose we let

$$l = \frac{a}{(a^2+b^2+c^2)^{\frac{1}{2}}}, \quad m = \frac{b}{(a^2+b^2+c^2)^{\frac{1}{2}}}, \quad \text{and} \quad n = \frac{c}{(a^2+b^2+c^2)^{\frac{1}{2}}}.$$

Also suppose we let d_0 be the distance between the plane and the origin. Then $l^2+m^2+n^2 = 1$ and an equation of the plane is

$$lx + my + nz + d_0 = 0. \tag{7-27}$$

This equation is said to be in *normal form*. If d_0 is positive (negative), then a point is at positive (negative) distance from the plane if and only if it is on the same side of the plane as the origin.

PROBLEMS

1. Prove that for any vectors $\mathbf{u}$ and $\mathbf{v}$ and any number t,
   (a) $\mathbf{u} \cdot \mathbf{v} = \mathbf{v} \cdot \mathbf{u}$;   (b) $t(\mathbf{u} \cdot \mathbf{v}) = (t\mathbf{u}) \cdot \mathbf{v} = \mathbf{u} \cdot (t\mathbf{v})$;   (c) $\mathbf{u} \cdot \mathbf{u} = |\mathbf{u}|^2$.

2. Prove the following.
   (a) $|\mathbf{u}+\mathbf{v}|^2 = |\mathbf{u}|^2 + 2(\mathbf{u} \cdot \mathbf{v}) + |\mathbf{v}|^2$.   (b) $(\mathbf{u}+\mathbf{v}) \cdot (\mathbf{u}-\mathbf{v}) = |\mathbf{u}|^2 - |\mathbf{v}|^2$.

3. Find the angle between the given vectors.

   (*a*) $\mathbf{i}$; $\mathbf{i}+\mathbf{j}+\sqrt{2}\mathbf{k}$.   (*c*) $\mathbf{i}+2\mathbf{j}-2\mathbf{k}$; $-2\mathbf{i}+\mathbf{j}+2\mathbf{k}$.

   (b) $3\mathbf{i}+4\mathbf{k}$; $2\mathbf{i}+\sqrt{5}\mathbf{j}$.   (d) $\mathbf{i}$; $\mathbf{i}+\mathbf{j}+\mathbf{k}$.

4. For each of the following, determine all vectors that make equal angles with each of the three given vectors.

   (*a*) $\mathbf{i}$; $\mathbf{i}+\mathbf{j}$; $\mathbf{i}+\mathbf{j}+\mathbf{k}$.   (*b*) $\mathbf{i}-\mathbf{j}+\mathbf{k}$; $-\mathbf{i}+\mathbf{j}+\mathbf{k}$; $2\mathbf{i}+\mathbf{j}-\mathbf{k}$.

5. For each of the following, find equations (parametric or otherwise) satisfied by the coordinates of all points that are equidistant from the lines passing through the given points.

   (*a*) $(0, 0, 0)$ and $(1, 0, 0)$; $(0, 0, 0)$ and $(3, -4, 0)$; $(0, 0, 0)$ and $(0, 0, 1)$.

   (*b*) $(1, 1, -1)$ and $(3, 3, 0)$; $(1, 1, -1)$ and $(2, -1, 1)$; $(1, 1, -1)$ and $(4, 1, 3)$.

   (*c*) $(1, 2, 1)$ and $(3, 0, 2)$; $(1, 2, 1)$ and $(6, 2, 13)$.

6. Two lines have the given parametric equations. Find the distance between these lines. [*Hint:* Find the shortest distance from a point of one line to a point of the other line.]

$$(a) \begin{cases} x = 1-s, \\ y = 1+2s, \\ z = 2-s; \end{cases} \quad \begin{cases} x = t, \\ y = 1+5t, \\ z = 4+t. \end{cases} \quad (b) \begin{cases} x = 1+t, \\ y = t, \\ z = 3-t; \end{cases} \quad \begin{cases} x = t, \\ y = 2-t, \\ z = 1+2t. \end{cases}$$

7. For each of the following, prove that the stated condition is necessary and sufficient for $\mathbf{u}$ to be orthogonal to $\mathbf{v}$.

(a) $|\mathbf{u}+\mathbf{v}|^2 = |\mathbf{u}|^2+|\mathbf{v}|^2.$ (b) $|\mathbf{u}+\mathbf{v}| = |\mathbf{u}-\mathbf{v}|.$

(c) $|\mathbf{u}+k\mathbf{v}| \geq |\mathbf{u}|$ for all numbers k.

8. Let $\mathbf{u}$ and $\mathbf{v}$ be any two vectors for which $|\mathbf{u}| \neq 0$. Show that the vectors $\mathbf{u}$ and $\mathbf{v}-(\mathbf{u}\cdot\mathbf{v})\mathbf{u}/|\mathbf{u}|^2$ are orthogonal.

9. Show that, for any vectors $\mathbf{u}$ and $\mathbf{v}$, the angle between $\mathbf{u}$ and $\mathbf{v}$ is bisected by the vector $|\mathbf{v}|\mathbf{u}+|\mathbf{u}|\mathbf{v}$.

10. (*a*) Find the point in the (x, y)-plane which is equidistant from the lines whose equations are $y = 0$, $3x = 4y$, $5x-12y = 10$, and is inside the triangle formed by these lines. (*b*) Find the other three points in the (x, y)-plane which are equidistant from the lines of part (a).

11. Find an equation for each plane that (*a*) is two units from the origin and is perpendicular to the line through the points $(3, 1, 2)$ and $(-1, 2, 3)$; (*b*) contains the point $(1, 3, 0)$ and the line of intersection of the planes whose equations are $13x+7y-3z+2 = 0$ and $17x+5y+11z+40 = 0$; (*c*) contains the point $(0, 6, 3)$ and the line whose parametric equations are $x = 3-t$, $y = 1+2t$, and $z = -4+3t$; (*d*) is two units from the point $(1, 1, 2)$ and is perpendicular to the line whose equations are $x = 2+5t$, $y = 1-3t$, and $z = 3+t$.

12. Find the center of the inscribed sphere of the tetrahedron whose faces lie in the planes whose equations are

$$x+2y-2z = 6; \quad 2x-y+2z = -3;$$
$$2x+3y+6z = 14; \quad 3y-4z+10 = 0.$$

How many spheres are there, each of which is tangent to these four planes? Why?

7-3. CROSS PRODUCT

Let us consider the problem of finding a vector that is orthogonal to each of two given vectors. If $\mathbf{u} = u_1\mathbf{i}+u_2\mathbf{j}+u_3\mathbf{k}$ and $\mathbf{v} = v_1\mathbf{i}+v_2\mathbf{j}+v_3\mathbf{k}$

are the given vectors, then for the vector $\mathbf{r} = x\mathbf{i} + y\mathbf{j} + z\mathbf{k}$ to be orthogonal to both $\mathbf{u}$ and $\mathbf{v}$ we need to have $\mathbf{r} \cdot \mathbf{u} = 0$ and $\mathbf{r} \cdot \mathbf{v} = 0$, or

$$xu_1 + yu_2 + zu_3 = 0,$$

$$xv_1 + yv_2 + zv_3 = 0.$$

Now we multiply the first of these equations by v_3 and the second by $-u_3$ and add to eliminate z; then multiply the first by $-v_2$ and the second by u_2 and add to eliminate y. We then have the equations

$$x(u_1v_3 - u_3v_1) + y(u_2v_3 - u_3v_2) = 0$$

and

$$x(u_2v_1 - u_1v_2) + z(u_2v_3 - u_3v_2) = 0.$$

If we let $x = u_2v_3 - u_3v_2$, then possible values for y and z are $y = u_3v_1 - u_1v_3$ and $z = u_1v_2 - u_2v_1$. Therefore, the vector

$$(u_2v_3 - u_3v_2)\mathbf{i} + (u_3v_1 - u_1v_3)\mathbf{j} + (u_1v_2 - u_2v_1)\mathbf{k}$$

is orthogonal to each of the vectors $\mathbf{u}$ and $\mathbf{v}$. Although any scalar multiple of this vector is also orthogonal to both $\mathbf{u}$ and $\mathbf{v}$, this vector is of particular interest for reasons to be discussed in this section.

DEFINITION 7-3.1. Suppose $\mathbf{u} = u_1\mathbf{i} + u_2\mathbf{j} + u_3\mathbf{k}$ and $\mathbf{v} = v_1\mathbf{i} + v_2\mathbf{j} + v_3\mathbf{k}$ are two vectors. The *cross product*† of $\mathbf{u}$ and $\mathbf{v}$ *in this order* is denoted by $\mathbf{u} \times \mathbf{v}$ and is given by the formula

$$\mathbf{u} \times \mathbf{v} = (u_2v_3 - u_3v_2)\mathbf{i} + (u_3v_1 - u_1v_3)\mathbf{j} + (u_1v_2 - u_2v_1)\mathbf{k}. \qquad (7\text{-}28)$$

We have seen that the cross product of two vectors is a vector orthogonal to each of the given vectors. The following theorem gives us a simple formula for the length of $\mathbf{u} \times \mathbf{v}$ and will enable us to develop some geometric interpretations of the cross product.

THEOREM 7-3.1. For two vectors, $\mathbf{u}$ and $\mathbf{v}$, let θ be an angle between $\mathbf{u}$ and $\mathbf{v}$. Then

$$|\mathbf{u} \times \mathbf{v}| = |\mathbf{u}|\,|\mathbf{v}|\,|\sin\theta|. \qquad (7\text{-}29)$$

---

† What we call the cross product sometimes is called the *vector product* or the *outer product*.

PROOF. Our proof is based on the equality,

$$(\mathbf{u} \cdot \mathbf{v})^2 + |\mathbf{u} \times \mathbf{v}|^2 = |\mathbf{u}|^2 |\mathbf{v}|^2. \tag{7-30}$$

To prove this equality, we first write it in the following form, using the notation $\mathbf{u} = (u_1, u_2, u_3)$ and $\mathbf{v} = (v_1, v_2, v_3)$:

$$(u_1 v_1 + u_2 v_2 + u_3 v_3)^2 + [(u_2 v_3 - u_3 v_2)^2 + (u_3 v_1 - u_1 v_3)^2 + (u_1 v_2 - u_2 v_1)^2]$$
$$= (u_1^2 + u_2^2 + u_3^2)(v_1^2 + v_2^2 + v_3^2).$$

It is easy to verify that when the squares in the left member are expanded, the squared terms are precisely the terms in the right member and the rest of the terms cancel. Now we let θ be an angle between $\mathbf{u}$ and $\mathbf{v}$. Then Eq. (7-30) can be written as

$$(|\mathbf{u}| \, |\mathbf{v}| \, \cos \theta)^2 + |\mathbf{u} \times \mathbf{v}|^2 = |\mathbf{u}|^2 |\mathbf{v}|^2,$$

or

$$|\mathbf{u} \times \mathbf{v}|^2 = \mathbf{u}^2 \mathbf{v}^2 (1 - \cos^2 \theta) = |\mathbf{u}|^2 |\mathbf{v}|^2 \sin^2 \theta.$$

Equality (7-29) follows from this.

We used Definition 7-3.1 to define $\mathbf{u} \times \mathbf{v}$. In addition, we know that, if $\mathbf{u} \times \mathbf{v} \neq 0$, then $\mathbf{u} \times \mathbf{v}$ is orthogonal to both $\mathbf{u}$ and $\mathbf{v}$ and therefore can be represented by an arrow perpendicular to planes parallel to both $\mathbf{u}$ and $\mathbf{v}$. Also, we can express $|\mathbf{u} \times \mathbf{v}|$ as $|\mathbf{u}||\mathbf{v}||\sin \theta|$, where θ is an angle between $\mathbf{u}$ and $\mathbf{v}$. This implies that $|\mathbf{u} \times \mathbf{v}|$ is the area of a parallelogram with $\mathbf{u}$ and $\mathbf{v}$ as adjacent sides. To complete a geometric description of $\mathbf{u} \times \mathbf{v}$, we need to describe the direction of $\mathbf{u} \times \mathbf{v}$ along a line perpendicular to planes parallel to $\mathbf{u}$ and $\mathbf{v}$. This is done in the following definition and the geometric interpretation of the definition we shall develop.

DEFINITION 7-3.2. An *ordered set* of three vectors is a set of three vectors for which one vector is designated as the first, another as the second, and the remaining one as the third. An *oriented trihedral* is an ordered set of three vectors, $\{\mathbf{u}, \mathbf{v}, \mathbf{w}\}$, such that $\mathbf{u} \cdot (\mathbf{v} \times \mathbf{w}) \neq 0$. An oriented trihedral $\{\mathbf{u}, \mathbf{v}, \mathbf{w}\}$ is *positively oriented* or *negatively oriented* according to whether $\mathbf{u} \cdot (\mathbf{v} \times \mathbf{w}) > 0$ or $\mathbf{u} \cdot (\mathbf{v} \times \mathbf{w}) < 0$.

To obtain a geometric description of the meaning of orientation, let us choose a particular rectangular coordinate system and represent $\mathbf{u}$, $\mathbf{v}$, and $\mathbf{w}$ by arrows with their initial points at the origin. We rotate the trihedral $(\mathbf{u}, \mathbf{v}, \mathbf{w})$ about the line through the origin perpendicular to the x-axis and $\mathbf{u}$, so that $\mathbf{u}$ lies along the positive x-axis. Then rotate about the x-axis until $\mathbf{v}$ is in the half of the (x, y)-plane whose points have positive y-coordinates. At the end of this process, $\mathbf{u} = \theta\mathbf{i}$, where $\theta > 0$, and $\mathbf{v} = \delta\mathbf{i} + \varepsilon\mathbf{j}$, where $\varepsilon > 0$. With $\mathbf{w}$ denoted by $A\mathbf{i} + B\mathbf{j} + C\mathbf{k}$, we have

$$
\begin{aligned}
\mathbf{u} \cdot (\mathbf{v} \times \mathbf{w}) &= (\theta\mathbf{i}) \cdot [(\delta\mathbf{i} + \varepsilon\mathbf{j}) \times (A\mathbf{i} + B\mathbf{j} + C\mathbf{k})] \\
&= (\theta\mathbf{i}) \cdot [\varepsilon C\mathbf{i} - \delta C\mathbf{j} + (\delta B - \varepsilon A)\mathbf{k}] \qquad (7\text{-}31) \\
&= (\theta\varepsilon)C.
\end{aligned}
$$

During the rotations, $\mathbf{v}$ and $\mathbf{w}$ are of constant length and the angle between them does not change. Therefore $|\mathbf{v} \times \mathbf{w}|$ is constant. Since $\mathbf{v} \times \mathbf{w}$ is perpendicular to the plane of $\mathbf{v}$ and $\mathbf{w}$, the acute angle θ between lines along $\mathbf{u}$ and $\mathbf{v} \times \mathbf{w}$ is constant and

$$
\mathbf{u} \cdot (\mathbf{v} \times \mathbf{w}) = \pm |\mathbf{u}| \, |\mathbf{v} \times \mathbf{w}| \cos \theta.
$$

Since $\mathbf{u} \cdot (\mathbf{v} \times \mathbf{w})$ varies continuously, only one of these values can be in its range.† Therefore, $\mathbf{u} \cdot (\mathbf{v} \times \mathbf{w})$ does not change sign and is positive after the rotation if and only if it was positive initially, so that C in (7-31) determines the orientation. Therefore, we can conclude that $\{\mathbf{u}, \mathbf{v}, \mathbf{w}\}$ is positively oriented or negatively oriented, according to whether $\mathbf{w}$ points upward or downward from the (x, y)-plane after the trihedral is rotated so that $\mathbf{u}$ lies along the positive x-axis and $\mathbf{v}$ is in the half of the (x, y)-plane whose points have positive y-coordinates. We can give the following nonmathematical description of this. We shall call a trihedral $\{\mathbf{u}, \mathbf{v}, \mathbf{w}\}$ *right-handed* if the thumb of the right hand points in the positive direction along $\mathbf{w}$ when the fingers are wrapped around $\mathbf{w}$ in such a way that $\mathbf{u}$ can be rotated through an angle less than π to lie along $\mathbf{v}$; otherwise, we shall call the trihedral *left-handed*. *An oriented trihedral is positively oriented if and only if it and the coordinate trihedral, $\{\mathbf{i}, \mathbf{j}, \mathbf{k}\}$, are both right-handed or both left-handed.*

THEOREM 7-3.2. If $\mathbf{u} \times \mathbf{v} \neq \mathbf{0}$, then the trihedral $\{\mathbf{u} \times \mathbf{v}, \mathbf{u}, \mathbf{v}\}$ is positively oriented.

PROOF. $(\mathbf{u} \times \mathbf{v}) \cdot (\mathbf{u} \times \mathbf{v}) = |\mathbf{u} \times \mathbf{v}|^2 > 0.$

---

† Explicitly, we might let θ_1 be the total angle of rotation during the first stage. Let t be a symbol which during the first stage denotes the angle through which the trihedral has rotated, and during the second stage denotes the sum of θ_1 and the angle of rotation about the x-axis. Now define f by $f(t) = \mathbf{u} \cdot (\mathbf{v} \times \mathbf{w})$. Then the components of $\mathbf{u}$, $\mathbf{v}$, and $\mathbf{w}$ are continuous functions of t and f is a continuous function.

The fact that $|\mathbf{u} \times \mathbf{v}|$ is the area of a parallelogram with $\mathbf{u}$ and $\mathbf{v}$ as adjacent sides leads to other interesting geometric facts. Suppose that $\mathbf{u}$ and $\mathbf{v}$ are drawn as arrows with their initial points at the origin, as indicated in Fig. 7-9, and let

$$A = |\mathbf{u} \times \mathbf{v}|.$$

Then

$$(u_1, u_2, 0) \times (v_1, v_2, 0) = (0, 0, u_1v_2 - u_2v_1) = (u_1v_2 - u_2v_1)\mathbf{k},$$

and this cross product is equal to the area of a parallelogram with $(u_1, u_2, 0)$ and $(v_1, v_2, 0)$ as adjacent sides. That is, the area of the projection into the (x, y)-plane of the parallelogram with $\mathbf{u}$ and $\mathbf{v}$ as adjacent sides is equal to the third component of $\mathbf{u} \times \mathbf{v}$, and therefore is equal to $A \cos \gamma$, where γ is as shown in Fig. 7-9. Similarly, the parallelogram determined by $\mathbf{u}$ and $\mathbf{v}$ projects into parallelograms in the (y, z)-plane and the (z, x)-plane whose areas are $A \cos \alpha$ and $A \cos \beta$, respectively. Also,

$$A^2 = (A \cos \alpha)^2 + (A \cos \beta)^2 + (A \cos \gamma)^2. \tag{7-32}$$

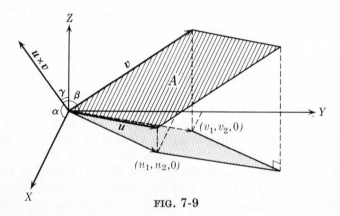

FIG. 7-9

That is, the square of the area of a parallelogram is equal to the sum of the squares of the areas of its projections into three mutually perpendicular planes.

It is often convenient to write the cross product of vectors in determinant notation. With this notation, we can write (7-28) as

$$\mathbf{u} \times \mathbf{v} = \mathbf{i} \begin{vmatrix} u_2 & u_3 \\ v_2 & v_3 \end{vmatrix} - \mathbf{j} \begin{vmatrix} u_1 & u_3 \\ v_1 & v_3 \end{vmatrix} + \mathbf{k} \begin{vmatrix} u_1 & u_2 \\ v_1 & v_2 \end{vmatrix}. \tag{7-33}$$

Since

$$(u_1\mathbf{i} + u_2\mathbf{j}) \times (v_1\mathbf{i} + v_2\mathbf{j}) = \begin{vmatrix} u_1 & u_2 \\ v_1 & v_2 \end{vmatrix}\mathbf{k},$$

the area of a parallelogram with $u_1\mathbf{i} + u_2\mathbf{j}$ and $v_1\mathbf{i} + v_2\mathbf{j}$ as adjacent sides is equal to the absolute value of the determinant

$$\begin{vmatrix} u_1 & u_2 \\ v_1 & v_2 \end{vmatrix}.$$

We can also write

$$\mathbf{u} \times \mathbf{v} = \begin{vmatrix} \mathbf{i} & \mathbf{j} & \mathbf{k} \\ u_1 & u_2 & u_3 \\ v_1 & v_2 & v_3 \end{vmatrix}, \tag{7-34}$$

since expansion of this determinant by the first row gives Eq. (7-33).

There are several very important algebraic properties of the cross product, each of which we shall state in two equivalent forms and list as parts of the following theorem. The proof of this theorem needs little more than formal evaluation of the various determinants and will be left as problems for the student.

THEOREM 7-3.3. For any vectors $\mathbf{u}$, $\mathbf{v}$, and $\mathbf{w}$, and any number t,

$$\mathbf{u} \times \mathbf{v} = -(\mathbf{v} \times \mathbf{u}), \quad \text{or} \quad \begin{vmatrix} \mathbf{i} & \mathbf{j} & \mathbf{k} \\ u_1 & u_2 & u_3 \\ v_1 & v_2 & v_3 \end{vmatrix} = -\begin{vmatrix} \mathbf{i} & \mathbf{j} & \mathbf{k} \\ v_1 & v_2 & v_3 \\ u_1 & u_2 & u_3 \end{vmatrix};$$

$$t(\mathbf{u} \times \mathbf{v}) = (t\mathbf{u}) \times \mathbf{v} = \mathbf{u} \times (t\mathbf{v}), \quad \text{or}$$

$$t\begin{vmatrix} \mathbf{i} & \mathbf{j} & \mathbf{k} \\ u_1 & u_2 & u_3 \\ v_1 & v_2 & v_3 \end{vmatrix} = \begin{vmatrix} \mathbf{i} & \mathbf{j} & \mathbf{k} \\ tu_1 & tu_2 & tu_3 \\ v_1 & v_2 & v_3 \end{vmatrix} = \begin{vmatrix} \mathbf{i} & \mathbf{j} & \mathbf{k} \\ u_1 & u_2 & u_3 \\ tv_1 & tv_2 & tv_3 \end{vmatrix};$$

$$\mathbf{u} \times (\mathbf{v} + \mathbf{w}) = (\mathbf{u} \times \mathbf{v}) + (\mathbf{u} \times \mathbf{w}), \quad \text{or}$$

$$\begin{vmatrix} \mathbf{i} & \mathbf{j} & \mathbf{k} \\ u_1 & u_2 & u_3 \\ v_1+w_1 & v_2+w_2 & v_3+w_3 \end{vmatrix} = \begin{vmatrix} \mathbf{i} & \mathbf{j} & \mathbf{k} \\ u_1 & u_2 & u_3 \\ v_1 & v_2 & v_3 \end{vmatrix} + \begin{vmatrix} \mathbf{i} & \mathbf{j} & \mathbf{k} \\ u_1 & u_2 & u_3 \\ w_1 & w_2 & w_3 \end{vmatrix}.$$

It follows from the original definition of cross product, or from the geometric interpretation of the cross product, that

$$\mathbf{i} \times \mathbf{j} = \mathbf{k}, \quad \mathbf{j} \times \mathbf{k} = \mathbf{i}, \quad \mathbf{k} \times \mathbf{i} = \mathbf{j},$$
$$\mathbf{j} \times \mathbf{i} = -\mathbf{k}, \quad \mathbf{k} \times \mathbf{j} = -\mathbf{i}, \quad \mathbf{i} \times \mathbf{k} = -\mathbf{j}. \tag{7-35}$$

The equations in (7-35) and Theorem 7-3.3 give an alternative method for evaluating cross products, which may be quite easy if several components are zero. For example,

$$\mathbf{i} \times (5\mathbf{i} - \mathbf{j} + 3\mathbf{k}) = 5(\mathbf{i} \times \mathbf{i}) - (\mathbf{i} \times \mathbf{j}) + 3(\mathbf{i} \times \mathbf{k}) = -3\mathbf{j} - \mathbf{k}.$$

Since $\mathbf{i} \times (\mathbf{i} \times \mathbf{j}) = \mathbf{i} \times \mathbf{k} = -\mathbf{j}$, but $(\mathbf{i} \times \mathbf{i}) \times \mathbf{j} = \mathbf{0} \times \mathbf{j} = \mathbf{0}$, we see that *the cross product is not associative* [also see problem 11].

The product $\mathbf{u} \cdot (\mathbf{v} \times \mathbf{w})$ is the *triple scalar product* of $\mathbf{u}$, $\mathbf{v}$, and $\mathbf{w}$. If in (7-33) or (7-34) we replace $\mathbf{u}$ by $\mathbf{v}$ and $\mathbf{v}$ by $\mathbf{w}$, then we can evaluate $\mathbf{u} \cdot (\mathbf{v} \times \mathbf{w})$ merely by replacing $\mathbf{i}$, $\mathbf{j}$, and $\mathbf{k}$ by u_1, u_2, and u_3, respectively. Therefore,

$$\mathbf{u} \cdot (\mathbf{v} \times \mathbf{w}) = \begin{vmatrix} u_1 & u_2 & u_3 \\ v_1 & v_2 & v_3 \\ w_1 & w_2 & w_3 \end{vmatrix}. \tag{7-36}$$

If $\mathbf{u}$, $\mathbf{v}$, $\mathbf{w}$, and $\mathbf{v} \times \mathbf{w}$ are represented by arrows with the same initial point, then the arrow $\mathbf{v} \times \mathbf{w}$ is perpendicular to the plane of $\mathbf{v}$ and $\mathbf{w}$ and is equal in length to the area of a parallelogram with $\mathbf{v}$ and $\mathbf{w}$ as adjacent sides. Also,

$$\mathbf{u} \cdot (\mathbf{v} \times \mathbf{w}) = |\mathbf{v} \times \mathbf{w}| \, |\mathbf{u}| \cos \theta,$$

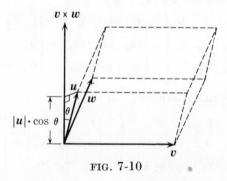

FIG. 7-10

where θ is the angle between **u** and **v** × **w** [see Fig. 7-10]. Since the trihedral (**v**, **w**, **v** × **w**) is positively oriented, θ is acute or obtuse according to whether the trihedral (**v**, **w**, **u**), or (**u**, **v**, **w**), is positively or negatively oriented. Then $|\mathbf{u}|$ cos θ is the signed length of the projection of **u** onto **v** × **w**, and the absolute value of **u** · (**v** × **w**) is the volume of a parallelepiped with **u**, **v**, and **w** as coterminal edges. This volume is **u** · (**v** × **w**) or − **u** · (**v** × **w**), according to whether the trihedral (**u**, **v**, **w**) is positively or negatively oriented.

THEOREM 7-3.4.   For any vectors, **u**, **v**, and **w**,

$$\mathbf{u}\cdot(\mathbf{v}\times\mathbf{w}) = -\mathbf{u}\cdot(\mathbf{w}\times\mathbf{v}) = \mathbf{w}\cdot(\mathbf{u}\times\mathbf{v}) = -\mathbf{w}\cdot(\mathbf{v}\times\mathbf{u})$$
$$= \mathbf{v}\cdot(\mathbf{w}\times\mathbf{u}) = -\mathbf{v}\cdot(\mathbf{u}\times\mathbf{w}). \qquad (7\text{-}37)$$

PROOF.   Interchanging two rows of a determinant is equivalent to changing the sign of the determinant. The truth of (7-37) follows from this when we observe that each member of (7-37) is obtained from the preceding member by changing the sign and interchanging two rows in the corresponding determinant. Alternatively, we can prove (7-37) by noting that, if two of three vectors are interchanged, the orientation of the corresponding trihedral is changed but the volume of the parallelepiped determined by the trihedral is not changed.

There is a very useful memory device for (7-37). If **u**, **v**, and **w** are represented by three points arranged counterclockwise around a circle, then a triple scalar product of **u**, **v**, and **w** in some order is equal to **u** · (**v** × **w**) if the order is counterclockwise around the circle. It is equal to − **u** · (**v** × **w**) if the order is clockwise. That is,

$$\mathbf{u}\cdot(\mathbf{v}\times\mathbf{w}) = \mathbf{v}\cdot(\mathbf{w}\times\mathbf{u}) = \mathbf{w}\cdot(\mathbf{u}\times\mathbf{v}),$$
$$\mathbf{u}\cdot(\mathbf{v}\times\mathbf{w}) = -\mathbf{u}\cdot(\mathbf{w}\times\mathbf{v}) = -\mathbf{w}\cdot(\mathbf{v}\times\mathbf{u}) = -\mathbf{v}\cdot(\mathbf{u}\times\mathbf{w}).$$

PROBLEMS

1. For each pair of vectors, find all vectors that are orthogonal to both given vectors.
   (*a*) **i** + **j**; **i** + **j** + **k**.   (*b*) **i** − **j**; **i** + **j** + **k**.   (c) **i** + 2**j** − **k**; 2**i** + **j** + 3**k**.

2. Find equations of the line that contains the point $(1, -2, 3)$ and is perpendicular to each of the vectors $3\mathbf{i}+\mathbf{j}-\mathbf{k}$ and $2\mathbf{i}-7\mathbf{j}+\mathbf{k}$.

3. For each of the following sets of three points, find an equation of the plane that contains the points. [*Hint:* First find an arrow perpendicular to the plane.]

(*a*) $(1, -1, 1)$; $(2, 3, 0)$; $(0, -2, 5)$.

(*b*) $(0, 0, 0)$; $(3, 5, -2)$; $(-2, 7, 11)$.

(*c*) $(2, 1, 0)$; $(0, 0, 3)$; $(1, 1, 1)$.

4. For each of the following, find the area of a triangle that has the given arrows as two of its sides.

(*a*) $\mathbf{i}$; $\mathbf{i}+2\mathbf{j}+3\mathbf{k}$.   (*b*) $\mathbf{i}+2\mathbf{j}$; $\mathbf{i}+6\mathbf{j}$.   (c) $\mathbf{i}+2\mathbf{j}+\mathbf{k}$; $3\mathbf{i}-\mathbf{j}+2\mathbf{k}$.

5. A line is parallel to the arrow $\mathbf{u}$ and passes through the point (x_0, y_0, z_0).   (a) Show that the distance from the point (x, y, z) to the line is

$$\left| \frac{\mathbf{u} \times [(x-x_0)\mathbf{i} + (y-y_0)\mathbf{j} + (z-z_0)\mathbf{k}]}{|\mathbf{u}|} \right|.$$

(b) Show that an equation of the line is

$$\mathbf{u} \times [(x-x_0)\mathbf{i} + (y-y_0)\mathbf{j} + (z-z_0)\mathbf{k}] = \mathbf{0}.$$

6. For each of the following, use problem 5(a) to determine the distance from the given point to the given line.

(*a*) $(0, 1, 5)$; $\begin{cases} x = 1+2t, \\ y = 3-t, \\ z = 5t. \end{cases}$ (b) $(2, 1, 3)$; $\begin{cases} x = 2-t, \\ y = 2t, \\ z = 1+2t. \end{cases}$

7. Show that $\mathbf{u} \cdot [\mathbf{u} \times (\mathbf{v} \times \mathbf{w})] = 0$ for any vectors $\mathbf{u}$, $\mathbf{v}$, and $\mathbf{w}$.

8. Prove that, for any vectors $\mathbf{u}$ and $\mathbf{v}$,

$$(\mathbf{u}+\mathbf{v}) \cdot [\mathbf{u} \times (\mathbf{v}+2\mathbf{u})] = 0.$$

9.* Show that $\mathbf{u} \times (\mathbf{v} \times \mathbf{w}) = (\mathbf{u} \cdot \mathbf{w})\mathbf{v} - (\mathbf{u} \cdot \mathbf{v})\mathbf{w}$ for any vectors $\mathbf{u}$, $\mathbf{v}$, and $\mathbf{w}$. [*Hint:* Because of the geometric descriptions of the scalar and cross products and the geometric method for multiplying arrows by numbers and subtracting arrows, the given equality is true if and only if it is true if $\mathbf{u}$, $\mathbf{v}$, and $\mathbf{w}$ are replaced by any vectors $\mathbf{u}^*$, $\mathbf{v}^*$, and $\mathbf{w}^*$ for which the trihedrals $(\mathbf{u}, \mathbf{v}, \mathbf{w})$ and $(\mathbf{u}^*, \mathbf{v}^*, \mathbf{w}^*)$ are congruent. Let $\mathbf{u}^* = a_1\mathbf{i}$, $\mathbf{v}^* = a_2\mathbf{i}+b_2\mathbf{j}$, $\mathbf{w}^* = a_3\mathbf{i}+b_3\mathbf{j}+c_3\mathbf{k}$.]

10. Use problem 9 to show that, for any vectors $\mathbf{r}$, $\mathbf{s}$, $\mathbf{u}$, and $\mathbf{v}$,

$$(\mathbf{r} \times \mathbf{s}) \cdot (\mathbf{u} \times \mathbf{v}) = (\mathbf{r} \cdot \mathbf{u})(\mathbf{s} \cdot \mathbf{v}) - (\mathbf{r} \cdot \mathbf{v})(\mathbf{s} \cdot \mathbf{u}).$$

11. Prove that $\mathbf{u} \times (\mathbf{v} \times \mathbf{w}) = (\mathbf{u} \times \mathbf{v}) \times \mathbf{w}$ if and only if $\mathbf{u}$ and $\mathbf{w}$ are parallel or $\mathbf{v}$ is orthogonal to both $\mathbf{u}$ and $\mathbf{w}$.

12. Prove that the area of the triangle whose vertices are (x_1, y_1), (x_2, y_2), and (x_3, y_3) is given by the absolute value of the indicated

expression. [*Hint:* Use the geometric interpretation of the triple scalar product.]

$$\frac{1}{2} \begin{vmatrix} x_1 & y_1 & 1 \\ x_2 & y_2 & 1 \\ x_3 & y_3 & 1 \end{vmatrix}$$

13. Find the volume of the parallelepiped whose vertices are $(2, 3, 4)$, $(1, -2, 3)$, $(4, 3, 4)$, $(3, -2, 3)$, $(3, 4, 5)$, $(2, -1, 4)$, $(5, 4, 5)$, and $(4, -1, 4)$.

7-4. CURVE LENGTH

Before discussing the length of a curve, we must have an explicit definition of curve. For this, we shall use parametric equations. We have seen that lines and planes have simple parametric representations. Let us consider a few cases that illustrate the general applicability of parametric equations for describing "curves." The graph in the (x, y)-plane of the equation $x^2/a^2 + y^2/b^2 = 1$ is an ellipse. This ellipse is also the graph of the parametric equations

$$\begin{cases} x = a \cos t, \\ y = b \sin t, \end{cases}$$

for $0 \leq t \leq 2\pi$. If the domain of a function f is an interval I, then the graph in the (x, y)-plane is also the graph of the parametric equations

$$\begin{cases} x = t, \\ y = f(t). \end{cases}$$

Similarly, the intersection of the graphs in three dimensions of two equations such as $y = F(x)$ and $z = G(x, y)$ is also the graph of the parametric equations

$$\begin{cases} x = t, \\ y = F(t), \\ z = G[t, F(t)]. \end{cases}$$

These examples show that parametric equations are widely applicable.

DEFINITION 7-4.1. A *curve* is the graph of a set of parametric equations

$$\begin{cases} x = f(t), \\ y = g(t), \\ z = h(t), \end{cases}$$

such that f, g, and h are continuous on an interval $[a, b]$. The points that correspond to a and b are the *end points* of the curve. A *simple curve* is a curve with the property that, with the possible exception of a and b, no two numbers in $[a, b]$ determine the same point on the curve. A *closed curve* is a curve whose end points are coincident.

It is readily apparent that a curve is a continuous image of an interval. If we let $P(t)$ be the point with coordinates $f(t)$, $g(t)$, and $h(t)$, then the distance between a fixed point $P(t_0)$ and the point $P(t)$ is

$$\{[f(t) - f(t_0)]^2 + [g(t) - g(t_0)]^2 + [h(t) - h(t_0)]^2\}^{\frac{1}{2}}. \qquad (7\text{-}38)$$

This approaches zero as $t \to t_0$ if f, g, and h are continuous. Thus, P is a continuous function of t. A very important reason for assuming continuity of the functions f, g, and h is that a curve is then connected, being a continuous image of an interval. However, even with this continuity assumption, curves can be quite strange. For example, the curve of Definition 7-4.1 consists of a single point if $a = b$, or if f, g, and h are constant on $[a, b]$. Although we shall not show this, for each square there is a curve that passes through each point of the square and its interior, and for each cube there is a curve that passes through each point of the cube and its interior! In either case, the interval can be the interval $[0, 1]$. It is clear from the existence of such curves that we should not expect all curves to have length.

A simple way of estimating the length of a curve is to select points along the curve and add the lengths of chords that join successive points. We might expect to obtain better approximations by choosing the points closer together. This concept is generalized in the following definition.

DEFINITION 7-4.2. Suppose C is a simple curve with the parametric equations

$$\begin{cases} x = f(t), \\ y = g(t), \\ z = h(t), \end{cases}$$

for $a \leqq t \leqq b$. For a partition $P = \{t_1, t_2, \cdots, t_{n+1}\}$ of $[a, b]$, suppose

$$\Delta_i x = f(t_{i+1}) - f(t_i), \quad \Delta_i y = g(t_{i+1}) - g(t_i), \quad \Delta_i z = h(t_{i+1}) - h(t_i),$$

(7-39)

and

$$L_P = \sum_{i=1}^{n} [(\Delta_i x)^2 + (\Delta_i y)^2 + (\Delta_i z)^2]^{1/2}. \tag{7-40}$$

Then C is *rectifiable* (or has length) if and only if the numbers L_P have an upper bound. If C is rectifiable, then the *length* of C is the number

$$\sup \{L_P : P \text{ a partition of } [a, b]\}.$$

The number L_P is the total length of the broken line path consisting of line segments joining points determined by successive points of the partition [see Fig. 7-11]. The definition of length for simple curves

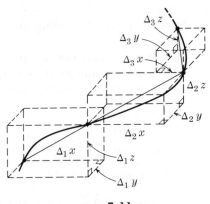

FIG. 7-11

was given in terms of a particular set of parametric equations for the curve. However, it is not difficult to show that for simple curves length is independent of the particular parametric equations used. To do this, let us suppose that a simple curve C has two sets of para-metric equations,

$$\begin{cases} x = f(t), \\ y = g(t), \\ z = h(t), \quad t \in [a, b]; \end{cases} \qquad \begin{cases} x = F(r), \\ y = G(r), \\ z = H(r), \quad r \in [\alpha, \beta], \end{cases}$$

where for each set of equations no two values of the parameter, except possibly the end points, correspond to the same point of C. We shall assume that C is not a closed curve and leave it to the student to extend our result to the case of simple closed curves. It is enough to show that the length determined by using the first set of parametric equations is not greater than the length determined by using the second set of equations, since the argument could then be reversed. To do this, we let $\{t_1, t_2, \cdots, t_{n+1}\}$ be a partition of $[a, b]$ and $\{P_1, P_2, \cdots, P_{n+1}\}$ be the corresponding points on the curve C as determined by the first set of parametric equations. All we need to show is that the numbers $\{r_1, r_2, \cdots, r_{n+1}\}$ corresponding to these points when we use the second set of parametric equations are arranged in order of size, since then L_P as defined by Eq. (7-40) is a valid sum of chords for the second set of parametric equations. It follows from Theorem 2-6.5 that the inverse of the map of $[a, b]$ onto C is continuous. Now we map $[\alpha, \beta]$ onto C and then C onto $[a, b]$. For any k, this gives a continuous map of the interval with end points r_{k-1} and r_{k+1} onto a subset of $[a, b]$ containing t_{k-1} and t_{k+1}. Since this subset is connected, it contains t_k. Therefore, r_k is between r_{k-1} and r_{k+1} and $\{r_1, r_2, \cdots, r_{n+1}\}$ is an increasing set or a decreasing set, according to whether $r_1 < r_2$ or $r_1 > r_2$.

We have yet to discuss conditions that assure a curve has length and to examine the problem of determining the length of such a curve. For both of these problems, we shall consider only curves with parametric equations

$$\begin{cases} x = f(t), \\ y = g(t), \\ z = h(t), \quad t \in [a, b], \end{cases} \tag{7-41}$$

for which f, g, and h are differentiable. With the help of the mean value theorem, we can deduce that

$$\begin{aligned} L_P &= \sum_{i=1}^{n} [(\Delta_i x)^2 + (\Delta_i y)^2 + (\Delta_i z)^2]^{1/2} \\ &= \sum_{i=1}^{n} \left[\left(\frac{\Delta_i x}{\Delta_i t}\right)^2 + \left(\frac{\Delta_i y}{\Delta_i t}\right)^2 + \left(\frac{\Delta_i z}{\Delta_i t}\right)^2 \right]^{1/2} \Delta_i t \\ &= \sum_{i=1}^{n} [f'(\alpha_i)^2 + g'(\beta_i)^2 + h'(\gamma_i)^2]^{1/2} \Delta_i t, \end{aligned} \tag{7-42}$$

where $\Delta_i t = t_{i+1} - t_i$ and the numbers α_i, β_i, and γ_i are in the open interval (t_i, t_{i+1}).

THEOREM 7-4.1. If C is a simple curve with the parametric equations in (7-41) and if f', g', and h' are bounded on $[a, b]$, then C is rectifiable.

PROOF. Suppose M is a number such that, if $t \in [a, b]$, then

$$|f'(t)| \leq M, \quad |g'(t)| \leq M, \quad |h'(t)| \leq M.$$

It follows from (7-42) that $L_P \leq \sqrt{3}M \sum_{i=1}^{n} |\Delta_i t| = \sqrt{3}M|b - a|$. Therefore, $\sqrt{3}M|b - a|$ is an upper bound for the set of all L_P and this set has a least upper bound—the length of C [see Definition 7-4.2].

THEOREM 7-4.2. If C is a simple curve with the parametric equations in (7-41) and if f', g', and h' are continuous on $[a, b]$ with $a \leq b$, then C is rectifiable and the length of C is equal to

$$\int_a^b [f'(t)^2 + g'(t)^2 + h'(t)^2]^{1/2}\, dt. \tag{7-43}$$

PROOF. First we note that f', g', and h' are bounded on $[a, b]$ if they are continuous [Theorem 2-8.2], so that it follows from Theorem 7-4.1 that C is rectifiable. Since adding more points to a partition does not decrease the corresponding sum L_P of lengths of chords, we can replace the partition defining L_P in (7-42) by a partition for which the largest of $\Delta_i t$ is as small as we wish without decreasing the value of L_P. Therefore, the length of C is equal to the following limit, provided this limit exists:

$$\lim_{\delta \to 0} \sum_{i=1}^{n} [f'(\alpha_i)^2 + g'(\beta_i)^2 + h'(\gamma_i)^2]^{1/2}\, \Delta_i t, \tag{7-44}$$

where δ is the largest of the numbers $\Delta_i t$ and the numbers α_i, β_i, and γ_i are in the interval $[t_i, t_{i+1}]$. Since f', g', and h' are continuous,

$$[(f')^2 + (g')^2 + (h')^2]^{1/2}$$

is continuous and (7-43) exists. Now it follows from Theorem 5-5.1 that (7-43) and (7-44) are equal, so that the integral in (7-43) is equal to the length of C.

ILLUSTRATION 1. The parabola whose equation is $y^2 = 4x$ has the parametric equations $x = t^2$, $y = 2t$. The length of the arc of this parabola that joins the points $(0, 0)$ and $(1, 2)$ is $\int_0^1 \sqrt{4t^2 + 4}\, dt$. If we substitute $t = \tan \theta$, this integral becomes

$$2\int_0^{1/4 \pi} \sec^3 \theta\, d\theta = [\sec \theta \tan \theta]_0^{1/4 \pi} + \int_0^{1/4 \pi} \sec \theta\, d\theta$$

$$= \sqrt{2} + [\ln (\sec \theta + \tan \theta)]_0^{1/4 \pi}$$

$$= \sqrt{2} + \ln (\sqrt{2} + 1).$$

PROBLEMS

1. For each of the following, determine the length of the graph in the (x, y)-plane of the given equation. Choose a parameter and limits of integration so that the graph is traced exactly once.

(a) $y^2 = x^3; \ 0 \leq x \leq 28$.

(b) $y = \frac{1}{2}(e^x + e^{-x}); \ 0 \leq x \leq k$.

(c) $y^3 = x^2; \ 0 \leq x \leq 8$.

(d) $y = \ln (\cos x); \ 0 \leq x \leq \frac{1}{4}\pi$.

(e) $\begin{cases} x = \sin t \cos t, \\ y = \cos t \cos t. \end{cases}$

(f) $\begin{cases} x = t - \sin t, \\ y = 1 - \cos t, \end{cases} \ 0 \leq t \leq 2\pi$.

(g) $\begin{cases} x = e^t \cos t, \\ y = e^t \sin t, \end{cases} \ 0 \leq t \leq \ln 2$.

2. For each of the following, determine the length of the graph of the given equations.

(a) $\begin{cases} x = t, \\ y = 2t, \\ z = 3t, \quad 0 \leq t \leq 1. \end{cases}$

(b) $\begin{cases} x = 3t, \\ y = 4t, \\ z = 5 \ln (\sec t), \quad 0 \leq t \leq \frac{1}{3}\pi. \end{cases}$

(c) $\begin{cases} x = \cos 2t, \\ y = 2t + \sin 2t, \\ z = 4 \cos t, \quad 0 \leq t \leq k. \end{cases}$

(d) $\begin{cases} x = a(t - \sin t) \\ y = a(1 - \cos t), \end{cases} \\ 0 \leq t \leq 2\pi$.

3. (a) Let C be the ellipse whose parametric equations are

$$\begin{cases} x = a \cos t, \\ y = b \sin t, \end{cases}$$

where $a \geq b > 0$. Show that the circumference of C is equal to

$$4a \int_0^{\frac{1}{2}\pi} (1 - e^2 \cos^2 t)^{\frac{1}{2}} \, dt = 4a \int_0^{\frac{1}{2}\pi} (1 - e^2 \sin^2 t)^{\frac{1}{2}} \, dt$$

$$= 4a \int_0^1 \frac{(1 - e^2 t^2)^{\frac{1}{2}}}{(1 - t^2)^{\frac{1}{2}}} \, dt,$$

where e is the eccentricity of the ellipse. This is an *elliptic integral of the second kind*. [*Hint:* Use the substitutions $t = \frac{1}{2}\pi - s$ and $\sin t = s$.]

(b) Determine the circumference of the ellipse for which $a = 1$ and $e = \frac{1}{2}$. [*Hint:* Use a table of elliptic integrals.†]

---

† See the table in, for example, *Tables of Higher Functions* by E. Jahnke and F. Emde, rev. by F. Lösch (New York: McGraw-Hill Book Co., Inc.), p. 57.

4. Show that a simple curve has length if it consists of a finite number of curves joined in succession, each of which has length.

5. Prove that the curve in the (x, y)-plane with the parametric equations, $x = t$, $y = t \sin t^{-1}$, is not rectifiable if the interval $[0, 1]$ is used for t with $y(0)$ defined as 0.

6. Prove that the curve in the (x, y)-plane with the parametric equations, $x = t$, $y = t^2 \sin t^{-1}$ if $t \neq 0$ and $y(0) = 0$, $0 \leq t \leq 1$, is rectifiable.

7. Let C be a curve that contains each point of the interior and perimeter of a square whose sides are of unit length. [*Note:* Such a curve cannot be a simple curve.] Show that if Definition 7-4.2 is used, even though C is not simple, then C is not rectifiable whatever parametric equations are used for C. [*Hint:* Let the square have vertices $(0, 0)$, $(1, 0)$, $(1, 1)$, and $(0, 1)$. Show that if a curve is rectifiable and contains the $(n + 1)^2$ points $(r/n, s/n)$, where $0 \leq r \leq n$ and $0 \leq s \leq n$, then the length is at least as large as $n + 2$.]

7-5. MORE ABOUT CURVE LENGTH

Suppose a curve has the parametric equations

$$\begin{cases} x = f(u), \\ y = g(u), \\ z = h(u), \end{cases}$$

where f', g', and h' are continuous. Also suppose that a and t are two values of the parameter and that $s(t)$ is the length of the curve between the points for which the parameter has the values a and t, if $a \leq t$, or the negative of this length, if $a > t$. Then

$$s(t) = \int_a^t [f'(u)^2 + g'(u)^2 + h'(u)^2]^{1/2} \, du,$$

and it follows from the fundamental theorem of calculus that

$$s'(t) = [f'(t)^2 + g'(t)^2 + h'(t)^2]^{1/2},$$
$$ds = [f'(t)^2 + g'(t)^2 + h'(t)^2]^{1/2} \, dt. \tag{7-45}$$

Therefore, $(ds)^2 = [f'(t) \, dt]^2 + [g'(t) \, dt]^2 + [h'(t) \, dt]^2$, which is the same as

$$(ds)^2 = (dx)^2 + (dy)^2 + (dz)^2. \tag{7-46}$$

Intuitively, this equation is related to the fact that if a chord joins two points for which the differences of coordinates are Δx, Δy, and Δz, then the length of the chord is $[(\Delta x)^2 + (\Delta y)^2 + (\Delta z)^2]^{1/2}$. Precise statements can be deduced as follows. If $ds/dt \neq 0$ and we denote the length of the chord by "chord" and $|\Delta s|$ by "arc," then

$$\lim_{\Delta t \to 0} \frac{\text{chord}}{\text{arc}} = \lim_{\Delta t \to 0} \frac{[(\Delta x)^2 + (\Delta y)^2 + (\Delta z)^2]^{1/2}}{|\Delta s|}$$

$$= \lim_{\Delta t \to 0} \frac{[(\Delta x/\Delta t)^2 + (\Delta y/\Delta t)^2 + (\Delta z/\Delta t)^2]^{1/2}}{\Delta s/\Delta t}$$

$$= \frac{ds/dt}{ds/dt} = 1, \tag{7-47}$$

$$\lim_{\Delta t \to 0} \frac{|ds|}{\text{arc}} = \lim_{\Delta t \to 0} \frac{s'(t)\,\Delta t}{\Delta s} = \lim_{\Delta t \to 0} \frac{ds/dt}{\Delta s/\Delta t} = 1.$$

Then

$$\lim_{\Delta t \to 0} \left(1 - \frac{\text{chord}}{\text{arc}}\right) = \lim_{\Delta t \to 0} \left(\frac{\text{arc} - \text{chord}}{\text{arc}}\right) = 0, \tag{7-48}$$

and

$$\lim_{\Delta t \to 0} \left(1 - \frac{|ds|}{\text{arc}}\right) = \lim_{\Delta t \to 0} \left(\frac{\text{arc} - |ds|}{\text{arc}}\right) = 0. \tag{7-49}$$

Equations (7-48) and (7-49) can be interpreted as meaning that if $ds/dt \neq 0$, then the arc may be replaced either by the chord or by $|ds|$ with an error that is a small part of the arc if Δt is sufficiently small.

It is interesting to note that the validity of Eq. (7-47) for chords and arcs of circles follows directly from the fact that $\lim_{x \to 0} (\sin x)/x = 1$. We need only observe that if the arc subtends an angle x at the center of a circle of radius r, then the length of the arc is rx and the length of the chord is larger than $r \cdot \sin x$. Therefore,

$$\frac{\sin x}{x} < \frac{\text{chord}}{\text{arc}} < 1 \quad \text{and} \quad \lim_{x \to 0} \frac{\text{chord}}{\text{arc}} = 1. \tag{7-50}$$

If a curve is in the (x, y)-plane and no two points on the curve have the same first coordinates and different second coordinates, then y is a function of x and we can write Eq. (7-46) as

$$(ds)^2 = (dx)^2 + (dy)^2 = \left[1 + \left(\frac{dy}{dx}\right)^2\right](dx)^2. \tag{7-51}$$

If no two points have different first coordinates and the same second coordinates, then

$$(ds)^2 = \left[\left(\frac{dx}{dy}\right)^2 + 1\right](dy)^2. \tag{7-52}$$

ILLUSTRATION 1. Suppose we wish to find the length of the arc that joins the points $(0, 0)$ and $(\frac{1}{6}\pi, \ln 2 - \frac{1}{2}\ln 3)$ on the graph of $y = \ln(\sec x)$. We have $ds = [1 + (dy/dx)^2]^{1/2}\,dx = (1 + \tan^2 x)^{1/2}\,dx = \sec x\,dx$, so the length of the arc is

$$\int_0^{\pi/6} \sec x\,dx = \left[\ln(\sec x + \tan x)\right]_0^{\pi/6} = \ln\left(\frac{2}{\sqrt{3}} + \frac{1}{\sqrt{3}}\right) = \tfrac{1}{2}\ln 3.$$

If a curve has a polar equation of type $r = f(\theta)$, then we can use θ as a parameter and write $x = r\cos\theta$, $y = r\sin\theta$. Then

$$dx = (\cos\theta)\,dr - (r\sin\theta)\,d\theta, \qquad dy = (\sin\theta)\,dr + (r\cos\theta)\,d\theta,$$

and

$$(ds)^2 = (dx)^2 + (dy)^2 = (dr)^2 + r^2(d\theta)^2 = \left[r^2 + \left(\frac{dr}{d\theta}\right)^2\right](d\theta)^2. \tag{7-53}$$

There is a useful geometric aid for remembering the formula

$$(ds)^2 = (dr)^2 + (r\,d\theta)^2. \tag{7-54}$$

As shown in Fig. 7-12, we can think of Δr, $r\,\Delta\theta$, and Δs as being the lengths of the sides of a figure that is a right triangle except for one side, which is an arc of a circle, and the hypotenuse, which is an arc of a curve! Thus, it seems reasonable that $(\Delta r)^2 + (r\,\Delta\theta)^2$ is a good

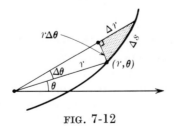

FIG. 7-12

approximation of $(\Delta s)^2$ when $\Delta\theta$ is small. In fact, since we have proved Eq. (7-54), we know that

$$\lim_{\Delta\theta\to 0} \frac{(\Delta r)^2 + (r\,\Delta\theta)^2}{(\Delta s)^2} = \lim_{\Delta\theta\to 0} \left[\left(\frac{\Delta r}{\Delta\theta}\right)^2 + r^2\right]\left(\frac{\Delta s}{\Delta\theta}\right)^{-2} = 1,$$

since these limits are equal to $[(dr/d\theta)^2 + r^2](ds/d\theta)^{-2}$ and from (7-54) we have $(dr/d\theta)^2 + r^2 = (ds/d\theta)^2$.

ILLUSTRATION 2. To find the length of the cardioid whose polar equation is $r = 1 + \cos\theta$, we can use (7-53) and express the length as

$$\int_0^{2\pi} \left[r^2 + \left(\frac{dr}{d\theta}\right)^2\right]^{1/2} d\theta = \int_0^{2\pi} [2 + 2\cos\theta]^{1/2}\, d\theta = \int_0^{2\pi} 2\left|\cos \tfrac{1}{2}\theta\right|\, d\theta.$$

Since $\cos\tfrac{1}{2}\theta$ is negative for $\pi < \theta < 2\pi$, the absolute value signs must be handled carefully. The cardioid is symmetric about the polar axis and its length can be computed by integrating between the limits 0 and π and doubling the result. Therefore, the length is

$$4\int_0^\pi \cos \tfrac{1}{2}\theta\, d\theta = \left[8\sin\tfrac{1}{2}\theta\right]_0^\pi = 8.$$

If for a curve C the derivatives, dx/dt, dy/dt, and dz/dt, are bounded, then any arc that joins two points of the curve has length. For such curves, we can describe the position of a point P on the curve by specifying the directed distance from some fixed point P_0 on the curve to P. This distance is positive or negative according to whether the parameter t has a larger or a smaller value at P than at P_0. This use of arc length as a parameter has considerable theoretical importance. The integral of Theorem 7-4.2 becomes

$$\int_{s_a}^{s_b} ds, \tag{7-55}$$

where the value of the integral is the length of the arc that joins the points for which the arc-length parameter has the values s_a and s_b. Direct evaluation of this integral gives $s_b - s_a$, which is certainly the distance between these points. However, the value of $s_b - s_a$ is usually unknown and the integral must be evaluated by change of variables, using equations such as (7-45), and (7-51) through (7-53).

ILLUSTRATION 3. A *helix* is a curve shaped like a coil spring that has parametric equations of type

$$\begin{cases} x = a \cos t, \\ y = a \sin t, \\ z = bt. \end{cases}$$

Then

$$\left(\frac{ds}{dt}\right)^2 = \left(\frac{dx}{dt}\right)^2 + \left(\frac{dy}{dt}\right)^2 + \left(\frac{dz}{dt}\right)^2 = a^2 + b^2,$$

so that the arc that joins the points for which t has the values t_1 and t_2 has length $(a^2 + b^2)^{1/2}|t_2 - t_1|$. The arc length $s(t)$ measured from the point for which $t = 0$ is $(a^2 + b^2)^{1/2}t$, and the equations of the curve using this arc length as parameter are

$$\begin{cases} x = a \cos [s(a^2 + b^2)^{-1/2}], \\ y = a \sin [s(a^2 + b^2)^{-1/2}], \\ z = b(a^2 + b^2)^{-1/2}s. \end{cases}$$

There are many useful applications for integrals of type

$$\int_{s_a}^{s_b} f(s)\, ds, \tag{7-56}$$

where f is a function of s. Again, it is usually necessary to express s in terms of a suitable parameter to evaluate this integral. Such an integral can be interpreted as being an integral along a curve [see Fig. 7-13]. It is the limit of sums of type $\sum_{i=1}^{n} f(\sigma_i)\, \Delta_i s$. This sum

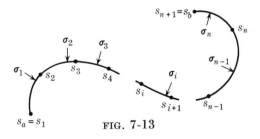

FIG. 7-13

is formed by choosing a partition $\{s_1, s_2, \cdots, s_{n+1}\}$ of the interval $[s_a, s_b]$. Then, for each i, we can let $\Delta_i s = s_{i+1} - s_i$ and σ_i be a point in the interval $[s_i, s_{i+1}]$. That is, the sum is formed by dividing the curve into arcs and then adding the products that are obtained by multiplying the length of each arc and a value of the function f at a point of that arc. The mathematical or physical interpretation of this integral depends on the interpretation of the function f. For example, if f is called "density," then the integral is called the "mass" of the curve. It follows from the fundamental theorem of calculus that $dm/ds = f(s)$, where $m(s)$ is the mass of the arc of the curve that joins a fixed point and the point at distance s along the curve from this point. This means that density is the instantaneous rate of change of mass— i.e., the limit of the average mass per unit distance as the length of the arc of the curve under consideration approaches zero. Integrals of type (7-56) are closely related to line integrals, which will be studied in Chapter 9.

ILLUSTRATION 4. Suppose that a curve C has the parametric equations

$$\begin{cases} x = \sin t, \\ y = \cos t, \\ z = t^2, \end{cases}$$

and that the density is equal to $|3t|$ at the point for which the parameter has the value t. Then the mass of the arc of C that joins the points for which $t = 0$ and $t = 2\pi$ is

$$\int_0^{2\pi} (3t)[\cos^2 t + \sin^2 t + 4t^2]^{1/2} \, dt = \int_0^{2\pi} (3t)[1 + 4t^2]^{1/2} \, dt$$

$$= \tfrac{1}{4}[(1 + 16\pi^2)^{3/2} - 1].$$

PROBLEMS

1. For each of the following, determine the length of the graph in the (x, y)-plane between the indicated points.

(*a*) $y = \tfrac{1}{3}x^3 + \tfrac{1}{4}x^{-1}$, $(1, 7/12)$, $(2, 67/24)$.

(*b*) $y = \ln (\sin x)$, $(\tfrac{1}{4}\pi, -\tfrac{1}{2}\ln 2)$, $(\tfrac{1}{2}\pi, 0)$.

(*c*) $x = \tfrac{1}{3}(y^2 + 2)^{3/2}$, $(\sqrt{3}, 1)$, $(2\sqrt{6}, 2)$.

2. Sketch and determine the lengths of the graphs of the following polar equations.

(*a*) $r = \theta^2$; $\quad 0 \leqq \theta \leqq 2\pi$. $\qquad$ (*c*) $r = \theta$; $\quad 0 \leqq \theta \leqq 2\pi$.

(b) $r = \sin \theta$. $\qquad\qquad\qquad$ (d) $\begin{cases} r = t^2, \\ \theta = \ln t; \end{cases} 1 \leq t \leq 2.$

3. For each of the following, find the mass of the graph of the given equations for the given density, ρ.

(*a*) $y = \sin x$; $0 \leqq x \leqq \pi$; $\rho(x) = 2\pi \sin x$.

(*b*) $\begin{cases} x = t, \\ y = 2t, \\ z = t^2; \quad 0 \leq t \leq 1; \quad \rho(t) = t. \end{cases}$

(*c*) $r = 1 + 2 \cos \theta$; $\rho(\theta) = |\sin \theta|$.

(*d*) $\begin{cases} x = a \cos t, \\ y = a \sin t, \\ z = bt; \quad 0 \leq t \leq 2\pi; \quad \rho(t) = t. \end{cases}$

7-6. DIFFERENTIATION OF VECTORS

Suppose that I is an interval of real numbers and that f, g, and h are real-valued functions having I as domains.   For each number t in I, let the vector $\mathbf{P}(t)$ be defined by

$$\mathbf{P}(t) = f(t)\mathbf{i} + g(t)\mathbf{j} + h(t)\mathbf{k}. \tag{7-57}$$

Then we define the derivative of the vector-valued function $\mathbf{P}$ as the vector-valued function $\mathbf{P}'$ for which a number t is in the domain of $\mathbf{P}'$ if and only if

$$\lim_{\Delta t \to 0} \frac{\mathbf{P}(t + \Delta t) - \mathbf{P}(t)}{\Delta t} \tag{7-58}$$

exists, the value of the limit being $\mathbf{P}'(t)$.   This limit can also be written as

$$\lim_{\Delta t \to 0} \left[\frac{f(t + \Delta t) - f(t)}{\Delta t} \mathbf{i} + \frac{g(t + \Delta t) - g(t)}{\Delta t} \mathbf{j} + \frac{h(t + \Delta t) - h(t)}{\Delta t} \mathbf{k} \right]. \tag{7-59}$$

For any vector $a\mathbf{i} + b\mathbf{j} + c\mathbf{k}$ and any vector-valued function $\mathbf{F}$ with $\mathbf{F}(t) = u(t)\mathbf{i} + v(t)\mathbf{j} + w(t)\mathbf{k}$, we have

$$|u(t) - a| \leqq |\mathbf{F}(t) - \mathbf{A}|, \quad |v(t) - b| \leqq |\mathbf{F}(t) - \mathbf{A}|, \quad |w(t) - c| \leqq |\mathbf{F}(t) - \mathbf{A}|,$$

and

$$|\mathbf{F}(t) - \mathbf{A}| = \{[u(t) - a]^2 + [v(t) - b]^2 + [w(t) - c]^2\}^{\frac{1}{2}}$$

$$\leqq \sqrt{3} \cdot [\text{largest of } \{|u(t) - a|, |v(t) - b|, |w(t) - c|\}].$$

Thus, for any number c that has a neighborhood contained in the domain of $\mathbf{F}$, it follows that $\lim_{t \to c} \mathbf{F}(t) = \mathbf{A}$ if and only if each of the following is true:

$$\lim_{t \to c} u(t) = a, \quad \lim_{t \to c} v(t) = b, \quad \lim_{t \to c} w(t) = c.$$

Therefore, the limit in (7-58) or (7-59) exists if and only if all of the following limits exist:

$$\lim_{\Delta t \to 0} \frac{f(t + \Delta t) - f(t)}{\Delta t} = f'(t),$$

$$\lim_{\Delta t \to 0} \frac{g(t + \Delta t) - g(t)}{\Delta t} = g'(t),$$

$$\lim_{\Delta t \to 0} \frac{h(t + \Delta t) - h(t)}{\Delta t} = h'(t),$$

in which case

$$\mathbf{P}'(t) = f'(t)\mathbf{i} + g'(t)\mathbf{j} + h'(t)\mathbf{k}. \tag{7-60}$$

We shall now discuss some laws of limits for vector-valued functions, so that these laws can be used in proving theorems about derivatives. Suppose we let u be a function whose range is a set of numbers and $\mathbf{F}$ be a function whose range is a set of vectors. Also, let S be a system of stages such that each stage contains a point in the intersection of the domains of u and $\mathbf{F}$.† If $\lim_S u = c$ and $\lim_S \mathbf{F} = \boldsymbol{\alpha}$, then

$$\lim_S (u\mathbf{F}) = c\boldsymbol{\alpha}. \tag{7-61}$$

If $\mathbf{G}$ is another function whose range is a set of vectors, if each stage contains a point in the intersection of the domains of $\mathbf{F}$ and $\mathbf{G}$, and if $\lim_S \mathbf{G} = \boldsymbol{\beta}$, then

$$\lim_S (\mathbf{F} + \mathbf{G}) = \boldsymbol{\alpha} + \boldsymbol{\beta}, \tag{7-62}$$

$$\lim_S (\mathbf{F} \cdot \mathbf{G}) = \boldsymbol{\alpha} \cdot \boldsymbol{\beta}, \tag{7-63}$$

$$\lim_S (\mathbf{F} \times \mathbf{G}) = \boldsymbol{\alpha} \times \boldsymbol{\beta}. \tag{7-64}$$

---

† For the purpose of visualizing a more concrete situation, the reader might imagine u and $\mathbf{F}$ to be defined on an interval about a number t_0, and the stages to be sets of the form $\{t: 0 < |t - t_0| < \varepsilon\}$.

For a vector-valued function $\mathbf{H}$, $\lim_S \mathbf{H}$ exists and equals $\boldsymbol{\gamma}$ if and only if the limit of each component of $\mathbf{H}$ is equal to the corresponding component of $\boldsymbol{\gamma}$. Because of this fact, Eqs. (7-61) through (7-64) are direct consequences of the laws of limits stated in Theorem 2-5.3. For example, if

$$\mathbf{F} = f_1\mathbf{i} + f_2\mathbf{j} + f_3\mathbf{k},$$

$$\mathbf{G} = g_1\mathbf{i} + g_2\mathbf{j} + g_3\mathbf{k},$$

$$\boldsymbol{\alpha} = \alpha_1\mathbf{i} + \alpha_2\mathbf{j} + \alpha_3\mathbf{k},$$

$$\boldsymbol{\beta} = \beta_1\mathbf{i} + \beta_2\mathbf{j} + \beta_3\mathbf{k},$$

then Eq. (7-63) is equivalent to all of the following being true:

$$\lim_S f_1 g_1 = \alpha_1 \beta_1, \quad \lim_S f_2 g_2 = \alpha_2 \beta_2, \quad \lim_S f_3 g_3 = \alpha_3 \beta_3.$$

We can also give proofs of (7-61) through (7-64) similar to the proofs of corresponding parts of Theorem 2-5.3. For example, to prove Eq. (7-64) we must show that, for any positive number ε, there is a stage A such that, for each t in the domain of $\mathbf{F} \times \mathbf{G}$, it is true that

$$|\mathbf{F}(t) \times \mathbf{G}(t) - \boldsymbol{\alpha} \times \boldsymbol{\beta}| < \varepsilon \quad \text{if} \quad t \in A.$$

To do this, we first note that

$$|\mathbf{F}(t) \times \mathbf{G}(t) - \boldsymbol{\alpha} \times \boldsymbol{\beta}| = |\mathbf{F}(t) \times [\mathbf{G}(t) - \boldsymbol{\beta}] + [\mathbf{F}(t) - \boldsymbol{\alpha}] \times \boldsymbol{\beta}|$$

$$\leq |\mathbf{F}(t) \times [\mathbf{G}(t) - \boldsymbol{\beta}]| + |[\mathbf{F}(t) - \boldsymbol{\alpha}] \times \boldsymbol{\beta}|.$$

Since $|\mathbf{A} \times \mathbf{B}| \leq |\mathbf{A}| \, |\mathbf{B}|$ for any two vectors $\mathbf{A}$ and $\mathbf{B}$, this implies that

$$|\mathbf{F}(t) \times \mathbf{G}(t) - \boldsymbol{\alpha} \times \boldsymbol{\beta}| \leq |\mathbf{F}(t)| \, |\mathbf{G}(t) - \boldsymbol{\beta}| + |\boldsymbol{\beta}| \, |\mathbf{F}(t) - \boldsymbol{\alpha}|. \qquad (7\text{-}65)$$

Now choosing a positive number ε, we can complete the proof by finding a stage A such that, if $t \in A$, then each of the last two terms is less than $\frac{1}{2}\varepsilon$. Since $\lim_S \mathbf{F} = \boldsymbol{\alpha}$, there is a stage A_1 such that

$$|\mathbf{F}(t) - \boldsymbol{\alpha}| < \frac{\varepsilon}{2|\boldsymbol{\beta}| + \varepsilon} \quad \text{if} \quad t \in A_1. \qquad (7\text{-}66)$$

Putting ε in the denominator of the last fraction has the advantage of making the fraction less than or equal to unity, even if $|\boldsymbol{\beta}| = 0$. Then

$$|\mathbf{F}(t)| < |\boldsymbol{\alpha}| + 1 \quad \text{if} \quad t \in A_1. \qquad (7\text{-}67)$$

Now we can let A_2 be a stage such that

$$|\mathbf{G}(t) - \boldsymbol{\beta}| < \frac{\varepsilon}{2(|\boldsymbol{\alpha}| + 1)} \quad \text{if} \quad t \in A_2. \tag{7-68}$$

If $A = A_1 \cap A_2$, it follows from inequalities (7-65) through (7-68) that, if $t \in A$, then

$$|\mathbf{F}(t) \times \mathbf{G}(t) - \boldsymbol{\alpha} \times \boldsymbol{\beta}| \leqq (|\boldsymbol{\alpha}| + 1)|\mathbf{G}(t) - \boldsymbol{\beta}| + |\boldsymbol{\beta}| \frac{\varepsilon}{2|\boldsymbol{\beta}| + \varepsilon}$$

$$< (|\boldsymbol{\alpha}| + 1) \frac{\varepsilon}{2(|\boldsymbol{\alpha}| + 1)} + \tfrac{1}{2}\varepsilon = \varepsilon.$$

We can use the laws of limits, Eqs. (7-61) through (7-64), to prove that if u, $\mathbf{F}$, and $\mathbf{G}$ are differentiable at a point t, where u is a real-valued function and $\mathbf{F}$ and $\mathbf{G}$ are vector-valued functions, then $u\mathbf{F}$, $\mathbf{F} + \mathbf{G}$, $\mathbf{F} \cdot \mathbf{G}$, and $\mathbf{F} \times \mathbf{G}$ are differentiable at t and

$$\frac{d(\mathbf{F} + \mathbf{G})}{dt} = \mathbf{F}'(t) + \mathbf{G}'(t), \tag{7-69}$$

$$\frac{d(u\mathbf{F})}{dt} = u(t)\mathbf{F}'(t) + u'(t)\mathbf{F}(t), \tag{7-70}$$

$$\frac{d(\mathbf{F} \cdot \mathbf{G})}{dt} = \mathbf{F}(t) \cdot \mathbf{G}'(t) + \mathbf{F}'(t) \cdot \mathbf{G}(t), \tag{7-71}$$

$$\frac{d(\mathbf{F} \times \mathbf{G})}{dt} = \mathbf{F}(t) \times \mathbf{G}'(t) + \mathbf{F}'(t) \times \mathbf{G}(t). \tag{7-72}$$

The proofs are similar to the proofs of the corresponding differentiation formulas for real-valued functions and are left for the student. Caution must be used in applying Eq. (7-72), since the order of the factors in each term is very important.

Suppose a curve is the graph of the set of parametric equations

$$\begin{cases} x = f(t), \\ y = g(t), \\ z = h(t). \end{cases}$$

Then, for a particular value of t, the vector

$$\mathbf{P}(t) = f(t)\mathbf{i} + g(t)\mathbf{j} + h(t)\mathbf{k}$$

can be represented by an arrow from the origin to the point $[f(t), g(t), h(t)]$ and is called the *position vector* for this point on the curve. The curve is the set of those points P for which there is a value of t such that the arrow $\mathbf{P}(t)$ with its initial point at the origin has its terminal point at P.

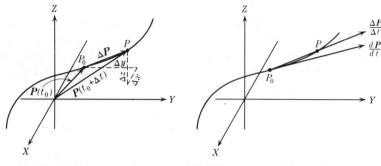

FIG. 7-14

We shall denote the vector $\mathbf{P}(t_0 + \Delta t) - \mathbf{P}(t_0)$ by $\Delta\mathbf{P}$.   The vector $\Delta\mathbf{P}$ can be represented by the arrow joining the points P_0 and P which are terminal points of $\mathbf{P}(t_0)$ and $\mathbf{P}(t_0 + \Delta t)$ when the initial points are at the origin [see Fig. 7-14].   If we let

$$\Delta x = f(t_0 + \Delta t) - f(t_0),$$
$$\Delta y = g(t_0 + \Delta t) - g(t_0),$$
$$\Delta z = h(t_0 + \Delta t) - h(t_0),$$

then

$$\frac{\Delta\mathbf{P}}{\Delta t} = \frac{\Delta x}{\Delta t}\mathbf{i} + \frac{\Delta y}{\Delta t}\mathbf{j} + \frac{\Delta z}{\Delta t}\mathbf{k},$$

and this vector can be represented by an arrow that lies along the secant line through the points P_0 and P.   If $\mathbf{P}'(t_0)$ exists and is nonzero, then, since $\Delta\mathbf{P}/\Delta t \to \mathbf{P}'(t_0)$, it follows that the angle between $\mathbf{P}'(t_0)$ and $\Delta\mathbf{P}/\Delta t$ approaches zero as $\Delta t \to 0$.   This means that if $\mathbf{P}'(t_0)$ is represented by an arrow whose initial point is at P_0, then this arrow lies along the tangent at P_0.   Also, the length of $\Delta\mathbf{P}/\Delta t$ approaches the length of $\mathbf{P}'(t_0)$ and this length is

$$|\mathbf{P}'(t_0)| = \left[\left(\frac{dx}{dt}\right)^2 + \left(\frac{dy}{dt}\right)^2 + \left(\frac{dz}{dt}\right)^2\right]^{\frac{1}{2}}. \tag{7-73}$$

We know from Theorem 7-4.2 that if the derivatives in this expression are continuous and the curve is simple, then any arc that joins two points of the curve has length and we can describe the position of a point P on the curve by specifying the directed distance s from some fixed point P_0 on the curve to P. This distance is positive or negative according to whether the parameter has a larger or a smaller value at P than at P_0. Moreover, $|\mathbf{P}'(t_0)| = [ds/dt]_{t=t_0}$.

The choice of a particular parameter determines an *orientation* for the curve, in the sense that P_2 follows P_1 if the parameter has a larger value at P_2 than at P_1. The value of the arc-length parameter s at a point P depends on the choice of the fixed point P_0 and on the orientation of the curve. If $ds/dt \neq 0$, then

$$\left| \frac{d\mathbf{P}}{ds} \right| = \left| \frac{d\mathbf{P}}{dt} \right| \left| \frac{dt}{ds} \right| = \frac{ds}{dt} \cdot \frac{dt}{ds} = 1.$$

This means that the vector $d\mathbf{P}/ds$, which we shall denote by $\mathbf{T}$, is a vector of unit length parallel to the tangent. Of course, once an arrow parallel to the tangent line at a particular point is known, then the equation of the tangent line can be written easily [see Section 7-1]. In practice, the unit vector $d\mathbf{P}/ds$ is obtained by computing $d\mathbf{P}/dt$ and multiplying by dt/ds, or dividing by ds/dt.

ILLUSTRATION. Suppose $\mathbf{P}(t) = (\cos t)\mathbf{i} + (\sin t)\mathbf{j} + (t)\mathbf{k}$. If $\mathbf{P}(t)$ is represented by an arrow whose initial point is at the origin, then the terminal point is on the curve whose parametric equations are

$$\begin{cases} x = \cos t, \\ y = \sin t, \\ z = t. \end{cases}$$

Since $x^2 + y^2 = 1$ for all values of t, the curve is on the cylinder whose equation is $x^2 + y^2 = 1$. As t increases, the curve continually rises as it winds around the cylinder, and we have

$$\mathbf{P}'(t) = (-\sin t)\mathbf{i} + (\cos t)\mathbf{j} + \mathbf{k}.$$

Parametric equations of the line tangent to this curve at the point for which $t = t_0$ are

$$\begin{cases} x = \cos t_0 + u(-\sin t_0), \\ y = \sin t_0 + u(\cos t_0), \\ z = t_0 + u. \end{cases}$$

Since $|ds/dt| = [(-\sin t)^2 + (\cos t)^2 + 1]^{1/2} = \sqrt{2}$, the unit tangent vector is

$$\mathbf{T} = \mathbf{P}'(t)\frac{dt}{ds} = \frac{\mathbf{P}'(t)}{\sqrt{2}} = (-\tfrac{1}{2}\sqrt{2}\sin t_0)\mathbf{i} + (\tfrac{1}{2}\sqrt{2}\cos t_0)\mathbf{j} + \tfrac{1}{2}\sqrt{2}\,\mathbf{k}.$$

If the arc-length parameter is measured from the point $(1, 0, 0)$, where $t = 0$, then $s = \sqrt{2}\,t$ and equations of the curve are

$$\begin{cases} x = \cos(\tfrac{1}{2}\sqrt{2}\,s), \\ y = \sin(\tfrac{1}{2}\sqrt{2}\,s), \\ z = \tfrac{1}{2}\sqrt{2}\,s. \end{cases}$$

This curve has the interesting geometric property that the angle between a tangent to the curve and the element of the cylinder through its point of tangency is the same for all tangents. To show this, we first note that all elements of the cylinder are parallel to the vector $\mathbf{k}$. Therefore, the cosine of the angle between the tangent and any element of the cylinder is equal to $\mathbf{T} \cdot \mathbf{k}$, or $\tfrac{1}{2}\sqrt{2}$.

PROBLEMS

1. Let $\mathbf{F}$ be differentiable at the point t and denote $\mathbf{F} \cdot \mathbf{F}$ by $\mathbf{F}^2$. Show that $D(\mathbf{F}^2) = 2(\mathbf{F} \cdot \mathbf{F}')$. What can be said about $\mathbf{F}'$ if $|\mathbf{F}|$ is constant?

2. For each of the following, find parametric equations for the tangent line at the specified point.

(a) $\begin{cases} x = 3 - 4t, \\ y = 2 + t^2, \\ z = 10 - t^3; \quad (-5, 6, 2). \end{cases}$ 　　(b) $\begin{cases} x = \cos 2t, \\ y = \sin 3t, \\ z = t; \quad (1, 0, 0). \end{cases}$

(c) $\mathbf{P}(t) = (\cosh t)\mathbf{i} + (\sinh t)\mathbf{j} + \mathbf{k}; \quad (1, 0, 1).$

3. Let $\mathbf{A}$ and $\mathbf{B}$ be vectors whose components are constants and let C be the curve defined by $\mathbf{P}(t) = \mathbf{A} + t\mathbf{B}$. Use differentiation and show that any arrow tangent to C is parallel to $\mathbf{B}$.

4. Let $\mathbf{A}$ and $\mathbf{B}$ be vectors whose components are constants and let C be the curve defined by $\mathbf{P}(t) = t\mathbf{A} + (1-t)\mathbf{B}$. Use differentiation and show that any arrow tangent to C is parallel to $\mathbf{A} - \mathbf{B}$. (C is the line through the end points of $\mathbf{A}$ and $\mathbf{B}$, when the initial points are at the origin.)

5. Let **A**, **B**, and **C** be vectors whose components are constants and let K be the curve defined by

$$\mathbf{P}(t) = u(t)\mathbf{A} + v(t)\mathbf{B} + [1 - u(t) - v(t)]\mathbf{C},$$

where u and v are differentiable functions of t. Use differentiation and show that any arrow tangent to K is perpendicular to the vector $(\mathbf{A} - \mathbf{C}) \times (\mathbf{B} - \mathbf{C})$. ($K$ is in the plane that contains the terminal points of **A**, **B**, and **C**, when the initial points are at the origin.)

6. Let

$$\mathbf{P}_1(t) = f(t)\mathbf{i} + g(t)\mathbf{j} + h(t)\mathbf{k} \quad \text{and} \quad \mathbf{P}_2(t) = F(t)\mathbf{i} + G(t)\mathbf{j} + H(t)\mathbf{k}$$

define two curves that intersect at the point P and let θ be the angle between the tangents at this point, where each tangent is directed in the direction for which t increases as one moves along the corresponding curve. Show that

$$\cos\theta = \frac{f'(t)F'(t) + g'(t)G'(t) + h'(t)H'(t)}{\{[f'(t)]^2 + [g'(t)]^2 + [h'(t)]^2\}^{\frac{1}{2}}\{[F'(t)]^2 + [G'(t)]^2 + [H'(t)]^2\}^{\frac{1}{2}}}.$$

7. For each of the following, use the method of problem 6 to determine the angle between tangents to the given curves at their point (or points) of intersection.

(*a*) $\begin{cases} x = 1 + 2t, \\ y = 1 + 3t, \\ z = 2 - t; \end{cases}$ $\begin{cases} x = 2 + 2s + s^2, \\ y = -2s - s^2, \\ z = 3 + s. \end{cases}$

(*b*) $\begin{cases} x = 3\cos t, \\ y = 2\sin t; \end{cases}$ $\begin{cases} x = \cosh s, \\ y = 2\sinh s. \end{cases}$

8. Prove that $\mathbf{P}(t)$ is perpendicular to $\mathbf{P}'(t)$ for all t, if

$$\mathbf{P}(t) = \frac{2t}{1 + t^2}\mathbf{i} + \frac{1 - t^2}{1 + t^2}\mathbf{j} + \mathbf{k}.$$

9. Let K be a curve with the property that the line from the origin to any point P on K is perpendicular to the tangent at P. Show that there is a number r such that K is on the sphere of radius r with center at the origin. [Compare with problem 1.]

10. Let $\mathbf{P}(t) = f(t)\mathbf{i} + g(t)\mathbf{j} + h(t)\mathbf{k}$. Show that **P** is continuous at a point t_0 if and only if all the functions f, g, and h are continuous at t_0.

11. Let **F** and **G** be vector-valued functions and t be a number for which $\mathbf{F}'(t)$ and $\mathbf{G}'(t)$ exist. Show that $(\mathbf{F} \cdot \mathbf{G})'$ and $(\mathbf{F} \times \mathbf{G})'$ exist and that

(a) $\dfrac{d(\mathbf{F} \cdot \mathbf{G})}{dt} = \mathbf{F}(t) \cdot \mathbf{G}'(t) + \mathbf{F}'(t) \cdot \mathbf{G}(t);$

(b) $\dfrac{d(\mathbf{F} \times \mathbf{G})}{dt} = \mathbf{F}(t) \times \mathbf{G}'(t) + \mathbf{F}'(t) \times \mathbf{G}(t).$

12. Let $\mathbf{F}'(t) = \mathbf{G}'(t)$ for all t in an interval I. Show that there is a constant vector $\mathbf{c}$ for which

$$\mathbf{F}(t) = \mathbf{G}(t) + \mathbf{c} \quad \text{if} \quad t \in I.$$

7-7. DIRECTIONAL DERIVATIVE AND GRADIENT

For a function f of three variables, the partial derivative $\partial f/\partial x$ is the rate of change of f with respect to x. This means that the value of $\partial f/\partial x$ at a point P_0 is the rate of change of f along the line through this point parallel to the x-axis. In general, if $\mathbf{P}_0$ is the position vector of a point and $\mathbf{T}$ is a unit vector, then $\mathbf{P}_0 + s\mathbf{T}$ is the position vector of the point along the line through P_0 in the direction of $\mathbf{T}$ and at distance s from P_0. The following definition gives a natural generalization of the concept of partial derivative.

DEFINITION 7-7.1. Suppose f is a function of three variables—i.e., a function of points with three coordinates—and $\mathbf{T}$ is a vector of unit length. The *directional derivative* of f in the direction of $\mathbf{T}$ is the function whose value at P_0 is equal to

$$\lim_{s \to 0} \frac{f(\mathbf{P}_0 + s\mathbf{T}) - f(\mathbf{P}_0)}{s},$$

for all points P_0 such that this limit exists.

It is customary to use df/ds to indicate a directional derivative, with the unit vector $\mathbf{T}$ specified in some way. Let us denote P_0 by (x_0, y_0, z_0) and $\mathbf{T}$ by $\lambda\mathbf{i} + \mu\mathbf{j} + \nu\mathbf{k}$, where $\lambda^2 + \mu^2 + \nu^2 = 1$. Then $f(\mathbf{P}_0 + s\mathbf{T})$ is a function of s. In fact, we can think of f as a function of x, y, and z, where x, y, and z are functions of s defined by

$$x = x_0 + \lambda s, \quad y = y_0 + \mu s, \quad z = z_0 + \nu s.$$

Then df/ds is simply the ordinary derivative of f with respect to s, evaluated at $s = 0$. We can use the chain rule to write

$$\frac{df}{ds} = \frac{\partial f}{\partial x}\frac{dx}{ds} + \frac{\partial f}{\partial y}\frac{dy}{ds} + \frac{\partial f}{\partial z}\frac{dz}{ds} = \frac{\partial f}{\partial x}\lambda + \frac{\partial f}{\partial y}\mu + \frac{\partial f}{\partial z}\nu. \tag{7-74}$$

It is easily seen from Eq. (7-74) that df/ds is the scalar product of two vectors. One is the unit tangent vector $\mathbf{T}$ and the other is the vector

$$\nabla f = \left(\frac{\partial f}{\partial x}\right)\mathbf{i} + \left(\frac{\partial f}{\partial y}\right)\mathbf{j} + \left(\frac{\partial f}{\partial z}\right)\mathbf{k}. \tag{7-75}$$

This vector is called the *gradient* of f. The symbol $\mathbf{\nabla}$ can be thought of as an operator (or function) defined by the statement that $\mathbf{\nabla}f$ is the vector of Eq. (7-75). We might then write

$$\mathbf{\nabla} = \left(\frac{\partial}{\partial x}\right)\mathbf{i} + \left(\frac{\partial}{\partial y}\right)\mathbf{j} + \left(\frac{\partial}{\partial z}\right)\mathbf{k}. \tag{7-76}$$

This operator is called the *del operator* and $\mathbf{\nabla}f$ is read as "del f." This operator is more complex than, but is similar to, the familiar differentiation operator d/dx or D_x.

Since the directional derivative is equal to $\mathbf{\nabla}f \cdot \mathbf{T}$ and $\mathbf{T}$ is a unit vector, it follows that the directional derivative is equal to $|\mathbf{\nabla}f|\cos\theta$, where θ is the angle between $\mathbf{\nabla}f$ and $\mathbf{T}$. That is, the directional derivative is the signed length of the projection of $\mathbf{\nabla}f$ onto $\mathbf{T}$. Therefore, $\mathbf{\nabla}f$ at a point (x_0, y_0, z_0) is a vector that points from (x_0, y_0, z_0) in the direction of maximum increase of the function f and whose magnitude is equal to this maximum rate of change of f. This shows that $\mathbf{\nabla}f$ is determined by f as a function of points P in space and that $\mathbf{\nabla}f$ does not depend on the particular coordinate system used to describe points. It follows directly from the definition of $\mathbf{\nabla}f$ that $|\mathbf{\nabla}f|$, which is the maximum rate of change of f, is given by

$$|\mathbf{\nabla}f| = \left[\left(\frac{\partial f}{\partial x}\right)^2 + \left(\frac{\partial f}{\partial y}\right)^2 + \left(\frac{\partial f}{\partial z}\right)^2\right]^{1/2}.$$

ILLUSTRATION 1. If $f(x, y, z) = xyz$, then

$$\mathbf{\nabla}f = (yz)\mathbf{i} + (xz)\mathbf{j} + (xy)\mathbf{k}.$$

At the point $(1, 0, 1)$, $\mathbf{\nabla}f = \mathbf{j}$. Therefore, at this point the maximum rate of change of f is in the direction of the y-axis and is equal to unity. The rate of change in any other direction can be obtained by projecting onto a vector in this direction and is equal to the cosine of the angle between this vector and $\mathbf{j}$. For example, the directional derivative of f is equal to $\frac{1}{2}$ in those directions that make an angle of $\frac{1}{3}\pi$ with the vector $\mathbf{j}$. Vectors in such directions form a cone whose elements make an angle of $\frac{1}{3}\pi$ with the line through $(1, 0, 1)$ parallel to the y-axis. The vectors in whose directions the directional derivative is zero are those vectors perpendicular to $\mathbf{j}$, since the projection of $\mathbf{j}$ onto such a vector is of zero length. This means that df/ds at $(1, 0, 1)$ is zero in the direction of any unit vector $\mathbf{T}$ in the (z, x)-plane. This is also a consequence of the fact that $f(x, y, z) = 0$ for all points in the (z, x)-plane.

Now suppose that we are given a curve through P_0 with parametric equations

$$x = x(t), \quad y = y(t), \quad z = z(t) \tag{7-77}$$

such that at P_0 each of $x'(t)$, $y'(t)$, $z'(t)$ exists and not all are zero. Then

$$\mathbf{T} = \frac{x'(t)\mathbf{i} + y'(t)\mathbf{j} + z'(t)\mathbf{k}}{[x'(t)^2 + y'(t)^2 + z'(t)^2]^{\frac{1}{2}}} \tag{7-78}$$

is a unit vector tangent to the curve. If f is a function of x, y, and z, then, with (x, y, z) restricted to being a point of this curve, f becomes a function of t. Therefore, if f is differentiable at P_0, then

$$\frac{df}{dt} = \frac{\partial f}{\partial x} x'(t) + \frac{\partial f}{\partial y} y'(t) + \frac{\partial f}{\partial z} z'(t).$$

The directional derivative of f in the direction of $\mathbf{T}$ is given by

$$\frac{df}{ds} = \frac{(\partial f/\partial x)x'(t) + (\partial f/dy)y'(t) + (\partial f/\partial z)z'(t)}{[x'(t)^2 + y'(t)^2 + z'(t)^2]^{\frac{1}{2}}}. \tag{7-79}$$

The value of df/ds depends on the particular curve being used only in that it depends on the direction of the tangent vector.

Suppose the graph of the equation $f(x, y, z) = 0$ is a surface with a tangent plane at the point P_0. For any curve in the surface, the rate of change of f along the curve is zero everywhere, since f has the same value (zero) at each point of the curve. Therefore, at points where the curve has a tangent line, the directional derivative in the direction of the tangent is zero (provided the conditions of the preceding paragraph are satisfied). On the other hand, if f has a gradient of nonzero length at P_0, then the directional derivative is zero in the direction of those vectors perpendicular to ∇f. This suggests that the tangent plane is the plane through P_0 perpendicular to ∇f.

THEOREM 7-7.1. Suppose f is a function with $\nabla f \neq 0$ at the point $P_0 = (x_0, y_0, z_0)$ on the graph of the equation

$$f(x, y, z) = 0. \tag{7-80}$$

Then this graph has a tangent plane at P_0 if f is differentiable at P_0. This plane is perpendicular to ∇f and has the equation

$$f_1(x_0, y_0, z_0)(x - x_0) + f_2(x_0, y_0, z_0)(y - y_0) + f_3(x_0, y_0, z_0)(z - z_0) = 0. \tag{7-81}$$

PROOF. The graph of Eq. (7-81) is the plane through P_0 perpendicular to ∇f, since the left member of (7-81) is the scalar product of the two vectors ∇f and $(x-x_0)\mathbf{i}+(y-y_0)\mathbf{j}+(z-z_0)\mathbf{k}$, and is zero if and only if (x, y, z) is some point in the plane. To prove that this plane actually is a tangent plane at (x_0, y_0, z_0), we must show that, for points P on the graph of Eq. (7-80), the angle θ between the plane and the line P_0P approaches zero as P approaches P_0 [see Fig. 7-15]. Since $\sin \theta$ is

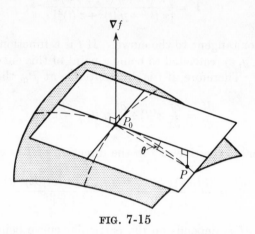

FIG. 7-15

the absolute value of the cosine of the angle between ∇f and the arrow $\mathbf{P}-\mathbf{P}_0$ from P_0 to P, $(\nabla f)\cdot(\mathbf{P}-\mathbf{P}_0) = |\nabla f|[d(P_0, P)] \sin \theta$, and

$$\sin \theta = \left| \frac{f_1(x_0, y_0, z_0)(x-x_0)+f_2(x_0, y_0, z_0)(y-y_0)+f_3(x_0, y_0, z_0)(z-z_0)}{|\nabla f|[d(P_0, P)]} \right|$$

$$= \left| \frac{[df]_{(x-x_0,\, y-y_0,\, z-z_0)}}{|\nabla f|[d(P_0, P)]} \right|. \tag{7-82}$$

Since f has the same value (zero) at P_0 as at P, the difference Δf of these values of f is zero and the numerator of the last member of Eq. (7-82) is equal to $df-\Delta f$. Since it follows from differentiability of f that $(df-\Delta f)/[d(P_0, P)] \to 0$ as $P \to P_0$, we see that $\sin \theta \to 0$ and that $\lim_{P\to P_0} \theta = 0$. Therefore, the plane of Eq. (7-81) is tangent to the graph of Eq. (7-80).

ILLUSTRATION 2. The graph of $4x^2 + 9y^2 = z^2 + 16$ is a surface, called a *hyperboloid of one sheet* [see Fig. 7-16]. Planes perpendicular to the z-axis intersect the surface in ellipses. The (y, z)-plane and the (z, x)-plane intersect the surface in hyperbolas. Suppose we wish to determine the equation of the tangent plane at $(2, 1, 3)$. We first note that the partial derivatives of $4x^2 + 9y^2 - z^2 - 16$ have the values 16,

18, and -6, respectively, at this point.   Therefore, an equation of the tangent plane is

$$16(x-2)+18(y-1)-6(z-3) = 0 \quad \text{or} \quad 8x+9y-3z = 16.$$

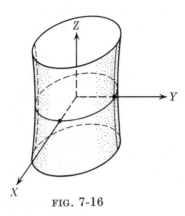

FIG. 7-16

The hyperboloid of one sheet is a *doubly ruled surface*.   This means that for each point of the surface there are two straight lines through that point which lie in the surface (taut strings could be used to construct a model of the surface).   For example, the two lines in the surface that pass through the point (2, 1, 3) have equations

$$\begin{cases} 2x+3y-z = 4, \\ 2x-3y+z = 4; \end{cases} \quad \begin{cases} 14x- 3y-7z = 4, \\ 2x+21y+ z = 28. \end{cases} \tag{7-83}$$

To see that the first of these lines is in the surface, we note that, if (x, y, z) is on the line, then

$$2x-z = 4-3y \quad \text{and} \quad 2x+z = 4+3y,$$

so that $(2x-z)(2x+z) = (4-3y)(4+3y)$ or $4x^2+9y^2 = z^2+16$.   Similarly, if (x, y, z) is on the second line, then

$$7(2x-z) = 4+3y \quad \text{and} \quad 2x+z = 7(4-3y),$$

so that $7(2x-z)\cdot(2x+z) = (4+3y)\cdot 7(4-3y)$, and again $4x^2+9y^2 = z^2+16$.   Each of the lines in (7-83) is in the tangent plane, since otherwise the angle between the tangent plane and the line that joins (2, 1, 3) and a point P on that line would not approach zero as P approaches (2, 1, 3).

PROBLEMS

1. Let $f(x, y, z) = x^2yz^3$. Compute the value of the directional derivative of f at $(1, 2, -1)$ in the direction toward $(2, 0, 3)$.

2. Starting from the point $(2, 1, 3)$, find which direction one should travel in order to obtain the most rapid rate of increase of the function f, if

$$f(x, y, z) = (x-y)^2 + (y-z)^2 + (z-x)^2.$$

What is the value of the directional derivative in this direction?

3. At the point $(2, 0, 3)$, the directional derivative of a given function f in the direction toward $(3, -2, 2)$ is $-1/\sqrt{6}$; in the direction toward $(2, 4, 4)$ it is $1/\sqrt{17}$; and in the direction toward $(4, -1, 2)$ it is zero. Determine the values of the three first-order partial derivatives of f at $(2, 0, 3)$ and the value of the directional derivative at $(2, 0, 3)$ in the direction toward $(0, 2, 14)$.

4. Let f be a function of two variables and $f(x, y) = 0$ be the equation of a curve. Show that, at a point (x_0, y_0) on this curve,

  (a) ∇f lies along the line whose slope is f_2/f_1;

  (b) the tangent line to the curve has slope $-f_1/f_2$;

  (c)
$$\nabla f = \{[f_1(x_0, y_0)]^2 + [f_2(x_0, y_0)]^2\}^{1/2}[(\cos \phi)\mathbf{i} + (\sin \phi)\mathbf{j}],$$

where ϕ is the angle between ∇f and $\mathbf{i}$.

5. Let $\mathbf{P} = x\mathbf{i} + y\mathbf{j} + z\mathbf{k}$ and let $\mathbf{A}$ be a constant vector. Show that $\nabla(\mathbf{A}\cdot\mathbf{P}) = \mathbf{A}$.

6. For each surface, find an equation of the tangent plane and equations of the normal line at the point indicated.

  (**a**) $x = y^2 + z^2$ at $(4, 2, 0)$.

  (**b**) $x^2 = yz$ at $(0, 0, 2)$.

  (c) $x^3 + y^3 + z^3 + 3xyz = 2$ at $(3, -2, 1)$.

  (d) $3y = x^2z + z^2 + 3$ at $(2, 0, -1)$.

7. Find equations of all lines through the origin which are perpendicular to the surface whose equation is $xy + z^4 = \frac{5}{8}$.

8. Find all points on the surface $(y+z)^2 + (z-x)^2 = 4$ at which the line perpendicular to the surface is parallel to the (y, z)-plane.

9. The graphs of $x^2 + y^2 + z^2 = 6$ and $2x^2 + 3y^2 + z^2 = 9$ both contain the point $(1, 1, 2)$. (a) Find the angle between the tangent planes at $(1, 1, 2)$. (**b**) Find equations of the line tangent at $(1, 1, 2)$ to the curve of intersection of the surfaces.

10. The graph of the equation $4x^2 + 9y^2 = z^2$ is an *elliptic cone*. Find an equation of the plane tangent to this surface at the point $(2, 1, 5)$ and show that this plane contains a line which lies in the surface.

11. The graph of

$$\frac{x^2}{a^2} + \frac{y^2}{b^2} + \frac{z^2}{c^2} = 1$$

is an *ellipsoid*. Show that, for any nonzero vector $\mathbf{N} = A\mathbf{i} + B\mathbf{j} + C\mathbf{k}$, there are two points of the ellipsoid at which $\mathbf{N}$ is perpendicular to the tangent plane.

12. The graph of $x^2 - 4y^2 - 9z^2 = 36$ is a *hyperboloid of two sheets*. The intersection with the (x, y)-plane or the (z, x)-plane is a hyperbola. The intersection with the plane $x = x_0$ is an ellipse if $|x_0| > 6$, a point if $|x_0| = 6$, and the empty set if $|x_0| < 6$. Find equations of the planes that are tangent to this hyperboloid and parallel to the plane whose equation is $6x + 3y - 9z = 5$. Sketch the surface.

13. The graph of

$$\frac{x^2}{a^2 - k} + \frac{y^2}{b^2 - k} + \frac{z^2}{c^2 - k} = 1,$$

where $a^2 > b^2 > c^2$, is an ellipsoid if $c^2 > k$, a hyperboloid of one sheet if $b^2 > k > c^2$, and a hyperboloid of two sheets if $a^2 > k > b^2$. Show that, for any point $P_0 = (x_0, y_0, z_0)$, each of the following is true.

(a) If such an ellipsoid, hyperboloid of one sheet, and hyperboloid of two sheets pass through P_0, then any two of the three tangent planes at P_0 are perpendicular. [*Hint:* Consider

$$\left(\frac{x_0^2}{a^2 - k_1} + \frac{y_0^2}{b^2 - k_1} + \frac{z_0^2}{c^2 - k_1} \right) - \left(\frac{x_0^2}{a^2 - k_2} + \frac{y_0^2}{b^2 - k_2} + \frac{z_0^2}{c^2 - k_2} \right)$$

for two of the three values of k.]

(b) If P_0 is not a point of the region of the (x, y)-plane inside or on the ellipse $x^2/(a^2 - c^2) + y^2/(b^2 - c^2) = 1$, then there is a value of k for which the ellipsoid passes through P_0.

(c) If P_0 is neither in the region of the (x, y)-plane outside or on the ellipse $x^2/(a^2 - c^2) + y^2/(b^2 - c^2) = 1$, nor in the region of the (z, x)-plane that is bounded by the two branches of the hyperbola $x^2/(a^2 - b^2) - z^2/(b^2 - c^2) = 1$, then there is a value of k for which the hyperboloid of one sheet passes through P_0.

(d) If P_0 is neither in one of the two regions of the (z, x)-plane bounded by a branch of the hyperbola $x^2/(a^2 - b^2) - z^2/(b^2 - c^2) = 1$, nor in the (y, z)-plane, then there is a value of k for which the hyperboloid of two sheets passes through P_0.

(e) Explain how one might assign coordinates (k_1, k_2, k_3) to each point of space, where $k_1 \leq c^2$, $c^2 \leq k_2 \leq b^2$, $b^2 \leq k_3 \leq a^2$.

14.* Let f and g be functions of three variables and let P_0 be a point for which f has a relative maximum or a relative minimum for points (x, y, z) such that $g(x, y, z) = 0$. Also assume that f and g are differentiable at P_0, that the intersection of the graph of $g(x, y, z) = 0$ and any plane through P_0 parallel to ∇g contains a curve through P_0 having parametric equations as described in (7-77) for t in an interval I, and that the value of t at P_0 is not an end point of I. Show that at P_0 the vectors ∇f and ∇g are parallel.

15.* Let $g(x, y) = 17x^2 - 12xy + 22y^2$. Use the method suggested by problem 14 to determine the line through the origin that passes through the points on the curve $g(x, y) = c$ in the (x, y)-plane at greatest distance from the origin, and the line that passes through the points at least distance. [*Hint:* If P is such an extreme point, then there is a number λ such that $\nabla g = \lambda \mathbf{P}$. Such a number is called a *Lagrange multiplier*. (See Section 8-6.)]

16. Use the method suggested by problem 14 to solve the following problems.

(**a**) Find the dimensions of the rectangular parallelepiped of greatest volume which has three faces in the coordinate planes and one vertex in the plane $15x + 10y + 6z = 90$.

(**b**) Find the volume of the rectangular parallelepiped of greatest volume which can be inscribed in the ellipsoid

$$\frac{x^2}{a^2} + \frac{y^2}{b^2} + \frac{z^2}{c^2} = 1.$$

(**c**) Find the dimensions of the rectangular box, without a top, of greatest volume whose surface area is 108 square feet.

(d) Find the greatest and least distances from the origin to a point of the curve $5x^2 + 6xy + 5y^2 = 8$.

8

TRANSFORMATIONS

8-1. CHANGE OF VARIABLES IN SINGLE INTEGRALS

We have seen that the following formula can be used to change variables in a single integral:

$$\int_a^b f(x)\, dx = \int_\alpha^\beta f[u(t)]u'(t)\, dt, \qquad (8\text{-}1)$$

where $a = u(\alpha)$ and $b = u(\beta)$ [see Theorem 3-6.3]. To establish this formula, we assumed that u' is continuous on the closed interval I_α^β with end points α and β and that f is continuous at $u(t)$ if $t \in I_\alpha^\beta$. The proof was based on the possibility of evaluating the integrals in Eq. (8-1) by using antiderivatives. This is not a natural method to use for multiple integrals.

We shall now give a proof of (8-1) that can be generalized to multiple integrals. To do this, we make the additional assumption that u' is either positive on I_α^β or negative on I_α^β, so that u is either increasing or decreasing on I_α^β. Also, we let $u(\alpha) = a$ and $u(\beta) = b$. Then u maps the interval I_α^β of the t-axis onto the closed interval of

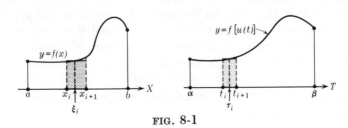

FIG. 8-1

the x-axis with end points a and b. Also, this transformation is one-to-one [see Fig. 8-1]. Any partition of one interval corresponds to a partition of the other. In particular, for the ith interval in a partition of I_α^β we can use the mean value theorem to obtain

$$\Delta_i x = x_{i+1} - x_i = u(t_{i+1}) - u(t_i) = u'(\tau_i)(t_{i+1} - t_i) = u'(\tau_i)\,\Delta_i t,$$

where τ_i is a suitable number in this ith interval. Since the integrand of the second integral in (8-1) is continuous on the interval I_α^β, the integral exists and is equal to

$$\lim_{\delta \to 0} \sum_{i=1}^{n} f[u(\theta_i)]u'(\theta_i)\,\Delta_i t,$$

where δ is the fineness of the partition of I_α^β, $\Delta_i t = t_{i+1} - t_i$, and θ_i is in the closed interval with end points t_i and t_{i+1}. Since this limit exists for arbitrary choices of θ_i in the corresponding interval, its value is not changed if we choose θ_i as τ_i, so that $u'(\tau_i)\,\Delta_i t = \Delta_i x$, and then let $\xi_i = u(\tau_i)$, to obtain

$$\lim_{\delta \to 0} \sum_{i=1}^{n} f[u(\tau_i)]\,\Delta_i x = \lim_{\delta \to 0} \sum_{i=1}^{n} f(\xi_i)\,\Delta_i x = \int_a^b f(x)\,dx.$$

We can think of $u'(t)$ in Eq. (8-1) as being a "local magnification factor," by which an interval of length Δt is multiplied to approximate the length Δx of the corresponding interval on the x-axis. In the next section, we shall see that, for a change from rectangular coordinates to polar coordinates, the "local magnification factor" is r. This is the factor by which the area of a set in the (r, θ)-plane with r and θ used as rectangular coordinates is multiplied to approximate the area of the corresponding set in the (x, y)-plane.

8-2. POLAR COORDINATES AND DOUBLE INTEGRALS

We defined the double integral of a function f over a region R as $\lim_{\delta \to 0} \sum_{i=1}^{n} f(p_i)\,\Delta_i A$, if this limit exists [see Definition 5-2.1]. The symbol $\Delta_i A$ denotes the area of $\Delta_i R$, where $\{\Delta_1 R, \Delta_2 R, \cdots, \Delta_n R\}$ is a partition of R. Also, δ is the fineness of this partition and p_i is a point in $\Delta_i R$. We shall soon see that a region bounded by two concentric circles whose radii differ by Δr, and by two radial lines whose angles of inclination differ by $\Delta \theta$, has area $r\,\Delta r\,\Delta \theta$, where r is the average of the two radii [see Fig. 8-4]. This suggests that one might be able to evaluate an integral $\int_R f(x, y)\,dA$ by transforming the integral into an integral of type $\int f(x, y)r\,dr\,d\theta$.

ILLUSTRATION 1. Suppose we wish to find the area of the region R enclosed by the cardioid whose equation is $r = 1 + \cos \theta$ [Fig. 8-2]. This area is equal to $\int_R dA$, which we can write as

$$\int_0^{2\pi} \int_0^{1+\cos\theta} r \, dr \, d\theta = \int_0^{2\pi} \tfrac{1}{2}(1 + \cos\theta)^2 \, d\theta$$

$$= \int_0^{2\pi} (\tfrac{3}{4} + \cos\theta + \tfrac{1}{4}\cos 2\theta) \, d\theta = \tfrac{3}{2}\pi.$$

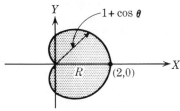

FIG. 8-2

ILLUSTRATION 2. A solid is bounded by the cylinder $x^2 + y^2 = 4$, the (x, y)-plane, and the surface $z = (x^2 + y^2)^{1/2}$. The volume is equal to $\int_R (x^2 + y^2)^{1/2} \, dA$, where R is the disk $x^2 + y^2 \leq 4$ in the (x, y)-plane. This disk is also the polar graph of $r \leq 2$ and the double integral can be written in polar coordinates as the iterated integral

$$\int_0^{2\pi} \int_0^2 r^2 \, dr \, d\theta = \int_0^{2\pi} \left(\frac{8}{3}\right) d\theta = \frac{16}{3} \pi.$$

We shall now justify this use of polar coordinates. Let us suppose that S is a bounded set in the (x, y)-plane and that R is a suitable corresponding set in a plane for which polar coordinates of a point in S are used as rectangular coordinates of a point in R. Explicitly, let us choose r to be nonnegative and θ so that $0 \leq \theta < 2\pi$, as in Fig. 8-3.

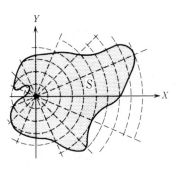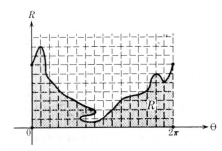

FIG. 8-3

THEOREM 8-2.1. Let S and R be the sets of Fig. 8-3 and suppose that S is compact and has area. If f is continuous on S, then

$$\int_S f(x, y) \, dA = \int_R r \cdot f(r \cos \theta, r \sin \theta) \, dA.$$

PROOF. It follows from Theorem 5-2.3 that f is integrable on S. Let us partition R by using a grid consisting of lines parallel to the coordinate axes in the (r, θ)-plane as indicated in Fig. 8-3, forming congruent rectangles with sides of length Δr and $\Delta \theta$. This grid corresponds to a grid in the (x, y)-plane consisting of a finite number of lines through the origin and circles with centers at the origin. Having agreed that r is to be nonnegative and θ in the interval $[0, 2\pi)$, each point of S corresponds to one and only one point of R. The area of a rectangle in the (r, θ)-plane is $\Delta r \, \Delta \theta$. The corresponding region of the (x, y)-plane is bounded by two line segments of length Δr and two circular arcs of length $r_1 \, \Delta \theta$ and $r_2 \, \Delta \theta$, where r_1 and r_2 are the radii of the corresponding circles [see Fig. 8-4]. We shall leave it to the student to show that, if $r = \frac{1}{2}(r_1 + r_2)$, then the area of this region is exactly equal to $r \, \Delta r \, \Delta \theta$.

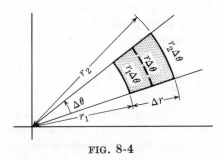

FIG. 8-4

For a positive number ε, let k be a positive integer and δ a positive number such that

$$\frac{(2\pi)^2}{k} < \tfrac{1}{2}\varepsilon \quad \text{and} \quad \frac{\delta k}{2\pi} < \tfrac{1}{2}\varepsilon.$$

Choose the grids in Fig. 8-3 so that the circle of radius $2\pi/k$ is used in the (x, y)-plane and the partition is fine enough that $s^* - s_* < \delta$ if s_* and s^* are inner and outer sums determined for S. The disc of radius $2\pi/k$ maps into a strip of area $(2\pi)^2/k$ in the (r, θ)-plane. For a member of the partition of S not in this disc, the area is greater than the product of $2\pi/k$ and the area of the corresponding rectangle in the (r, θ)-plane.

Therefore, if r_* and r^* are inner and outer sums determined for R, then

$$r^* - r_* < \frac{(2\pi)^2}{k} + \frac{\delta k}{2\pi} < \tfrac{1}{2}\varepsilon + \tfrac{1}{2}\varepsilon = \varepsilon.$$

It now follows from Theorem 3-2.2 that R has area. Since f is continuous on S, f is bounded on S [Theorem 2-8.2]. Since S is compact, S is bounded [see problem 2, page 75]. Therefore, there is a number M such that

$$|f(x, y)| \leqq M \text{ if } (x, y) \in S,$$

$$|r \cdot f(r \cos \theta, r \sin \theta)| \leqq M \text{ if } (r, \theta) \in R.$$

Then it follows from Theorem 5-2.4 that $r \cdot f$ is integrable on R. Now choose Δr and $\Delta\theta$ small enough so that, for the grids illustrated in Fig. 8-3,

$$\left| \int_S f(x, y) \, dA - \sum_S f(x_i, y_i) \, \Delta_i A \right| < \tfrac{1}{4}\varepsilon, \tag{8-2}$$

$$\left| \int_R r \cdot f(r \cos \theta, r \sin \theta) \, dA - \sum_R r_i \cdot f(r_i \cos \theta_i, r_i \sin \theta_i) \, \Delta_i A \right| < \tfrac{1}{4}\varepsilon, \tag{8-3}$$

and $s^* - s_* < \tfrac{1}{4}\varepsilon/M$ and $r^* - r_* < \tfrac{1}{4}\varepsilon/M$, where $\sum_S f(x_i, y_i) \, \Delta_i A$ is any Riemann sum taken over S, using the partition of S determined by the grid in the (x, y)-plane; and $\sum_R r_i \cdot f(r_i \cos \theta_i, r_i \sin \theta_i) \, \Delta_i A$ is any Riemann sum taken over R, using the partition of R determined by the grid in the (r, θ)-plane. For a rectangle contained in R, we choose (r_i, θ_i) in (8-3) so that $r_i \, \Delta r \, \Delta\theta$ is the area of the corresponding region in the (x, y)-plane, and then choose (x_i, y_i) so that $x_i = r_i \cos \theta_i$ and $y_i = r_i \sin \theta_i$. Then, with primes denoting that we include only those terms corresponding to rectangles contained in R, when summing over R, and only the corresponding terms when summing over S, we have

$$\sum_S{}' f(x_i, y_i) \, \Delta_i A = \sum_S{}' f(x_i, y_i)(r_i \, \Delta r \, \Delta\theta)$$

$$= \sum_R{}' r_i \cdot f(r_i \cos \theta_i, r_i \sin \theta_i) \, \Delta r \, \Delta\theta$$

$$= \sum_R{}' r_i \cdot f(r_i \cos \theta_i, r_i \sin \theta_i) \, \Delta_i A.$$

Thus, the sums in (8-2) and (8-3) become identical, except for terms corresponding to rectangles only partially contained in R and the corresponding sets partially contained in S. However, the absolute values of the sums over such sets are less than $\frac{1}{4}\varepsilon$, since for both planes the total area involved is less than $\frac{1}{4}\varepsilon/M$ and M is an upper bound to both $|f(x, y)|$ and $|r \cdot f(r \cos \theta, r \sin \theta)|$. Thus, it follows from (8-2) and (8-3) that

$$\left| \int_S f(x, y)\, dA \;-\; {\sum_S}' f(x_i, y_i)\, \Delta_i A \right| < \tfrac{1}{2}\varepsilon,$$

$$\left| \int_R r \cdot f(r \cos \theta, r \sin \theta)\, dA - {\sum_R}' r_i \cdot f(r_i \cos \theta_i, r_i \sin \theta_i)\, \Delta_i A \right| < \tfrac{1}{2}\varepsilon.$$

Since the two primed sums are equal, we have

$$\left| \int_S f(x, y)\, dA \;-\; \int_R r \cdot f(r \cos \theta, r \sin \theta)\, dA \right| < \varepsilon.$$

Since ε was arbitrary, $\displaystyle \int_S f(x, y)\, dA \;=\; \int_R r \cdot f(r \cos \theta, r \sin \theta)\, dA.$

ILLUSTRATION 3. Suppose S is the first quadrant in the (x, y)-plane. To evaluate the improper integral

$$\int_S e^{-(x^2+y^2)}\, dA, \tag{8-4}$$

we change to polar coordinates and consider the improper integral,

$$\int_R e^{-r^2} \cdot r\, dA,$$

where R is the strip in the (r, θ)-plane defined by $0 \le \theta \le \frac{1}{2}\pi$ and $r \ge 0$. To evaluate this improper integral, we shall let R_ρ be the subset of R defined by $0 \le \theta \le \frac{1}{2}\pi$ and $0 \le r \le \rho$ and use an iterated integral:

$$\int_{R_\rho} e^{-r^2}\, r\, dA \;=\; \int_0^{1/2\pi} \int_0^\rho e^{-r^2}\, r\, dr\, d\theta \;=\; \tfrac{1}{2} \int_0^{1/2\pi} (1 - e^{-\rho^2})\, d\theta$$

$$= \tfrac{1}{4}\pi(1 - e^{-\rho^2}).$$

Since $\lim_{\rho \to +\infty} (1 - e^{-\rho^2}) = 1$, we can conclude that the original integral is equal to $\frac{1}{4}\pi$. If we had tried to evaluate (8-4) without changing to polar coordinates, we might have let S_r be the rectangle defined by $0 \le x \le r$ and $0 \le y \le r$. Then

$$\int_{S_r} e^{-(x^2+y^2)}\, dA \;=\; \int_0^r \int_0^r e^{-(x^2+y^2)}\, dx\, dy \;=\; \int_0^r e^{-y^2} \left[\int_0^r e^{-x^2}\, dx \right] dy$$

$$= \left[\int_0^r e^{-x^2}\, dx \right] \cdot \left[\int_0^r e^{-y^2}\, dy \right] = \left[\int_0^r e^{-x^2}\, dx \right]^2.$$

Thus, this iterated integral is the product of two equal definite integrals! Now we let r increase and equate the limits, to obtain

$$\int_S e^{-(x^2+y^2)}\, dA = \left[\int_0^{+\infty} e^{-x^2}\, dx\right]^2. \tag{8-5}$$

Since we know that the left member of (8-5) is equal to $\frac{1}{4}\pi$, it follows that

$$\int_0^{+\infty} e^{-x^2}\, dx = \frac{1}{2}\sqrt{\pi}. \tag{8-6}$$

Although we have not succeeded in evaluating (8-4) by using rectangular coordinates, we have obtained an extremely useful mathematical fact as a by-product. It is also interesting to note that we have evaluated a difficult integral *without* first determining an antiderivative.

ILLUSTRATION 4. The gamma function discussed in Illustration 2, page 164, is related intimately to the beta function B defined for $\xi > 0$ and $\eta > 0$ by

$$B(\xi, \eta) = \int_0^1 t^{\xi-1}(1-t)^{\eta-1}\, dt. \tag{8-7}$$

In fact, we shall prove that

$$\Gamma(\xi)\Gamma(\eta) = \Gamma(\xi+\eta)B(\xi, \eta). \tag{8-8}$$

We have $\Gamma(\xi) = \int_0^{+\infty} t^{\xi-1}e^{-t}\, dt = 2\int_0^{+\infty} x^{2\xi-1}e^{-x^2}\, dx$, with $t = x^2$. By arguments similar to that which lead to Eq. (8-5), we have

$$\Gamma(\xi)\Gamma(\eta) = 4\int_S x^{2\eta-1}y^{2\xi-1}e^{-(x^2+y^2)}\, dA,$$

where S is the first quadrant in the (x, y)-plane. As in Illustration 3, we can let R be the strip in the (r, θ)-plane with $0 \leq \theta \leq \frac{1}{2}\pi$ and $r \geq 0$. Then, with R_ρ defined by $0 \leq \theta \leq \frac{1}{2}\pi$ and $0 \leq r \leq \rho$, we have

$$\begin{aligned}
\Gamma(\xi)\Gamma(\eta) &= \lim_{\rho \to +\infty} 4\int_{R_\rho} (r\cos\theta)^{2\eta-1}(r\sin\theta)^{2\xi-1}e^{-r^2}r\, dA \\
&= \lim_{\rho \to +\infty} 4\int_0^\rho \int_0^{\frac{1}{2}\pi} r^{2\xi+2\eta-1}e^{-r^2}(\cos\theta)^{2\eta-1}(\sin\theta)^{2\xi-1}\, dA \\
&= 4\int_0^{+\infty} r^{2\xi+2\eta-1}e^{-r^2}\, dr \int_0^{\frac{1}{2}\pi} (\cos\theta)^{2\eta-1}(\sin\theta)^{2\xi-1}\, d\theta \\
&= \Gamma(\xi+\eta)\cdot 2\int_0^{\frac{1}{2}\pi} (\cos\theta)^{2\eta-1}(\sin\theta)^{2\xi-1}\, d\theta. \tag{8-9}
\end{aligned}$$

Now let $\sin^2 \theta = t$, so that

$$2 \int_0^{\frac{1}{2}\pi} (\cos \theta)^{2\eta - 1}(\sin \theta)^{2\xi - 1} \, d\theta = \int_0^1 \frac{t^{\xi - \frac{1}{2}}(1 - t)^{\eta - \frac{1}{2}}}{\sin \theta \cos \theta} \, dt$$

$$= \int_0^1 t^{\xi - 1}(1 - t)^{\eta - 1} \, dt = B(\xi, \eta).$$

Substitution in (8-9) gives us (8-8). Of course, we also have

$$B(\xi, \eta) = 2 \int_0^{\frac{1}{2}\pi} (\sin \theta)^{2\eta - 1}(\cos \theta)^{2\xi - 1} \, d\theta. \qquad (8\text{-}10)$$

PROBLEMS

1. Find the areas of each of the following regions. (**a**) The region inside the lemniscate whose equation is $r^2 = 2 \cos 2\theta$. (**b**) The intersection of the interiors of the circles whose equations are $r = 2a \cos \theta$ and $r = 2a \sin \theta$. (**c**) The region that is inside the graph of $r = 3 \cos \theta$ and outside the graph of $r = 1 + \cos \theta$. (**d**) The region inside one loop of the graph of $r = 2 \sin 3\theta$. (**e**) The region between the two loops of the limaçon whose equation is $r = 2 + 4 \cos \theta$.

2. Use polar coordinates and find the volume of each of the following. (**a**) The region between the graph of $z = (x^2 + y^2)^{-\frac{1}{2}}$ and the plane region bounded by the polar graph of $r = 2 \cos \theta$. (**b**) A slab of unit thickness whose base is bounded by the polar graph of $r = \theta$ for $0 \leq \theta \leq \frac{1}{2}\pi$ and the polar graph of $\theta = \frac{1}{2}\pi$. (**c**) The piece of the cylinder $x^2 + y^2 \leq 1$ which is between the (x, y)-plane and the surface whose equation is $z = x^2$. (**d**) The piece of the cylinder $x^2 + y^2 \leq 1$ which is between the (x, y)-plane and the surface that is generated by rotating about the z-axis the graph of $z = x^2$ in the (x, z)-plane. [*Hint:* Show that the surface is the graph of $z = r^2$.] (**e**) The region between the graph of $z = (x^2 + y^2)^{-\frac{1}{2}}$ and the piece of the (x, y)-plane between the two loops of the limaçon whose equation is $r = 2 + 4 \cos \theta$.

3. For each of the following, determine whether the region between the set R in the (x, y)-plane and the graph of the given function has volume. Determine the volume if it exists.

(**a**) $(x^2 + y^2)^{-\frac{1}{2}}$; $R = \{(x, y): x^2 + y^2 \leq 9\}$.

(**b**) $(x^2 + y^2)^{-1}$; $R = \{(x, y): x \geq 0 \text{ and } 0 \leq y \leq x\}$.

(**c**) $(x^2 + y^2)^{-1}$; R is the set of points in the first quadrant that are inside the circle $x^2 + y^2 = \frac{1}{4}$ and under the polar graph of $r = \theta$ for $0 \leq \theta \leq \frac{1}{4}\pi$.

(**d**) $2xy(x^2 + y^2)^{-1}$; $R = \{(x, y): x^2 + y^2 \leq 1, x \geq 0, \text{ and } y \geq 0\}$.

4. (a) Use (8-6) and problem 2(a) of Section 3-7 to show that $\Gamma(\frac{1}{2})$ $= \sqrt{\pi}$. (b) Show that $\Gamma(\frac{3}{2}) = \frac{1}{2}\sqrt{\pi}$ and $\Gamma(\frac{5}{2}) = \frac{3}{4}\sqrt{\pi}$.

5. Use properties of the beta and gamma functions to evaluate each of the following.

(**a**) $\displaystyle\int_0^1 t^6(1-t)^3\,dt.$

(**c**) $\displaystyle\int_0^{\frac{1}{2}\pi} \sin^4\theta\cos^5\theta\,d\theta.$

(**b**) $\displaystyle\int_0^1 x^{\frac{3}{2}}(1-x)^{-\frac{1}{2}}\,dx.$

(**d**) $\displaystyle\int_0^{\frac{1}{2}\pi} \sin^3\theta\cos^{\frac{1}{2}}\theta\,d\theta.$

6. Prove that $\displaystyle\int_0^1 \frac{dx}{\sqrt{x\ln(1/x)}} = \sqrt{2\pi}.$

7. Prove that $\displaystyle\int_0^1 \frac{dx}{\sqrt{-\ln x}} = \sqrt{\pi}.$

8. Prove that $\displaystyle\Gamma(x)\Gamma(1-x) = \int_0^{+\infty} \frac{t^{x-1}}{1+t}\,dt$ if $0 < x < 1$. -

[*Note:* This integral is equal to $\pi/(\sin\pi x)$. See *Modern Analysis*, by E. T. Whittaker and G. N. Watson (Cambridge, Mass.: Cambridge University Press, 1940), p. 239.]

9. Find an appropriate change of variables and prove that

$$\int_s^x (x-t)^{m-1}(t-s)^{n-1}\,dt = (x-s)^{m+n-1}B(m,n)$$
$$= (x-s)^{m+n-1}\frac{\Gamma(m)\Gamma(n)}{\Gamma(m+n)}.$$

10. Suppose that S is a bounded set in the (x,y)-plane and that R is the corresponding set in a plane for which polar coordinates of a point in S are used as rectangular coordinates of a point in R, with $r \geqq 0$ and $\theta \in [0, 2\pi)$. Prove that S has area if R has area.

8-3. LINEAR TRANSFORMATIONS

In this section and in Section 8-5, we shall discuss linear transformations, matrices, and determinants. This discussion is needed to develop and understand the inverse transformation and implicit function theorems and the general method of change of variables in multiple integrals. The methods of evaluating determinants, Cramer's rule for solving linear equations, and the usual properties of determinants will not be derived, since the student has studied this at least for determinants of third order. A general treatment is best left for a course in algebra. The following are some of these properties:

I. A determinant is not changed in value if the rows and columns are interchanged.

II. Multiplying each term of one row (or one column) of a determinant by a number t is equivalent to multiplying the determinant by t.

III. The value of a determinant is not changed if the same multiples of the terms of one row are added to the corresponding terms of another row, or if the same multiples of the terms of one column are added to the corresponding terms of another column.

The concept of three-dimensional vectors may easily be generalized. For any positive integer n, we can define an n-dimensional vector to be a sequence

$$\mathbf{u} = (u_1, u_2, \cdots, u_n)$$

of n real numbers, with addition and multiplication by real numbers defined as follows:

$$(u_1, u_2, \cdots, u_n) + (v_1, v_2, \cdots, v_n) = (u_1 + v_1, u_2 + v_2, \cdots, u_n + v_n),$$

$$t(u_1, u_2, \cdots, u_n) = (tu_1, tu_2, \cdots, tu_n).$$

The numbers $u_1, \cdots, u_n$ are the *components* of $\mathbf{u}$. The set of all such vectors is *n-dimensional real coordinate space*, customarily denoted by R^n. Sometimes we shall call this space *n-dimensional vector space* or simply *n-dimensional space*. Since we shall have no need for it, we shall not discuss complex coordinate spaces or axioms for abstract vector spaces.

DEFINITION 8-3.1. A *linear transformation* of R^n is a function T whose domain is R^n, whose range is contained in R^n, and which has the following properties:

(i) T is *additive*; i.e., for any vectors $\mathbf{x}$ and $\mathbf{y}$,

$$T(\mathbf{x} + \mathbf{y}) = T(\mathbf{x}) + T(\mathbf{y});$$

(ii) T is *homogeneous*; i.e., for any vectors $\mathbf{x}$ and $\mathbf{y}$ and any number t,

$$T(t\mathbf{x}) = t \cdot T(\mathbf{x}).$$

DEFINITION 8-3.2. The *product* P of two linear transformations A and B of R^n is denoted by AB and is the transformation defined for $\mathbf{x}$ in R^n by

$$P(\mathbf{x}) = A[B(\mathbf{x})].$$

It is important to understand the notation $P = AB$. The result of letting the transformation AB operate on a vector $\mathbf{x}$ is determined by first letting B operate on x and then operating on the result with A. In other words, if the symbol AB is thought of as a recipe for performing a certain process, then the instructions are to be read from right to left. As we shall illustrate by an example, multiplication of linear transformations is not commutative.

> **ILLUSTRATION 1.** Suppose A and B are linear transformations of R^3 and that
>
> $$A(x, y, z) = (x, y, 0) \quad \text{and} \quad B(x, y, z) = (y, z, x).$$
>
> The linear transformation A can be described as a projection of the space onto the (x, y)-plane; B is a rigid motion that can be described as a clockwise rotation of 120 degrees about the line $x = y = z$ (the coordinate axes are thought of as lines which do not move and are used to determine rectangular coordinates for a point before the rigid motion B and new coordinates after B has moved the point to a new position). For these transformations,
>
> $$(AB)(x, y, z) = A[B(x, y, z)] = A(y, z, x) = (y, z, 0),$$
> $$(BA)(x, y, z) = B[A(x, y, z)] = B(x, y, 0) = (y, 0, x).$$
>
> The transformations AB and BA are quite different. In fact, the range of AB is the (x, y)-plane and the range of BA is the (x, z)-plane.

Multiplication of linear transformations differs from multiplication of numbers in several respects. We have seen that multiplication of linear transformations does not satisfy the commutative law. The next illustration provides an example of linear transformations whose product is zero, although neither factor is zero.

> **ILLUSTRATION 2.** We shall let the transformations A and B be defined on R^2 by the equalities $A(x, y) = (x, 0)$ and $B(x, y) = (0, x+y)$. Then
>
> $$(AB)(x, y) = A[B(x, y)] = A(0, x+y) = (0, 0),$$
>
> so that $AB = 0$. However,
>
> $$(BA)(x, y) = B[A(x, y)] = B(x, 0) = (0, x),$$
>
> so that $BA \neq 0$.

The following theorem gives an important fact about multiplication of linear transformations which the student may have assumed to be true, though it has not yet been stated or proved.

THEOREM 8-3.1. The product of two linear transformations is a linear transformation.

PROOF. Given a product P of linear transformations A and B, we must show that, for any vectors $\mathbf{u}$ and $\mathbf{v}$ in the domain of P and any scalar t, $P(\mathbf{u}+\mathbf{v}) = P(\mathbf{u})+P(\mathbf{v})$ and $P(t\mathbf{u}) = t\cdot P(\mathbf{u})$. This is done using linearity of A and B, as follows:

$$P(\mathbf{u}+\mathbf{v}) = A[B(\mathbf{u}+\mathbf{v})] = A[B(\mathbf{u})+B(\mathbf{v})]$$
$$= A[B(\mathbf{u})]+A[B(\mathbf{v})] = P(\mathbf{u})+P(\mathbf{v});$$
$$P(t\mathbf{u}) = A[B(t\mathbf{u})] = A[t\cdot B(\mathbf{u})] = t\cdot A[B(\mathbf{u})] = t\cdot P(\mathbf{u}).$$

We shall denote by $\mathbf{e}_k$ the vector in R^n whose kth component is $+1$, with all other components zero. Then, for each $\mathbf{u}$ in R^n, we have

$$\mathbf{u} = (u_1, u_2, \cdots, u_n) = \sum_{i=1}^{n} u_i\mathbf{e}_i.$$

The next theorem uses this fact to show that a linear transformation is determined completely when its effect on the vectors $\mathbf{e}_1, \cdots, \mathbf{e}_n$ is known.

THEOREM 8-3.2. If $\mathbf{v}_1, \mathbf{v}_2, \cdots, \mathbf{v}_n$ are n vectors in R^n, not necessarily all different, then there is exactly one linear transformation T of R^n such that

$$T(\mathbf{e}_j) = \mathbf{v}_j \quad \text{for all} \quad j. \tag{8-11}$$

This is the linear transformation with the property that

$$T\left(\sum_{1}^{n} a_j\mathbf{e}_j\right) = \sum_{1}^{n} a_j\mathbf{v}_j, \tag{8-12}$$

for all numbers $a_1, a_2, \cdots, a_n$.

PROOF. Let $\mathbf{v}_1, \cdots, \mathbf{v}_n$ be vectors in R^n. To show that there is at least one linear transformation T that maps $\mathbf{e}_j$ onto $\mathbf{v}_j$ for each j, we shall define T by the following equality and then prove that it is the desired linear transformation:

$$T\left(\sum_{1}^{n} a_j\mathbf{e}_j\right) = \sum_{1}^{n} a_j\mathbf{v}_j. \tag{8-13}$$

Since any vector in R^n is a linear combination of the vectors $\mathbf{e}_1, \cdots, \mathbf{e}_n$, we obtain linearity of T from the following equalities:

$$T\left[\left(\sum_1^n a_j \mathbf{e}_j\right) + \left(\sum_1^n b_j \mathbf{e}_j\right)\right] = T\left[\sum_1^n (a_j + b_j)\mathbf{e}_j\right] = \sum_1^n (a_j + b_j)\mathbf{v}_j$$

$$= \sum_1^n a_j \mathbf{v}_j + \sum_1^n b_j \mathbf{v}_j$$

$$= T\left(\sum_1^n a_j \mathbf{e}_j\right) + T\left(\sum_1^n b_j \mathbf{e}_j\right);$$

$$T\left[t\left(\sum_1^n a_j \mathbf{e}_j\right)\right] = T\left[\sum_1^n (ta_j)\mathbf{e}_j\right] = \sum_1^n (ta_j)\mathbf{v}_j$$

$$= t\left(\sum_1^n a_j \mathbf{v}_j\right) = t \cdot T\left(\sum_1^n a_j \mathbf{e}_j\right).$$

If into Eq. (8-13) we put $a_j = 1$ and $a_i = 0$ when $i \neq j$, we obtain

$$T(\mathbf{e}_j) = \mathbf{v}_j.$$

We now know that T has the properties stated in the theorem. The only step in the proof that remains is to show that there is no other linear transformation that maps $\mathbf{e}_j$ onto $\mathbf{v}_j$ for each j. Suppose that S is such a linear transformation. Then it follows from linearity of S that

$$S\left(\sum_1^n a_j \mathbf{e}_j\right) = \sum_1^n S(a_j \mathbf{e}_j) = \sum_1^n a_j S(\mathbf{e}_j) = \sum_1^n a_j \mathbf{v}_j.$$

It follows from this and Eq. (8-13) that

$$T\left(\sum_1^n a_j \mathbf{e}_j\right) = S\left(\sum_1^n a_j \mathbf{e}_j\right)$$

for all numbers $a_1, a_2, \cdots, a_n$. This implies that $T = S$.

It is convenient to represent members $\mathbf{x}$ of R^n as columns of n numbers:

$$\mathbf{x} = \begin{pmatrix} x_1 \\ x_2 \\ \vdots \\ x_n \end{pmatrix}.$$

If T is a linear transformation of R^n, then T can be described by specifying its effect on $\mathbf{e}_1, \cdots, \mathbf{e}_n$:

$$T(\mathbf{e}_1) = \mathbf{v}_1 = \begin{pmatrix} a_{11} \\ a_{21} \\ a_{31} \\ \vdots \\ a_{n1} \end{pmatrix}, \cdots, T(\mathbf{e}_j) = \mathbf{v}_j = \begin{pmatrix} a_{1j} \\ a_{2j} \\ a_{3j} \\ \vdots \\ a_{nj} \end{pmatrix}, \cdots.$$

Then $T(\mathbf{x}) = \sum_1^n x_i T(\mathbf{e}_i) = x_1\mathbf{v}_1 + x_2\mathbf{v}_2 + \cdots + x_n\mathbf{v}_n$, so that

$$T(\mathbf{x}) = \begin{pmatrix} a_{11}x_1 + a_{12}x_2 + a_{13}x_3 + \cdots + a_{1n}x_n \\ a_{21}x_1 + a_{22}x_2 + a_{23}x_3 + \cdots + a_{2n}x_n \\ a_{31}x_1 + a_{32}x_2 + a_{33}x_3 + \cdots + a_{3n}x_n \\ \cdots \cdots \cdots \cdots \cdots \cdots \\ a_{n1}x_1 + a_{n2}x_2 + a_{n3}x_3 + \cdots + a_{nn}x_n \end{pmatrix}. \qquad (8\text{-}14)$$

As the student may know, an $m \times n$ *matrix* is a rectangular array of mn objects that contains m rows with n objects in each row. A *square matrix* of *order* n is an $m \times n$ matrix with $m = n$. It is customary to denote a matrix by symbols such as

$$\begin{pmatrix} a_{11} & a_{12} & \cdots & a_{1n} \\ a_{21} & a_{22} & \cdots & a_{2n} \\ \cdot & \cdot & \cdot & \cdot \\ a_{m1} & a_{m2} & \cdots & a_{mn} \end{pmatrix} \quad \text{or} \quad (a_{ij}),$$

where a_{ij} denotes the object in the ith row and the jth column. The index i on a_{ij} is the *row index* and j is the *column index*. If the matrix is square, then the *principal diagonal* is the set of all a_{ij} with $i = j$.

With a given matrix $A = (a_{ij})$, we associate the linear transformation T_A described by the formula

$$T_A(x_1, x_2, \cdots, x_n) = \begin{pmatrix} a_{11} & a_{12} & \cdots & a_{1n} \\ a_{21} & a_{22} & \cdots & a_{2n} \\ \cdot & \cdot & \cdot & \cdot \\ a_{n1} & a_{n2} & \cdots & a_{nn} \end{pmatrix} \begin{pmatrix} x_1 \\ x_2 \\ \vdots \\ x_n \end{pmatrix}$$

$$= \begin{pmatrix} a_{11}x_1 + a_{12}x_2 + \cdots + a_{1n}x_n \\ a_{21}x_1 + a_{22}x_2 + \cdots + a_{2n}x_n \\ \cdot \cdot \cdot \cdot \cdot \cdot \cdot \\ a_{n1}x_1 + a_{n2}x_2 + \cdots + a_{nn}x_n \end{pmatrix}. \qquad (8\text{-}15)$$

This formula includes a definition of the *product of a square matrix and a column matrix*.   This product is represented as a column matrix and is determined by the rule that the ith term in the product matrix is equal to the sum of the products of the terms of the ith row of the square matrix and the corresponding terms of the given column matrix.

From the discussion preceding Eq. (8-14), it follows that the transformation T_A defined by Eq. (8-15) actually is linear.   In fact, T_A is the linear transformation with the property that, for each j,

$$T(\mathbf{e}_j) = \sum_{i=1}^{n} a_{ij}\mathbf{e}_i.$$

Although it is immaterial whether a vector is represented by a column or a row matrix, it often is important to know which representation is being used.   For this reason, we shall introduce the convention that $\mathbf{v}_c$ denotes the representation of $\mathbf{v}$ as a column matrix. The terms in the column matrix are the coefficients of the basis vectors in the representation of $\mathbf{v}$ as a linear combination of the basis vectors.

THEOREM 8-3.3.   For each linear transformation T of R^n, there is a unique square matrix A such that

$$T(\mathbf{v}) = A\mathbf{v}_c \text{ if } \mathbf{v} \in R^n. \tag{8-16}$$

Moreover, the columns of A are the images under T of $\mathbf{e}_1, \cdots, \mathbf{e}_n$.

PROOF.   A linear transformation of R^n is determined if the images of the vectors $\mathbf{e}_1, \cdots, \mathbf{e}_n$ are specified [Theorem 8-3.2].   Moreover, if $T(\mathbf{e}_j) = \mathbf{v}_j$ for each j, and if the matrix $A = (a_{ij})$ is chosen so that

$$\mathbf{v}_j = \sum_{i=1}^{n} a_{ij}\mathbf{e}_i,$$

we know that T is the linear transformation T_A defined by Eq. (8-15). It remains for us to show that A in Eq. (8-16) must be this matrix. To do this, we can replace $\mathbf{v}$ in (8-16) by $\mathbf{e}_j$ and note that $A \cdot (\mathbf{e}_j)_c$ is simply the jth column of A.   That is, the columns of A must be the images of the vectors $\mathbf{e}_1, \cdots, \mathbf{e}_n$.

We shall now consider the problem of defining the product of two square matrices A and B in such a way that multiplication of matrices corresponds to multiplication of the associated linear transformations— that is, so that $T_A T_B = T_{AB}$.   To see what the definition must be, we observe first that B is the matrix whose columns are the vectors onto which T_B maps the basis vectors $\mathbf{e}_1, \mathbf{e}_2, \cdots, \mathbf{e}_n$. That is,

$$B = ([T_B(\mathbf{e}_1)]_c, [T_B(\mathbf{e}_2)]_c, \cdots, [T_B(\mathbf{e}_n)]_c).$$

Similarly, we must have

$$AB = ([T_A T_B(\mathbf{e}_1)]_c, [T_A T_B(\mathbf{e}_2)]_c, \cdots, [T_A T_B(\mathbf{e}_n)]_c). \tag{8-17}$$

We can now see how AB must be defined if we study a general column of AB. It follows from Eqs. (8-15) and (8-17) that the jth column of AB is

$$[T_A T_B(\mathbf{e}_j)]_c = \begin{pmatrix} a_{11} & a_{12} & \cdots & a_{1n} \\ a_{21} & a_{22} & \cdots & a_{2n} \\ \cdot & \cdot & \cdots & \cdot \\ a_{n1} & a_{n2} & \cdots & a_{nn} \end{pmatrix} \begin{pmatrix} b_{1j} \\ b_{2j} \\ \vdots \\ b_{nj} \end{pmatrix}.$$

As for Eq. (8-15), we can use row-by-column multiplication to evaluate this product. Therefore, the term in the ith row and jth column of AB is obtained by multiplying each term of the ith row of A by the corresponding term in the jth column of B and then adding. In practice, we can do as indicated by the following diagram:

$$\rightarrow \begin{pmatrix} \cdot & \cdot & & \cdot \\ \cdot & \cdot & & \cdot \\ a_{i1} & a_{i2} & \cdots & a_{in} \\ \cdot & \cdot & & \cdot \\ \cdot & \cdot & & \cdot \end{pmatrix} \begin{pmatrix} \cdots & b_{1j} & \cdots \\ \cdots & b_{2j} & \cdots \\ & \cdot & \\ & \cdot & \\ \cdots & b_{nj} & \cdots \end{pmatrix} = \rightarrow \begin{pmatrix} & \cdot & \\ & \cdot & \\ \cdots & c_{ij} & \cdots \\ & \cdot & \end{pmatrix}.$$

We can determine the term c_{ij} in the ith row and jth column of AB by tracing to the right across the ith row of A and simultaneously tracing down the jth column of B, then multiplying the terms in corresponding positions, and adding the products obtained. This gives us

$$c_{ij} = a_{i1}b_{1j} + a_{i2}b_{2j} + a_{i3}b_{3j} + \cdots + a_{in}b_{nj}.$$

DEFINITION 8-3.3. The *product* of two square matrices of order n, (a_{ij}) and (b_{ij}), is the square matrix (c_{ij}), where

$$c_{ij} = \sum_{k=1}^{n} a_{ik} b_{kj}.$$

The *determinant of a square matrix* $A = (a_{ij})$ is denoted by det (A) or $|A|$. It is simply the number obtained by evaluating the square array of A by the usual methods for determining the value of a determinant. The *cofactor* of a_{pq} is $(-1)^{p+q}$ *times* the determinant of the matrix of order $n-1$ obtained from the given matrix A by deleting the pth row and qth column. We shall use but not prove the formula

$$\det (A) = \sum_{k=1}^{n} a_{ik} A_{ik} = \sum_{k=1}^{n} a_{kj} A_{kj}. \tag{8-18}$$

DEFINITION 8-3.4. The *identity transformation* of R^n is the transformation I for which $I(\mathbf{x}) = \mathbf{x}$ for all $\mathbf{x}$ in R^n. An *invertible linear transformation* is a linear transformation T for which there is a linear transformation T^{-1} such that $T^{-1}T = I$.

It should be clear that the matrix of the identity transformation I is the identity matrix, i.e., the matrix that has 1's along the principal diagonal and zeros elsewhere.

THEOREM 8-3.4. If det $(A) \neq 0$, then the linear transformation T whose matrix is A is invertible and the matrix of T^{-1} is

$$A^{-1} = \left(\frac{A_{ij}}{\det (A)} \right), \tag{8-19}$$

where A_{ij} is the cofactor of a_{ij}.

PROOF. If det $(A) \neq 0$, we let T^{-1} be the linear transformation whose matrix is A^{-1} as defined by (8-19). Then the matrix (c_{ij}) of $T^{-1}T$ is $A^{-1}A$. That is,

$$(c_{ij}) = \left(\frac{A_{ji}}{\det (A)} \right)(a_{ij}) = \left(\sum_{k=1}^{n} \frac{A_{ki} a_{kj}}{\det (A)} \right).$$

Then from (8-18), $c_{ii} = \sum_{k=1}^{n} A_{ki} a_{ki} / \det (A) = 1$ for all i. If $i \neq j$, then $c_{ij} = 0$, since c_{ij} is then the determinant of a matrix with the ith and jth columns identical. Thus, (c_{ij}) is the identity matrix and $T^{-1}T = I$.

THEOREM 8-3.5. If det $(A) = 0$, then the linear transformation whose matrix is A is not invertible.

PROOF.   We shall assume without proof that

$$\det (AB) = \det (A) \det (B), \qquad (8\text{-}20)$$

if A and B are square matrices of order n.† If A and B are the matrices of T^{-1} and T, then the matrix of I is AB. If det $(B) = 0$, then det (AB) $= 0$. But det $(AB) \neq 0$, since AB is the identity matrix and det (AB) $= 1$.

PROBLEMS

1. For each of the following, determine the vector into which $(1, 2, -3)$ is transformed by the indicated linear transformation.

(a) T^2, where $T(x, y, z) = (y, x, -z)$.

(b) RS, where $R(x, y, z) = (x+y, z, y-z)$ and $S(x, y, z) = (y, x-z, x+z)$.

(c) SR, where R and S are the linear transformations of part (b).

2.   Let T be a linear transformation of R^n.   Show that $T(\mathbf{0}) = \mathbf{0}$.

3.   In each of the following, T is a linear transformation of the vector space of three-dimensional vectors.   Determine in each case whether the range of T is the entire vector space.

(a) $T(u_1\mathbf{i}+u_2\mathbf{j}+u_3\mathbf{k}) = u_1\mathbf{i}+u_2\mathbf{j}+u_3\mathbf{k}$.

(b) $T(u_1\mathbf{i}+u_2\mathbf{j}+u_3\mathbf{k}) = u_1\mathbf{i}+u_2\mathbf{j}$.

(c) $T(u_1\mathbf{i}+u_2\mathbf{j}+u_3\mathbf{k}) = u_2\mathbf{i}-u_3\mathbf{j}+u_1\mathbf{k}$.

(d) $T(u_1\mathbf{i}+u_2\mathbf{j}+u_3\mathbf{k}) = (u_1+u_3)\mathbf{i}-u_2\mathbf{j}+(u_2-u_3)\mathbf{k}$.

(e) $T(u_1\mathbf{i}+u_2\mathbf{j}+u_3\mathbf{k}) = (u_1+2u_2)\mathbf{i}+(u_1+u_2)\mathbf{j}-u_2\mathbf{k}$.

(f) $T(u_1\mathbf{i}+u_2\mathbf{j}+u_3\mathbf{k}) = 2u_1\mathbf{i}+(3u_1+u_2+2u_3)\mathbf{j}+(u_1+u_2+2u_3)\mathbf{k}$.

4.   Let R and S be the linear transformations of two-dimensional real coordinate space for which $R(x, y) = (-y, x)$ and $S(x, y) = (2x, y)$. Show that

(a) $R^4(x, y) = (x, y)$;   (b) $RSRS = SRSR$;

(c) $(RSRS)^2 = R^3S^2RS^2$.

5.   Let R, S, and T be the linear transformations of three-dimensional real coordinate space for which

$$R(x, y, z) = (x, 0, 0), \quad S(x, y, z) = (0, x, y), \quad T(x, y, z) = (y, z, x)$$

---

† See James, *op. cit.*, p. 764, Theorem 12-9.2.

Describe each of the following transformations by stating the vector into which (x, y, z) is transformed.

(*a*) RT.   (*c*) SR.   (*e*) RSR.

(*b*) R^2T.   (*d*) RS.   (*f*) SR^2.

6. Let T and T^* be the linear transformations defined on three-dimensional real coordinate space by the following equations:

$$T(x, y, z) = (x-z, 3x+y+z, y+3z),$$
$$T^*(x, y, z) = (-2x+y-z, 9x-3y+4z, -3x+y-z).$$

Show that $(TT^*)(x, y, z) = (T^*T)(x, y, z) = (x, y, z)$ for all (x, y, z).

7. A certain linear transformation takes $(1, 1, 3)$ into $(0, 3, 1)$, $(1, 1, 4)$ into $(1, -1, 2)$, and $(2, 1, 3)$ into $(2, 5, 7)$. Into what vectors does this linear transformation take $(1, 0, 0)$, $(0, 1, 0)$, and $(0, 0, 1)$?

8. A certain linear transformation takes $(1, 0, 1)$ into $(2, 3, 4)$ and $(2, 1, 1)$ into $(1, -1, 0)$. Into what vectors does this linear transformation take $(3, 1, 2)$ and $(1, 1, 0)$?

9. Compute AB and BA, where

$$A = \begin{pmatrix} 1 & -1 & -1 \\ 1 & -1 & -1 \\ 1 & -1 & -1 \end{pmatrix} \quad \text{and} \quad B = \begin{pmatrix} 1 & 2 & 3 \\ 2 & 1 & 3 \\ -1 & 1 & 0 \end{pmatrix}.$$

10. Let T be the linear transformation of four-dimensional real coordinate space for which $T(a, b, c, d) = (c, a, d, b)$. Find the matrix of this linear transformation.

11. Determine which of the following matrices are matrices of invertible linear transformations and find the inverses of the ones that are.

(*a*) $\begin{pmatrix} 1 & 2 \\ 0 & 3 \end{pmatrix}$.   (*b*) $\begin{pmatrix} 0 & 1 \\ 2 & 0 \end{pmatrix}$.   (*c*) $\begin{pmatrix} 1 & 2 \\ 1 & 2 \end{pmatrix}$.

(*d*) $\begin{pmatrix} 0 & 1 & 0 \\ 0 & 0 & 1 \\ 1 & 0 & 0 \end{pmatrix}$.   (*e*) $\begin{pmatrix} 0 & 2 & 0 \\ 1 & 0 & 1 \\ 0 & 2 & 0 \end{pmatrix}$.   (*f*) $\begin{pmatrix} 2 & 1 & 1 \\ -1 & 1 & -1 \\ 1 & 0 & 1 \end{pmatrix}$.

12. If we identify (a_0, a_1, a_2, a_3) with the polynomial $a_0+a_1x+a_2x^2+a_3x^3$, then a linear transformation of polynomials of degree three or less corresponds to a linear transformation of R^4.

(*a*) Determine the matrix of the differentiation operator $D = d/dx$.

(*b*) Determine the matrix of the transformation $1-D+D^2-D^3$. Show that this transformation is invertible and find its inverse.

13. Since linear transformations are functions, addition of linear transformations can be defined just as for functions. Show that (a) the sum of two linear transformations is a linear transformation; (b) $R(S+T) = RS+RT$ if R, S, and T are linear transformations.

14. Let T be a linear transformation of R^n for which there is an integer k such that $T^k(\mathbf{x}) = 0$ for all $\mathbf{x}$. Show that

$$(I - T)(I + T + T^2 + T^3 + \cdots + T^{k-1}) = I,$$

so that $I - T$ is invertible [see problem 13].

15.* Prove that, if T is an invertible linear transformation and $T^*T = I$, then $TT^* = I$ and T^* is invertible.

16. Let k be a positive integer. Explain why T^k is invertible if and only if T is invertible.

17. Show that the range of an invertible linear transformation of R^n is R^n.

18. Show that a linear transformation T of R^n is invertible if the range of T is R^n.

8-4. INVERSE TRANSFORMATION AND IMPLICIT FUNCTION THEOREMS

The inverse transformation theorem of this section is analogous to Cramer's rule. In fact, the proof is based on approximations of nonlinear transformations by linear transformations.

We know that if the domain of a function f is an interval I and f is either increasing on I or decreasing on I, then f has a continuous inverse g. If f is differentiable, then g is differentiable and $f'(x)g'(y) = 1$ whenever $y = f(x)$ [see Theorems 2-6.4 and 2-7.2].

Now suppose that f is a function whose derivative is continuous at a point x_0. Since $f'(x) \to f'(x_0)$ as $x \to x_0$, it follows that if $f'(x_0) \neq 0$, then there is a neighborhood of x_0 on which f' is nonzero. In particular, if $f'(x_0) > 0$, then there is an interval $[x_0 - \varepsilon, x_0 + \varepsilon]$ on which f' is positive [see Fig. 8-5]. Then f is increasing on this interval and therefore has an inverse that is differentiable on the interval $[f(x_0 - \varepsilon), f(x_0 + \varepsilon)]$.

The purpose of this section is to generalize this theory about inverses of functions of one variable to transformations defined by systems of equations. Given functions f and g of two variables, we may denote by (u, v) the image of a point (x, y) as determined by the two equations

$$\begin{cases} u = f(x, y), \\ v = g(x, y). \end{cases} \tag{8-21}$$

These equations define a transformation T whose domain and range are sets of points in the plane. We shall study the problem of solving these equations for x and y as functions of u and v—that is, the problem of determining the inverse of T. For the transformation T, the "Jacobian" in the following definition is a useful generalization of the concept of "derivative" of a function of one variable.

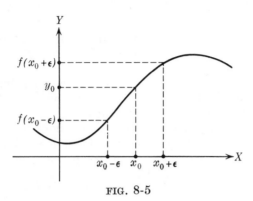

FIG. 8-5

DEFINITION 8-4.1. For the transformation defined by the equations in (8-21), the Jacobian matrix is the matrix

$$\begin{pmatrix} \dfrac{\partial u}{\partial x} & \dfrac{\partial u}{\partial y} \\[2mm] \dfrac{\partial v}{\partial x} & \dfrac{\partial v}{\partial y} \end{pmatrix} = \begin{pmatrix} f_1(x, y) & f_2(x, y) \\ g_1(x, y) & g_2(x, y) \end{pmatrix},$$

which has as rows the gradients of the functions u and v. The determinant of this matrix is said to be the *Jacobian determinant* of T, or simply the *Jacobian* of T. The Jacobian can be denoted by using the ordinary determinant notation, but we shall also denote it by the symbol $\partial(u, v)/\partial(x, y)$.

These concepts of Jacobian matrix and Jacobian determinant for transformations of the plane have obvious generalizations to spaces of higher dimensions. We shall state the following theorem for spaces of arbitrary dimensions; the proof, given at the end of this section, is only for transformations of the plane. For higher-dimension spaces, the proof is essentially the same, but it needs more variables and functions and more complicated notation. A transformation T on R^n defines n functions, each of which is a function of n variables. Explicitly, if

$$T(x_1, x_2, \cdots, x_n) = (y_1, y_2, \cdots, y_n),$$

then we can write

$$y_i = f^i(x_1, x_2, \cdots, x_n),$$

for $1 \leq i \leq n$. These functions f^i are called the *component functions* of T.

THEOREM 8-4.1 (INVERSE TRANSFORMATION THEOREM). Suppose that $\mathbf{v}_0 = (x_1, x_2, \cdots, x_n)$ is a vector in R^n and that T is a transformation with the following properties.

(i) There is a neighborhood of $\mathbf{v}_0$ on which all first-order partial derivatives of component functions are continuous.

(ii) The Jacobian of T is nonzero at $\mathbf{v}_0$.

Then there is a neighborhood U of $\mathbf{v}_0$ and a neighborhood W of $T(\mathbf{v}_0)$ such that T is a one-to-one transformation of U onto W and the first-order partial derivatives of the component functions of T^{-1} are continuous at each point of W.

Although the proof of this theorem for $n = 2$ will be given at the end of the section, it is instructive to consider the following special case. Suppose that $T(x, y) = (u, v)$ and $T(x_0, y_0) = (u_0, v_0)$, where

$$\begin{cases} u = a_1x + b_1y + c_1, \\ v = a_2x + b_2y + c_2; \end{cases} \quad \text{or} \quad \begin{pmatrix} u \\ v \end{pmatrix} = \begin{pmatrix} a_1 & b_1 \\ a_2 & b_2 \end{pmatrix}\begin{pmatrix} x \\ y \end{pmatrix} + \begin{pmatrix} c_1 \\ c_2 \end{pmatrix}.$$

If $\Delta x = x - x_0$, $\Delta y = y - y_0$, $\Delta u = u - u_0$, and $\Delta v = v - v_0$, then we have

$$\begin{cases} \Delta u = a_1\,\Delta x + b_1\,\Delta y, \\ \Delta v = a_2\,\Delta x + b_2\,\Delta y, \end{cases} \quad \text{or} \quad \begin{pmatrix} \Delta u \\ \Delta v \end{pmatrix} = \begin{pmatrix} a_1 & b_1 \\ a_2 & b_2 \end{pmatrix}\begin{pmatrix} \Delta x \\ \Delta y \end{pmatrix}. \quad (8\text{-}22)$$

Also, the Jacobian is the determinant

$$\begin{vmatrix} \dfrac{\partial u}{\partial x} & \dfrac{\partial u}{\partial y} \\ \dfrac{\partial v}{\partial x} & \dfrac{\partial v}{\partial y} \end{vmatrix} = \begin{vmatrix} a_1 & b_1 \\ a_2 & b_2 \end{vmatrix}.$$

Since the Jacobian is nonzero, the linear transformation of (8-22) has an inverse. This implies that T has an inverse. In this case, the domain of T and the domain of T^{-1} are the entire plane. All partial derivatives of u and v with respect to x or y, or of x and y with respect to u or v, are constants and are continuous everywhere. Intuitively, the proof of Theorem 8-4.1 will be based on the fact that, near (x_0, y_0), the equations in (8-21) are approximately equivalent to the equations

$$\begin{cases} \Delta u = f_1(x_0, y_0)\, \Delta x + f_2(x_0, y_0)\, \Delta y, \\ \Delta v = g_1(x_0, y_0)\, \Delta x + g_2(x_0, y_0)\, \Delta y, \end{cases}$$

or

$$\begin{pmatrix} \Delta u \\ \Delta v \end{pmatrix} = \begin{pmatrix} f_1(x_0, y_0) & f_2(x_0, y_0) \\ g_1(x_0, y_0) & g_2(x_0, y_0) \end{pmatrix} \begin{pmatrix} \Delta x \\ \Delta y \end{pmatrix}. \tag{8-23}$$

Under the hypotheses of Theorem 8-4.1, the inverse T^{-1} exists. We shall consider a method for computing values of T^{-1} which is a generalization of Newton's method. It will be recalled that Newton's method involved replacing a curve by the tangent line at a chosen point.† For the following generalization of Newton's method, we shall replace a transformation by the linear transformation whose matrix is the Jacobian matrix of the given transformation evaluated at a chosen point [the equations in (8-23) give the two-dimensional case].

GENERALIZED NEWTON'S METHOD. Suppose we are given a vector **v** in R^n and a transformation T. If we have an approximation $\boldsymbol{\alpha}$ to a vector **u** for which $T(\mathbf{u}) = \mathbf{v}$, we replace $T(\mathbf{u})$ by $T(\boldsymbol{\alpha}) + J(\boldsymbol{\alpha})(\boldsymbol{\beta} - \boldsymbol{\alpha})$ and determine the next approximation $\boldsymbol{\beta}$ by using the formula

$$\mathbf{v} - T(\boldsymbol{\alpha}) = J(\boldsymbol{\alpha})(\boldsymbol{\beta} - \boldsymbol{\alpha})_c \quad \text{or} \quad \boldsymbol{\beta} = \boldsymbol{\alpha} - J^{-1}(\boldsymbol{\alpha})[T(\boldsymbol{\alpha}) - \mathbf{v}]_c, \tag{8-24}$$

where $J(\boldsymbol{\alpha})$ is the Jacobian matrix of T evaluated at $\boldsymbol{\alpha}$.

ILLUSTRATION 1. We shall let T be the transformation such that

$$\begin{cases} u = x^3 + 2y, \\ v = 5x + y^3, \end{cases} \quad \text{if} \quad T(x, y) = (u, v).$$

Suppose we wish to determine $T^{-1}(\frac{1}{2}, \frac{1}{2})$—that is, the point (x, y) such that $\frac{1}{2} = x^3 + 2y$ and $\frac{1}{2} = 5x + y^3$. As a first approximation, we can use $(x, y) = (0, 0)$. Then

$$J(0, 0) = \begin{pmatrix} 0 & 2 \\ 5 & 0 \end{pmatrix} \quad \text{and} \quad J^{-1}(0, 0) = \begin{pmatrix} 0 & \frac{1}{5} \\ \frac{1}{2} & 0 \end{pmatrix}.$$

---

† For a discussion of Newton's method analogous to the present discussion of the generalized Newton's method, see James, *op. cit.*, pp. 278–280.

The equations in (8-24) with $\boldsymbol{\alpha} = \mathbf{0}$ and $\mathbf{v} = (\frac{1}{2}, \frac{1}{2})$ give us

$$\begin{pmatrix} \frac{1}{2} \\ \frac{1}{2} \end{pmatrix} - \begin{pmatrix} 0 \\ 0 \end{pmatrix} = \begin{pmatrix} 0 & 2 \\ 5 & 0 \end{pmatrix} \left[\boldsymbol{\beta} - \begin{pmatrix} 0 \\ 0 \end{pmatrix} \right] \quad \text{or} \quad \boldsymbol{\beta} = \begin{pmatrix} 0 \\ 0 \end{pmatrix} + \begin{pmatrix} 0 & \frac{1}{5} \\ \frac{1}{2} & 0 \end{pmatrix} \begin{pmatrix} \frac{1}{2} \\ \frac{1}{2} \end{pmatrix} = \begin{pmatrix} \frac{1}{10} \\ \frac{1}{4} \end{pmatrix}.$$

Then $u(\frac{1}{10}, \frac{1}{4}) = .5010$, $v(\frac{1}{10}, \frac{1}{4}) = .5156$, and the first of the equations in (8-24), with $\boldsymbol{\alpha} = (\frac{1}{10}, \frac{1}{4})$ and $\boldsymbol{\beta} = (\beta_1, \beta_2)$, becomes

$$\begin{pmatrix} \frac{1}{2} \\ \frac{1}{2} \end{pmatrix} - \begin{pmatrix} .5010 \\ .5156 \end{pmatrix} = \begin{pmatrix} .030 & 2 \\ 5 & .188 \end{pmatrix} \left[\begin{pmatrix} \beta_1 \\ \beta_2 \end{pmatrix} - \begin{pmatrix} \frac{1}{10} \\ \frac{1}{4} \end{pmatrix} \right],$$

or

$$\begin{cases} -.0010 = .030(\beta_1 - \frac{1}{10}) + 2(\beta_2 - \frac{1}{4}), \\ -.0156 = 5(\beta_1 - \frac{1}{10}) + .188(\beta_2 - \frac{1}{4}). \end{cases}$$

When these equations are solved, we have $\beta_1 - \frac{1}{10} = -.0031$ and $\beta_2 - \frac{1}{4} = -.0005$. Therefore, $\boldsymbol{\beta}$, our next approximation of (x, y), is the vector $(.0969, .2495)$. The values of u and v at $(.0969, .2495)$ are .499,910 and .500,031. From (8-24) with $\boldsymbol{\alpha} = (.0969, .2495)$, we have

$$\begin{pmatrix} \frac{1}{2} \\ \frac{1}{2} \end{pmatrix} - \begin{pmatrix} .499,910 \\ .500,031 \end{pmatrix} = \begin{pmatrix} .028,169 & 2 \\ 5 & .186,751 \end{pmatrix} \left[\begin{pmatrix} \beta_1 \\ \beta_2 \end{pmatrix} - \begin{pmatrix} .0969 \\ .2495 \end{pmatrix} \right],$$

or

$$\begin{cases} .000,090 = .028,169(\beta_1 - .0969) + 2(\beta_2 - .2495), \\ -.000,031 = 5(\beta_1 - .0969) + .186,751(\beta_2 - .2495). \end{cases}$$

These equations give $\beta_1 - .0969 = -.000,008$ and $\beta_2 - .2495 = .000,045$, so that our approximation of (x, y) is now $(.096,892, .249,545)$.

The convergence in Illustration 1 appears to be rapid. The following theorem shows that this is to be expected in general, provided the first approximation is good enough. This theorem is proved for two-dimensional spaces, but similar results can be obtained in similar ways for higher dimensional spaces.

THEOREM 8-4.2 Suppose T is a transformation of R^2 and that $T(\mathbf{u}) = \mathbf{v}$. Also suppose that there is a neighborhood M of $\mathbf{u}$ and positive numbers L, U_1, and U_2 such that

(i) $|J(\mathbf{x})| \geq L$ for all $\mathbf{x}$ in M, where J is the Jacobian determinant of T;

(ii) U_1 is an upper bound for the absolute values of first-order partial derivatives of component functions of T at points of M;

(iii) U_2 is an upper bound for the absolute values of second-order partial derivatives of the component functions of T at points of M.

Then there is a neighborhood N of $\mathbf{u}$ such that, if $\boldsymbol{\alpha} \in N$ and $\boldsymbol{\alpha}$ and $\boldsymbol{\beta}$ are successive approximations obtained by the generalized Newton's method, then $\boldsymbol{\beta} \in N$ and

$$|\boldsymbol{\beta} - \mathbf{u}| \leq \frac{2\sqrt{2}\,U_1 U_2}{L} |\boldsymbol{\alpha} - \mathbf{u}|^2. \tag{8-25}$$

PROOF. We shall let N be $\{\mathbf{w}: |\mathbf{w} - \mathbf{u}| < \varepsilon\}$, where $\varepsilon < L/(2\sqrt{2}\,U_1 U_2)$ and ε is small enough that $N \subset M$. We shall denote by f and g the component functions of T and write the first of the equations in (8-24) in the form

$$\begin{pmatrix} v_1 \\ v_2 \end{pmatrix} - \begin{pmatrix} f(\alpha_1, \alpha_2) \\ g(\alpha_1, \alpha_2) \end{pmatrix} = \begin{pmatrix} f_1(\alpha_1, \alpha_2) & f_2(\alpha_1, \alpha_2) \\ g_1(\alpha_1, \alpha_2) & g_2(\alpha_1, \alpha_2) \end{pmatrix} \begin{pmatrix} \beta_1 - \alpha_1 \\ \beta_2 - \alpha_2 \end{pmatrix},$$

or

$$\begin{cases} v_1 - f(\alpha_1, \alpha_2) = (\beta_1 - \alpha_1)f_1(\alpha_1, \alpha_2) + (\beta_2 - \alpha_2)f_2(\alpha_1, \alpha_2), \\ v_2 - g(\alpha_1, \alpha_2) = (\beta_1 - \alpha_1)g_1(\alpha_1, \alpha_2) + (\beta_2 - \alpha_2)g_2(\alpha_1, \alpha_2). \end{cases} \tag{8-26}$$

Then we can define E_1 and E_2 by

$$\begin{cases} v_1 - f(\alpha_1, \alpha_2) = (u_1 - \alpha_1)f_1(\alpha_1, \alpha_2) + (u_2 - \alpha_2)f_2(\alpha_1, \alpha_2) + E_1, \\ v_2 - g(\alpha_1, \alpha_2) = (u_1 - \alpha_1)g_1(\alpha_1, \alpha_2) + (u_2 - \alpha_2)g_2(\alpha_1, \alpha_2) + E_2. \end{cases} \tag{8-27}$$

It follows from Taylor's theorem that there is a point (ξ, η) on the line segment joining (u_1, u_2) and (α_1, α_2) for which

$$|E_1| = \tfrac{1}{2}|(u_1 - \alpha_1)^2 f_{11}(\xi, \eta) \\ + 2(u_1 - \alpha_1)(u_2 - \alpha_2)f_{12}(\xi, \eta) + (u_2 - \alpha_2)^2 f_{22}(\xi, \eta)|.$$

Since $(\xi, \eta) \in N$ and $N \subset M$, we have

$$|E_1| \leq \tfrac{1}{2}U_2[|u_1 - \alpha_1| + |u_2 - \alpha_2|]^2.$$

We shall leave it to the student to show that we must then have

$$|E_1| \leq U_2[(u_1 - \alpha_1)^2 + (u_2 - \alpha_2)^2] = U_2|\mathbf{u} - \boldsymbol{\alpha}|^2.$$

Similarly, $|E_2| \leq U_2|\mathbf{u} - \boldsymbol{\alpha}|^2$, so that

$$(E_1^2 + E_2^2)^{1/2} \leq \sqrt{2}\,U_2|\mathbf{u} - \boldsymbol{\alpha}|^2. \tag{8-28}$$

Now we use subtraction to eliminate the left members of the equations in (8-26) and (8-27). The results can be written as follows:

$$\begin{cases} (\beta_1 - u_1)f_1(\alpha_1, \alpha_2) + (\beta_2 - u_2)f_2(\alpha_1, \alpha_2) = E_1, \\ (\beta_1 - u_1)g_1(\alpha_1, \alpha_2) + (\beta_2 - u_2)g_2(\alpha_1, \alpha_2) = E_2; \end{cases}$$

or

$$\beta_1 - u_1 = \frac{\begin{vmatrix} E_1 & f_2(\alpha_1, \alpha_2) \\ E_2 & g_2(\alpha_1, \alpha_2) \end{vmatrix}}{\begin{vmatrix} f_1(\alpha_1, \alpha_2) & f_2(\alpha_1, \alpha_2) \\ g_1(\alpha_1, \alpha_2) & g_2(\alpha_1, \alpha_2) \end{vmatrix}},$$

$$\beta_2 - u_2 = \frac{\begin{vmatrix} f_1(\alpha_1, \alpha_2) & E_1 \\ g_1(\alpha_1, \alpha_2) & E_2 \end{vmatrix}}{\begin{vmatrix} f_1(\alpha_1, \alpha_2) & f_2(\alpha_1, \alpha_2) \\ g_1(\alpha_1, \alpha_2) & g_2(\alpha_1, \alpha_2) \end{vmatrix}}.$$

Since the determinants in the numerators are not larger than the product of the lengths of their columns [see problem 10 of Section 8-5] and L is a lower bound for the Jacobian determinant of T, we have

$$|\beta_1 - u_1| \leqq \frac{(E_1^2 + E_2^2)^{1/2}[f_2(\alpha_1, \alpha_2)^2 + g_2(\alpha_1, \alpha_2)^2]^{1/2}}{L},$$

$$|\beta_2 - u_2| \leqq \frac{(E_1^2 + E_2^2)^{1/2}[f_1(\alpha_1, \alpha_2)^2 + g_1(\alpha_1, \alpha_2)^2]^{1/2}}{L},$$

and

$$|\beta - u| \leqq \frac{(E_1^2 + E_2^2)^{1/2}[f_1(\alpha_1, \alpha_2)^2 + f_2(\alpha_1, \alpha_2)^2 + g_1(\alpha_1, \alpha_2)^2 + g_2(\alpha_1, \alpha_2)^2]^{1/2}}{L}.$$

Now we can use (8-28) and the fact that U_1 is an upper bound for the first-order partial derivatives of f and g to obtain

$$|\beta - u| \leqq \frac{2\sqrt{2}U_1U_2}{L}|\alpha - u|^2.$$

Since $\alpha \in N$, we have $|\alpha - u| < L/(2\sqrt{2}U_1U_2)$. Therefore, $|\beta - u| \leqq |\alpha - u|$, and $\beta \in N$.

The inverse transformation theorem is a special case of the following "implicit function theorem." The implicit function theorem appears to be more general than the inverse transformation theorem, but can be proved by using the inverse transformation theorem. We shall state the theorem and give the proof of a typical special case.

THEOREM 8-4.3 (IMPLICIT FUNCTION THEOREM). Suppose we have a system of n equations,

$$\begin{cases} f^1(x_1, x_2, \cdots, x_p; u_1, u_2, \cdots, u_n) = 0, \\ f^2(x_1, x_2, \cdots, x_p; u_1, u_2, \cdots, u_n) = 0, \\ \quad \cdot \quad \cdot \quad \cdot \quad \cdot \quad \cdot \quad \cdot \quad \cdot \quad \cdot \quad \cdot \\ f^n(x_1, x_2, \cdots, x_p; u_1, u_2, \cdots, u_n) = 0. \end{cases}$$

Also suppose that these equations are satisfied by the point

$$(x_1^0, x_2^0, \cdots, x_p^0; u_1^0, u_2^0, \cdots, u_n^0),$$

that all first-order partial derivatives are continuous in a neighborhood of this point, and that at this point the following Jacobian is nonzero:

$$\frac{\partial(f^1, f^2, \cdots, f^n)}{\partial(u_1, u_2, \cdots, u_n)}.$$

Under these conditions, there exists one and only one set of functions, $\phi^1, \phi^2, \cdots, \phi^n$, whose first-order partial derivatives are continuous in a neighborhood of $(x_1^0, \cdots, x_p^0)$, whose values are $u_1^0, \cdots, u_n^0$ when $x_1, \cdots, x_p$ have the values $x_1^0, \cdots, x_p^0$, and for which there is a neighborhood of $(x_1^0, \cdots, x_p^0)$ in which the given equations are satisfied if

$$\begin{cases} u_1 = \phi^1(x_1, x_2, \cdots, x_p), \\ u_2 = \phi^2(x_1, x_2, \cdots, x_p), \\ \quad \cdot \quad \cdot \quad \cdot \quad \cdot \quad \cdot \quad \cdot \\ u_n = \phi^n(x_1, x_2, \cdots, x_p). \end{cases}$$

ILLUSTRATION 2. The point $(1, 1, -1)$ satisfies the equations

$$\begin{cases} \cos(x-y) + e^{x+z} - 2 = 0, \\ xz + \sin(x-y) + 1 = 0. \end{cases}$$

Suppose we wish to determine the values of y and z when $x = 1.2$. We introduce the transformation T defined by

$$T(x, y, z) = [x, \cos(x-y) + e^{x+z} - 2, xz + \sin(x-y) + 1].$$

Then $T(1, 1, -1) = (1, 0, 0)$. Our problem is to determine (x_0, y_0, z_0) such that $T(x_0, y_0, z_0) = (1.2, 0, 0)$. Of course, we must have $x_0 = 1.2$. The Jacobian matrix of T is

$$J(x, y, z) = \begin{pmatrix} 1 & 0 & 0 \\ -\sin(x-y) + e^{x+z} & \sin(x-y) & e^{x+z} \\ z + \cos(x-y) & -\cos(x-y) & x \end{pmatrix}.$$

With $\boldsymbol{\alpha} = (1.2, 1, -1)$, we have $T(\boldsymbol{\alpha}) = (1.2, .201, -.001)$, and the first of the equations in (8-24) becomes

$$\begin{pmatrix} 1.2 \\ 0 \\ 0 \end{pmatrix} - \begin{pmatrix} 1.2 \\ .201 \\ -.001 \end{pmatrix} = \begin{pmatrix} 1 & 0 & 0 \\ ? & .199 & 1.221 \\ ? & -.980 & 1.200 \end{pmatrix} \begin{pmatrix} \beta_1 - 1.2 \\ \beta_2 - 1 \\ \beta_3 + 1 \end{pmatrix},$$

or

$$\beta_1 - 1.2 = 0 \quad \text{and} \quad \begin{cases} .199(\beta_2 - 1) + 1.221(\beta_3 + 1) = -.201, \\ -.980(\beta_2 - 1) + 1.200(\beta_3 + 1) = +.001. \end{cases} \quad (8\text{-}29)$$

The question marks were inserted in the Jacobian matrix in place of the correct entries, since $\beta_1 = 1.2$ and these entries would not affect the remaining computation. Then $\boldsymbol{\beta} = (1.2, 0.83, -1.14)$, and we can use this vector for $\boldsymbol{\alpha}$ in (8-24) to obtain a new value for $\boldsymbol{\beta}$:

$$\begin{pmatrix} 1.2 \\ 0 \\ 0 \end{pmatrix} - \begin{pmatrix} 1.2 \\ -.0059 \\ -.0064 \end{pmatrix} = \begin{pmatrix} 1 & 0 & 0 \\ ? & .3617 & 1.0618 \\ ? & -.9323 & 1.2000 \end{pmatrix} \begin{pmatrix} \beta_1 - 1.2 \\ \beta_2 - .83 \\ \beta_3 + 1.14 \end{pmatrix},$$

or

$$\beta_1 = 1.2 \quad \text{and} \quad \begin{cases} .3617(\beta_2 - .83) + 1.0618(\beta_3 + 1.14) = +.0059, \\ -.9323(\beta_2 - .83) + 1.2000(\beta_3 + 1.14) = +.0064. \end{cases}$$

$$(8\text{-}30)$$

Then $\boldsymbol{\beta} = (1.2, 0.8302, -1.1345)$. Now we could use this vector for $\boldsymbol{\alpha}$ in (8-24) and continue the process. The student should note that (8-29) and (8-30) also result from considering x as fixed at 1.2 and setting the differentials of the left members of the given equations equal to the negatives of their values at the point currently being used as an estimate, with Δy and Δz the difference between the new and old estimates for y and z.

PROOF OF A TYPICAL SPECIAL CASE OF THE IMPLICIT FUNCTION THEOREM. Suppose that the simultaneous equations

$$\begin{cases} f(x, y, z, u, v) = 0, \\ g(x, y, z, u, v) = 0 \end{cases} \quad (8\text{-}31)$$

are satisfied by $(x_0, y_0, z_0, u_0, v_0)$, that all first-order partial derivatives of f and g are continuous in some neighborhood of $(x_0, y_0, z_0, u_0, v_0)$, and that at this point

$$\begin{vmatrix} \dfrac{\partial f}{\partial u} & \dfrac{\partial f}{\partial v} \\[2mm] \dfrac{\partial g}{\partial u} & \dfrac{\partial g}{\partial v} \end{vmatrix} \neq 0.$$

We shall introduce the transformation T of five-dimensional real coordinate space for which $T(x, y, z, u, v) = (\bar{x}, \bar{y}, \bar{z}, \bar{u}, \bar{v})$ if and only if

$$\bar{x} = x, \quad \bar{y} = y, \quad \bar{z} = z, \quad \bar{u} = f(x, y, z, u, v), \quad \bar{v} = g(x, y, z, u, v). \tag{8-32}$$

Since the equations in (8-31) are satisfied by $(x_0, y_0, z_0, u_0, v_0)$, we have $\bar{u}_0 = 0$ and $\bar{v}_0 = 0$. All functions in the right members of the equations in (8-32) have continuous first-order partial derivatives and the Jacobian of T is the following determinant, which is nonzero at $(x_0, y_0, z_0, u_0, v_0)$:

$$\begin{vmatrix} 1 & 0 & 0 & 0 & 0 \\ 0 & 1 & 0 & 0 & 0 \\ 0 & 0 & 1 & 0 & 0 \\ f_1 & f_2 & f_3 & f_4 & f_5 \\ g_1 & g_2 & g_3 & g_4 & g_5 \end{vmatrix} = \begin{vmatrix} f_4 & f_5 \\ g_4 & g_5 \end{vmatrix} = \begin{vmatrix} \dfrac{\partial f}{\partial u} & \dfrac{\partial f}{\partial v} \\ \dfrac{\partial g}{\partial u} & \dfrac{\partial g}{\partial v} \end{vmatrix}.$$

Therefore, it follows from Theorem 8-4.1 that there is a neighborhood U of $(x_0, y_0, z_0, u_0, v_0)$ such that, if T is restricted to U, then T has an inverse T^{-1} and the domain of T^{-1} is a neighborhood of $(\bar{x}_0, \bar{y}_0, \bar{z}_0, \bar{u}_0, \bar{v}_0)$. Since $x = \bar{x}$, $y = \bar{y}$, $z = \bar{z}$ there are functions F and G such that the transformation T^{-1} can be described by the following equations:

$$\begin{cases} x = \bar{x}, \\ y = \bar{y}, \\ z = \bar{z}, \end{cases} \quad \begin{cases} u = F(\bar{x}, \bar{y}, \bar{z}, \bar{u}, \bar{v}) \\ \quad = F[x, y, z, f(x, y, z, u, v), g(x, y, z, u, v)], \\ v = G(\bar{x}, \bar{y}, \bar{z}, \bar{u}, \bar{v}) \\ \quad = G[x, y, z, f(x, y, z, u, v), g(x, y, z, u, v)]. \end{cases} \tag{8-33}$$

If we wish to define u and v as functions θ and ϕ of (x, y, z) that satisfy the equations in (8-31), then it follows from the equations in (8-33) that we have no choice but to give the following definitions:

$$\begin{cases} u = F(x, y, z, 0, 0) = \theta(x, y, z), \\ v = G(x, y, z, 0, 0) = \phi(x, y, z). \end{cases} \tag{8-34}$$

Since $\bar{u}_0 = 0$ and $\bar{v}_0 = 0$, it follows from (8-33) that, with these definitions of θ and ϕ, we have $u_0 = \theta(x_0, y_0, z_0)$ and $v_0 = \phi(x_0, y_0, z_0)$. It follows from Theorem 8-4.1 that F and G, and therefore also θ and ϕ, have continuous first-order partial derivatives. To see that the values of u and v given by (8-34) satisfy the equations in (8-31), we note that it follows from (8-34) and the equations in (8-33) that

$$(x, y, z, u, v) = T^{-1}(x, y, z, 0, 0).$$

Then

$$T(x, y, z, u, v) = (x, y, z, 0, 0),$$

or

$$0 = f(x, y, z, u, v) \quad \text{and} \quad 0 = g(x, y, z, u, v).$$

PROOF OF THE INVERSE TRANSFORMATION THEOREM FOR TRANSFORMATIONS OF THE PLANE. Suppose T is a transformation of the plane. We shall use the notation

$$T(x, y) = (u, v), \quad \begin{cases} u = f(x, y), \\ v = g(x, y). \end{cases}$$

Also, we shall assume that the partial derivatives of f and g are continuous on a neighborhood of (x_0, y_0), and assume that $J(x_0, y_0) \neq 0$, where

$$J(x, y) = \begin{vmatrix} f_1(x, y) & f_2(x, y) \\ g_1(x, y) & g_2(x, y) \end{vmatrix}.$$

Since a determinant is a continuous function of its elements, and since each partial derivative in J is continuous on a neighborhood of (x_0, y_0), there is a circular neighborhood U of (x_0, y_0), such that

$$\begin{vmatrix} f_1(\alpha, \beta) & f_2(\alpha, \beta) \\ g_1(\gamma, \delta) & g_2(\gamma, \delta) \end{vmatrix} \neq 0 \tag{8-35}$$

if (α, β) and (γ, δ) belong to U. [In particular, we could demand that in this neighborhood the absolute value of the Jacobian be not less than half the value at (x_0, y_0).] To complete the proof, we must show that, if T maps U onto W, then

(1) T is one-to-one on U;

(2) W is a neighborhood of $T(x_0, y_0)$;

(3) the first-order partial derivatives of the component functions of T^{-1} are continuous on W.

To show that T is one-to-one on U, we shall let (x_1, y_1) and (x_2, y_2) be points in U. It follows from Taylor's theorem [Section 6-5] that there are two points, (α, β) and (γ, δ), on the line segment joining (x_1, y_1) and (x_2, y_2), such that

$$\begin{cases} f(x_2, y_2) - f(x_1, y_1) = f_1(\alpha, \beta)(x_2 - x_1) + f_2(\alpha, \beta)(y_2 - y_1), \\ g(x_2, y_2) - g(x_1, y_1) = g_1(\gamma, \delta)(x_2 - x_1) + g_2(\gamma, \delta)(y_2 - y_1). \end{cases}$$

Since U is circular, the points (α, β) and (γ, δ) are in U. Therefore, (8-35) is valid and the determinant of the coefficients of the preceding system of two equations in the variables $x_2 - x_1$ and $y_2 - y_1$ is nonzero. Therefore, these equations can be solved by Cramer's rule and it follows that $x_2 = x_1$ and $y_2 = y_1$ if $f(x_2, y_2) = f(x_1, y_1)$ and $g(x_2, y_2) = g(x_1, y_1)$. That is, $(x_1, y_1) = (x_2, y_2)$ if $T(x_1, y_1) = T(x_2, y_2)$. Therefore, T is one-to-one on U.

Now we shall show that W is a neighborhood of $T(x_0, y_0)$—that is, W contains a disk with center at $T(x_0, y_0)$. Let C be a circle with center at (x_0, y_0) that is contained in U, but has a smaller radius than U. Let S be the union of C and its interior. Since T is one-to-one on U, the image of C does not contain $T(x_0, y_0)$. Since C is compact, it follows from the maximum value theorem [Theorem 2-8.2] that the distance between $T(x, y)$ and $T(x_0, y_0)$ attains its minimum on C. This minimum is not zero. Thus, we can write

$$\inf \{d[T(x, y), T(x_0, y_0)]: (x, y) \in C\} = \delta > 0. \qquad (8\text{-}36)$$

We shall show that W contains the interior of the disk with center $T(x_0, y_0)$ and radius δ. If (u^*, v^*) is in the interior of this disk, then $d[T(x_0, y_0), (u^*, v^*)] < \delta$. Thus, if (x^*, y^*) is a point of S at which $d[T(x, y), (u^*, v^*)]$ attains its absolute minimum on S, then this absolute minimum is less than δ. From (8-36), we see that (x^*, y^*) is in the interior of S. Then the first-order partial derivatives of $[f(x, y) - u^*]^2 + [g(x, y) - v^*]^2$ are zero at (x^*, y^*). That is,

$$f_1(x^*, y^*)[f(x^*, y^*) - u^*] + g_1(x^*, y^*)[g(x^*, y^*) - v^*] = 0,$$
$$f_2(x^*, y^*)[f(x^*, y^*) - u^*] + g_2(x^*, y^*)[g(x^*, y^*) - v^*] = 0.$$

Since the Jacobian is nonzero at (x^*, y^*), this implies that

$$u^* = f(x^*, y^*) \quad \text{and} \quad v^* = g(x^*, y^*), \quad \text{or} \quad (u^*, v^*) = T(x^*, y^*).$$

Therefore, (u^*, v^*) belong to W.

Now suppose that T^{-1} is expressed by the equations $x = F(u, v)$, $y = G(u, v)$. To prove that F and G have continuous first-order partial derivatives at a point (u, v) of W, we can first let (x, y) denote $T^{-1}(u, v)$, Δu be nonzero, and $\Delta v = 0$. Then there are points, (α, β) and (γ, δ), between (x, y) and $(x + \Delta x, y + \Delta y)$, such that

$$f(x + \Delta x, y + \Delta y) - f(x, y) = \Delta u = f_1(\alpha, \beta)\, \Delta x + f_2(\alpha, \beta)\, \Delta y,$$
$$g(x + \Delta x, y + \Delta y) - g(x, y) = 0 = g_1(\gamma, \delta)\, \Delta x + g_2(\gamma, \delta)\, \Delta y.$$

These equations can be solved to obtain

$$\frac{\Delta x}{\Delta u} = \frac{g_2(\gamma, \delta)}{f_1(\alpha, \beta) g_2(\gamma, \delta) - f_2(\alpha, \beta) g_1(\gamma, \delta)},$$
$$\frac{\Delta y}{\Delta u} = \frac{-g_1(\gamma, \delta)}{f_1(\alpha, \beta) g_2(\gamma, \delta) - f_2(\alpha, \beta) g_1(\gamma, \delta)}.$$

Since we have proved (1) and (2), we know that any sufficiently small neighborhood U' of (x, y) is mapped by T onto a neighborhood W' of $T(x, y)$. This implies that there is a neighborhood of $T(x, y)$ that T^{-1} maps into U'—namely, the neighborhood W'. Therefore, T^{-1} is continuous. This implies that x and y are continuous functions of (u, v), so that Δx and Δy approach zero as $\Delta u \to 0$. Therefore, $(\alpha, \beta) \to (x, y)$ and $(\gamma, \delta) \to (x, y)$ as $\Delta u \to 0$, and we have

$$\frac{\partial x}{\partial u} = \frac{g_2(x, y)}{f_1(x, y)g_2(x, y) - f_2(x, y)g_1(x, y)},$$

$$\frac{\partial y}{\partial u} = \frac{-g_1(x, y)}{f_1(x, y)g_2(x, y) - f_2(x, y)g_1(x, y)}.$$

Similarly,

$$\frac{\partial x}{\partial v} = \frac{-f_2(x, y)}{f_1(x, y)g_2(x, y) - f_2(x, y)g_1(x, y)},$$

$$\frac{\partial y}{\partial v} = \frac{f_1(x, y)}{f_1(x, y)g_2(x, y) - f_2(x, y)g_1(x, y)}.$$

Since the first-order partial derivatives of f and g are continuous functions of (x, y), and the Jacobian in the denominator is nonzero, all these partial derivatives are continuous functions of (x, y). Since x and y are continuous functions of (u, v), these partial derivatives are continuous functions of (u, v).

PROBLEMS

1. For each of the following, determine the points at which the Jacobian is zero.

   (*a*) $T(x, y) = \left(\dfrac{x}{x+y}, \dfrac{y}{x+y} \right)$.

   (*b*) $T(x, y) = (x \cos y, x \sin y)$.

   (*c*) $T(x, y, z) = (xy, yz, zx)$.

   (*d*) $T(\rho, \theta, \phi) = (\rho \cos \theta \sin \phi, \rho \sin \theta \sin \phi, \rho \cos \phi)$.

2. For each of the following, determine the inverse of T valid near the indicated point, determine directly the Jacobian matrices of T and T^{-1} at this point, and check to see whether the product of these matrices is I.

   (*a*) $T(x, y) = (2x + 3y, 5x + 7y)$, $(0, 0)$.

   (*b*) $T(x, y) = \left(\dfrac{x+1}{x+y}, x+y \right)$, $(2, 1)$.

   (*c*) $T(x, y, z) = (xy, yz, zx)$, $(1, 1, 1)$.

   (*d*) $T(x, y) = [xy, \tfrac{1}{2}(x^2 - y^2)]$, $(2, 3)$.

3. Let $(x, y) = T^{-1}(u, v)$ be given implicitly by

$$u = \ln \tfrac{1}{3}(x+y)+x, \quad v = \ln (x-y)+y.$$

Use $T(2, 1) = (2, 1)$ and determine $T^{-1}(2.1, 1)$ to two-decimal-place accuracy.

4. Let u and v be given implicitly near $x = 1$, $u = 2$, $v = 3$, by

$$xu + \cos (x+u-v) = 3, \quad x^2u - u^3 + v^3 = 21.$$

Determine to two-decimal-place accuracy solutions for u and v when $x = 1.1$.

5. For each of the following, determine the value of u to two decimal places when the other variables have the indicated values.

    (a) $x+y+u = \sin (xyu)$ near $(0, 0, 0)$, $u(.1, .2) = $?

    (b) $xu + \ln (xu) = 1$ near $(1, 1)$, $u(\tfrac{1}{2}) = $?

    (c) $xyu + \ln (xu) = 1$ near $(1, 1, 1)$, $u(1, \tfrac{1}{2}) = $?

    (d) $x \cos (\pi xu) + uy = 0$ near $(2, \tfrac{1}{2}, -4)$, $u(\tfrac{7}{8}, \tfrac{1}{2}) = $?

6. Let z be given implicitly by $z^3 + 3z^2y - 7x^2y^2z + 9 = 0$ near $(1, -1, 1)$. Determine an approximate solution for z near $(x, y) = (1, -1)$.

7. Let $T(x, y) = [f(x, y), g(x, y)]$ and $T^{-1}(u, v) = [F(u, v), G(u, v)]$, where f, g, F, G have continuous first-order partial derivatives. Explain why $\partial(x, y)/\partial(u, v) \neq 0$ and

$$\frac{\partial(x, y)}{\partial(u, v)} \frac{\partial(u, v)}{\partial(x, y)} = 1.$$

8. Let R and S be transformations defined, respectively, by

$$\begin{cases} u = f(x, y, z), \\ v = g(x, y, z), \\ w = h(x, y, z), \end{cases} \text{and} \begin{cases} u = F(x, y, z), \\ v = G(x, y, z), \\ w = H(x, y, z), \end{cases}$$

where F, G, and H have continuous first-order partial derivatives in a neighborhood of (x_0, y_0, z_0), and f, g, and h have continuous first-order partial derivatives in a neighborhood of $S(x_0, y_0, z_0)$. Explain why the Jacobian matrix of RS exists and equals the product of the Jacobian matrices of R and S. [*Note:* This implies the Jacobian matrix of R^{-1} is the inverse of the Jacobian matrix of R.]

9. (a) Let r and s be differentiable functions of u, v, and w, which in turn are differentiable functions of x and y. Show that

$$\frac{\partial(r, s)}{\partial(x, y)} = \frac{1}{2}\left[\frac{\partial(r, s)}{\partial(u, v)}\frac{\partial(u, v)}{\partial(x, y)} + \frac{\partial(r, s)}{\partial(v, w)}\frac{\partial(v, w)}{\partial(x, y)} + \frac{\partial(r, s)}{\partial(w, u)}\frac{\partial(w, u)}{\partial(x, y)}\right].$$

    (b) Check this equality for the case $r = u = x$, $s = v = y$, $w = 0$.

10. Use Theorem 8-4.1 to prove that, if f has first-order partial derivatives continuous near (x_0, y_0), $f(x_0, y_0) = 0$, and $f_2(x_0, y_0) \neq 0$, then there is a function ϕ such that $y_0 = \phi(x_0)$ and, if x is near x_0, then $f[x, \phi(x)] = 0$ and

$$\phi'(x) = \frac{-f_1(x, y)}{f_2(x, y)} \quad \text{if} \quad y = \phi(x).$$

8-5. VOLUME AND LINEAR TRANSFORMATIONS

Before starting the basic discussion of this section, let us summarize some facts about linear algebra. If the student is not familiar with these facts, he can study them later in an algebra course.

A *linearly independent* set is a set $\{\mathbf{u}_1, \cdots, \mathbf{u}_k\}$ such that $\sum_1^k a_i \mathbf{u}_i = \mathbf{0}$ only if each a_i is zero. A *linearly dependent* set is a set that is not linearly independent. The *linear span* of $\mathbf{u}_1, \cdots, \mathbf{u}_k$ is the set of all vectors of type $\sum_1^k a_i \mathbf{u}_i$. A system of n linear equations in n unknowns,

$$\sum_{j=1}^{n} a_{ij} x_j = c_i,$$

can be solved by *Cramer's rule* if the determinant of the coefficients is not zero. If each c_i is zero, then there is a solution, other than the trivial one for which each x_j is zero, if and only if the determinant of the coefficients is zero. The student is urged to try proving the following statements, which can be done by using these facts about linear equations.

I. If a set $\{\mathbf{u}_1, \cdots, \mathbf{u}_k\}$ of k vectors in R^n is linearly independent, then $k \leq n$.

II. If a set of n vectors in R^n is linearly independent, then the linear span of these n vectors is R^n.

III. If a set of k vectors in R^n is linearly independent and the linear span of these k vectors is R^n, then $k = n$.

A third-order determinant with real-number elements is equal to the volume of the parallelepiped that has as coterminal edges the three arrows $\mathbf{u}$, $\mathbf{v}$, and $\mathbf{w}$ whose components form the three rows of the determinant [see Fig. 8-6], or it is the negative of this volume, according to whether the trihedral $\{\mathbf{u}, \mathbf{v}, \mathbf{w}\}$ is positively or negatively oriented [see Section 7-3]. If we describe points as the terminal points of arrows with initial points at the origin, then the (solid) parallelepiped determined by $\mathbf{u}$, $\mathbf{v}$, and $\mathbf{w}$ is the set of points $A\mathbf{u} + B\mathbf{v}$

$+C\mathbf{w}$ for which A, B, and C are numbers in the interval $[0, 1]$. The faces contain the points for which at least one of A, B, and C is either 0 or 1, and the edges contain the points for which at least two of A, B, and C are either 0 or 1. For R^n, it is immaterial whether we call $\mathbf{u} = (u_1, \cdots, u_n)$ a vector or a point. Usually we shall call it a vector when operations of addition or multiplication are being used. The following definitions are generalizations of concepts we have used in R^3.

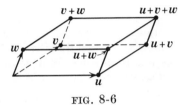

FIG. 8-6

DEFINITION 8-5.1. The *length* of a vector $(u_1, \cdots, u_n)$ is the number $(\sum_1^n u_i^2)^{1/2}$. The *scalar product* of vectors $(u_1, \cdots, u_n)$ and $(v_1, \cdots, v_n)$ is the number $\sum_1^n u_i v_i$. *Orthogonal vectors* are vectors whose scalar product is zero. The length of $\mathbf{u}$ is denoted by $|\mathbf{u}|$. The scalar product of $\mathbf{u}$ and $\mathbf{v}$ is denoted by $\mathbf{u} \cdot \mathbf{v}$. We write $\mathbf{u} \perp \mathbf{v}$ to indicate that $\mathbf{u}$ and $\mathbf{v}$ are orthogonal.

DEFINITION 8-5.2. An *n-dimensional parallelepiped* is a set P for which there are vectors $\mathbf{u}$ and $\mathbf{v}_1, \cdots, \mathbf{v}_n$ such that P is the set of all vectors

$$\mathbf{u} + \alpha_1 \mathbf{v}_1 + \alpha_2 \mathbf{v}_2 + \cdots + \alpha_n \mathbf{v}_n, \quad \text{with } 0 \leqq \alpha_i \leqq 1 \text{ for all } i. \quad (8\text{-}37)$$

Such a parallelepiped is *rectangular* if and only if $\mathbf{v}_i \perp \mathbf{v}_j$ if $i \neq j$.

For the parallelepiped defined by (8-37), the vectors $\mathbf{v}_1, \cdots, \mathbf{v}_n$ are *adjacent edges*. We can now use n-dimensional parallelepipeds and generalize Definitions 5-1.1 through 5-1.3 to obtain definitions of *n-D inner sums*, *n-D outer sums*, and *n-D volume* (or *hypervolume*). The basic properties of volume discussed in Section 5-1 can then be established for *n-D* volume. We shall omit the details, since they are analogous to the methods used with area and volume in Sections 3-2, 3-3, and 5-1. The next theorem is a natural generalization of Theorem 5-1.2. It can be proved in much the same way.

DEFINITION 8-5.3. A *line* in R^n is a set L for which there are vectors $\mathbf{u}$ and $\mathbf{v}$ with $\mathbf{v} \neq \mathbf{0}$ and

$$L = \{\mathbf{u} + t\mathbf{v} : t \text{ a real number}\}. \quad (8\text{-}38)$$

If $|\mathbf{v}| = 1$, then t is the distance from the point $\mathbf{u}$ to the point $\mathbf{u} + t\mathbf{v}$. For a particular number t, let R_t^{n-1} denote the set of all vectors which can be written as $(\mathbf{u} + t\mathbf{v}) + \mathbf{w}$ for some $\mathbf{w}$ orthogonal to $\mathbf{v}$. This set R_t^{n-1} can be translated so as to coincide with the set of all vectors orthogonal to $\mathbf{v}$. We merely subtract $\mathbf{u} + t\mathbf{v}$ from each member of R_t^{n-1}. Thus, we can consider R_t^{n-1} to be equivalent to R^{n-1} [see problems 15 and 16]. We shall call R_t^{n-1} the $(n-1)$-*dimensional space orthogonal to L at t*.

THEOREM 8-5.1. Suppose W is a set in R^n that has n-D volume. Also suppose L is a directed line and that the symbol t denotes distances of points along this line from some fixed point on the line. If the $(n-1)$-dimensional space orthogonal to L at t intersects W in a set that has $(n-1)$-D volume equal to $V(t)$, then

$$(\text{volume of } W) = \int_a^b V(t)\, dt,$$

where the numbers a and b are any two numbers for which W is between the $(n-1)$-dimensional space orthogonal to L at a and the $(n-1)$-dimensional space orthogonal to L at b.

The principal result of this section will be a formula for the volume of an n-dimensional parallelepiped [Theorem 8-5.3]. It follows from Theorem 8-5.1 that this volume is equal to the product of the altitude of the parallelepiped and the $(n-1)$-D volume of the corresponding $(n-1)$-dimensional base. This suggests that mathematical induction might be used. For this purpose, it is helpful to introduce the concept of an orthogonal transformation.

DEFINITION 8-5.4. An *orthogonal matrix* is a square matrix whose columns are mutually orthogonal vectors of unit length. An *orthogonal transformation* is a linear transformation whose matrix is an orthogonal matrix.

An orthogonal transformation is invertible. In fact, suppose A is an orthogonal transformation and A^T is the *transpose* of A; that is, A^T is the matrix obtained from A by interchanging each row and the corresponding column. Then it follows directly from the definition of an orthogonal matrix that $A^T A = I$. Therefore, $A A^T = I$ and the rows of A are mutually orthogonal vectors of unit length [see problem 15 of Section 8-3].

THEOREM 8-5.2.   Each of the following is a necessary and sufficient condition for a linear transformation T of R^n to be an orthogonal transformation:

    (i) $\mathbf{u} \cdot \mathbf{v} = T(\mathbf{u}) \cdot T(\mathbf{v})$ for all $\mathbf{u}$ and $\mathbf{v}$ in R^n;

    (ii) $|T(\mathbf{u})| = |\mathbf{u}|$ for all $\mathbf{u}$ in R^n.

PROOF.   Suppose first that T is an orthogonal transformation and A is its matrix. Multiplication of matrices is associative, since it corresponds to multiplication of transformations.† The following equalities can then be justified by imagining that the row vector has $n-1$ rows of zeros below it and the column vector has $n-1$ columns of zeros to its right. We use the notation $T(\mathbf{u}) = (u_1', \cdots, u_n')$ and $T(\mathbf{v}) = (v_1', \cdots, v_n')$:

$$\mathbf{u} \cdot \mathbf{v} = (u_1, \cdots, u_n)\begin{pmatrix} v_1 \\ \vdots \\ v_n \end{pmatrix} = (u_1, \cdots, u_n)(A^T A)\begin{pmatrix} v_1 \\ \vdots \\ v_n \end{pmatrix}$$

$$= [(u_1, \cdots, u_n)A^T] \cdot A \begin{pmatrix} v_1 \\ \vdots \\ v_n \end{pmatrix} = (u_1', \cdots, u_n')\begin{pmatrix} v_1' \\ \vdots \\ v_n' \end{pmatrix} = T(\mathbf{u}) \cdot T(\mathbf{v}).$$

Thus, $\mathbf{u} \cdot \mathbf{v} = T(\mathbf{u}) \cdot T(\mathbf{v})$. With $\mathbf{v}$ replaced by $\mathbf{u}$, we have $|\mathbf{u}| = |T(\mathbf{u})|$. Therefore, (i) implies (ii). Now suppose that $|\mathbf{u}| = |T(\mathbf{u})|$ for all vectors $\mathbf{u}$. Since the vectors $\mathbf{e}_i$ have unit length, the columns of the matrix A of T have unit length. Now let us consider $\mathbf{e}_p + \mathbf{e}_q$ with $p \neq q$. We have

$$\sqrt{2} = \left[\sum_{i=1}^{n} (a_{ip} + a_{iq})^2 \right]^{\frac{1}{2}}$$

$$= \left[\sum_{i=1}^{n} (a_{ip})^2 + \sum_{i=1}^{n} (a_{iq})^2 + 2 \sum_{i=1}^{n} a_{ip}a_{iq} \right]^{\frac{1}{2}}$$

$$= \left[2 + 2 \sum_{i=1}^{n} a_{ip} a_{iq} \right]^{\frac{1}{2}}.$$

This statement of equality is true if and only if $\sum_{i=1}^{n} a_{ip}a_{iq} = 0$—that is, if and only if columns p and q are orthogonal, Thus we have shown that if T preserves length, then the columns of A are mutually orthogonal vectors of unit length. That is, T is an orthogonal transformation.

It follows from this theorem that both length and orthogonality are preserved by orthogonal transformations. Thus, an orthogonal transformation maps a rectangular parallelepiped onto a rectangular

---

† Associativity of transformation multiplication follows from the fact that both $f(gh)$ and $(fg)h$ map x onto $f\{g[h(x)]\}$.

parallelepiped with adjacent edges of the same length. This implies that an orthogonal transformation maps any set with n-D volume onto a set with the same volume.

We know [see pp. 328 and 330] that the area of a parallelogram with adjacent edges $\mathbf{u}_1 = (u_{11}, u_{21})$ and $\mathbf{u}_2 = (u_{12}, u_{22})$ is the absolute value of the determinant

$$\begin{vmatrix} u_{11} & u_{12} \\ u_{21} & u_{22} \end{vmatrix}.$$

Also, the volume of a parallelepiped with adjacent edges,

$$\mathbf{u}_1 = (u_{11}, u_{21}, u_{31}), \quad \mathbf{u}_2 = (u_{12}, u_{22}, u_{32}), \quad \mathbf{u}_3 = (u_{13}, u_{23}, u_{33}),$$

is the absolute value of the determinant

$$\begin{vmatrix} u_{11} & u_{12} & u_{13} \\ u_{21} & u_{22} & u_{23} \\ u_{31} & u_{32} & u_{33} \end{vmatrix}.$$

THEOREM 8-5.3. The absolute value of the determinant whose columns are $\mathbf{u}_1, \cdots, \mathbf{u}_n$ is the volume of the n-dimensional parallelepiped with adjacent edges $\mathbf{u}_1, \cdots, \mathbf{u}_n$.

PROOF. This theorem is true trivially if $n = 1$. As just noted, it is true if $n = 2$ or $n = 3$. To complete the proof by mathematical induction, we need only prove the theorem is valid for $n = k$ if it is valid for $n = k-1$. Let A be the matrix with columns $\mathbf{u}_1, \cdots, \mathbf{u}_k$. If $|A| = 0$, then the vectors $\mathbf{u}_1, \cdots, \mathbf{u}_k$ are linearly dependent and their linear span is not R^k. Then the k-D volume of the parallelepiped with edges $\mathbf{u}_1, \cdots, \mathbf{u}_k$ is zero [see problem 12]. Now we assume that $|A| \neq 0$. Choose $\mathbf{v}_k$ of unit length and orthogonal to each of $\mathbf{u}_1, \cdots, \mathbf{u}_{k-1}$ [see problem 14]. Then choose any vectors $\mathbf{v}_1, \cdots, \mathbf{v}_{k-1}$ with unit lengths and such that $\mathbf{v}_i \perp \mathbf{v}_j$ if $i \neq j$. Then, with the $\mathbf{v}$'s as row vectors,

$$\begin{pmatrix} v_{11} & v_{12} & \cdots & v_{1k} \\ v_{21} & v_{22} & \cdots & v_{2k} \\ & & \cdot \cdot \cdot & \\ v_{k1} & v_{k2} & \cdots & v_{kk} \end{pmatrix} \begin{pmatrix} u_{11} & u_{12} & \cdots & u_{1k} \\ u_{21} & u_{22} & \cdots & u_{2k} \\ & & \cdot \cdot \cdot & \\ u_{k1} & u_{k2} & \cdots & u_{kk} \end{pmatrix}$$

$$= \begin{pmatrix} u'_{11} & u'_{12} & \cdots & u'_{1, k-1} & u'_{1k} \\ u'_{21} & u'_{22} & \cdots & u'_{2, k-1} & u'_{2k} \\ & & \cdot \cdot \cdot & & \\ 0 & 0 & & 0 & u'_{kk} \end{pmatrix}. \quad (8\text{-}39)$$

Let T be the orthogonal transformation whose matrix has the $\mathbf{v}$'s as rows. Then T maps the $(n-1)$-dimensional parallelepiped with edges $\mathbf{u}_1, \cdots, \mathbf{u}_{k-1}$ onto the parallelepiped with edges

$$\mathbf{u}_1' = (u_{11}', u_{21}', \cdots, u_{k-1,1}', 0), \cdots,$$

$$\mathbf{u}_{k-1}' = (u_{1,k-1}', u_{2,k-1}', \cdots, u_{k-1,k-1}', 0),$$

which by our induction assumption has volume equal to the absolute value of the determinant

$$\begin{vmatrix} u_{11}' & \cdots & u_{1,k-1}' \\ & \cdot \ \ \cdot \ \ \cdot & \\ u_{k-1,1}' & \cdots & u_{k-1,k-1}' \end{vmatrix}.$$

The absolute value of the determinant whose columns are $\mathbf{u}_1, \cdots, \mathbf{u}_k$ is equal to the absolute value of the determinant of the last member of (8-39) [see problem 11]. Thus, we need to show that, for the n-dimensional parallelepiped with edges $\mathbf{u}_1, \cdots, \mathbf{u}_k$, the number u_{kk}' is the altitude corresponding to the base with edges $\mathbf{u}_1, \cdots, \mathbf{u}_{k-1}$. To do this, let us write

$$\mathbf{u}_k = \sum a_i \mathbf{v}_i = a_k \mathbf{v}_k + \left(\sum_1^{k-1} a_i \mathbf{v}_i \right).$$

Since $\mathbf{v}_k$ is orthogonal to each of $\mathbf{v}_1, \cdots, \mathbf{v}_{k-1}$, and also to each of $\mathbf{u}_1, \cdots, \mathbf{u}_{k-1}$, it follows that the linear span of $\{\mathbf{v}_1, \cdots, \mathbf{v}_{k-1}\}$ is the linear span of $\{\mathbf{u}_1, \cdots, \mathbf{u}_{k-1}\}$ [see problem 15]. Also, a_k is the desired altitude and

$$a_k = \mathbf{v}_k \cdot \mathbf{u}_k = u_{kk}'.$$

THEOREM 8-5.4. Suppose T is a linear transformation of R^n with matrix A. If T maps an n-dimensional parallelepiped P onto a parallelepiped P^*, then

$$\text{(volume of } P^*) = |\det (A)|(\text{volume of } P). \tag{8-40}$$

PROOF. If P has the adjacent edges $\mathbf{u}_1, \cdots, \mathbf{u}_n$, then the volume of P is $|\det (B)|$, where B is the matrix whose columns are $\mathbf{u}_1, \cdots, \mathbf{u}_n$. Then adjacent edges of P^* are the columns of the matrix AB and the volume of P^* is the absolute value of $\det (AB)$. Since $\det (AB) = \det (A) \det (B)$, this gives us Eq. (8-40).

PROBLEMS

1. Show that, for any vectors $\mathbf{u}$, $\mathbf{v}$, and $\mathbf{w}$ in R^n and any number t,
   (a) $\mathbf{u} \cdot \mathbf{v} = \mathbf{v} \cdot \mathbf{u}$.   (b) $(t\mathbf{u}) \cdot \mathbf{v} = t(\mathbf{u} \cdot \mathbf{v})$.
   (c) $\mathbf{u} \cdot (\mathbf{v} + \mathbf{w}) = \mathbf{u} \cdot \mathbf{v} + \mathbf{u} \cdot \mathbf{w}$.

2. Prove *Schwarz's inequality* for R^n: $|\mathbf{u} \cdot \mathbf{v}| \leqq |\mathbf{u}|\,|\mathbf{v}|$.

3. Construct a 2×2 nonorthogonal matrix whose determinant is $+1$.

4. In each case, determine an orthogonal matrix A whose first column is a vector parallel to the given vector. Check by showing that $AA^T = A^T A = I$.   (*a*) $(3, 4)$.   (b) $(1, 1)$.   (c) $(3, 5)$.

5. For each of the following, determine an orthogonal matrix A whose first row is parallel to the first of the two given vectors and whose second row is parallel to the other given vector. Check by showing that $AA^T = A^T A = I$.   (a) $(5, 12, 0)$, $(12, -5, 0)$.   (b) $(2, 2, 1)$, $(1, 2, -6)$.

6. Explain why the product of two orthogonal matrices is an orthogonal matrix.

7. Explain why an orthogonal transformation of the plane is either a rotation or a rotation followed by a reflection. [*Hint:* Use the fact that a linear transformation of the plane is determined if the images of two perpendicular vectors are known.]

8. In each of the following, let R and S be the indicated rotations of three-dimensional real coordinate space. [Use a right-handed coordinate system and the convention that angles are measured counterclockwise as viewed from the positive side of planes perpendicular to the axis of rotation.] Determine the vector onto which $(1, 1, 1)$ is mapped by RS. [*Hint:* Determine the matrix RS.]

(*a*) R rotates $90°$ about the x-axis; S rotates $45°$ about the y-axis.

(*b*) R rotates $120°$ about the line $x = y = z$ and the positive side of a plane perpendicular to this line is the side that contains an unbounded piece of the first octant; S rotates $45°$ about the z-axes. [*Hint:* R takes the x-axis into the y-axis.]

9. (a) Let $A = (a_{ij})$ be a 3×3 orthogonal matrix whose determinant is $+1$. Determine an orthogonal matrix M_z that describes a rotation about the z-axis and for which $M_z A$ is a matrix $B = (b_{ij})$ with $b_{21} = 0$.

(b) Let B be the matrix of part (a). Explain why there is a choice of sign such that the matrix

$$M_y = \begin{pmatrix} b_{11} & 0 & b_{31} \\ 0 & 1 & 0 \\ \mp b_{31} & 0 & \pm b_{11} \end{pmatrix}$$

is the matrix of a rotation about the y-axis with the property that the matrix $M_y B = M_x$ describes a rotation about the x-axis.

(c) Use parts (a) and (b) to show that any orthogonal linear transformation whose determinant is $+1$ is equal to the product of three rotations about the coordinate axes.

10. Suppose the columns of a matrix A are the vectors $\mathbf{v}_1, \cdots, \mathbf{v}_n$. Explain why

$$|\det(A)| \leq |\mathbf{v}_1|\,|\mathbf{v}_2|\,|\mathbf{v}_3|\cdots|\mathbf{v}_n|$$

and the equality holds if and only if A is orthogonal. [*Note:* This is the special case for real matrices of what is called *Hadamard's inequality*.]

11. Explain why $|\det (A)| = 1$ if A is an orthogonal matrix.

12. Show that if the linear span of $\mathbf{u}_1, \cdots, \mathbf{u}_n$ is not R^n, then the parallelepiped with edges $\mathbf{u}_1, \cdots, \mathbf{u}_n$ has n-D volume equal to zero.

13. Suppose $\mathbf{u}_1, \cdots, \mathbf{u}_n$ are mutually orthogonal nonzero vectors in R^n. Use II and prove that the linear span of $\{\mathbf{u}_1, \cdots, \mathbf{u}_n\}$ is R^n.

14. Let U be the linear span of vectors $\mathbf{u}_1, \cdots, \mathbf{u}_k$ in R^n. Prove that, if R^n contains a vector $\mathbf{w}$ not in U, then there is a nonzero vector $\mathbf{v}$ in R^n with $\mathbf{v} \perp \mathbf{u}$ if $\mathbf{u} \in U$ and $\mathbf{v}$ not orthogonal to $\mathbf{w}$. [*Hint:* Show that $\mathbf{v}$ can be of type $\mathbf{w} + \sum_1^k a_i \mathbf{u}_i$.]

15. Let $\mathbf{u}$ be a nonzero vector in R^n and let U be the set of all vectors orthogonal to $\mathbf{u}$. Show that there are $n-1$ mutually orthogonal members $\mathbf{u}_1, \cdots, \mathbf{u}_{n-1}$ of U whose linear span is U and for which $|\mathbf{u}_i| = 1$ for each i. [*Hint:* Make repeated use of problem 14.]

16. Let U be the linear span of vectors $\mathbf{u}_1, \cdots, \mathbf{u}_k$ in R^n. Also suppose that $\mathbf{u}_i \perp \mathbf{u}_j$ if $i \neq j$ and that $|\mathbf{u}_i| = 1$ for each i. Define f by

$$f\left(\sum_1^k a_i \mathbf{u}_i\right) = \sum_1^k a_i \mathbf{e}_i,$$

where the a_i's are arbitrary real numbers and for each i the vector $\mathbf{e}_i$ is the member of R^k whose components are zeros except for the ith component which is $+1$. Show that, for each $\mathbf{x}$ and $\mathbf{y}$ in U,

$$\mathbf{x} \cdot \mathbf{y} = f(\mathbf{x}) \cdot f(\mathbf{y}) \quad \text{and} \quad |\mathbf{x}| = |f(\mathbf{x})|.$$

8-6. LAGRANGE MULTIPLIERS

We have seen that, if functions f and g with domains in R^3 are such that f has a relative maximum at P_0 for points (x, y, z) such that $g(x, y, z) = 0$, then there are sufficient conditions for the vectors ∇f and ∇g at P_0 to be parallel [see problem 14, page 362]. Now that more mathematical tools are available, we shall generalize this type of problem and clarify the conditions that suffice to justify use of the method. We shall first consider an example. Then we shall prove a general theorem that justifies the procedure used. This theorem makes use of the implicit function theorem and the theory of orthogonality in R^n.

ILLUSTRATION. Suppose we wish to find the points farthest from the origin, and the points closest to the origin, that are on both the ellipsoid and the plane whose equations are

$$x^2 + y^2 + 9z^2 = 25, \quad x + 3y - 2z = 0. \tag{8-41}$$

That is, we wish to find the extreme values of $x^2 + y^2 + z^2$, subject to conditions (8-41). We shall do this by introducing auxiliary variables λ_1 and λ_2, called *Lagrange multipliers*, and using the expression

$$(x^2 + y^2 + z^2) + \lambda_1(x^2 + y^2 + 9z^2 - 25) + \lambda_2(x + 3y - 2z).$$

The equations we shall need to solve are obtained by taking partial derivatives of this expression. They are

$$\begin{cases} 2x + \lambda_1(2x) + \lambda_2(1) = 0, \\ 2y + \lambda_1(2y) + \lambda_2(3) = 0, \\ 2z + \lambda_1(18z) + \lambda_2(-2) = 0. \end{cases} \tag{8-42}$$

Elimination of λ_1 and λ_2 gives $3xz - yz = 0$. This equation and the equation of the plane have the following common solutions for (x, y, z):

$$t(3, -1, 0) \quad \text{and} \quad t(1, 3, 5), \quad t \text{ arbitrary.} \tag{8-43}$$

Substitution in the equation of the ellipsoid yields $t = \pm \sqrt{5/2}$ and $t = \pm \sqrt{5/47}$. The four points we want are given by using these values of t in (8-43). The intersection of the ellipsoid and the plane is an ellipse. The points we have found are the ends of the axes of this ellipse.

The next theorem, when applied to this illustration, assures us that every extremal point is among the solutions obtained by using Eqs. (8-42). As for the auxiliary variables λ_1 and λ_2 used in this illustration, the symbols $\lambda_1, \cdots, \lambda_m$ in the statement of Theorem 8-6.1 are called *Lagrange multipliers*.

THEOREM 8-6.1. Suppose f and $g^1, g^2, \cdots, g^m$ are functions with domains in R^n and that $m < n$. Also suppose that all first-order partial derivatives of these functions are continuous in a neighborhood of a point $\mathbf{x}^0 = (x_1^0, \cdots, x_n^0)$, which is in the set

$$S = \{\mathbf{x}: g^i(\mathbf{x}) = 0 \text{ for } 1 \leqq i \leqq m\},$$

and that at this point the following Jacobian is nonzero:

$$\frac{\partial(g^1, g^2, \cdots, g^m)}{\partial(x_1, x_2, \cdots, x_m)}. \tag{8-44}$$

If f, when restricted to S, has a local extreme at $\mathbf{x}^0$, then there exists a set of m real numbers $\{\lambda_1, \lambda_2, \cdots, \lambda_m\}$ that satisfies the following n equations:

$$f_k(x_1^0, \cdots, x_n^0) + \sum_{i=1}^{m} \lambda_i g_k^i(x_1^0, \cdots, x_n^0) = 0, \quad k = 1, 2, \cdots, n. \tag{8-45}$$

PROOF. It follows from the Implicit Function Theorem that there is a set of functions $\{\phi^1, \cdots, \phi^m\}$ whose domains are in R^{n-m}, whose first-order partial derivatives are continuous in a neighborhood of $(x_{m+1}^0, \cdots, x_n^0)$, for which

$$\phi^i(x_{m+1}^0, \cdots, x_m^0) = x_i^0 \text{ for } i = 1, 2, \cdots, m,$$

and for which there is a neighborhood of $(x_{m+1}^0, \cdots, x_n^0)$ in which

$$g^i[\phi^1(x_{m+1}, \cdots, x_n), \cdots, \phi^m(x_{m+1}, \cdots, x_n), \quad x_{m+1}, \cdots, x_n] = 0$$

$$\text{for } 1 \leqq i \leqq m. \tag{8-46}$$

Now suppose $\mathbf{v} = (v_1, \cdots, v_n)$ is a vector with the property that

$$\sum_{k=1}^{n} [g_k^i(x_1^0, \cdots, x_n^0)]v_k = 0 \text{ for } i = 1, 2, \cdots, m. \tag{8-47}$$

For numbers s sufficiently small, let $\mathbf{v}(s)$ be the point defined by

$$\mathbf{v}(s) = [\phi^1(x_{m+1}^0 + v_{m+1}s, \cdots, x_n^0 + v_n s), \cdots,$$

$$\phi^m(x_{m+1}^0 + v_{m+1}s, \cdots, x_n^0 + v_n s), x_{m+1}^0 + v_{m+1}s, \cdots, x_n^0 + v_n s].$$

Because of (8-46), we know that, if each g_i is made a function of s by substituting $\mathbf{v}(s)$, then g_i is identically zero. Therefore,

$$\sum_{k=1}^{n} [g_k^i(x_1^0, \cdots, x_n^0)]\left[\frac{d\phi^k}{ds}\right]_{s=0} + \sum_{k=m+1}^{n} [g_k^i(x^0, \cdots, x_n^0)]v_k = 0$$

$$\text{for } i = 1, 2, \cdots, m. \quad (8\text{-}48)$$

Since the Jacobian (8-44) is nonzero at $(x_1^0, \cdots, x_n^0)$, it follows from Cramer's rule and (8-47) and (8-48) that

$$\left[\frac{d\phi^k}{ds}\right]_{s=0} = v_k \text{ for } k = 1, 2, \cdots, m.$$

Now for $f[\mathbf{v}(s)]$, we have

$$\left[\frac{df}{ds}\right]_{s=0} = \sum_{k=1}^{m}\left[f_k\frac{d\phi^k}{ds}\right]_{s=0} + \sum_{k=m+1}^{n} [f_k]_{s=0}v_k = \sum_{k=1}^{n} [f_k]_{s=0}v_k.$$

Since f has a relative extreme at $(x_1^0, \cdots, x_n^0)$, we must have $[df/ds]_{s=0}$ $=0$. Thus, we have proved that any vector $\mathbf{v}$ that is orthogonal to each of the vectors

$$\boldsymbol{\nabla}g^i = [g_1^i(x_1^0, \cdots, x_n^0), \cdots, g_n^i(x_1^0, \cdots, x_n^0)], \quad i = 1, 2, \cdots, m,$$

also is orthogonal to the vector

$$\boldsymbol{\nabla}f = [f_1(x_1^0, \cdots, x_n^0), \cdots, f_n(x_1^0, \cdots, x_n^0)].$$

This implies that $\boldsymbol{\nabla}f$ is in the linear span of the vectors $\boldsymbol{\nabla}g^i$, which is equivalent to the existence of numbers $\lambda_1, \cdots, \lambda_m$ that satisfy (8-45).

PROBLEMS

1. Find the shortest distance from the origin to the hyperbola whose equation in the (x, y)-plane is $x^2 + 8xy + 7y^2 = 9$.

2. Determine the dimensions of the largest rectangular parallelepiped that has three faces in the coordinate planes and one vertex on the first octant part of the graph of

$$(x+1)(y+3)(z+2) = 48.$$

3. Determine the largest value of z among the points (x, y, z) that satisfy $2x + 6y = 14$ and $x^2 + z^2 = 2y$.

4. Find the largest distance from the origin to a point in the intersection of the graphs of $25x^2 + 20y^2 + 4z^2 = 100$ and $z = x + y$.

5. Find the maximum value of $x^2 + 4y^2 + 2x$ for $x^2 + y^2 \leq 1$.

6. Find all extreme values of xyz subject to the condition that x, y, and z are positive and

$$\frac{1}{x} + \frac{1}{y} + \frac{1}{z} = 3.$$

Determine whether this is a minimum, a maximum, or neither.

7. Determine the minimum distance between the graphs of $x^2 + y^2 = 1$ and $x^2 y = 2$ in the (x, y)-plane.

8. Determine the maximum value of $x^2 + y^2 + z^2 + w^2$, subject to the conditions $2x + 3y = 6$, $4y - z = 1$, and $y + z + w = 15$.

8-7.   CHANGE OF VARIABLES IN MULTIPLE INTEGRALS

In Sections 8-1 and 8-2 we discussed the formula

$$\int_a^b f(x)\, dx = \int_\alpha^\beta f[u(t)]u'(t)\, dt$$

for change of variables in a single integral, and the formula

$$\int_S f(x, y)\, dA = \int_R f(r\cos\theta, r\sin\theta) r\, dA$$

for the change from rectangular to polar coordinates.   We then spoke of "local magnification factors" of $u'(t)$ for the first formula and r for the second formula.

We now wish to obtain a formula for the "magnification factor" to be used with a general transformation of R^n.   We shall discuss this for linear transformations first, since the situation is then relatively simple.   Also, since rather general transformations can be approximated by linear transformations, we can use the theory developed for linear transformations to study nonlinear transformations.   We have seen that a linear transformation of R^n maps an n-dimensional parallelepiped onto a parallelepiped whose n-D volume is changed by a magnification factor equal to the absolute value of the determinant of the matrix of the transformation [see Theorem 8-5.4].   For example, suppose we let T be a linear transformation that maps the (u, v)-plane of Fig. 8-7 onto the entire (x, y)-plane; i.e., the determinant of the matrix of T is nonzero. Let us denote this determinant by det (T). If s_* and s^* are inner and outer sums for a set R in the (u, v)-plane, then the rectangles used in these inner and outer sums are mapped onto parallelograms in the (x, y)-plane. Moreover, the sum of the areas of those parallelograms that correspond to rectangles used in s_* is equal to $|\det (T)| s_*$, and the sum of the areas of parallelograms that correspond to rectangles used in s^* is equal to $|\det (T)| s^*$. It follows from this that S has area if and only if R has area and that the area of S is equal to $|\det (T)|$ times the area of R. Now suppose that f is continuous on S and that S is compact and has area. Then f is integrable on S and $f[T(q)]|\det (T)|$ is integrable on R. We have

$$\int_S f(p)\, dA = \lim_{\delta \to 0} \sum_{i=1}^{n} f(p_i) \cdot \text{area } (\Delta_i S). \tag{8-49}$$

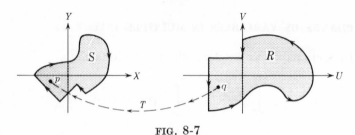

FIG. 8-7

Here we use the conventions of Section 5-2: S is the union of sets $\Delta_1 S, \cdots, \Delta_n S$ which have area and are such that the area of $\Delta_i S \cap \Delta_j S$ is zero if $i \neq j$; the point p_i is in $\Delta_i S$ for all i; and the number δ is the least upper bound of distances between two points that are both in the same one of the sets $\Delta_1 S, \cdots, \Delta_n S$. The transformation T^{-1} maps the sets $\Delta_1 S, \cdots, \Delta_n S$ onto sets $\Delta_1 R, \cdots, \Delta_n R$ of the (u, v)-plane and we have

$$\text{area } (\Delta_i S) = |\det (T)| \cdot \text{area } (\Delta_i R).$$

Also, T^{-1} maps p_i into a point q_i such that $p_i = T(q_i)$. Therefore, we can write for the right member of Eq. (8-49) the expression

$$\lim_{\delta \to 0} \sum_{i=1}^{n} f[T(q_i)]|\det (T)|\,\text{area } (\Delta_i R) = \int_R f[T(q)]|\det (T)|\, dA.$$

Thus, we see that

$$\int_S f(p)\, dA = \int_R f[T(q)]|\det (T)|\, dA. \tag{8-50}$$

ILLUSTRATION 1.   Suppose T is the linear transformation defined by the equations

$$\begin{cases} x = u+v, \\ y = 2u-v. \end{cases}$$

It can be shown that this linear transformation maps the region R of Fig. 8-8 onto the region S. Suppose we wish to evaluate $\int_S (3x-y)\, dA$. We note that $\det(T) = -3$ and that $3x-y = u+4v$. Therefore, Eq. (8-50) becomes

$$\int_S (3x-y)\, dA = \int_R (u+4v)\cdot 3\, dA.$$

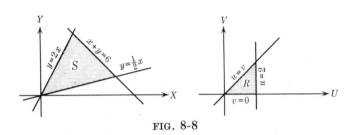

FIG. 8-8

The integral over R can be evaluated as the following iterated integral:

$$\int_0^2 \int_0^u (3u+12v)\, dv\, du = \int_0^2 (9u^2)\, du = 24.$$

Although we established formula (8-50) for two-dimensional spaces, it should be clear that a similar derivation can be given for R^n. It is not nearly as clear whether a formula similar to (8-50) can be given if T is not a linear transformation. However, in our study of the inverse transformation theorem of Section 8-4, we saw that near a point p a transformation T can be approximated by the linear transformation whose matrix is the Jacobian matrix of T evaluated at p. This suggests that we might substitute the Jacobian of T for $\det (T)$ in Eq. (8-50). Before discussing this in more detail, let us consider an application.

ILLUSTRATION 2.   Suppose we wish to evaluate

$$\int_S \frac{x}{4x^2+y^2}\, dA,$$

where S is the region in the first quadrant bounded by the coordinate axes, the ellipse whose equation is $4x^2+y^2 = 16$, and the ellipse whose equation is $4x^2 + y^2 = 1$. With the hope of simplifying the integrand, let us make the substitution

$$\begin{cases} x = u \cos v, \\ y = 2u \sin v. \end{cases}$$

The student can check to see that as a point p traces out the boundary of S [see Fig. 8-9], the transformation T^{-1} maps p onto a point that traces out the boundary of the region R. The Jacobian of T is

$$\begin{vmatrix} \cos v & -u \sin v \\ 2 \sin v & 2u \cos v \end{vmatrix} = 2u,$$

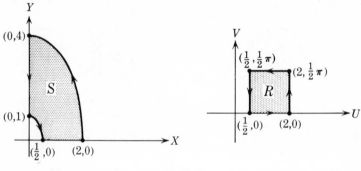

FIG. 8-9

so that we have

$$\int_S \frac{x}{4x^2 + y^2} \, dA = \int_R \frac{x}{4x^2 + y^2} \, |2u| \, dA.$$

After substituting for x and y, this becomes

$$\int_R \frac{u \cos v}{4u^2} \, (2u) \, dA = \tfrac{1}{2} \int_R \cos v \, dA = \tfrac{1}{2} \int_{1/2}^2 \int_0^{\pi/2} \cos v \, dv \, du = \tfrac{3}{4}.$$

In Section 8-4, we proved the inverse transformation and implicit function theorems only for special cases. It should have been clear that a general proof for R^n would have been similar and would use neighborhoods and open sets defined by using distance as given by

$$d(\mathbf{u}, \mathbf{v}) = |\mathbf{u} - \mathbf{v}|.$$

In fact, R^n then is a metric space. To show this, we need to show that properties (a) through (c) of Definition 2-1.1 are satisfied. In vector notation, these properties are:

(a) $|\mathbf{u} - \mathbf{v}| = 0$ if and only if $\mathbf{u} = \mathbf{v}$;

(b) $|\mathbf{u} - \mathbf{v}| = |\mathbf{v} - \mathbf{u}|$ for all $\mathbf{u}$ and $\mathbf{v}$;

(c) $|\mathbf{u} - \mathbf{w}| \leq |\mathbf{u} - \mathbf{v}| + |\mathbf{v} - \mathbf{w}|$ for all $\mathbf{u}$, $\mathbf{v}$, and $\mathbf{w}$.

Clearly (a) and (b) are valid. If we let $\mathbf{u} - \mathbf{v} = \mathbf{x}$ and $\mathbf{v} - \mathbf{w} = \mathbf{y}$, then (c) becomes

$$|\mathbf{x} + \mathbf{y}| \leq |\mathbf{x}| + |\mathbf{y}| \quad \text{for all } \mathbf{x} \text{ and } \mathbf{y}.$$

This can be proved by the same nongeometric method used to prove (7-4) in Section 7-1.

The proof of Theorem 2-3.2 given for R^2 can be generalized in a natural way to give the following theorem.

THEOREM 8-7.1 (HEINE-BOREL). A subset T of R^n is compact if it is bounded and closed in R^n.

Now suppose that T is a transformation whose domain and range are contained in R^n. As in Section 8-4, we note that T defines n *component functions* $f^1, \cdots, f^n$ for which

$$y_i = f^i(x_1, \cdots, x_n) \quad \text{if} \quad T(x_1, \cdots, x_n) = (y_1, \cdots, y_n).$$

We shall use superscripts to distinguish component functions and subscripts to indicate partial derivatives. Also, we shall assume that all first-order partial derivatives of component functions are continuous on a compact set R. Then it follows from Theorem 2-3.3 that each such partial derivative is uniformly continuous on R. Thus, for an arbitrary positive number ε, there is a positive number δ such that, for all i and j through n,

$$|\Delta f^i_j| = |f^i_j(x_1 + r_1, \cdots, x_n + r_n) - f^i_j(x_1, \cdots, x_n)|$$
$$< \frac{\varepsilon}{n^{3/2}} \quad \text{if} \quad |\mathbf{r}| < \delta \tag{8-51}$$

and $\mathbf{x} = (x_1, \cdots, x_n)$ and $\mathbf{x} + \mathbf{r} = (x_1 + r_1, \cdots, x_n + r_n)$ are points in R.

Now we make the additional hypothesis that R is contained in an open set U that is contained in all of the domains of first-order partial derivatives of component functions. By using the same method that led to Eq. (6-6), it follows from (8-51) that, if

$$\Delta f^i = f^i(x_1 + r_1, \cdots, x_n + r_n) - f^i(x_1, \cdots, x_n)$$

and

$$df^i = \sum_{j=1}^{n} f_j^i(x_1, \cdots, x_n) r_j,$$

then

$$|\Delta f^i - df^i| \leqq \frac{\varepsilon}{n^{3/2}} \sum |r_j| \quad \text{if} \quad |\mathbf{r}| < \delta.$$

If $|r_k|$ is the largest of $|r_1|, \cdots, |r_n|$, then

$$\sum |r_j| \leqq n|r_k| \leqq n|\mathbf{r}|.$$

Therefore, for $1 \leqq i \leqq n$,

$$|\Delta f^i - df^i| \leqq \frac{\varepsilon}{n^{1/2}} |\mathbf{r}| \quad \text{if} \quad |\mathbf{r}| < \delta. \tag{8-52}$$

The Jacobian matrix of T at x is the matrix $J_x(T)$ for which the element in the ith row and jth column is $f_j^i(x_1, \cdots, x_n)$. It follows from Ineq. (8-52) that each component of $[T(\mathbf{x}+\mathbf{r}) - T(\mathbf{x})] - J_x(T)\mathbf{r}_c$ has absolute value not greater than $\varepsilon|\mathbf{r}|/n^{1/2}$, so that

$$\left| [T(\mathbf{x}+\mathbf{r}) - T(\mathbf{x})] - J_x(T) \begin{pmatrix} r_1 \\ \vdots \\ r_n \end{pmatrix} \right| \leqq \varepsilon|\mathbf{r}| \quad \text{if} \quad |\mathbf{r}| < \delta. \tag{8-53}$$

Critical use will be made of this inequality in the proofs of both of the next two theorems.

THEOREM 8-7.2. Suppose T is a one-to-one transformation whose domain and range are in R^n and that there is an open set U on which the component functions of T have continuous first-order partial derivatives and the Jacobian of T is nonzero. If a compact subset S of U has n-D volume and is mapped by T onto a set R, then R has n-D volume.

PROOF. Since T is continuous on U, the inverse image of an open set is an open set [see Theorem 2-2.2]. This implies that if $\mathbf{x}$ belongs to the boundary of S, then $T(\mathbf{x})$ belongs to the boundary of R. It follows from the inverse transformation theorem of Section 8-4 that T maps open sets onto open sets. Thus, if $T(\mathbf{x})$ belongs to the boundary of R, then $\mathbf{x}$ belongs to the boundary of S. Therefore, T maps the boundary of S onto the boundary of R. Moreover, R is compact and therefore bounded [see Theorem 2-8.1 and problem 12]. We shall show that R has n-D volume by showing that the boundary of R has n-D volume zero [see problem 13]. Choose a positive number δ for which (8-53) is true with $\varepsilon = 1$. Since S is compact and first-order partial derivatives of component functions are continuous on S, they are bounded on S [see Theorem 2-8.2]. If the absolute value of each of these partial derivatives is less than ϕ on S and if $|r_i| < \delta$ for all i, then

$$\left| J_{\mathbf{x}}(T)\begin{pmatrix} r_1 \\ \vdots \\ r_n \end{pmatrix} \right| = \left[\sum_{i=1}^{n} (f_1^i r_1 + \cdots + f_n^i r_n)^2 \right]^{\frac{1}{2}} < [n(n\phi\delta)^2]^{\frac{1}{2}} = n^{\frac{3}{2}}\phi\delta. \tag{8-54}$$

It follows from (8-54), and (8-53) with $\varepsilon = 1$, that there is a number M such that

$$|T(\mathbf{x}+\mathbf{r}) - T(\mathbf{x})| \leq M|\mathbf{r}|, \tag{8-55}$$

if $\mathbf{x}$ and $\mathbf{x}+\mathbf{r}$ are in S and $|\mathbf{r}| < \delta$.

Now let η be an arbitrary positive number and choose a system of n-dimensional cubes with diameters less than δ and small enough that

$$s^* - s_* < \frac{\eta}{(2M)^n n^{\frac{1}{2}n}}$$

if s_* and s^* are the inner and outer sums for S determined by this system of cubes. Let d be the diameter and C be a particular cube. If $\mathbf{x}$ and $\mathbf{y}$ are in $C \cap S$, then from (8-55) we have $|T(\mathbf{y}) - T(\mathbf{x})| \leq Md$, so that $T(\mathbf{y})$ is in the cube with center $T(\mathbf{x})$ and edge of length $2Md$. The volume of C is $n^{-\frac{1}{2}n}d^n$. All points of $C \cap S$ map onto points of a cube with volume $(2M)^n d^n$. The boundary of S is contained in a union of cubes with n-D volume equal to $s^* - s_*$. Therefore, the boundary of R is contained in a union of cubes with n-D volume

$$(s^* - s_*)(2M)^n n^{\frac{1}{2}n} < \eta.$$

Since η was an arbitrary positive number, this implies that the boundary of R has n-D volume zero.

The definition of an integral over a subset S of R^n is formally very similar to the definitions of double and triple integrals. Therefore, we shall refer the student to Definition 5-4.1 rather than formally define general multiple integrals. The proof of the generalization of

Theorem 5-2.4 involves considerable detail, but it is not significantly different from the proof of Theorem 5-2.4. We shall omit the proof but use the fact that if the domain of f is a compact subset S of R^n with n-D volume and f is bounded, then f is integrable on S if and only if the set of discontinuities of f is of n-D measure zero. In particular, f is integrable if f is continuous on S.

> **THEOREM 8-7.3.** Suppose T is a one-to-one transformation whose domain and range are in R^n and that there is an open set U on which the component functions of T have continuous first-order partial derivatives and the Jacobian of T is nonzero. Let R be a subset of U that is mapped onto a compact set S that has n-D volume. If f is continuous on S, then
>
> $$\int_S f(p)\, dV = \int_R f[T(q)]\,|J(T)|\, dV. \qquad (8\text{-}56)$$

PROOF. It follows from the inverse transformation theorem that T^{-1} satisfies all of the hypotheses stated for T. Then it follows from Theorem 2-8.1 that R is compact, and it follows from Theorem 8-7.2 that R has n-D volume. We shall show next that, if ΔR is a compact subset of R with n-D volume and ΔR is mapped by T onto the subset ΔS of S, then

$$m(\text{volume of } \Delta R) \leqq (\text{volume of } \Delta S) \leqq M(\text{volume of } \Delta R), \quad (8\text{-}57)$$

if m and M are lower and upper bounds for $|\det[J(T)]|$ on ΔR. Each element of the matrix $J(T^{-1})$ is continuous and therefore bounded on S. Therefore, if $\mathbf{x}$ is a particular point of R and L is defined on S by

$$L(\mathbf{y}) = \mathbf{x} + J_{\mathbf{x}}^{-1}(T)\begin{pmatrix} s_1 \\ \vdots \\ s_n \end{pmatrix}, \quad \text{where } \mathbf{s} = \mathbf{y} - T(\mathbf{x}), \qquad (8\text{-}58)$$

then there is a number μ such that, for all $\mathbf{x}$ in R and all $\mathbf{y}$ in S,

$$|L(\mathbf{y}) - \mathbf{x}| \leqq \mu |\mathbf{y} - T(\mathbf{x})|. \qquad (8\text{-}59)$$

Now let ε be an arbitrary positive number and δ be a positive number for which (8-53) is true for $\mathbf{x}$ and $\mathbf{x} + \mathbf{r}$ in R. Since ΔS has n-D volume, there is a system of cubes that satisfies both of the following conditions:

(i) (volume of $\Delta S) \leqq (1 + \varepsilon)s_*$, where s_* is the inner sum for S determined by this system of cubes.

(ii) The diameter of each cube is less than $2\delta/\mu$.

Let $T(\mathbf{x})$ be the center of a cube C used in s_* and let P be the parallelepiped onto which C is mapped by L of (8-58). It follows from (8-53) that, if $\mathbf{y} \in C$ and $\mathbf{s} = \mathbf{y} - T(\mathbf{x})$, then

$$|\{T[L(\mathbf{y})] - T(\mathbf{x})\} - [\mathbf{y} - T(\mathbf{x})]| \leq \varepsilon|L(\mathbf{y}) - \mathbf{x}| \quad \text{if} \quad |L(\mathbf{y}) - \mathbf{x}| < \delta.$$

Because of (8-59) and (ii), we have $|L(\mathbf{y}) - \mathbf{x}| \leq \mu|\mathbf{y} - T(\mathbf{x})| < \delta$. Therefore,

$$|T[L(\mathbf{y})] - \mathbf{y}| \leq \varepsilon|L(\mathbf{y}) - \mathbf{x}| \leq \varepsilon\mu|\mathbf{y} - T(\mathbf{x})| \leq \tfrac{1}{2}\varepsilon\mu\sqrt{n}\,\sigma,$$

where σ is the length of an edge of C. This implies that, if C' is the cube obtained from C by shrinking distances from the center by the factor $1 - \varepsilon\mu\sqrt{n}$, then L maps C' onto a parallelepiped P' that is mapped by T into C. We have

$$\text{(volume of } C) = (1 - \varepsilon\mu\sqrt{n})^{-n}(\text{volume of } C')$$

$$= (1 - \varepsilon\mu\sqrt{n})^{-n}|\det[J_{\mathbf{x}}(T)]|(\text{volume of } P')$$

$$\leq (1 - \varepsilon\mu\sqrt{n})^{-n}M(\text{volume of } P').$$

Summing over all cubes used in s_*, we obtain

$$\text{(volume of } \Delta S) \leq (1+\varepsilon)s_* \leq (1+\varepsilon)(1 - \varepsilon\mu\sqrt{n})^{-n}M(\text{volume of } \Delta R).$$

Since ε was an arbitrary positive number, this implies that

$$\text{(volume of } \Delta S) \leq M \cdot (\text{volume of } \Delta R). \tag{8-60}$$

Since $1/m$ is an upper bound for $|\det[J^{-1}(T)]|$ and T and T^{-1} satisfy the same hypotheses, (8-60) implies that

$$m(\text{volume of } \Delta R) \leq (\text{volume of } \Delta S).$$

This completes the proof of (8-57). Since both integrands in (8-56) are continuous and R and S are compact sets with n-D volume, both integrals exist. Let $\sum f(p_i)(\text{area of } \Delta_i S)$ and $\sum f[T(q_i)]|J(T)|(\text{area of } \Delta_i R)$ be Riemann sums for these integrals, where T maps $\Delta_i R$ onto $\Delta_i S$ and $T(q_i) = p_i$. Since the area of $\Delta_i S$ is between $m_i(\text{area of } \Delta_i R)$ and $M_i(\text{area of } \Delta_i R)$ if m_i and M_i are greatest lower and least upper bounds for $|J(T)|$ on R, the absolute value of the difference between these Riemann sums is not greater than

$$\sum |f(p_i)|(M_i - m_i)(\text{area of } \Delta_i R)$$
$$\leq (\text{area of } R)[\sup\{M_i - m_i\}][\sup\{|f(p)| : p \in S\}].$$

Since sup $\{M_i - m_i\}$ approaches zero as the fineness of the partitions used approaches zero, Eq. (8-56) is proved.

COROLLARY. If, in addition to the hypotheses of Theorem 8-7.3, R has n-D volume, then formula (8-56) is still valid if the Jacobian is zero on a subset of R with zero n-D measure.

PROOF. Continuity of $J(T)$ implies $\{z: J_z(T) = 0\}$ is closed in R and therefore compact. Using the Heine-Borel theorem, for each positive number η, let R_η be the union of the interiors of cubes and have the following properties:

(a) R_η contains all points at which the Jacobian of T is zero.

(b) R_η has n-D volume less than η and R_η maps onto a set that is contained in a union of cubes with n-D volume less than η [establish and use (8-55) as in the proof of Theorem 8-7.2].

It follows from Theorem 8-7.2 that $R - R_\eta$ maps onto a set that has n-D volume. Then we can apply Theorem 8-7.3 to $R - R_\eta$ and let η approach zero.

PROBLEMS

1. For each of the following, determine the "local magnification factor" of area.

   (**a**) $x = u+3$, $y = v+7$.   (**c**) $x = u(1-v)$, $y = uv$.

   (**b**) $x = 2u$, $y = 3v$.   (d) $x = u^2$, $y = v^2$.

2. For each of the following, determine the "local magnification factor" of volume.

   (**a**) $x = 3u$, $y = v+5$, $z = 2w$.   (**b**) $x = u - uv$, $y = uv$, $z = uvw$.

3. Suppose a linear transformation T is defined by $x = u+v$, $y = u-v$.

   (a) Describe the region in the (u, v)-plane that corresponds to the triangle in the (x, y)-plane with vertices at $(0, 0)$, $(2, 2)$, $(-1, 1)$.

   (**b**) Use the transformation T to evaluate

$$\int_{-1}^{0} \int_{-x}^{\frac{1}{3}(x+4)} dy\, dx + \int_{0}^{2} \int_{x}^{\frac{1}{3}(x+4)} dy\, dx.$$

4. Let S be the parallelogram with vertices at $(0, 0)$, $(2, 1)$, $(5, 0)$, $(3, -1)$. Express $\int_S (x+y)\, dA$ in the form $\iint (\quad)\, du\, dv$ and evaluate, where $x = 2u + 3v$ and $y = u - v$.

5. Let S be the parallelogram in the (x, y)-plane whose vertices are at $(0, 0)$, $(1, 3)$, $(2, 5)$, $(3, 8)$. Determine a linear transformation that maps the unit square in the first quadrant with one vertex at the origin onto S and use this linear transformation to evaluate $\int_S x\, dA$.

6. Let S be the parallelepiped whose vertices are $(0, 0, 0)$, $(1, 0, 1)$, $(2, 3, 4)$, $(3, 3, 5)$, $(2, 0, 1)$, $(3, 0, 2)$, $(4, 3, 5)$, $(5, 3, 6)$. Determine a linear transformation that maps the unit cube in the first octant with one vertex at the origin onto S and use this linear transformation to make a change of variables and evaluate $\int_S y^2 \, dV$.

7. Evaluate $\int_S e^{-(x^2 + y^2)} \, dA$, where S is the region bounded by the graph of $x^2 + y^2 = a^2$. Use the substitution $x = u \cos v$, $y = u \sin v$.

8. Evaluate $\int_S e^{-(x^2 + 4y^2)} \, dA$, where S is the region bounded by the graph of $x^2 + 4y^2 = a^2$. Use the substitution $x = 2u \cos v$, $y = u \sin v$.

9. Express

$$\int_{-1}^{0} \int_{-x}^{x+2} \frac{1}{\sqrt{y - x}} \, dy \, dx$$

in the form $\int \int (\quad) \, du \, dv$ and evaluate the latter, where $x = u - v^2$ and $y = u + v^2$.

10. Let a transformation T be defined by $x = u^2 - v^2$, $y = 2uv$. (a) Sketch a few of the curves in the (u, v)-plane that correspond to lines parallel to the coordinate axes in the (x, y)-plane. (b) Sketch a few of the curves in the (x, y)-plane that correspond to lines parallel to the coordinate axes in the (u, v)-plane. (c) Use the transformation T to evaluate the following double integral:

$$\int_{0}^{2} \int_{\frac{1}{4}y^2 - 1}^{1 - \frac{1}{4}y^2} (x^2 + y^2)^{-\frac{1}{2}} \, dx \, dy.$$

11. Make the change of variables $u = x^3 - 3xy^2$, $v = 3x^2y - y^3$ and evaluate $\int_S (x^2 + y^2)^2 (x^3 - 3xy^2) \, dA$, where S is the region bounded by the first-quadrant pieces of the graphs of $\sqrt{3}y = x$, $y = \sqrt{3}x$, and $x^2 + y^2 = 1$. [*Note:* $u^2 + v^2 = (x^2 + y^2)^3$.]

12. Prove that a compact subset of R^n is closed and bounded.

13. Prove that a bounded subset S of R^n has n-D volume if and only if the boundary of S has n-D volume zero. [Compare to problem 5, page 126, and problem 11, page 133.]

14. Suppose T is a transformation whose domain and range are in R^n and that there is an open set U on which the component functions of T have continuous first-order partial derivatives. Also suppose that R is a compact subset of U and that W is a subset of R with n-D volume zero. Show that T maps W onto a set that has n-D volume zero. [*Hint:* Show that for a suitable number M, (8-55) is valid for $\mathbf{x}$ and $\mathbf{x} + \mathbf{r}$ in R.]

15. With the notation and hypotheses of Theorem 8-7.3, explain why the n-D volume of S is equal to $\int_R |J(T)| \, dV$.

8-8. CYLINDRICAL AND SPHERICAL COORDINATES

Cylindrical coordinates in R^3 consist of polar coordinates (r, θ) used instead of (x, y) to locate the projection of a point into the (x, y)-plane, coupled with the z-coordinate. The change from cylindrical to rectangular coordinates is the linear transformation T_c defined by

$$x = r \cos \theta, \quad y = r \sin \theta, \quad z = z.$$

As was done in Section 8-2 for polar coordinates, we must make restrictions on the values of r and θ in order to assure that T be one-to-one; e.g., $r \geqq 0$ and $0 \leqq \theta < 2\pi$. The Jacobian of this transformation is

$$\frac{\partial(x, y, z)}{\partial(r, \theta, z)} = \begin{vmatrix} \cos \theta & -r \sin \theta & 0 \\ \sin \theta & r \cos \theta & 0 \\ 0 & 0 & 1 \end{vmatrix} = r.$$

Thus, if R is a set in R^3 with coordinates denoted by r, θ, and z, and S is the corresponding set with coordinates denoted by x, y, and z, then we have

$$\int_S f(p) \, dV = \int_R f[T(q)]|r| \, dV, \tag{8-61}$$

provided f is continuous on S and S is compact and has volume. The coordinate surfaces for cylindrical coordinates are as indicated in Fig. 8-10(a). The surface $r = c_1$ is a circular cylinder whose axis is on the

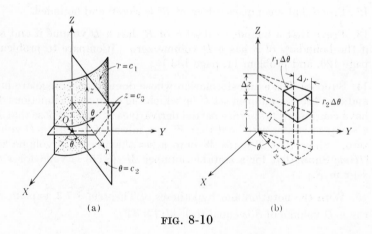

(a)   (b)

FIG. 8-10

z-axis; the surface $\theta = c_2$ is a plane containing the z-axis; and the surface $z = c_3$ is a plane perpendicular to the z-axis. Figure 8-10(b) shows a region of space bounded by such coordinate surfaces. If we let $r = \frac{1}{2}(r_1 + r_2)$, then $r \, \Delta\theta \, \Delta r$ is the area of the base of this solid, so that the volume is equal to $r \, \Delta\theta \, \Delta r \, \Delta z$. This gives an intuitive justification of Eq. (8-61), but could be the basis of a careful proof similar to the corresponding proof for polar coordinates in Section 8-2.

ILLUSTRATION 1. Suppose we wish to determine the moment of inertia about the y-axis of the cylinder K of Fig. 8-11, assuming the density is a constant δ. That is, we wish to evaluate the integral

$$\int_K (x^2 + z^2) \, dm.$$

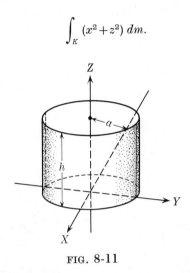

FIG. 8-11

If we change to cylindrical coordinates, the integral becomes

$$\int_0^{2\pi} \int_0^a \int_0^h (r^2 \cos^2 \theta + z^2) \delta \, r \, dz \, dr \, d\theta$$

$$= \delta \int_0^{2\pi} \int_0^a (hr^3 \cos^2 \theta + \tfrac{1}{3}h^3 r) \, dr \, d\theta$$

$$= \delta \int_0^{2\pi} (\tfrac{1}{4}ha^4 \cos^2 \theta + \tfrac{1}{6}h^3 a^2) \, d\theta$$

$$= \delta(\tfrac{1}{4}\pi ha^4 + \tfrac{1}{3}\pi h^3 a^2) = M(\tfrac{1}{4}a^2 + \tfrac{1}{3}h^2),$$

where M is the mass of the cylinder.

In a problem where there is symmetry with respect to a point, it may be convenient to choose that point as the origin and to use spherical coordinates. Spherical coordinates are defined as shown in Fig. 8-12(a), with the restriction that $0 \leq \phi \leq \pi$. If ϕ is measured to PO extended through O, and θ to $P'O$ extended through O, then ρ is taken to be negative. The coordinate surfaces are spheres with centers at the origin ($\rho = c$), planes through the z-axis ($\theta = c$), and cones with axes on the z-axis ($\phi = c$). Figure 8-12(b) shows a region bounded by coordinate surfaces. This region corresponds to a rectangular parallelepiped of volume $\Delta\rho \, \Delta\theta \, \Delta\phi$ in (ρ, θ, ϕ)-space. If $\rho \neq 0$ and $\phi \neq 0$, this region in (x, y, z)-space is approximately a rectangular parallelepiped when $\Delta\rho$, $\Delta\theta$, and $\Delta\phi$ are sufficiently small. The edges are of length $\Delta\rho$, $\rho \, \Delta\phi$, and $\rho \sin \phi \, \Delta\theta$, so that we might estimate the volume as $\rho^2 \sin \phi \, \Delta\rho \, \Delta\theta \, \Delta\phi$. This suggests that $\rho^2 \sin \phi$ is the "local magnification factor" for the transformation from spherical to rectangular coordinates and also provides a useful way of remembering the "local magnification factor." Let us now use Theorem 8-7.3 and its corollary to justify this. Spherical coordinates are related to rectangular coordinates by the following equations:

$$x = \rho \sin \phi \cos \theta, \quad y = \rho \sin \phi \sin \theta, \quad z = \rho \cos \phi. \quad (8\text{-}62)$$

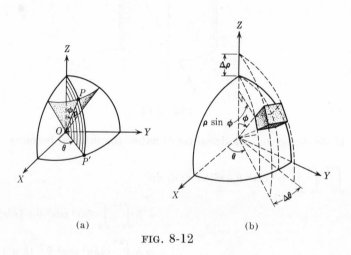

(a)   (b)

FIG. 8-12

The Jacobian of the transformation defined by these equations is

$$\frac{\partial(x, y, z)}{\partial(\rho, \theta, \phi)} = \begin{vmatrix} \sin \phi \cos \theta & -\rho \sin \phi \sin \theta & \rho \cos \phi \cos \theta \\ \sin \phi \sin \theta & \rho \sin \phi \cos \theta & \rho \cos \phi \sin \theta \\ \cos \phi & 0 & -\rho \sin \phi \end{vmatrix} = -\rho^2 \sin \phi.$$

Therefore, if R and S are sets in (ρ, θ, ϕ)-space and (x, y, z)-space, respectively, such that T is a one-to-one transformation of R onto S, then

$$\int_S f(p)\, dV = \int_R f[T(q)]\rho^2 \sin \phi\, dV,$$

provided f is continuous on S and S is compact and has volume.

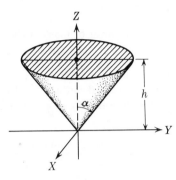

FIG. 8-13

ILLUSTRATION 2. A solid right circular cone has density proportional to the distance from the origin. The altitude is h and the semi-vertical angle is α [see Fig. 8-13]. If the density is $c\rho$ and the mass is M, then

$$M = \int_0^\alpha \int_0^{h/\cos \phi} \int_0^{2\pi} c\rho^3 \sin \phi\, d\theta\, d\rho\, d\phi$$

$$= 2\pi c \int_0^\alpha \int_0^{h/\cos \phi} \rho^3 \sin \phi\, d\rho\, d\phi$$

$$= \tfrac{1}{2}\pi c h^4 \int_0^\alpha \frac{\sin \phi}{\cos^4 \phi}\, d\phi = \tfrac{1}{6}\pi c h^4 \left(\frac{1}{\cos^3 \alpha} - 1\right).$$

PROBLEMS

1. Show that the Jacobian matrix of the transformation from cylindrical to rectangular coordinates and the Jacobian matrix of the transformation from spherical to rectangular coordinates are both equal to products of a diagonal matrix and an orthogonal matrix.

2. Determine the center of mass of a solid right circular cone whose density is proportional to the distance from the vertex [see Illustration 2].

3. Find the center of mass of the "ice cream cone" bounded above by the sphere $\rho = h$ and below by the cone $\phi = \frac{1}{6}\pi$, if the density is (a) constant; (b) proportional to the distance from the vertex; (c) proportional to the distance from the (x, y)-plane.

4. For each of the following, use cylindrical coordinates and triple integration to determine the volume of the region S. (a) S is the region inside the sphere $x^2 + y^2 + z^2 = 4a^2$ and inside the cylinder $x^2 + y^2 = a^2$. (b) S is bounded above by the sphere $x^2 + y^2 + z^2 = 8$ and below by the paraboloid $2z = x^2 + y^2$.

5. Find the volume and center of mass of the solid of constant density bounded by the graph of $\rho = a(1 - \cos \phi)$.

6. Let $p_0 = (0, 0, a)$ be a point on the z-axis outside a sphere S of mass M with center at the origin and radius r. Also assume that the density μ of the sphere is a function only of ρ. Use spherical coordinates to show that

$$\int_S \frac{\cos \omega}{[d(p_0, p)]^2} \, dm = \int_0^r \frac{2\pi\mu(\rho)\rho^2}{a^2} \left[\frac{a - \rho}{|a - \rho|} + 1 \right] d\rho = \frac{M}{a^2},$$

where ω is the angle between the z-axis and the line joining p_0 and p, so that $\cos \omega = (a - \rho \cos \phi)/d(p_0, p)$. [*Note:* It follows from this that the gravitational attraction on a particle outside a sphere is the same as if the mass of the sphere were concentrated at its center, provided the density depends only on the distance from the center of the sphere.]

7. Let S be the region between two concentric spheres with centers at the origin and let p_0 be a point on the z-axis *inside* the inner sphere. Show that if the density of S is a function only of the distance from the origin, then in the notation of problem 6 the first equality in the displayed expression is valid and

$$\int_S \frac{\cos \omega}{[d(p_0, p)]^2} \, dm = 0.$$

[*Note:* It follows from this that the gravitational attraction on a particle inside a spherical shell is zero.]

8. Imagine a small cylindrical hole bored through a solid sphere of constant density. Use problems 6 and 7 to show that if one neglects the effect of removal of mass when the hole is bored, then the gravitational attraction of the sphere on a particle in the hole is proportional to the distance of the particle from the center of the sphere.

9. Let S be the four-dimensional ball of radius r. This means that S is the set of all vectors (x_1, x_2, x_3, x_4) such that $x_1^2 + x_2^2 + x_3^2 + x_4^2 \leq r^2$.

Show that, except for the points such that ρ, A or B is zero, the equations

$$\begin{cases} x_1 = \rho \sin A \sin B \sin C, \\ x_2 = \rho \sin A \sin B \cos C, \\ x_3 = \rho \sin A \cos B, \\ x_4 = \rho \cos A, \end{cases}$$

define a one-to-one transformation of the rectangular parallelepiped $0 \leq A \leq \pi, 0 \leq B \leq \pi, 0 \leq C \leq 2\pi, 0 \leq \rho \leq r$, onto the four-dimensional ball. Determine the "local magnification factor" of this transformation and compute the volume of the sphere by integrating over the rectangular parallelepiped [see problem 4, page 264].

10. Extend problem 9 to a five-dimensional ball.

VECTOR THEOREMS

9-1. LINE INTEGRALS

Line integrals are generalizations of the definite integral $\int_a^b f(x)\,dx$. For a line integral, the interval $[a, b]$ is replaced by a curve. It will be recalled that a curve is the graph of a set of parametric equations

$$x = f(t), \quad y = g(t), \quad z = h(t), \quad t \in I, \tag{9-1}$$

where f, g, and h are continuous on the interval I. In this and the following section, we shall use only rectifiable curves.

DEFINITION 9-1.1. Suppose C is a rectifiable curve with the parametric equations in (9-1) defined on the interval $[a, b]$, and that the position vector of the point for which the parameter has the value t is denoted by $\mathbf{P}(t)$, so that

$$\mathbf{P}(t) = f(t)\mathbf{i} + g(t)\mathbf{j} + h(t)\mathbf{k}.$$

Also suppose that $\mathbf{F}$ is a vector function whose domain includes C and that $\{a = t_1, t_2, \cdots, t_{n+1} = b\}$ is a partition of $[a, b]$. For each i, we shall let τ_i be a point of the interval $[t_i, t_{i+1}]$ [Fig. 9-1]. We then form the sum

$$\sum_{i=1}^{n} \mathbf{F}(\tau_i) \cdot \Delta_i \mathbf{P}, \tag{9-2}$$

where $\Delta_i \mathbf{P} = \mathbf{P}(t_{i+1}) - \mathbf{P}(t_i)$. If this sum has a limit as the fineness of the partition approaches zero, this limit is defined as the value of the *line integral* of $\mathbf{F}$ over C and is denoted by

$$\int_C \mathbf{F}(t) \cdot d\mathbf{P}.$$

424

To avoid cumbersome notation, in (9-2) we have indicated the value of $\mathbf{F}$ at the point for which the parameter is τ_i by $\mathbf{F}(\tau_i)$ rather than $\mathbf{F}[\mathbf{P}(\tau_i)]$. Whenever it is not likely to cause confusion, we shall indicate points by specifying the value of the parameter at that point. This is done, for example, in Fig. 9-1.

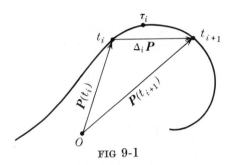

FIG 9-1

Since $\Delta_i \mathbf{P} = \mathbf{i}\,\Delta_i x + \mathbf{j}\,\Delta_i y + \mathbf{k}\,\Delta_i z$, we can write expression (9-2) as

$$\sum_{i=1}^{n} \mathbf{F}(\tau_i)\cdot(\mathbf{i}\,\Delta_i x + \mathbf{j}\,\Delta_i y + \mathbf{k}\,\Delta_i z). \tag{9-3}$$

Let us write $\mathbf{F}$ as $L\mathbf{i} + M\mathbf{j} + N\mathbf{k}$. Then if x, y, and z are differentiable on $[a, b]$, it follows from the mean value theorem that there are numbers α_i, β_i, and γ_i for each i, such that expression (9-3) is equal to

$$\sum_{i=1}^{n} \mathbf{F}(\tau_i)\cdot[\mathbf{i}x'(\alpha_i) + \mathbf{j}y'(\beta_i) + \mathbf{k}z'(\gamma_i)]\,\Delta_i t$$

$$= \sum_{i=1}^{n} [L(\tau_i)x'(\alpha_i) + M(\tau_i)y'(\beta_i) + N(\tau_i)z'(\gamma_i)]\,\Delta_i t. \tag{9-4}$$

Now suppose that $\mathbf{F}$ is continuous (so that L, M, and N are continuous), and that x', y', and z' are continuous. Then it follows from Theorem 5-5.1 that the sum in (9-4) approaches the following integral as the fineness of the partition approaches zero:

$$\int_a^b [L(t)x'(t) + M(t)y'(t) + N(t)z'(t)]\,dt.$$

Since $\mathbf{P}'(t) = x'(t)\mathbf{i} + y'(t)\mathbf{j} + z'(t)\mathbf{k}$, we finally have

$$\int_C \mathbf{F}(t)\cdot d\mathbf{P} = \int_a^b (Lx' + My' + Nz')\,dt = \int_a^b (\mathbf{F}\cdot\mathbf{P}')\,dt. \tag{9-5}$$

We can also write formula (9-5) as

$$\int_C \mathbf{F}(t) \cdot d\mathbf{P} = \int_a^b Lx' \, dt + \int_a^b My' \, dt + \int_a^b Nz' \, dt$$

$$= \int_C L \, dx + \int_C M \, dy + \int_C N \, dz. \tag{9-6}$$

ILLUSTRATION 1. Suppose we wish to evaluate $\int \mathbf{F} \cdot d\mathbf{P}$ from $(1, 0, 0)$ to $(1, 0, 2\pi)$ along one turn of the helix defined by

$$\mathbf{P}(t) = \mathbf{i} \cos t + \mathbf{j} \sin t + \mathbf{k}t, \quad \text{where} \quad \mathbf{F}(t) = -\mathbf{i} \sin t + \mathbf{j} \cos t.$$

Then

$$\int_C \mathbf{F}(t) \cdot d\mathbf{P} = \int_0^{2\pi} [\mathbf{F}(t) \cdot \mathbf{P}'(t)] \, dt$$

$$= \int_0^{2\pi} (-\mathbf{i} \sin t + \mathbf{j} \cos t) \cdot (-\mathbf{i} \sin t + \mathbf{j} \cos t + \mathbf{k}) \, dt$$

$$= \int_0^{2\pi} dt = 2\pi.$$

If there is a point of C that is not in the domains of all of x', y', and z', or is a discontinuity of one of these functions, it may be possible to divide C into a finite number of pieces on each of which x', y', and z' are defined and are continuous. Then we can apply Eq. (9-6) to each piece separately.

ILLUSTRATION 2. Suppose we let

$$\mathbf{F}(x, y, z) = \mathbf{i}(2x+y) + \mathbf{j}(x+2z) + \mathbf{k}(3x+y+z).$$

Then Eq. (9-6) becomes

$$\int_C \mathbf{F} \cdot d\mathbf{P} = \int_C (2x+y) \, dx + (x+2z) \, dy + (3x+y+z) \, dz.$$

Suppose we wish to evaluate this integral along a curve C that joins the points $(0, 0, 0)$ and $(1, 2, 3)$ of Fig. 9-2. First we let C be the straight line C_1 from $(0, 0, 0)$ to $(1, 2, 3)$, so that along C we have $y = 2x$ and $z = 3x$. We can use x as a parameter and write

$$\int_{C_1} \mathbf{F} \cdot d\mathbf{P} = \int_0^1 (4x) \, dx + \int_0^1 (7x) \, 2dx + \int_0^1 (8x) \, 3dx$$

$$= \int_0^1 (42x) \, dx = 21.$$

Now we let C be the curve C_2 that consists of the line segments from $(0, 0, 0)$ to $(1, 0, 0)$, from $(1, 0, 0)$ to $(1, 2, 0)$, and from $(1, 2, 0)$ to $(1, 2, 3)$. Along each of these segments, the assumptions made to establish Eq. (9-6) are satisfied and we have

$$\int_{C_2} \mathbf{F}(t) \cdot d\mathbf{P} = \int_0^1 (2x) \, dx + \int_0^2 (1) \, dy + \int_0^3 (5+z) \, dz = \frac{45}{2}.$$

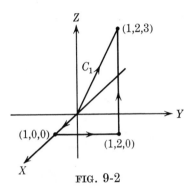

FIG. 9-2

We know that if $\mathbf{P}$ is the position vector of points on a curve C and if $\mathbf{P}$ is differentiable, then

$$\mathbf{P}'(t) = \frac{ds}{dt} \mathbf{T},$$

where $\mathbf{T}$ is the unit tangent vector [see page 352]. Since $\mathbf{F} \cdot \mathbf{T}$ is the tangential component of $\mathbf{F}$, we can write Eq. (9-5) as

$$\int_C \mathbf{F}(t) \cdot d\mathbf{P} = \int (\mathbf{F} \cdot \mathbf{T}) \, ds = \int F_T \, ds, \tag{9-7}$$

where F_T is the tangential component of $\mathbf{F}$ and appropriate limits are to be put on the integrals.

A vector function for which the vector at each point of the domain is called a force is a *force field*. If $\mathbf{F}$ is a force field, then $\int_C \mathbf{F}(t) \cdot d\mathbf{P}$ is the *work* done by the force on a particle of unit mass moving along the curve C from the initial point to the terminal point. Equation (9-7) can be interpreted as stating that the work done on a particle of unit mass moving along the curve is the limit of the sum of products, each of which has as its two factors the length of a segment of the curve and the tangential component of the force at a point of the segment, as the length of the longest segment approaches zero.

It is to be expected that assumptions must be made about the nature of **F** or the nature of the curve C before we can be assured that $\int_C \mathbf{F} \cdot d\mathbf{P}$ exists. We know that it is sufficient to have **F**, x', y', and z' continuous. For most applications, this is enough information about the question of existence of a line integral. However, sometimes it is useful to have more general results than these. In the next theorem we assume only that **F** is continuous and that the curve over which the line integral is evaluated is rectifiable. The proof is difficult, since x', y', and z' may not even exist and we cannot use formulas such as (9-4) and (9-6).

THEOREM 9-1.1. If C is a rectifiable simple curve with the position vector **P**, and **F** is a vector function that is continuous at each point of C, then $\int_C \mathbf{F} \cdot d\mathbf{P}$ exists.†

PROOF. We shall let C be a rectifiable curve of length L and suppose that **P** is defined by $\mathbf{P} = x\mathbf{i} + y\mathbf{j} + z\mathbf{k}$ and the parametric equations

$$x = f(t), \quad y = g(t), \quad z = h(t), \quad a \leqq t \leqq b,$$

where the functions f, g, and h are continuous on $[a, b]$. If **F** is a vector function that is continuous on $[a, b]$, then each component of **F** is continuous on $[a, b]$, so that each component of **F** is uniformly continuous on $[a, b]$. Therefore, **F** itself is uniformly continuous on $[a, b]$. We must show that the expression

$$\sum_{i=1}^{n} \mathbf{F}(\tau_i) \cdot \Delta_i \mathbf{P} \tag{9-8}$$

has a limit as the fineness of the partition used in forming this sum approaches zero. Uniform continuity is the essential tool to be used. For a positive number ε, we can choose a positive number δ_ε such that, for all r and s in $[a, b]$,

$$|\mathbf{F}(r) - \mathbf{F}(s)| < \varepsilon \quad \text{if} \quad |r - s| < \delta_\varepsilon.$$

Now we shall select a partition $\{t_1 = a, t_2, \cdots, t_{n+1} = b\}$, which we denote by Π, whose fineness is less than δ_ε. We shall let Π' be any other

---

† We could define *rectifiable* for nonsimple curves and corresponding sets of parametric equations in such a way that the proof of Theorem 9-1.1 would apply, but then the length of a curve might have different values for different sets of parametric equations. Also, we can use problem 11 to extend Theorem 9-1.1 to curves that can be divided into a finite number of simple curves.

partition that *uses the same points and some additional ones.* [For example, the piece of C between values t_i and t_{i+1} of t might be subdivided as shown in Fig. 9-3.] Each interval of Π' is contained in an interval of Π, so that the ith term of Eq. (9-8) for the partition Π corresponds to several terms of the sum for Π'. For the arc shown in Fig. 9-3 and the special case of three subarcs, we have the corresponding sums

$$\mathbf{F}(\tau_i)\cdot\Delta_i\mathbf{P} \quad \text{and} \quad \mathbf{F}(\tau_k^*)\cdot\Delta_k^*\mathbf{P}+\mathbf{F}(\tau_{k+1}^*)\cdot\Delta_{k+1}^*\mathbf{P}+\mathbf{F}(\tau_{k+2}^*)\cdot\Delta_{k+2}^*\mathbf{P}.$$

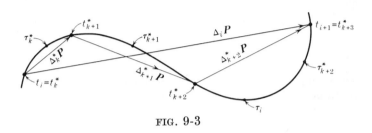

FIG. 9-3

Since $t_{i+1}-t_i<\delta_\varepsilon$, we have for this special case

$$|\mathbf{F}(\tau_j^*)-\mathbf{F}(\tau_i)| \; < \; \varepsilon$$

for $j = k$, $k+1$, $k+2$. Therefore,

$$
\begin{aligned}
|\mathbf{F}(\tau_i)\cdot\Delta_i\mathbf{P}&-[\mathbf{F}(\tau_k^*)\cdot\Delta_k^*\mathbf{P}+\mathbf{F}(\tau_{k+1}^*)\cdot\Delta_{k+1}^*\mathbf{P}+\mathbf{F}(\tau_{k+2}^*)\cdot\Delta_{k+2}^*\mathbf{P}]| \\
&\leqq \; |\mathbf{F}(\tau_i)\cdot\Delta_i\mathbf{P}-[\mathbf{F}(\tau_i)\cdot\Delta_k^*\mathbf{P}+\mathbf{F}(\tau_i)\cdot\Delta_{k+1}^*\mathbf{P}+\mathbf{F}(\tau_i)\cdot\Delta_{k+2}^*\mathbf{P}]| \\
&\quad + \varepsilon[|\Delta_k^*\mathbf{P}|+|\Delta_{k+1}^*\mathbf{P}|+|\Delta_{k+2}^*\mathbf{P}|] \\
&\leqq \; |\mathbf{F}(\tau_i)\cdot[\Delta_i\mathbf{P}-(\Delta_k^*\mathbf{P}+\Delta_{k+1}^*\mathbf{P}+\Delta_{k+2}^*\mathbf{P})]| + \varepsilon L_i \; = \; \varepsilon L_i,
\end{aligned}
$$

where L_i is the length of the arc of C between the points for which t has the values t_i and t_{i+1}. It should be clear that this can be done for each interval of Π, so that the absolute value of the difference between a sum of type (9-8) for the partition Π and a sum for the partition Π' is less than εL. Now suppose we have two partitions Π_1 and Π_2 that have fineness less than δ_ε. If we use all values of t that are used for either of these partitions, then we have a partition that, because of what we have just shown, has a sum of type (9-8) that differs from such sums for Π_1 or for Π_2 by less than εL. Thus, for any positive number ε, there is a positive number δ_ε such that

$$|S'-S''| \; < \; 2\varepsilon L, \tag{9-9}$$

if S' and S'' are sums of type (9-8) for partitions with fineness less than δ_ε. Now choose sequences $\{\delta_{1/n}\}$ and $\{S_n\}$ such that S_n is a sum of type (9-8) for a partition with fineness less than $\delta_{1/n}$ and $\lim \delta_{1/n} = 0$. Then

$$|S_p - S_q| < \frac{2L}{n} \text{ if } p > n \text{ and } q > n.$$

Thus, $\{S_n\}$ is a Cauchy sequence, and it follows from Theorem 2-10.2 that $\{S_n\}$ has a limit σ. Now suppose ε is an arbitrary positive number and use (9-9) to obtain a positive number δ for which $|S' - S''| < \frac{1}{2}\varepsilon$ if S' and S'' are sums of type (9-8) for partitions with fineness less than δ. Then choose n so that $\delta_{1/n} < \delta$ and $|\sigma - S_n| < \frac{1}{2}\varepsilon$. If S is a sum of type (9-8) for a partition with fineness less than δ, then we have

$$|\sigma - S| \leq |\sigma - S_n| + |S_n - S| < \varepsilon.$$

Therefore, σ is the limit of expression (9-8) as the fineness of the partitions used approaches zero.†

PROBLEMS

1. For each of the following, evaluate $\int \mathbf{F} \cdot d\mathbf{P}$ by using either formula (9-5) or formula (9-6) of the text.

   (a) $\mathbf{F} = t\mathbf{i} + \mathbf{j} - t^2\mathbf{k}$, where $\mathbf{P}(t) = \mathbf{i} + t\mathbf{j} + t^2\mathbf{k}$ for $-1 \leq t \leq 1$.

   (b) $\mathbf{F} = (y \sin x)\mathbf{i} - (x \cos y)\mathbf{j}$; $\mathbf{P}(t) = t\mathbf{i} + t\mathbf{j}$ for $0 \leq t \leq 1$.

   (c) $\mathbf{F} = (x^2 y)\mathbf{i} + (x^2 - y^2)\mathbf{j}$; $\mathbf{P}(t) = t\mathbf{i} + 3t^2\mathbf{j}$ for $0 \leq t \leq 1$.

   (d) $\mathbf{F} = (1 - x^2)^{1/2}\mathbf{i} + (y^2 + z)\mathbf{j} + x\mathbf{k}$; $\mathbf{P}(t) = (\cos \pi t)\mathbf{i} + t\mathbf{j} - t^2\mathbf{k}$ for $0 \leq t \leq 2$.

2. Evaluate $\int_{(1,1,0)}^{(0,0,\sqrt{2})} x^2 yz \, ds$ along each of the following paths. (a) The graph of $x = \cos t$, $y = \cos t$, $z = \sqrt{2} \sin t$, $0 \leq t \leq \frac{1}{2}\pi$. (b) The straight line from $(1, 1, 0)$ to $(0, 0, \sqrt{2})$.

3. Evaluate $\int (x + 2) \, ds$ between the points $(0, 0, 0)$ and $(1, 1, 0)$ along (a) the straight lines between these points; (b) the line segments from $(0, 0, 0)$ to $(1, 0, 0)$ and from $(1, 0, 0)$ to $(1, 1, 0)$.

4. Evaluate $\int (xy) \, ds$ from $(3, 0, 0)$ to $(15/4, 3, \ln 8)$ along each of the following curves. (a) $x = 3 \cosh t$, $y = 4 \sinh t$, $z = 3t$. (b) The line segments from $(3, 0, 0)$ to $(15/4, 0, 0)$, from $(15/4, 0, 0)$ to $(15/4, 3, 0)$, and from $(15/4, 3, 0)$ to $(15/4, 3, \ln 8)$.

---

† We might also have used problem 6, page 119.

5. Evaluate $\int_C F_T \, ds$, where $\mathbf{F} = (2xy^2z)\mathbf{i} + (2x^2yz)\mathbf{j} + (x^2y^2)\mathbf{k}$ and C is (**a**) the circle $x^2 + y^2 = 1$, $z = 1$; (**b**) the polygonal path from $(0, 0, 0)$ to $(2, 1, 3)$ with corners at $(2, 0, 0)$ and $(2, 1, 0)$; (**c**) the line segment from $(0, 0, 0)$ to $(2, 1, 3)$.

6. Evaluate $\int_{(1,0,0)}^{(-1,0,0)} (x^3 - y^3) \, dy$ in each of the following ways. (**a**) Along the x-axis. (**b**) Along the semi-circle $x = \cos t$, $y = \sin t$, $z = 0$, $0 \le t \le \pi$. (**c**) Along the semi-circle $x = \cos(-t)$, $y = \sin(-t)$, $z = 0$, $0 \le t \le \pi$.

7. Evaluate $\int_C xy^2 \, dx + x^2y \, dy$, where C is (**a**) the arc of the graph of $y = x^2$ from $(0, 0)$ to $(-1, 1)$; (b) the segment joining $(0, 0)$ to $(0, 1)$ and the segment from $(0, 1)$ to $(-1, 1)$.

8. Evaluate $\int_C y^2 \, dx + x^2 \, dy$, where C is (**a**) the triangle with vertices at $(0, 0)$ $(1, 0)$, and $(1, 1)$; (b) the graph of $x^2 + y^2 = 1$.

9. Evaluate the following line integrals. (**a**) $\int_C y \, dx - x \, dy$, where C is the circle $x^2 + y^2 = 1$, $z = 0$, oriented counterclockwise. (b) $\int_C x^2yz \, dx - y^3 \, dy + x^2z \, dz$, where C is the closed polygonal curve with successive vertices $(0, 2, 3)$, $(1, 2, 3)$, $(1, 2, 6)$, $(1, 4, 3)$, $(0, 2, 3)$.

10. For each of the following, evaluate $\int_C \mathbf{F} \cdot d\mathbf{P}$.

(**a**) $\mathbf{F} = \sqrt{y}\,\mathbf{i} + 2x\mathbf{j} + 3y\mathbf{k}$ and $\mathbf{P}(t) = t\mathbf{i} + t^2\mathbf{j} + t^3\mathbf{k}$ for $1 \le t \le 2$.

(**b**) $\mathbf{F} = x\left(\dfrac{1-y^2}{y^2+z^2}\right)^{1/2}\mathbf{i}$ and C is the first-octant part of the intersection of $x = y$ and $2y^2 + z^2 = 1$, oriented from $(0, 0, 1)$ to $(\frac{1}{2}\sqrt{2}, \frac{1}{2}\sqrt{2}, 0)$.

(**c**) $\mathbf{F} = (z/y)\mathbf{i} + (x^2 + y^2 + 2z^2)\mathbf{k}$ and C is the first-octant arc of $x^2 + y^2 = 1$, $z = 2x + 4$, oriented from $(0, 1, 4)$ to $(1, 0, 6)$.

(**d**) $\mathbf{F} = y\mathbf{i} - y(x-1)\mathbf{j} + y^2z\mathbf{k}$ and C is the first-octant arc of the curve $x^2 + y^2 + z^2 = 4$, $(x-1)^2 + y^2 = 1$, oriented from $(2, 0, 0)$ to $(0, 0, 2)$.

11.* Let C_1 and C_2 be two curves such that the terminal point of C_1 is the initial point of C_2. Show that if $\int_{C_1} \mathbf{F} \cdot d\mathbf{P}$ and $\int_{C_2} \mathbf{F} \cdot d\mathbf{P}$ exist, then the integral over $C_1 \cup C_2$ exists and

$$\int_{C_1 \cup C_2} \mathbf{F} \cdot d\mathbf{P} = \int_{C_1} \mathbf{F} \cdot d\mathbf{P} + \int_{C_2} \mathbf{F} \cdot d\mathbf{P}.$$

12. Let C be a rectifiable curve and $\mathbf{F}$ a vector-valued function such that $\int_C \mathbf{F} \cdot d\mathbf{P}$ exists. Show that

$$\left| \int_C \mathbf{F} \cdot d\mathbf{P} \right| \le (\sup_C |\mathbf{F}|)(\text{length of } C).$$

9-2. SURFACES AND AREAS OF SURFACES

For plane sets, we have given a careful definition of area and a detailed development of properties of area. We now wish to extend this definition to sets of points on surfaces. It is essential that any definition we shall give for the area of a surface include the property that for sets in a plane the area is the same as that given by our previous definition. Before we go further, we must emphasize that care should be taken in approximating the area of a surface as the sum of areas of plane sets. For example, by selecting appropriate triplets of points evenly distributed over a given surface as vertices of plane triangles, a crinkled surface can be made that approximates the given surface. The area of the crinkled surface is the sum of the areas of its triangular parts. It might seem reasonable that as more and more points are chosen closer and closer together, the areas of the crinkled surfaces approach the area of the given surface. However, if the surface is a right circular cylinder, the points can be chosen so that not only do the areas of the crinkled surfaces not approach the area of the cylinder, but there is no upper bound to the areas of the crinkled surfaces!

For example, suppose the altitude and the radius of the base of a cylinder are both unity. Let the cylinder be divided into n congruent cylinders with altitude $1/n$ by planes parallel to the base. Then choose n equally spaced points around each circle, so that the element of the cylinder through a particular point bisects the arc joining the neighboring points on either adjacent circle. These points determine $2mn$ congruent triangles. For each triangle, we take as the base the chord joining the two vertices in a plane parallel to the base of the cylinder. Let b_m be the length of the base and let $d_{m,n}$ be the length of the altitude from the center of the base to the opposite vertex. Then the total area of all triangles is

$$A_{m,n} = mnb_m d_{m,n}.$$

If m is kept constant, then b_m is constant and $d_{m,n}$ approaches the positive number equal to the distance from the center of the base to the cylinder. Then $A_{m,n}$ increases indefinitely as n increases. If n is kept constant, then $mb_m \to 2\pi$ and $nd_{m,n} \to 1$, so that $A_{m,n}$ approaches the area of the cylinder as m increases. By controlling carefully the way m and n increase, we can make $A_{m,n}$ approach any number not smaller than the area of the cylinder!

In Section 7-3, we saw that if the area of a parallelogram is A and if a vector perpendicular to the parallelogram makes angles α, β, and γ with the coordinate axes, then the areas A_1, A_2, A_3 of the projections of the parallelogram into the coordinate planes $x = 0$, $y = 0$, $z = 0$, respectively, are given by the formulas

$$A_1 = A|\cos \alpha|, \quad A_2 = A|\cos \beta|, \quad A_3 = A|\cos \gamma|.$$

Since $\cos^2 \alpha + \cos^2 \beta + \cos^2 \gamma = 1$, we have

$$A = [(A_1)^2 + (A_2)^2 + (A_3)^2]^{1/2}. \tag{9-10}$$

Clearly this formula can be used with any plane set. If $A_3 \neq 0$, for example, then we can write (9-10) as

$$A = \frac{[(A_1)^2 + (A_2)^2 + (A_3)^2]^{1/2}}{A_3} \cdot A_3 = \frac{1}{|\cos \gamma|} A_3. \tag{9-11}$$

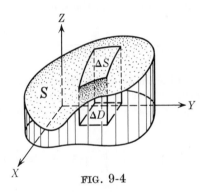

FIG. 9-4

Equations (9-10) and (9-11) are exact for sets in a plane. However, if a surface has a tangent plane at a point (x_0, y_0, z_0), then it is reasonable to approximate the surface near the point by its projection into the tangent plane. Suppose we let D be the projection into the (x, y)-plane of the surface S shown in Fig. 9-4. As an approximation for the area of a piece ΔS of S, we might use $\Delta A_3/|\cos \gamma|$, where ΔA_3 is the area of the projection ΔD of ΔS into the (x, y)-plane and $\cos \gamma$ is evaluated at some point of ΔS. Then we might expect the area of S to be given by the formula

$$\text{area of } S = \int_D |\cos \gamma|^{-1} \, dA. \tag{9-12}$$

Use of this formula requires a technique for evaluating $\cos \gamma$. However, this problem was solved in Section 7-7. We showed that if a surface has the equation $f(x, y, z) = 0$, where the first-order partial derivatives of f are continuous, then the gradient

$$\nabla f = \frac{\partial f}{\partial x}\mathbf{i} + \frac{\partial f}{\partial y}\mathbf{j} + \frac{\partial f}{\partial z}\mathbf{k}$$

is perpendicular to the surface at any point where not all three partial derivatives are zero. Therefore,

$$\cos \gamma = \frac{\dfrac{\partial f}{\partial z}}{\left[\left(\dfrac{\partial f}{\partial x}\right)^2 + \left(\dfrac{\partial f}{\partial y}\right)^2 + \left(\dfrac{\partial f}{\partial z}\right)^2\right]^{\frac{1}{2}}}. \tag{9-13}$$

ILLUSTRATION 1. Suppose we wish to determine the area of the surface of a sphere whose radius is a. If the center of the sphere is at the origin, so that the equation of the sphere is $x^2 + y^2 + z^2 = a^2$, then

$$\cos \gamma = \frac{2z}{[(2x)^2 + (2y)^2 + (2z)^2]^{\frac{1}{2}}} = \frac{z}{(x^2 + y^2 + z^2)^{\frac{1}{2}}} = \frac{z}{a}.$$

Now we can determine the area of the upper hemisphere by evaluating the following integral over D, where D is the set in the (x, y)-plane bounded by the graph of $x^2 + y^2 = a^2$ (to perform the actual integration, we use polar coordinates):

$$\int_D \frac{a}{z} \, dA = a \int_0^a \int_0^{2\pi} (a^2 - r^2)^{-\frac{1}{2}} r \, d\theta \, dr$$

$$= 2\pi a \int_0^a (a^2 - r^2)^{-\frac{1}{2}} r \, dr = 2\pi a^2.$$

Therefore, the area of the entire sphere is $4\pi a^2$.

The preceding discussion does not deal with the question of an explicit definition of "surface" and "area of a surface." Intuitively, a surface is the locus of a point that has two "degrees of freedom." Mathematically, this means that two parameters should be used to describe points in the surface. We shall first define "surface elements," which will be used in the next section to build more general surfaces.

DEFINITION 9-2.1. A *surface element* is a set S that is the range of a continuous one-to-one transformation T whose domain is the union $\bar{D}$ of a bounded open plane set D and its boundary, with the boundary a rectifiable simple closed curve. The *edge* of S is the image of the boundary of D.

It follows from Theorem 2-6.5 that the inverse of the transformation T of Definition 9-2.1 is continuous. A one-to-one continuous transformation whose inverse is continuous is called a *topological transformation* or *homeomorphism*. The domain and range are said to be *topologically equivalent* or *homeomorphic*. Thus, the sets S and $\bar{D}$ of Definition 9-2.1 are topologically equivalent.

We can relate Definition 9-2.1 to the concept of a surface being the graph of an equation of type $z = f(x, y)$. If the domain of f is a set $\bar{D}$ as described in Definition 9-2.1, and if f is continuous on $\bar{D}$, then we can let x and y be parameters and define the transformation of $\bar{D}$ onto S by the equations $x = x$, $y = y$, and $z = f(x, y)$. Thus, Definition 9-2.1 gives a generalization of the concept that a surface is the graph of an equation of type $z = f(x, y)$.

We shall generalize Eq. (9-12). However, we shall not attempt to determine area for general surface elements, but only for surface elements that are "smooth" in the sense of the following definition.

DEFINITION 9-2.2. A *smooth surface element* is a surface element described by equations

$$x = f(u, v), \quad y = g(u, v), \quad z = h(u, v), \tag{9-14}$$

where the first-order partial derivatives of f, g, and h are continuous at all points of the interior D of their common domain $\bar{D}$, and there is no point of D at which the following Jacobians are all zero:

$$J_1 = \frac{\partial(y, z)}{\partial(u, v)}, \quad J_2 = \frac{\partial(z, x)}{\partial(u, v)}, \quad J_3 = \frac{\partial(x, y)}{\partial(u, v)}. \tag{9-15}$$

We must first establish the existence of a tangent plane at points of a smooth surface element. Having done this, it will be easy to give motivation for a definition of surface area.

THEOREM 9-2.1. Suppose S is a smooth surface element described by (9-14), (x_0, y_0, z_0) is a point of S not on the edge of S, and (u_0, v_0) is the corresponding point of D. Then S has a tangent plane at (x_0, y_0, z_0) and parametric equations of the tangent plane are

$$\begin{cases} x = x_0 + f_1(u_0, v_0) \cdot s + f_2(u_0, v_0) \cdot t, \\ y = y_0 + g_1(u_0, v_0) \cdot s + g_2(u_0, v_0) \cdot t, \\ z = z_0 + h_1(u_0, v_0) \cdot s + h_2(u_0, v_0) \cdot t. \end{cases} \tag{9-16}$$

PROOF. If we let $\mathbf{P}(u, v)$ denote the position vector of points on the surface, then

$$\mathbf{P}(u, v) = f(u, v)\mathbf{i} + g(u, v)\mathbf{j} + h(u, v)\mathbf{k}. \tag{9-17}$$

We must show first that the equations in (9-16) are equations of a plane Π—i.e., that the vectors $\partial \mathbf{P}/\partial u$ and $\partial \mathbf{P}/\partial v$ are not parallel. To do this, we observe that

$$\left|\frac{\partial \mathbf{P}}{\partial u} \times \frac{\partial \mathbf{P}}{\partial v}\right| = \left\| \begin{array}{ccc} \mathbf{i} & \mathbf{j} & \mathbf{k} \\ f_1(u, v) & g_1(u, v) & h_1(u, v) \\ f_2(u, v) & g_2(u, v) & h_2(u, v) \end{array} \right\| = [(J_1)^2 + (J_2)^2 + (J_3)^2]^{\frac{1}{2}}.$$

(9-18)

This is nonzero, since there is no point of D at which all of J_1, J_2, and J_3 are zero. Now we shall let θ be the angle between the plane Π and the line segment joining (x_0, y_0, z_0) to another point (x, y, z) on S. We must show that θ approaches zero as $(x, y, z) \to (x_0, y_0, z_0)$ [see Definition 6-1.3]. We shall let $\Delta x, \Delta y, \Delta z$ denote $x - x_0$, $y - y_0$, and $z - z_0$ respectively. Also, we shall let (u, v) be the point of D corresponding to (x, y, z), $\Delta u = u - u_0$, and $\Delta v = v - v_0$. Since (x_0, y_0, z_0) is not on the edge of S, there is a neighborhood of (u_0, v_0) contained in D. We can choose this neighborhood to be convex. Then if (u, v) is in this neighborhood of (u_0, v_0), it follows from Taylor's theorem [page 303] that there are points (u_1, v_1), (u_2, v_2), (u_3, v_3) on the line segment joining (u_0, v_0) and (u, v) such that

$$\begin{cases} \Delta x = f_1(u_1, v_1) \, \Delta u + f_2(u_1, v_1) \, \Delta v, \\ \Delta y = g_1(u_2, v_2) \, \Delta u + g_2(u_2, v_2) \, \Delta v, \\ \Delta z = h_1(u_3, v_3) \, \Delta u + h_2(u_3, v_3) \, \Delta v. \end{cases}$$

(9-19)

The vector $(\Delta x)\mathbf{i} + (\Delta y)\mathbf{j} + (\Delta z)\mathbf{k}$ is orthogonal to the cross product of the vectors whose components are the coefficients of Δu and Δv, respectively, in (9-19)—i.e., the vector

$$\left| \begin{array}{ccc} \mathbf{i} & \mathbf{j} & \mathbf{k} \\ f_1(u_1, v_1) & g_1(u_2, v_2) & h_1(u_3, v_3) \\ f_2(u_1, v_1) & g_2(u_2, v_2) & h_2(u_3, v_3) \end{array} \right|.$$

As $(u, v) \to (u_0, v_0)$, this vector approaches the value at (u_0, v_0) of $(\partial \mathbf{P}/\partial u) \times (\partial \mathbf{P}/\partial v)$ which is perpendicular to the plane Π. Since θ is the angle between Π and $(\Delta x)\mathbf{i} + (\Delta y)\mathbf{j} + (\Delta z)\mathbf{k}$, it follows that $\theta \to 0$ as $(u, v) \to (u_0, v_0)$. The transformation (9-14) from $\bar{D}$ onto S has a continuous inverse; hence, $(u, v) \to (u_0, v_0)$ if $(x, y, z) \to (x_0, y_0, z_0)$. Therefore, $\theta \to 0$ as $(x, y, z) \to (x_0, y_0, z_0)$.

We are now prepared to give motivation for a definition of area for smooth surface elements. We shall consider a rectangle with sides Δu and Δv in the set D in the (u, v)-plane. The image of this rectangle is a piece of the surface and can be approximated in the tangent plane by a parallelogram with sides of length $|\partial \mathbf{P}/\partial u| \, \Delta u$ and $|\partial \mathbf{P}/\partial v| \, \Delta v$, as shown in Fig. 9-5. The area of this parallelogram is $|(\partial \mathbf{P}/\partial u) \times (\partial \mathbf{P}/\partial v)| \, \Delta u \, \Delta v$. This suggests the following definition.

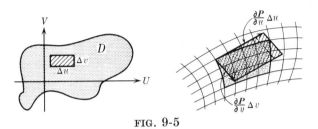

FIG. 9-5

DEFINITION 9-2.3. If S is a smooth surface element with the position vector $\mathbf{P}(u, v)$ and D is the domain of $\mathbf{P}$, then the area of S is equal to

$$\int_{D} \left| \frac{\partial \mathbf{P}}{\partial u} \times \frac{\partial \mathbf{P}}{\partial v} \right| dA. \tag{9-20}$$

This definition is particularly easy to apply if $\partial \mathbf{P}/\partial u$ and $\partial \mathbf{P}/\partial v$ are orthogonal, since the area is then equal to

$$\int_{D} \left| \frac{\partial \mathbf{P}}{\partial u} \right| \left| \frac{\partial \mathbf{P}}{\partial v} \right| dA. \tag{9-21}$$

ILLUSTRATION 2. The following equation defines a position vector $\mathbf{P}$ for a hemisphere of radius a:

$$\mathbf{P}(\phi, \theta) = (a \sin \phi \cos \theta)\mathbf{i} + (a \sin \phi \sin \theta)\mathbf{j} + (a \cos \phi)\mathbf{k},$$

where $0 \leq \phi \leq \pi$ and $0 \leq \theta \leq \pi$. To determine the area of this hemisphere, we first evaluate the partial derivatives of $\mathbf{P}$:

$$\frac{\partial \mathbf{P}}{\partial \phi} = (a \cos \phi \cos \theta)\mathbf{i} + (a \cos \phi \sin \theta)\mathbf{j} + (-a \sin \phi)\mathbf{k},$$

$$\frac{\partial \mathbf{P}}{\partial \theta} = (-a \sin \phi \sin \theta)\mathbf{i} + (a \sin \phi \cos \theta)\mathbf{j}.$$

Then

$$\left| \frac{\partial \mathbf{P}}{\partial \phi} \right| = [(a \cos \phi \cos \theta)^2 + (a \cos \phi \sin \theta)^2 + (-a \sin \phi)^2]^{1/2} = a,$$

$$\left| \frac{\partial \mathbf{P}}{\partial \theta} \right| = [(-a \sin \phi \sin \theta)^2 + (a \sin \phi \cos \theta)^2]^{1/2} = a \sin \phi,$$

and

$$\left|\frac{\partial \mathbf{P}}{\partial \phi} \times \frac{\partial \mathbf{P}}{\partial \theta}\right| = \left|\frac{\partial \mathbf{P}}{\partial \phi}\right| \left|\frac{\partial \mathbf{P}}{\partial \theta}\right| = a^2 \sin \phi.$$

Therefore, the area of the hemisphere is equal to

$$\int_0^\pi \int_0^\pi a^2 \sin \phi \, d\phi \, d\theta = 2a^2 \int_0^\pi d\theta = 2\pi a^2.$$

Because of (9-18), we can write (9-20) as

$$\int_D [(J_1)^2 + (J_2)^2 + (J_3)^2]^{\frac{1}{2}} \, dA. \qquad (9\text{-}22)$$

This equation has an interesting geometric interpretation. Let us consider the transformation from the (u, v)-plane to the (x, y)-plane defined by the equations

$$\begin{cases} x = f(u, v), \\ y = g(u, v). \end{cases}$$

We know that the local magnification factor of this transformation is the absolute value of the Jacobian J_3 [see Section 8-7]. Therefore, if ΔS is the subset of the surface that corresponds to a subset ΔD of D with area ΔA, then we might approximate the area of the projection of ΔS into the (x, y)-plane by $|J_3| \Delta A$. Similarly, the areas of the projections of ΔS into the (y, z)-plane and the (z, x)-plane might be approximated by $|J_1| \Delta A$ and $|J_2| \Delta A$. Thus, $[J_1^2 + J_2^2 + J_3^2]^{\frac{1}{2}} \Delta A$ is an approximation of ΔS [see (7-32), page 330].

We should show that Definition 9-2.3 gives the same formula for area as Eq. (9-12), in case the surface is defined by an equation of type $f(x, y, z) = 0$. To do this, we shall think of x and y as being parameters and z as being an implicit function of x and y. Then

$$\frac{\partial f}{\partial x} + \frac{\partial f}{\partial z} \frac{\partial z}{\partial x} = 0, \qquad \frac{\partial f}{\partial y} + \frac{\partial f}{\partial z} \frac{\partial z}{\partial y} = 0,$$

and, with $\mathbf{P}(x, y) = x\mathbf{i} + y\mathbf{j} + z\mathbf{k}$, we have

$$\frac{\partial \mathbf{P}}{\partial x} \times \frac{\partial \mathbf{P}}{\partial y} = \begin{vmatrix} \mathbf{i} & \mathbf{j} & \mathbf{k} \\ 1 & 0 & -(\partial f/\partial x)/(\partial f/\partial z) \\ 0 & 1 & -(\partial f/\partial y)/(\partial f/\partial z) \end{vmatrix} = \frac{\dfrac{\partial f}{\partial x}}{\dfrac{\partial f}{\partial z}} \mathbf{i} + \frac{\dfrac{\partial f}{\partial y}}{\dfrac{\partial f}{\partial z}} \mathbf{j} + \mathbf{k}.$$

Therefore,

$$\left|\frac{\partial \mathbf{P}}{\partial x} \times \frac{\partial \mathbf{P}}{\partial y}\right| = \frac{\left[\left(\dfrac{\partial f}{\partial x}\right)^2 + \left(\dfrac{\partial f}{\partial y}\right)^2 + \left(\dfrac{\partial f}{\partial z}\right)^2\right]^{1/2}}{\left|\dfrac{\partial f}{\partial z}\right|}.$$

Thus, (9-20) becomes formula (9-12), with $\cos \gamma$ obtained from (9-13).

A good definition of area should not depend on the particular parametric representation of the surface. We shall leave it to the student to show that area as given by Definition 9-2.3 does not change if the parameters are changed [problem 17]. There are several other methods for defining area of a surface. To show the equivalence of different definitions is in some cases extremely difficult. Study of such problems has occupied the attention of many able mathematicians over the last 50 years and there are still questions that need more study. For smooth surface elements, we must be content with using Definition 9-2.3. We know that this definition is equivalent to the usual definition of area when the surface is in a plane and that it is equivalent to using such formulas as Eq. (9-12) in suitable special cases [also see problem 5]. It is easy to extend this definition to surfaces obtained by piecing together several smooth surface elements, such as the surface of a polyhedron or a sphere. One merely adds the areas of the pieces.

Definition 9-2.3 leads to an especially simple formula for the area of a surface of revolution. Suppose that f is nonnegative and f' is continuous on the interval $[a, b]$. As indicated in Fig. 9-6, rotating the graph of $y = f(x)$ around the x-axis generates a surface with parametric equations $x = x$, $y = f(x) \cos \omega$, $z = f(x) \sin \omega$. With

$$\mathbf{P}(x, \omega) = x\mathbf{i} + [f(x) \cos \omega]\mathbf{j} + [f(x) \sin \omega]\mathbf{k},$$

we have

$$\frac{\partial \mathbf{P}}{\partial x} \times \frac{\partial \mathbf{P}}{\partial \omega} = \begin{vmatrix} \mathbf{i} & \mathbf{j} & \mathbf{k} \\ 1 & f'(x) \cos \omega & f'(x) \sin \omega \\ 0 & -f(x) \sin \omega & f(x) \cos \omega \end{vmatrix},$$

and

$$\left|\frac{\partial \mathbf{P}}{\partial x} \times \frac{\partial \mathbf{P}}{\partial \omega}\right| = \left|\frac{\partial \mathbf{P}}{\partial x}\right|\left|\frac{\partial \mathbf{P}}{\partial \omega}\right| = |f(x)|\{1 + [f'(x)]^2\}^{1/2}.$$

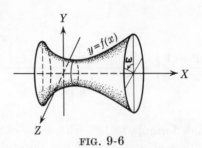

FIG. 9-6

The area of the surface is equal to

$$\int_a^b \int_0^{2\pi} f(x)\{1+[f'(x)]^2\}^{1/2}\, d\omega\, dx = \int_a^b 2\pi f(x)\{1+[f'(x)]^2\}^{1/2}\, dx.$$

If we integrate with respect to arc length s, this becomes

$$\int 2\pi f(x)\, ds, \tag{9-23}$$

with appropriate limits to be put on the integral. The student should try to give a direct intuitive justification of this formula.

PROBLEMS

1. Find the area of the region cut from the graph of $x+2y+z=1$ by the cylinder whose equation is $x^2+y^2=1$.

2. A piece S of the cone with equation $x^2+y^2=z^2$ is above the (x, y)-plane, and its projection into the (x, y)-plane has area A. Show that the area of S is equal to $\sqrt{2}A$.

3. Find the area of that piece of the graph of $x^2+y^2+z^2=a^2$ which is above the (x, y)-plane and inside the cylinder whose equation is $x^2+y^2 = ax$. [*Hint:* Use polar coordinates.]

4. Find the area of the piece of the graph of $y^2+z^2=2x$ between the planes $x=0$ and $x=2$.

5. Suppose a surface S has the equation $z=h(x, y)$, where the domain of h is a set D in the (x, y)-plane. Explain why formula (9-12) for the area of S can be written as

$$\int_D \left[1+\left(\frac{\partial z}{\partial x}\right)^2+\left(\frac{\partial z}{\partial y}\right)^2\right]^{1/2} dA.$$

6. For each of the following, determine the area of the graph of the given equation for (x, y) in the specified set $\bar{D}$.

(a) $z = (4 - x^2 - y^2)^{1/2}$; $\bar{D} = \{(x, y): x^2 + y^2 \leq 1\}$.

(b) $z = x^2 + y^2$; $\bar{D} = \{(x, y): x^2 + y^2 \leq 1\}$.

(c) $z \leq xy$; $\bar{D} = \{(x, y): x^2 + y^2 \leq 1\}$.

7. Show that the area of the ellipsoid whose equation is

$$\frac{x^2}{a^2} + \frac{y^2}{b^2} + \frac{z^2}{c^2} = 1$$

is equal to

(a) $2\pi a^2 + 2\pi ac^2(c^2 - a^2)^{-1/2} \cos^{-1}(a/c)$ if $a = b < c$;

(b) $2\pi a^2 + 2\pi ac^2(a^2 - c^2)^{-1/2} \cosh^{-1}(a/c)$ if $a = b > c$.

8. For each of the following, determine parametric equations of the tangent plane to the given surface at the point indicated.

(a) $x = u^3 - v$, $y = u^2v^3 - 3v$, $z = 2v$; $(-1, 2, 4)$.

(b) $x = 2e^{2u} \sin v$, $y = 2e^{3u} \cos v$, $z = e^{uv}$; $(1, \sqrt{3}, 1)$.

(c) $x = 4 \cos \theta \sin \Phi$, $y = 4\sqrt{3} \sin \theta \sin \Phi$, $z = 2 \cos \Phi$; $0 \leq \Phi \leq \pi$, $0 \leq \theta \leq 2\pi$; $(3, 3, 1)$.

9. For each of the following, determine a vector of unit length perpendicular to the given surface at the point indicated.

(a) $x = 2 \cos u$, $y = 4 \sin u$, $z = v$; $(\sqrt{2}, 2\sqrt{2}, 1)$.

(b) $x = 3u + v$, $y = u + 2v$, $z = 7u - 6v$; $(4, 3, 1)$.

(c) $x = \cosh u \cosh v$, $y = \cosh u \sinh v$, $z = \sinh u$; $(1, 0, 0)$.

10. Show that at all points of intersection of the following surfaces the tangent planes are perpendicular:

$$\begin{cases} x = u, \\ y = v, \\ z = uv; \end{cases} \qquad \begin{cases} x = a \sin \Phi \cos \theta, \\ y = \sqrt{2} \, a \sin \Phi \sin \theta, \\ z = \frac{1}{3}\sqrt{2} \, a \cos \Phi. \end{cases}$$

11. For each of the following, choose parametric equations for the surface S and use Definition 9-2.3 to determine the area of S.   (a) S is cut from the graph of $2x + 3y + z = 1$ by the coordinate planes.   (b) S is the piece of the graph of $2z = x^2 + y^2$ above the disk $x^2 + y^2 \leq 1$.   (c) S is the piece of the graph of $x^2 + z^2 = 2y$ between the planes $y = 0$ and $y = 2$.   (d) S is the piece of the sphere $x^2 + y^2 + z^2 = a^2$ above the disk $x^2 + y^2 \leq \frac{1}{4}a^2$.

12. The graph of $x = y^2 + z^2$ is a paraboloid. This paraboloid has parametric equations $x = t^2$, $y = t \cos \theta$, $z = t \sin \theta$. Determine the area of the piece of this paraboloid that is between the graphs of $x = 0$ and $x = 12$.

13. (a) Show that the following sets of parametric equations are parametric equations of the same surface and sketch the surface. [The surface is half of a hyperboloid of two sheets.]

$$\begin{cases} x = \cosh u \cosh v, \\ y = \cosh u \sinh v, \\ z = \sinh u; \end{cases} \qquad \begin{cases} x = t, \\ y = (t^2-1)^{\frac{1}{2}} \cos \theta, \\ z = (t^2-1)^{\frac{1}{2}} \sin \theta;\ t \geq 1. \end{cases}$$

(b) Choose one of the sets of parametric equations of part (a) and determine the area of the piece of the hyperboloid of two sheets between the planes $x = 1$ and $x = 5$.

14. The graph of the parametric equations,

$$x = 2 \cosh u \cos v,\ y = 2 \cosh u \sin v,\ z = 2 \sinh u,$$

is a hyperboloid of one sheet. Determine the area of the part of this hyperboloid between the (x, y)-plane and the plane $z = 4$.

15. Show that the hyperboloid of one sheet of problem 14 has parametric equations

$$x = (4+t^2)^{\frac{1}{2}} \cos \theta,\ y = (4+t^2)^{\frac{1}{2}} \sin \theta,\ z = t.$$

Use these equations to determine the area of the part of this hyperboloid between the (x, y)-plane and the plane $z = 4$.

16. Let R be the solid generated by rotating about the x-axis the set of points in the (x, y)-plane that are between the graphs of $y = 1/x$ and the x-axis and to the right of the graph of $x = 1$. Explain why R has volume π, but the surface of R does not have area.

17. Let S be a smooth surface element described by parametric equations $x = f(u, v), y = g(u, v), z = h(u, v)$, where $\bar{D}$ is the common domain of f, g, and h. Let $u = \theta(r, s)$ and $v = \Phi(r, s)$, where these equations define a one-to-one transformation of a set $\bar{D}^*$ in the (r, s)-plane onto the set $\bar{D}$. Show that

$$\int_D \left| \frac{\partial \mathbf{P}}{\partial u} \times \frac{\partial \mathbf{P}}{\partial v} \right| dA = \int_{D\star} \left| \frac{\partial \mathbf{Q}}{\partial r} \times \frac{\partial \mathbf{Q}}{\partial s} \right| dA,$$

where

$$\mathbf{P}(u, v) = f(u, v)\mathbf{i} + g(u, v)\mathbf{j} + h(u, v)\mathbf{k},$$

and

$$\mathbf{Q}(r, s) = \mathbf{P}[\theta(r, s),\ \Phi(r, s)].$$

9-3. SURFACE INTEGRALS

In this section we shall define surface integrals only for smooth surface elements.   In Section 9-7 we shall generalize this definition to "orientable" surfaces that are unions of several smooth surface elements.

Suppose that S is a smooth surface element with the position vector

$$\mathbf{P}(u, v) = f(u, v)\mathbf{i} + g(u, v)\mathbf{j} + h(u, v)\mathbf{k}, \tag{9-24}$$

where the common domain of f, g, and h is a set $\bar{D}$ in the (u, v)-plane. We know that S has a tangent plane at each point not on the edge, so it is possible to choose at each point a unit vector perpendicular to the tangent plane—i.e., perpendicular to the surface.   In fact, it follows from Theorem 9-2.1, Eq. (9-18), and the definition of smooth surface element, that all values of the following vector function are of unit length and perpendicular to the surface:

$$\frac{(\partial \mathbf{P}/\partial u) \times (\partial \mathbf{P}/\partial v)}{[(J_1)^2 + (J_2)^2 + (J_3)^2]^{\frac{1}{2}}}. \tag{9-25}$$

DEFINITION 9-3.1.   Suppose that S is a smooth surface element with the position vector $\mathbf{P}$ whose domain is $\bar{D}$, and that we are given a continuous vector function $\mathbf{n}$ whose domain is the interior D of $\bar{D}$† and whose values are all of unit length and perpendicular to S. With respect to $\mathbf{n}$, the *surface integral* of a vector-valued function $\mathbf{F}$ over S is denoted by $\int_S (\mathbf{F} \cdot \mathbf{n})\, d\sigma$ and is defined by

$$\int_S (\mathbf{F} \cdot \mathbf{n})\, d\sigma = \int_D (\mathbf{F} \cdot \mathbf{n}) \left| \frac{\partial \mathbf{P}}{\partial u} \times \frac{\partial \mathbf{P}}{\partial v} \right| dA. \tag{9-26}$$

There is little choice for the value of $\mathbf{n}$ to be used in this definition. In fact, $\mathbf{n}$ must either be the vector $(\partial \mathbf{P}/\partial u) \times (\partial \mathbf{P}/\partial v)$ divided by its length, or the vector obtained by multiplying this quotient by -1. For the first of these choices for $\mathbf{n}$, we have

$$\int_S (\mathbf{F} \cdot \mathbf{n})\, d\sigma = \int_D \mathbf{F} \cdot \left(\frac{\partial \mathbf{P}}{\partial u} \times \frac{\partial \mathbf{P}}{\partial v} \right) dA. \tag{9-27}$$

---

† An equivalent assumption is that the domain of $\mathbf{n}$ is S without its edge, since there is a continuous transformation with domain $\bar{D}$ and range S which has a continuous inverse [see the paragraph following Definition 9-2.1].

We know that if J_1, J_2, and J_3 are the Jacobians defined by the equations in (9-15) in the last section, then

$$\frac{\partial \mathbf{P}}{\partial u} \times \frac{\partial \mathbf{P}}{\partial v} = J_1 \mathbf{i} + J_2 \mathbf{j} + J_3 \mathbf{k}.$$

If $\mathbf{F} = L\mathbf{i} + M\mathbf{j} + N\mathbf{k}$, then we can write Eq. (9-27) as

$$\int_S (\mathbf{F} \cdot \mathbf{n}) \, d\sigma = \int_D (LJ_1 + MJ_2 + NJ_3) \, dA. \tag{9-28}$$

Now suppose that, for each coordinate plane, S can be divided into a finite number of smooth surface elements, each of which has the property that its projection onto that coordinate plane is one-to-one and the corresponding Jacobian J_i is nonzero except on a set of zero measure. Also suppose $\mathbf{F}$ is continuous on S (so that L, M, and N also are continuous). Then it follows from the formula for change of variables in multiple integrals [see the corollary to Theorem 8-7.3] that

$$\int_D L|J_1| \, dA = \int\int_{S_1} L \, dy \, dz,$$

$$\int_D M|J_2| \, dA = \int\int_{S_2} M \, dz \, dx,$$

$$\int_D N|J_3| \, dA = \int\int_{S_3} N \, dx \, dy,$$

where the integrals in the right members are evaluated over suitable pieces of the projections, S_1, S_2, and S_3, of S onto the coordinate planes. Thus, we can write Eq. (9-28) as

$$\int_S (\mathbf{F} \cdot \mathbf{n}) \, d\sigma = \int\int_{S_1} L(\pm dy \, dz) + \int\int_{S_2} M(\pm dz \, dx) + \int\int_{S_3} N(\pm dx \, dy), \tag{9-29}$$

where the signs are $+$ or $-$ according to whether J_1, J_2, or J_3, respectively, is positive or negative (that is, according to whether the vector $\mathbf{n}$ points toward the positive or the negative side of the corresponding coordinate plane when its initial point is in the plane).

The use of Theorem 8-7.3 to derive (9-29) by making changes of variables in (9-28) gives formal justification for the following manipulations.   If α, β, and γ are the angles between the coordinate axes and the vector $\mathbf{n}$, then

$$\mathbf{n} = (\cos\alpha)\mathbf{i} + (\cos\beta)\mathbf{j} + (\cos\gamma)\mathbf{k},$$

and

$$\mathbf{n}\,d\sigma = (\cos\alpha)\,d\sigma\mathbf{i} + (\cos\beta)\,d\sigma\mathbf{j} + (\cos\gamma)\,d\sigma\mathbf{k}.$$

Now we can use our intuitive feeling that $d\sigma$ replaces a symbol $\Delta\sigma$ that denotes a small, approximately planar piece of S occurring in an approximating sum for the surface integral.   This suggests that we replace the last equality by

$$\mathbf{n}\,d\sigma = (\pm\,dy\,dz)\mathbf{i} + (\pm\,dz\,dx)\mathbf{j} + (\pm\,dx\,dy)\mathbf{k},$$

where the signs are to be chosen as the signs of $\cos\alpha$, $\cos\beta$, and $\cos\gamma$, respectively.   With $\mathbf{F} = L\mathbf{i} + M\mathbf{j} + N\mathbf{k}$, we can use this expression for $\mathbf{n}\,d\sigma$ to obtain Eq. (9-29).

ILLUSTRATION.   Suppose we wish to evaluate the integral of $\mathbf{F}$ over the plane of Fig. 9-7, where $\mathbf{n}$ is directed upward and

$$\mathbf{F}(x, y, z) = x\mathbf{i} + y\mathbf{j} + z\mathbf{k}.$$

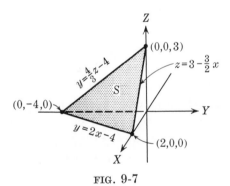

FIG. 9-7

Let us first make direct use of Definition 9-3.1, using the following parametric equations of the plane and Eq. (9-27):

$$x = u, \quad y = v, \quad z = -\tfrac{3}{2}u + \tfrac{3}{4}v + 3.$$

Then

$$\int_S (\mathbf{F}\cdot\mathbf{n})\,d\sigma = \int_D \begin{vmatrix} x & y & z \\ 1 & 0 & -\tfrac{3}{2} \\ 0 & 1 & \tfrac{3}{4} \end{vmatrix}\,dA = \int_D (+\tfrac{3}{2}x - \tfrac{3}{4}y + z)\,dA.$$

Since $z = -\frac{3}{2}x + \frac{3}{4}y + 3$, this gives us

$$\int_S (\mathbf{F} \cdot \mathbf{n})\, d\sigma = \int_0^2 \int_{2x-4}^0 3\, dy\, dx = \int_0^2 (12 - 6x)\, dx = 12.$$

Now if we use Eq. (9-29), we have

$$\int_S (\mathbf{F} \cdot \mathbf{n})\, d\sigma = \int_0^3 \int_{4z/3-4}^0 x\, dy\, dz + \int_0^2 \int_0^{3-3x/2} y(-dz\, dx)$$

$$+ \int_{-4}^0 \int_0^{y/2+2} z\, dx\, dy.$$

Since $6x - 3y + 4z = 12$ on S, this can be written as

$$\int_0^3 \int_{4z/3-4}^0 (\tfrac{1}{2}y - \tfrac{2}{3}z + 2)\, dy\, dz - \int_0^2 \int_0^{3-3x/2} (2x + \tfrac{4}{3}z - 4)\, dz\, dx$$

$$+ \int_{-4}^0 \int_0^{y/2+2} (-\tfrac{3}{2}x + \tfrac{3}{4}y + 3)\, dx\, dy.$$

After considerable computation, this gives $4 + 4 + 4 = 12$.

PROBLEMS

1. For each of the following, evaluate the surface integral with $\mathbf{n}$ directed upward. [That is, the third component of $\mathbf{n}$ is nonnegative.]

  (*a*) $\int_S (x\mathbf{i} + y\mathbf{j} + z\mathbf{k}) \cdot \mathbf{n}\, d\sigma$, where S is the part of the graph of $z = x^2 + y$ that is between the planes $x = \pm 3$ and between the planes $y = \pm 2$.

  (*b*) $\int_S (xz\mathbf{i} + yz\mathbf{j}) \cdot \mathbf{n}\, d\sigma$, where S is the graph of $z = (4 - x^2 - y^2)^{\frac{1}{2}}$.

  (c) $\int_S (x\mathbf{i} + y\mathbf{j} + z\mathbf{k}) \cdot \mathbf{n}\, d\sigma$, where S is the upper half of the sphere $x^2 + y^2 + z^2 = 4$.

2. For each of the following, assume that $\mathbf{n}$ is directed upward and use formula (9-29) to evaluate the surface integral.

  (*a*) $\int_S (x\mathbf{i} + y\mathbf{j} + z\mathbf{k}) \cdot \mathbf{n}\, d\sigma$, where S is the triangle with vertices $(1, 0, 0)$, $(0, 1, 0)$, $(0, 0, 1)$.

  (*b*) $\int_S (\mathbf{i} + \mathbf{j} + \mathbf{k}) \cdot \mathbf{n}\, d\sigma$, where S is the graph of $z = (1 - x^2 - y^2)^{\frac{1}{2}}$.

3. Evaluate $\int_S (x^2\mathbf{i} + y\mathbf{j} + z\mathbf{k}) \cdot \mathbf{n}\, d\sigma$, where S is the piece of the graph of $y = (4 - x^2)^{\frac{1}{2}}$ between the planes $z = 0$ and $z = 3$ and $\mathbf{n}$ is the normal whose y-component is nonnegative.

4. Evaluate each of the following surface integrals. [In each case, the integrand is the scalar **F**·**n** of Definition 9-3.1.]

(a) $\int_S yz \, d\sigma$, where S is the first-octant piece of the plane $x + 2y + 3z = 6$.

(b) $\int_S x^2 \, d\sigma$, where S is the piece of the cylinder $x^2 + y^2 = 1$ that is in the first octant and between the planes $z = 0$ and $z = 1$.

(c) $\int_S (x^2 + z^2) \, d\sigma$, where S is the half of the sphere $x^2 + y^2 + z^2 = 1$ on which $x \geq 0$.

5. Evaluate $\int_S (\mathbf{k} \cdot \mathbf{n}) \, d\sigma$, where S has the parametric equations $x = -t \cos \theta$, $y = -t \sin \theta$, $z = t$, $0 \leq t \leq 2$, $0 \leq \theta \leq \pi$, and

$$\mathbf{n} = \left(\frac{\partial \mathbf{P}}{\partial t} \times \frac{\partial \mathbf{P}}{\partial \theta} \right) \Big/ \left| \frac{\partial \mathbf{P}}{\partial t} \times \frac{\partial \mathbf{P}}{\partial \theta} \right|.$$

6. Evaluate $\int_S (x\mathbf{i} + y\mathbf{j} - z\mathbf{k}) \cdot \mathbf{n} \, d\sigma$, where S has the parametric equations $x = u + v$, $y = u - v$, $z = u^2 - v^2$, $0 \leq u \leq 1$, $0 \leq v \leq 1$, and

$$\mathbf{n} = \left(\frac{\partial \mathbf{P}}{\partial u} \times \frac{\partial \mathbf{P}}{\partial v} \right) \Big/ \left| \frac{\partial \mathbf{P}}{\partial u} \times \frac{\partial \mathbf{P}}{\partial v} \right|.$$

7. Suppose that a smooth surface element has parametric equations of type $x = x$, $y = y$, $z = h(x, y)$, where the domain of h is $\bar{D}$. Show that Eq. (9-26) of the text can be written as

$$\int_S \mathbf{F} \cdot \mathbf{n} \, d\sigma = \int_D (\mathbf{F} \cdot \mathbf{n}) \left[1 + \left(\frac{\partial z}{\partial x} \right)^2 + \left(\frac{\partial z}{\partial y} \right)^2 \right]^{\frac{1}{2}} dx \, dy,$$

where

$$\mathbf{n} = \pm \frac{\dfrac{\partial z}{\partial x} \mathbf{i} + \dfrac{\partial z}{\partial y} \mathbf{j} - \mathbf{k}}{\left[\left(\dfrac{\partial z}{\partial x} \right)^2 + \left(\dfrac{\partial z}{\partial y} \right)^2 + 1 \right]^{\frac{1}{2}}}.$$

9-4. POTENTIAL FUNCTIONS

There are some vector fields for which the line integral from a point P to a point Q is independent of the curve used to join P and Q. As indicated in Fig. 9-8, this means that the line integral around any closed curve is zero. A curve that contains points P and Q consists of a curve C_1 from P to Q and a curve C_2 from Q to P. If we denote by $-C_2$ the curve C_2 with its direction reversed, then the line integral of a function **F** around the closed curve is

$$\int_{C_1} \mathbf{F} \cdot d\mathbf{P} + \int_{C_2} \mathbf{F} \cdot d\mathbf{P} = \int_{C_1} \mathbf{F} \cdot d\mathbf{P} - \int_{-C_2} \mathbf{F} \cdot d\mathbf{P},$$

so that the line integral of **F** around the closed curve is zero if and only if the line integral along C_1 is equal to the line integral along $-C_2$.

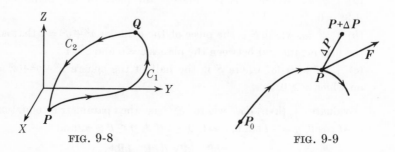

FIG. 9-8   FIG. 9-9

A force field **F** is said to be *conservative* on a set R if the line integral of **F** is zero around any rectifiable closed curve contained in R. In this section we shall investigate the nature of conservative force fields. As a first step, we note that if **F** is a conservative force field and $\mathbf{P}_0$ is the position vector of a fixed point, then the line integral of **F** from $\mathbf{P}_0$ to a variable point with position vector **P** is independent of the curve used to join the points. That is, the value of the line integral is determined once **P** has been specified, so that we can define a function Φ by

$$\Phi(\mathbf{P}) = \int_{\mathbf{P}_0}^{\mathbf{P}} \mathbf{F} \cdot d\mathbf{P},$$

where the integral is a line integral over some rectifiable curve joining $\mathbf{P}_0$ to **P**. Now we note that $\Phi(\mathbf{P}+\Delta\mathbf{P})$ can be evaluated by integrating along a curve from $\mathbf{P}_0$ to **P** and then along a line segment from **P** to $\mathbf{P}+\Delta\mathbf{P}$ [see Fig. 9-9]. If **F** were constant along this line segment, we would have

$$\Phi(\mathbf{P}+\Delta\mathbf{P}) - \Phi(\mathbf{P}) = \int_{\mathbf{P}}^{\mathbf{P}+\Delta\mathbf{P}} \mathbf{F} \cdot d\mathbf{P} = \mathbf{F} \cdot \Delta\mathbf{P}$$

and

$$\frac{\Phi(\mathbf{P}+\Delta\mathbf{P}) - \Phi(\mathbf{P})}{|\Delta\mathbf{P}|} = \mathbf{F} \cdot \frac{\Delta\mathbf{P}}{|\Delta\mathbf{P}|},$$

so that the projection of **F** onto this line segment is equal to the directional derivative of Φ in the direction of the line segment. It would then follow that **F** is the gradient $\nabla\Phi$ of Φ. Let us now replace this intuitive argument with a theorem and give a careful proof of the theorem. Rather than the severe assumption that **F** be constant, we shall assume only that **F** is continuous. Clearly, we want the domain of

F to be connected. Actually, it is convenient to assume more—namely, that the domain of **F** is open in R^3 as well as connected. It then follows that the domain of **F** is *polygonally connected* in the sense that any two points of S are the end points of a polygonal curve contained in S [see problem 15, page 61].

THEOREM 9-4.1. Suppose S is a nonempty connected open set in R^3. If **F** is a function that is continuous on S and is such that

$$\int_{C_1} \mathbf{F} \cdot d\mathbf{P} = \int_{C_2} \mathbf{F} \cdot d\mathbf{P},$$

whenever C_1 and C_2 are polygonal curves in S having the same initial and terminal points, then there exists a function Φ whose domain is S and for which $\mathbf{F} = \nabla \Phi$.

PROOF. We shall choose a point in S and let $\mathbf{P}_0$ denote the position vector of this point. For any point **P** in S, we shall select a polygonal curve C in S that joins $\mathbf{P}_0$ to **P** [see Fig. 9-10] and define

$$\Phi(\mathbf{P}) = \int_C \mathbf{F} \cdot d\mathbf{P}. \tag{9-30}$$

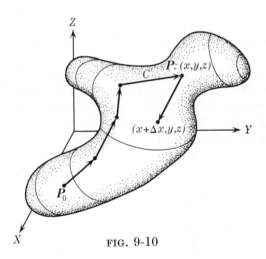

FIG. 9-10

By hypothesis, the number $\Phi(\mathbf{P})$ is completely determined by **P** and does not depend on the particular polygonal curve used to join $\mathbf{P}_0$ to **P**. To complete the proof, we shall show that each partial derivative of Φ exists and is equal to the corresponding component of **F**. We shall give an explicit proof only for the x-component, since the proof is the same for the other components. Let us denote by (x, y, z) the point with position vector $\mathbf{P}$ and consider the difference quotient,

$$\frac{\Phi(x+\Delta x,\, y,\, z) - \Phi(x,\, y,\, z)}{\Delta x}. \tag{9-31}$$

We evaluate $\Phi(x, y, z)$ as the line integral from $\mathbf{P}_0$ to $\mathbf{P}$ along C, and evaluate $\Phi(x+\Delta x, y, z)$ as the line integral from $\mathbf{P}_0$ to $(x+\Delta x, y, z)$ along the polygonal path consisting of C and a line segment from (x, y, z) to $(x+\Delta x, y, z)$. Then the numerator of (9-31) is simply the line integral of $\mathbf{F}$ along this line segment [see problem 11 of Section 9-1]. If L is the x-component of $\mathbf{F}$, then using Eq. (9-6), we see that

$$\frac{\Phi(x+\Delta x,\, y,\, z) - \Phi(x,\, y,\, z)}{\Delta x} = \frac{1}{\Delta x}\int_x^{x+\Delta x} L\, dx.$$

By hypothesis, $\mathbf{F}$ is continuous. Therefore, L is continuous and it follows from the first form of the fundamental theorem of calculus that the right member of this equality approaches the value of L at (x, y, z) as Δx approaches zero. Therefore, $\partial\Phi/\partial x = L$, as we wished to prove.

We have shown that a conservative force field is the gradient of a function Φ. Such a function Φ is said to be a (scalar) *potential function* of the function $\mathbf{F}$. We shall now show that the gradient of a function Φ is a conservative force field, without using the assumption that Φ was constructed from a conservative force field. We must show that the line integral of $\nabla\Phi$ from a point $\mathbf{P}_0$ to a point $\mathbf{P}$ is independent of the curve used to join $\mathbf{P}_0$ and $\mathbf{P}$. This can be done by demonstrating that this integral is equal to the difference between the value of Φ at $\mathbf{P}$ and the value of Φ at $\mathbf{P}_0$. Our first method of showing this applies to curves with a parametrization such that x', y', and z' are all continuous. We first establish the following equality:

$$\int_C \nabla\Phi\cdot d\mathbf{P} = \int_a^b \left[\frac{\partial\Phi}{\partial x} x'(t) + \frac{\partial\Phi}{\partial y} y'(t) + \frac{\partial\Phi}{\partial z} z'(t)\right] dt$$

$$= \int_a^b \frac{d\Phi}{dt}\, dt = \Phi(\mathbf{P}) - \Phi(\mathbf{P}_0), \tag{9-32}$$

where $\mathbf{P}_0$ and $\mathbf{P}$ are the end points of the curve C and the numbers a and b are the corresponding values of the parameter. To assure that $\int_C (\nabla\Phi)\cdot d\mathbf{P}$ exists, we assume that C is rectifiable and that $\nabla\Phi$ is continuous—i.e., the first-order partial derivatives of Φ are continuous. The first equality,

$$\int_C \nabla\Phi\cdot d\mathbf{P} = \int_a^b \left[\frac{\partial\Phi}{\partial x}\,x'(t)+\frac{\partial\Phi}{\partial y}\,y'(t)+\frac{\partial\Phi}{\partial z}\,z'(t)\right]dt,$$

is formula (9-6). To use formula (9-6), we need the information already assumed—namely, that the first-order partial derivatives of Φ are continuous on C—and the additional information that x', y', and z' are continuous on $[a, b]$. The next equality in Eq. (9-32) follows from the chain rule

$$\frac{\partial\Phi}{\partial x}\,x'(t)+\frac{\partial\Phi}{\partial y}\,y'(t)+\frac{\partial\Phi}{\partial z}\,z'(t) = \frac{d\Phi}{dt},$$

proved in Section 6-2. To use the chain rule, we can also assume that the domains of the first-order partial derivatives of Φ contain a neighborhood of each point of C. The last equality in Eq. (9-32) uses only the second form of the fundamental theorem of calculus [Theorem 3-6.2], for which we need know only that the integral involved exists (since the antiderivative of the integrand clearly exists).

ILLUSTRATION 1. If $\Phi(x, y, z) = 1+2x+yz^2$, then

$$\nabla\Phi = 2\mathbf{i}+z^2\mathbf{j}+2yz\mathbf{k}.$$

First let us evaluate $\int_{C_1} \nabla\Phi\cdot d\mathbf{P}$, where C_1 is the path from $(0, 0, 0)$ to $(1, 2, 3)$ shown in Fig. 9-11. We have $y = 2x$ and $z = 3x$ on C_1, so that

$$\int_{C_1} \nabla\Phi\cdot d\mathbf{P} = \int_{C_1} (2\,dx+z^2\,dy+2yz\,dz) = \int_0^1 (2+54x^2)\,dx = 20.$$

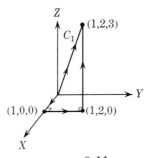

FIG. 9-11

Along the path C_2 that consists of line segments from $(0, 0, 0)$ to $(1, 0, 0)$, from $(1, 0, 0)$ to $(1, 2, 0)$, and from $(1, 2, 0)$ to $(1, 2, 3)$ we have

$$\int_{C_2} \boldsymbol{\nabla}\Phi\cdot d\mathbf{P} = \int_0^1 2\,dx + \int_0^2 (0)\,dy + \int_0^3 4z\,dz = 20. \qquad (9\text{-}33)$$

The integral along C_2 has the same value as the integral along C_1, as we might have expected. We might also expect this to be equal to the difference of the values of Φ at the end points of the curve—i.e., equal to

$$\Phi(1, 2, 3) - \Phi(0, 0, 0) = 21 - 1 = 20.$$

The student should note that the curve C_2 does not satisfy the assumptions used to establish (9-32). In fact, x', y', and z' cannot all exist at $(1, 0, 0)$, or at $(1, 2, 0)$, since the curve does not have a tangent at these points. However, we avoided this difficulty in Eq. (9-33) by evaluating the line integral along each segment of C separately. This gives as the total answer

$$[\Phi(1, 0, 0) - \Phi(0, 0, 0)] + [\Phi(1, 2, 0) - \Phi(1, 0, 0)]$$

$$+ [\Phi(1, 2, 3) - \Phi(1, 2, 0)] = \Phi(1, 2, 3) - \Phi(0, 0, 0).$$

We shall now summarize the preceding discussion as a theorem. In fact, we can show that $\int_C \boldsymbol{\nabla}\Phi\cdot d\mathbf{P} = \Phi(\mathbf{P}) - \Phi(\mathbf{P}_0)$ without making any assumption about the curve C with end points $\mathbf{P}_0$ and $\mathbf{P}$ other than that it is rectifiable. With this result, it would not be necessary, for example, to break the curve C_2 of the preceding illustration into three pieces. The method of proof used for this stronger result also gives meaning to the intuitive feeling that $\int_C \boldsymbol{\nabla}\Phi\cdot d\mathbf{P}$ is the total change in Φ as one moves from the initial point to the terminal point of C.

THEOREM 9-4.2. If the first-order partial derivatives of Φ are continuous in a neighborhood of each point of a rectifiable curve C, then

$$\int_C \boldsymbol{\nabla}\Phi\cdot d\mathbf{P} = \Phi(\mathbf{P}) - \Phi(\mathbf{P}_0),$$

where $\mathbf{P}_0$ and $\mathbf{P}$ are the initial and terminal points of C.

PROOF. Since the first-order partial derivatives of Φ are continuous, we know that $\int_C \boldsymbol{\nabla}\Phi\cdot d\mathbf{P}$ exists [see Theorem 9-1.1]. Also, this integral is the limit, as the fineness of the partition approaches zero, of a sum of type

$$\sum_{i=1}^{n} \boldsymbol{\nabla}\Phi\cdot\Delta_i\mathbf{P} = \sum_{i=1}^{n} \left(\frac{\partial\Phi}{\partial x}\Delta_i x + \frac{\partial\Phi}{\partial y}\Delta_i y + \frac{\partial\Phi}{\partial z}\Delta_i z\right), \qquad (9\text{-}34)$$

where the partial derivatives in the ith term are evaluated at a point of the arc of C that joins $\mathbf{P}(t_i)$ and $\mathbf{P}(t_{i+1})$. It follows from Taylor's theorem [Section 6-5] that if for each i the partial derivatives in Eq. (9-34) are continuous on the chord joining $\mathbf{P}(t_i)$ and $\mathbf{P}(t_{i+1})$, then there is a point on this chord such that, if the partial derivatives are evaluated at this point, then

$$\Delta_i\Phi = \frac{\partial\Phi}{\partial x}\Delta_i x + \frac{\partial\Phi}{\partial y}\Delta_i y + \frac{\partial\Phi}{\partial z}\Delta_i z, \qquad (9\text{-}35)$$

where $\Delta_i\Phi$ is the value of Φ at $\mathbf{P}(t_{i+1})$ *minus* the value of Φ at $\mathbf{P}(t_i)$. If these points on the chords could be used in (9-34), we would have

$$\sum_{i=1}^{n} \boldsymbol{\nabla}\Phi\cdot\Delta_i\mathbf{P} = \sum_{i=1}^{n} \Delta_i\Phi = \Phi(\mathbf{P}) - \Phi(\mathbf{P}_0).$$

Actually, if we evaluate the partial derivatives in (9-34) at one of the end points of $\Delta_i\mathbf{P}$, then we have

$$\sum \boldsymbol{\nabla}\Phi\cdot\Delta_i\mathbf{P} = \Phi(\mathbf{P}) - \Phi(\mathbf{P}_0) + \sum [(\boldsymbol{\nabla}\Phi)_C - (\boldsymbol{\nabla}\Phi)_{\text{chord}}]\cdot\Delta_i\mathbf{P},$$

where $(\boldsymbol{\nabla}\Phi)_C$ is the value of $\boldsymbol{\nabla}\Phi$ when evaluated at one of the points $\mathbf{P}(t_i)$ or $\mathbf{P}(t_{i+1})$ on C, and $(\boldsymbol{\nabla}\Phi)_{\text{chord}}$ is the value of $\boldsymbol{\nabla}\Phi$ when evaluated at a suitable point on the chord joining these points. If η is the largest of $|(\boldsymbol{\nabla}\Phi)_C - (\boldsymbol{\nabla}\Phi)_{\text{chord}}|$ for all intervals $[t_i, t_{i+1}]$, then

$$|\sum [(\boldsymbol{\nabla}\Phi)_C - (\boldsymbol{\nabla}\Phi)_{\text{chord}}]\cdot\Delta_i\mathbf{P}| \leqq \eta \sum |\Delta_i\mathbf{P}| \leqq \eta\cdot(\text{length of } C). \qquad (9\text{-}36)$$

Now let ε be an arbitrary positive number. For each point p of C, there is a number $\delta_{p,\varepsilon}$ such that the partial derivatives of Φ are continuous in the $2\delta_{p,\varepsilon}$-neighborhood of p and

$$|(\boldsymbol{\nabla}\Phi)_p - (\boldsymbol{\nabla}\Phi)_r| < \frac{\varepsilon}{2(\text{length of } C)} \text{ if } d(p, r) < 2\delta_{p,\varepsilon}, \qquad (9\text{-}37)$$

where $(\boldsymbol{\nabla}\Phi)_p$ and $(\boldsymbol{\nabla}\Phi)_r$ are the values of $\boldsymbol{\nabla}\Phi$ at p and r, respectively. Since C is the continuous image of a compact interval $[a, b]$, C is compact [Theorem 2-8.1]. Therefore, there is a finite collection of $\delta_{p,\varepsilon}$-neighborhoods of points on C that cover C. Let δ be the radius of the smallest of these neighborhoods and choose a partition $\{a = t_1, t_2, \cdots,$ $t_{n+1} = b\}$ of $[a, b]$ which is fine enough to have the following properties:

(i) $\left| \int_C \nabla \Phi \cdot d\mathbf{P} - \sum_{i=1}^{n} \nabla \Phi \cdot \Delta_i \mathbf{P} \right| < \frac{1}{2}\varepsilon$, if the partial derivatives in the ith term of the sum are evaluated at a point of the arc of C that joins $\mathbf{P}(t_i)$ and $\mathbf{P}(t_{i+1})$;

(ii) $d[\mathbf{P}(t_i), \mathbf{P}(t_{i+1})] < \delta$ for all i.

The inequality in (ii) can be satisfied, since $\mathbf{P}$ is uniformly continuous on $[a, b]$.

If $\mathbf{P}(t_i)$ is in the δ-neighborhood of a point p, then the chord joining $\mathbf{P}(t_i)$ and $\mathbf{P}(t_{i+1})$ is in the 2δ-neighborhood of p. Therefore, the partial derivatives of Φ are continuous on this chord and Eq. (9-35) can be used. Also, it follows from (9-37) that

$$\left| (\nabla \Phi)_C - (\nabla \Phi)_{\text{chord}} \right| < \frac{\varepsilon}{2(\text{length of } C)},$$

for each interval, so that (9-36) implies

$$\left| \sum \left[(\nabla \Phi)_C - (\nabla \Phi)_{\text{chord}} \right] \cdot \Delta_i \mathbf{P} \right| < \frac{1}{2}\varepsilon.$$

It follows from this and (i) that

$$\left| \int_C \nabla \Phi \cdot d\mathbf{P} - \sum (\nabla \Phi)_{\text{chord}} \cdot \Delta_i \mathbf{P} \right|$$

$$= \left| \int_C \nabla \Phi \cdot d\mathbf{P} - [\Phi(\mathbf{P}) - \Phi(\mathbf{P}_0)] \right| < \varepsilon.$$

Therefore, $\int_C \nabla \Phi \cdot d\mathbf{P} = \Phi(\mathbf{P}) - \Phi(\mathbf{P}_0)$.

PROBLEMS

1. For each of the following vector-valued functions, show that the line integral between two points is independent of the curve used to join the points. Do this by showing that the given function is the gradient of a potential function.

(a) $\mathbf{F} = x\mathbf{i} + y\mathbf{j} + z\mathbf{k}$.

(b) $\mathbf{F} = 3x^2 y\mathbf{i} + x^3\mathbf{j}$.

(c) $\mathbf{F} = (e^x \sin y)\mathbf{i} + (e^x \cos y)\mathbf{j} + z\mathbf{k}$.

(d) $\mathbf{F} = (3x^2 y + 5 + y^2 z)\mathbf{i} + (x^3 + 2xyz)\mathbf{j} + (xy^2)\mathbf{k}$.

(e) $\mathbf{F} = [(2x - yz) \sin xy + x^2 y \cos xy]\mathbf{i} + (x^3 \cos xy - xz \sin xy)\mathbf{j}$
$+ (\cos xy)\mathbf{k}$.

2. For each of the following, evaluate $\int \nabla \Phi \cdot d\mathbf{P}$ between the points P and Q by choosing a suitable path and evaluating the line integral explicitly. Check by using Theorem 9-4.2.

(a) $\Phi = xyz$; $P = (0, 0, 0)$; $Q = (1, 3, 5)$.

(b) $\Phi = x + 3yz$; $P = (1, 0, 2)$; $Q = (2, 3, 3)$.

(c) $\Phi = z \sin (2x + 3y)$; $P = (0, 0, 0)$; $Q = (2, 3, -1)$.

3. Show that if C does not contain the origin, then

$$\int_C \frac{x \, dx + y \, dy}{x^2 + y^2} = \ln \frac{r_2}{r_1},$$

where r_1 and r_2 are the distances of the end points of C from the origin.

4. Show that $\int_C (x^2 + y^2)^{-1}(-y \, dx + x \, dy) = \theta_2 - \theta_1$, where θ_1 and θ_2 are suitable angles from the positive x-axis to the lines from the origin to the initial and terminal points of C.

5. A gravitational force field $\mathbf{G}$ is defined by

$$\mathbf{G}(x, y, z) = \frac{c\mathbf{N}}{x^2 + y^2 + z^2} = \frac{-c(x\mathbf{i} + y\mathbf{j} + z\mathbf{k})}{(x^2 + y^2 + z^2)^{3/2}},$$

where $\mathbf{N}$ is a unit vector pointing toward the origin and c is a constant. Show that $\mathbf{G}$ is conservative and that the work done by $\mathbf{G}$ along a rectifiable curve can be expressed in terms of the distances of the end points from the origin.

6. Find a potential function Φ for $\mathbf{F}$, where

$$\mathbf{F}(x, y, z) = -y(x^2 - y^2)^{-1/2}x^{-1}\mathbf{i} + (x^2 - y^2)^{-1/2}\mathbf{j} + \mathbf{k}$$

in the region $|x| > |y|$. Do this by integrating from $(1, 0, 0)$ to (x, y, z) along straight lines. Check by showing that $\nabla \Phi = \mathbf{F}$.

7. Let C be a simple closed curve that lies in a plane perpendicular to the (x, y)-plane and is such that x', y', and z' are continuous on C. Show that

$$\int_C z \, dx + (x + y) \, dy + x \, dz = 0.$$

8.* Let $\mathbf{F}$ be a conservative force field. Use Newton's law $\mathbf{F} = m\mathbf{a}$ to show that the work done by $\mathbf{F}$ on a moving particle is equal to the change in kinetic energy [kinetic energy is $\frac{1}{2}m|\mathbf{v}|^2$, where $\mathbf{v}$ is velocity and m is mass].

9. Suppose that Φ and ψ are both potential functions for a vector-valued function $\mathbf{F}$. Show that $\Phi - \psi$ is a constant.

9-5. GREEN'S THEOREM

For functions of points on the real-number line, the most fundamental relation between differentiation and integration is given by the formula

$$\int_a^b f'(x)\, dx = f(b) - f(a).$$

The equality of Theorem 9-4.2, $\int_C \nabla\Phi\cdot d\mathbf{P} = \Phi(\mathbf{P}) - \Phi(\mathbf{P}_0)$, is a similar formula. We shall now develop another formula—Green's theorem†— for functions of points in the plane. Here again a differentiation is neutralized by an integration, in the sense that a *double* integral over a set S is equal to the *line* integral around the boundary of the set, where the integrand of the double integral involves derivatives of functions in the integrand of the line integral.

Let us consider first the simple case for which we have a line integral around a rectangle. We shall let S be the rectangle of Fig. 9-12 and let L and M be functions such that L, M, and the partial derivatives, $\partial L/\partial y$ and $\partial M/\partial x$, are continuous on the boundary and interior of S. Green's theorem states that

$$\int_C (L\, dx + M\, dy) = \int_S \left(\frac{\partial M}{\partial x} - \frac{\partial L}{\partial y} \right) dA, \qquad (9\text{-}38)$$

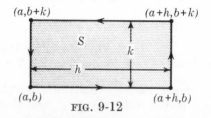

FIG. 9-12

where the boundary of S is denoted by C and is oriented counterclockwise as shown in the figure, so that the interior of S is on the left as one moves around C. To establish Eq. (9-38), let us consider $\int_S (\partial M/\partial x)\, dA$ and $\int_S (-\partial L/\partial y)\, dA$ separately. These double integrals exist, since the integrands are continuous on the rectangle and its

---

† Green's theorem is often credited to George Green (1828), but appeared earlier in the work of Gauss (1813) and Lagrange (1760).

boundary. We know that each of the double integrals can be evaluated as two successive ordinary integrals. Explicitly, we have

$$\int_S \left(\frac{\partial M}{\partial x}\right) dA = \int_b^{b+k} \int_a^{a+h} \frac{\partial M}{\partial x}\, dx\, dy = \int_b^{b+k} [M(a+h,\, y) - M(a,\, y)]\, dy$$

$$= \int_b^{b+k} M(a+h,\, y)\, dy + \int_{b+k}^b M(a,\, y)\, dy = \int_C M\, dy,$$

$$\int_S \left(-\frac{\partial L}{\partial y}\right) dA = \int_a^{a+h} \int_b^{b+k} \left(-\frac{\partial L}{\partial y}\right) dy\, dx$$

$$= \int_a^{a+h} [L(x,\, b) - L(x,\, b+k)]\, dx$$

$$= \int_a^{a+h} L(x,\, b)\, dx + \int_{a+h}^a L(x,\, b+k)\, dx = \int_C L\, dx.$$

This completes the proof of (9-38) for the rectangle S.

ILLUSTRATION 1. If S is the rectangle of Fig. 9-13, then

$$\int_C (x-y)\, dx + x^2\, dy = \int_0^2 x\, dx + \int_0^1 4\, dy + \int_2^0 (x-1)\, dx = 6.$$

This should be equal to the double integral,

$$\int_S \left[\frac{\partial(x^2)}{\partial x} - \frac{\partial(x-y)}{\partial y}\right] dA = \int_0^1 \int_0^2 (2x+1)\, dx\, dy = \int_0^1 6\, dy = 6.$$

It is possible to use the method of the preceding discussion to establish Eq. (9-38) for more general sets than rectangles. For the set S of Fig. 9-14, we can write

$$\int_S \left(-\frac{\partial L}{\partial y}\right) dA = \int_a^b \int_{u(x)}^{v(x)} \left(-\frac{\partial L}{\partial y}\right) dy\, dx = \int_a^b \{L[x,\, u(x)] - L[x,\, v(x)]\}\, dx$$

$$= \int_a^b L[x,\, u(x)]\, dx + \int_b^a L[x,\, v(x)]\, dx = \int_C L\, dx.$$

Similarly, $\int_S (\partial M/\partial x)\, dA = \int_C M\, dy$. These two equalities can be combined to give (9-38). This argument can be used if L and M have continuous first-order partial derivatives, S is between the graphs of two continuous functions of x, and S is between the graphs of two continuous functions of y. We can then generalize to any set, such as

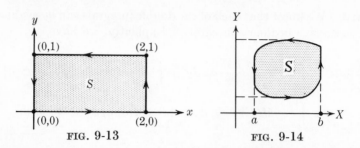

FIG. 9-13   FIG. 9-14

the one of Fig. 9-15, that can be divided into a finite number of pieces each of which is between the graphs of two continuous functions of x and between the graphs of two continuous functions of y. To do this, we need only observe that a double integral over a set is the sum of the double integrals over component sets, and that the line integral around the boundary of the entire set is the sum of the line integrals around the boundaries of the pieces (as indicated in Fig. 9-15, integrals over arcs that are boundaries of the two pieces are evaluated twice in opposite directions). Figure 9-16 shows a region to which the discussion of this paragraph is not applicable.

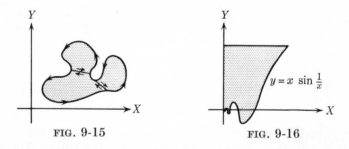

FIG. 9-15   FIG. 9-16

It is customary to say that *Green's theorem* is any theorem which states that an equation similar to (9-38) is true when certain conditions are satisfied by the set S, the boundary C, and the functions L and M. We have proved Green's theorem for rectangles and for sets of the type indicated in Fig. 9-15. Green's theorem can be proved for much more general sets than these. In fact, we shall eventually state Green's theorem for sets whose boundaries are rectifiable simple closed curves. However, we must first discuss the meaning of "simple closed curve." It will be recalled that a curve is defined by a continuous position vector **P** whose domain is an interval. Also, the *boundary in T* of a subset S of T is the set of all those points (x, y) with the property that each neighborhood of (x, y) contains points that are in S and also points that are in $T-S$. A *simple closed curve*, it will be remembered, is a curve with a position vector $\mathbf{P}(t)$, $a \leqq t \leqq b$, such that $\mathbf{P}(a)$ and $\mathbf{P}(b)$ are coincident and a and b are the only distinct values of t at which $\mathbf{P}$ has the same values; i.e., the curve does not touch or cross itself except at the ends [see Definition 7-4.1]. A simple closed curve C divides the plane into three sets, no two of which have a point in common [see Figs. 9-17 and 9-18]. One of the sets is C itself; each of the sets has C as its boundary; and exactly one set other than C is bounded (this set is said to be the *interior* of C). This statement may seem rather obvious for certain familiar simple closed curves, such as circles, ellipses, and polygons. However, the proof for an arbitrary simple closed curve is not simple and will not be given here.†

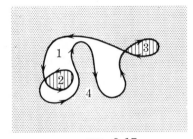   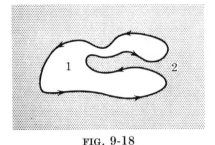

FIG. 9-17   FIG. 9-18

A curve that divides its com-   A simple closed curve and
plement into four pieces.   the two pieces into which
                                     it divides its complement.

Now suppose R is a set whose boundary is a rectifiable simple closed curve C. If we are to evaluate a double integral over R, we need to know that R has area. This will be left for the student to do [see problem 11]. Suppose that for R we choose an inner sum whose squares have a connected union, as shown in Fig. 9-19. Let us evaluate a line integral, $\int L \, dx + M \, dy$, around each of these squares. It is important to note that, since the integral is taken twice in opposite directions along each segment that is a common side of two squares, the sum of these line integrals is equal to the line integral around the boundary Γ of the union S of all the squares. Thus, if $\partial L/\partial y$ and $\partial M/\partial x$ are continuous on each square, so that Eq. (9-38) can be used for each square, then

$$\int_{\Gamma} L \, dx + M \, dy = \int_{S} \left(\frac{\partial M}{\partial x} - \frac{\partial L}{\partial y} \right) dA.$$

† Camille Jordan (1892) was the first to point out that this statement needs a proof. Jordan and others published incomplete "proofs." A correct proof was given first in 1905 by Oswald Veblen.

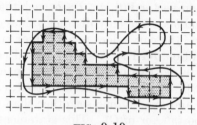

FIG. 9-19

If $\partial L/\partial y$ and $\partial M/\partial x$ are bounded on all of R, then

$$\int_S \left(\frac{\partial M}{\partial x} - \frac{\partial L}{\partial y}\right) dA \to \int_R \left(\frac{\partial M}{\partial x} - \frac{\partial L}{\partial y}\right) dA,$$

as the area of $R-S$ approaches zero. We shall show in Lemmas 1 and 2 that it is possible to choose the system of squares so that not only does the area of $R-S$ approach zero, but also $\int_\Gamma L\,dx + M\,dy$ approaches $\int_C (L\mathbf{i} + M\mathbf{j})\cdot d\mathbf{P}$, where C is "positively oriented" as described prior to the proof of Lemma 2. (Intuitively, a curve is "positively oriented" if the region bounded by the curve is on the left as one moves around the curve.) Once the two lemmas have been proved, we will have a proof of the following theorem.†

THEOREM 9-5.1 (GREEN'S THEOREM). If R is a bounded set in the (x, y)-plane whose boundary is a rectifiable simple closed curve C not equal to R, L and M are two functions continuous at all points of $R \cup C$, and $\partial L/\partial y$ and $\partial M/\partial x$ are bounded on R and continuous at all points of R, then

$$\int_C (L\mathbf{i} + M\mathbf{j})\cdot d\mathbf{P} = \int_R \left(\frac{\partial M}{\partial x} - \frac{\partial L}{\partial y}\right) dA, \qquad (9\text{-}39)$$

where C is "positively oriented," as described prior to the proof of Lemma 2 on page 465.

ILLUSTRATION 2. Suppose we wish to evaluate

$$\int (x^2 + y^2)\,dx + (x^2 - y^2)\,dy$$

---

† If the student needs additional evidence that the proof of this form of Green's theorem is not easy, he might study another proof given in *Mathematical Analysis: A Modern Approach to Advanced Calculus* by T. M. Apostol (Reading, Mass.: Addison-Wesley Publishing Co., Inc., 1957), pp. 287–292.

around the triangle of Fig. 9-20. It follows from Green's theorem that the line integral is equal to

$$\int_R \left[\frac{\partial(x^2 - y^2)}{\partial x} - \frac{\partial(x^2 + y^2)}{\partial y} \right] dA = \int_0^1 \int_0^y 2(x - y) \, dx \, dy$$

$$= \int_0^1 (-y^2) \, dy = -\frac{1}{3}.$$

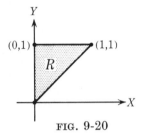

FIG. 9-20

There is a simple gimmick that makes it possible to use Green's theorem for sets bounded by several rectifiable simple closed curves. For example, suppose we wish to verify that

$$\int_C (L\mathbf{i} + M\mathbf{j}) \cdot d\mathbf{P} = \int_R \left(\frac{\partial M}{\partial x} - \frac{\partial L}{\partial y} \right) dA, \qquad (9\text{-}40)$$

for the set R of Fig. 9-21, where C consists of the two circles and the boundary of the rectangle. By drawing the four short lines as indicated we can create three regions whose boundaries are simple closed curves. Now we take the sum of the line integrals along each of these simple closed curves. Since Green's theorem applies to each region separately and *the integrals along the short lines cancel*, Eq. (9-40) is valid for the original boundary C of R.

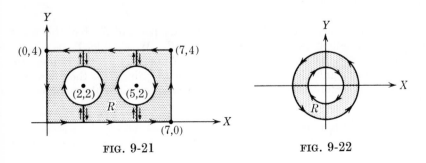

FIG. 9-21   FIG. 9-22

ILLUSTRATION 3. Suppose we wish to evaluate $\int \mathbf{F} \cdot d\mathbf{P}$ around the entire boundary of the set R of Fig. 9-22, where

$$\mathbf{F}(x, y) = \left(\frac{-y}{x^2+y^2}\right)\mathbf{i} + \left(\frac{x}{x^2+y^2}\right)\mathbf{j}.$$

Since

$$\frac{\partial}{\partial x}\left(\frac{x}{x^2+y^2}\right) - \frac{\partial}{\partial y}\left(\frac{-y}{x^2+y^2}\right) = \frac{y^2-x^2}{(x^2+y^2)^2} - \frac{y^2-x^2}{(x^2+y^2)^2} = 0,$$

it follows from Green's theorem, as modified in the preceding paragraph, that the line integral around the boundary of R is zero. Thus, the work done by $\mathbf{F}$ around the outer circle is equal to the work around the inner circle, if both are computed in the counterclockwise direction. This work can most easily be computed by letting $x = r \cos t$ and $y = r \sin t$, where r is the radius of the circle. Then the work is equal to the line integral

$$\int \mathbf{F} \cdot d\mathbf{P} = \int_0^{2\pi} \left[\left(\frac{-\sin t}{r}\right)\mathbf{i} + \left(\frac{\cos t}{r}\right)\mathbf{j}\right] \cdot [(-r \sin t)\mathbf{i} + (r \cos t)\mathbf{j}]\, dt$$

$$= \int_0^{2\pi} dt = 2\pi.$$

LEMMA 1. If R is a bounded set in the (x, y)-plane whose boundary is a rectifiable simple closed curve C not equal to R, and $\Delta > 0$, then for any points $\mathbf{P}_1, \mathbf{P}_2, \cdots, \mathbf{P}_{n+1} = \mathbf{P}_1$, sufficiently close together around C, and any $\varepsilon > 0$, there is a connected union of squares S contained in R for which the boundary of S is a single simple closed polygonal curve and there are points $\mathbf{Q}_1, \mathbf{Q}_2, \cdots, \mathbf{Q}_{n+1} = \mathbf{Q}_1$ on the boundary of S such that for all k the following are true:

(i) $|\mathbf{P}_k - \mathbf{Q}_k| < \varepsilon$.

(ii) The length of the boundary of S is less than twelve times the length of C.

(iii) The area of $R - S$ is less than Δ.

PROOF.† If a point of R is not a boundary point of R, then this point has a neighborhood that is contained in R. We shall let $\mathbf{P}_0$ be a point of R that is not a boundary point of R and let r be the radius of a circular neighborhood of $\mathbf{P}_0$ contained in R. Since C is the range of a continuous function $\mathbf{P}$ whose domain is an interval $[a, b]$, we know that

---

† Gaps will be left in the proof at certain places, but are indicated in brackets. The proof should be read first without concern for these gaps. Interested students might attempt to provide the missing explanations.

P is uniformly continuous. Therefore, there are points $\mathbf{P}_1, \mathbf{P}_2, \cdots,$ $\mathbf{P}_{n+1} = \mathbf{P}_1$ on C such that the length of arc between successive points is less than r [*gap*]. The curve C has zero area [problem 11]. Therefore, we may choose a system of squares whose mesh is less than $\varepsilon/\sqrt{2}$, small enough that the outer sum for C determined by this system of squares is less than Δ, and small enough so that for each k the point $\mathbf{P}_k$ is in the interior of a square (which we shall call a *vertex square* and denote by S_k) such that

(1) the distance of a point of C from S_k is greater than the diagonal of S_k, unless the point is on the arc joining $\mathbf{P}_k$ to $\mathbf{P}_{k-1}$ or on the arc joining $\mathbf{P}_k$ to $\mathbf{P}_{k+1}$ [*gap*]; and

(2) the sum of the areas of these vertex squares is less than $\frac{1}{2}\varepsilon$.

Now let us consider the (possibly disconnected) part C_k of C that is between $\mathbf{P}_k$ and $\mathbf{P}_{k+1}$ and outside $S_k \cup S_{k+1}$. We may subdivide the original system of squares to obtain a system of squares as indicated in Fig. 9-23, whose mesh we denote by σ and which is such that

(3) it is not possible for two squares with a point in common to contain points of both C_i and C_j if $i \neq j$ [*gap*].

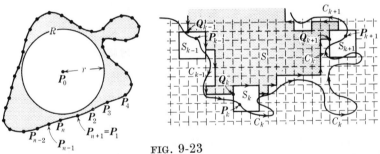

FIG. 9-23

Now we may choose S to be the largest connected union of squares such that $S \subset R$; $\mathbf{P}_0 \in S$; no square of S is contained in a vertex square; and each square of S has at least one side in common with another square of S (S has no squares "hanging on" by a corner). We note first that S has no "holes," so that its boundary is a single simple closed polygonal curve [*gap*].

If we now trace along the boundary of S in the positive direction— that is, keeping S always on the left or moving along each segment of the boundary in the counterclockwise direction with respect to the center of the square of S that has this segment as a side—we find that the vector from $\mathbf{P}_0$ to a point $\mathbf{P}$ on the boundary of S moves through 360 degrees (counterclockwise) as $\mathbf{P}$ moves around the boundary of S [*gap*]. Each segment of the boundary of S either lies along a side of a vertex square or is a side of a square that contains a point of one of the sets C_k (in the latter case, we say that the segment is "near" C_k), since otherwise the square not in S that has this segment as a side would have been included in S. It follows from (3) that if $i \neq j$, then a segment that is "near" C_i cannot join a segment that is "near" C_j; hence, two such segments must be separated by at least one segment that lies along a side of a vertex square. Moreover, it follows from (1) that a segment "near" C_k can connect only with other segments "near" C_k, or with a boundary segment of one of the vertex squares S_k or S_{k+1}. If we refer to the first diagram of Fig. 9-23, we see that it is not possible to encircle S with a path of segments that are either all boundary segments of a vertex square or are all "near" the same set C_k, since the arc joining two vertices $\mathbf{P}_k$ and $\mathbf{P}_{k+1}$ is shorter than r. From these facts, it is possible to show that if the first vertex square to be hit after S_k is S_{k+1}, then the next one must be S_{k+2} [*gap*]. In this case, we must continue in succession through the remaining $\mathbf{P}_i$'s. Similarly, if the first vertex square to be hit after S_k is S_{k-1}, then the next one is S_{k-2}, etc. In this case, we shall change the orientation of the curve by changing the sign of the parameter. After relabeling the points $\mathbf{P}_1, \mathbf{P}_2, \cdots$, $\mathbf{P}_{n+1}$ to correspond to the new orientation, traversing the boundary of S in the positive direction again corresponds to moving successively between these points. Thus, in the first case, or after relabeling in the second case, it is true that as we move successively between these points, the vector from $\mathbf{P}_0$ rotates through a total angle of 360 degrees, just as for the boundary of S.

Now for each k we shall let $\mathbf{Q}_k$ be the first point of the boundary of S that is on the boundary of S_k. Then (i) is satisfied, since S_k contains $\mathbf{P}_k$ and the diagonal of S_k is shorter than ε. The boundary Γ of S contains pieces of the boundaries of the vertex squares. Because of (1), $|\mathbf{P}_{k+1} - \mathbf{P}_k|$ is greater than the diagonal of the vertex square S_k, so that the perimeter of S_k is less than $2\sqrt{2}|\mathbf{P}_{k+1} - \mathbf{P}_k|$. The rest of Γ consists of segments of length σ each of which can be associated with a point of C that is in a square with the segment as one side. Let us arrange these points in order along C (one point may correspond to several squares, in which case it is regarded as being several coincident points). It is not possible for an arc of C joining eight consecutive points to have length less than σ, since there would then be four squares whose union is a square containing all eight points, and the boundary of this union of four squares would then be part of Γ. Therefore, the number of successive groups of eight points is not greater than the length of C divided by σ. Since each such set of eight points corresponds to pieces of Γ of total length 8σ, and there need be at most seven points not in such sets, we have

$$(\text{length of } \Gamma) < 2\sqrt{2} \sum |\mathbf{P}_{k+1} - \mathbf{P}_k| + 8(\text{length of } C) + 7\sigma,$$

$$< 11 \cdot (\text{length of } C) + 7\sigma < 12 \cdot (\text{length of } C).$$

To complete the proof, we observe that (iii) follows from the facts that the outer sum for $R - S$ determined by either of the systems of squares we have used is less than an outer sum for C, and the first system of squares was chosen so that this is less than Δ.

In the proof of Lemma 1 we saw that, given an interior point $\mathbf{P}_0$, it is possible to give an orientation to the rectifiable simple closed curve C by changing the sign of the parameter if necessary so that, if points $\mathbf{P}_1, \mathbf{P}_2, \cdots, \mathbf{P}_{n+1}$ are spaced closely enough around C, then the vector from $\mathbf{P}_0$ to $\mathbf{P}_i$ rotates through 360 degrees as we move in succession between these points. Such a curve is said to be *positively oriented*.†

LEMMA 2. Suppose that R is a bounded set in the (x, y)-plane whose boundary is a positively oriented rectifiable simple closed curve C not equal to R. Also suppose that $\mathbf{F}$ is a vector-valued function that is continuous at all points of the union of R and C. Then for any positive numbers Δ and ε there is a connected union of squares S contained in R for which the following are true.

(i) The area of $R - S$ is less than Δ.
(ii) If Γ is the boundary of S, then

$$\left| \int_C \mathbf{F} \cdot d\mathbf{P} - \int_\Gamma \mathbf{F} \cdot d\mathbf{P} \right| < \varepsilon.$$

PROOF. It follows from $\mathbf{F}$ being continuous on $R \cup C$ that $\mathbf{F}$ is uniformly continuous on $R \cup C$. Likewise, C is the range of a function $\mathbf{P}$ that is uniformly continuous on its domain. Therefore, for any positive number θ, there are points $\mathbf{P}_1, \mathbf{P}_2, \cdots, \mathbf{P}_{n+1} = \mathbf{P}_1$ on C sufficiently close together that Lemma 1 can be applied and with the properties:

(a) For each k, there is a disk with center at $\mathbf{P}_k$ for which

$$|\mathbf{F}(\mathbf{P}_k) - \mathbf{F}(\mathbf{Q})| < \theta,$$

if $\mathbf{Q}$ is in the disk and in the domain of $\mathbf{F}$.

(b) The arc joining $\mathbf{P}_{k-1}$ and $\mathbf{P}_{k+1}$ is contained in the disk with center at $\mathbf{P}_k$ and half the radius of the disk described in (a).

Now we shall choose S of Lemma 1 so that the area of $R - S$ is less than Δ and the length of the boundary Γ of S is less than 12 times the length of C. We let Γ^* denote the path for which Γ^* coincides with Γ, except that for each k we shall follow Γ to $\mathbf{Q}_k$, then a straight line from $\mathbf{Q}_k$ to $\mathbf{P}_k$, then a straight line from $\mathbf{P}_k$ to $\mathbf{Q}_k$, and then follow Γ

---

† To show that this definition is independent of the interior point being used, we can show that, given two interior points, the number Δ of Lemma 1 can be chosen sufficiently small that the resulting set S contains both points.

from $\mathbf{Q}_k$ to $\mathbf{Q}_{k+1}$ [see Fig. 9-24]. Also, we shall let the fineness of the system of squares used be small enough that the boundary of S between $\mathbf{Q}_k$ and $\mathbf{Q}_{k+1}$ is within the disk with center at $\mathbf{P}_k$ described in (a) [*gap*]. Then we have

$$\int_C \mathbf{G} \cdot d\mathbf{P} - \int_{\Gamma^*} \mathbf{G} \cdot d\mathbf{P} = 0,$$

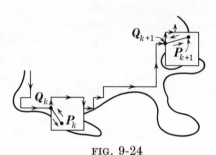

FIG. 9-24

if $\mathbf{G}$ at each point of C or Γ^* is defined as the value of $\mathbf{F}$ at the preceding one of the points $\mathbf{P}_1, \mathbf{P}_2, \cdots, \mathbf{P}_{n+1}$. Since $\mathbf{F}$ nowhere differs from $\mathbf{G}$ by more than θ, and $\int_{\Gamma^*} \mathbf{G} \cdot d\mathbf{P}$ is equal to $\int_{\Gamma} \mathbf{G} \cdot d\mathbf{P}$, we have

$$\left| \int_C \mathbf{F} \cdot d\mathbf{P} - \int_{\Gamma} \mathbf{F} \cdot d\mathbf{P} \right| \leqq \theta[(\text{length of } C) + (\text{length of } \Gamma)]$$

$$< 13\theta \cdot (\text{length of } C).$$

Now if we let $\theta = \varepsilon/[13(\text{length of } C)]$, the preceding inequality becomes (ii) of the lemma.

PROBLEMS

1. For each of the following, evaluate $\int_C (y+x)\, dx + (y-x)\, dy$ in two ways—by direct evaluation as a line integral and by use of Green's theorem. (a) C is the circle $x^2 + y^2 = 16$, oriented counterclockwise. (b) C is the square with successive vertices $(0, 0)$, $(1, 0)$, $(1, 1)$, $(0, 1)$.

2. Evaluate $\int_C y^2\, dx + x\, dy$ around the triangle with successive vertices $(0, 0)$, $(1, 0)$, and $(1, 1)$. Check by using Green's theorem.

3. Use Green's theorem to evaluate $\int (xy+x)\, dx + (x^2+xy)\, dy$ counterclockwise around the closed curve bounding the set of points between the graphs of $y = x^2$ and $y^2 = x$.

4. For each of the following, use Green's theorem to evaluate the line integral.

(a) $\int xy^2 \, dx + (x^2y + 7x) \, dy$ counterclockwise around the graph of $(x-1)^2 + (y+2)^2 = 4$.

(b) $\int (e^x \sin y) \, dx + (e^x \cos y) \, dy$ counterclockwise around the graph of $x^2 + 4y^2 = 7$.

(c) $\int (2x^3 - y^3) \, dx + (x^3 + y^3) \, dy$ around the circle $x^2 + y^2 = 1$.

(d) $\int \mathbf{V}(x^2y) \cdot d\mathbf{P}$ counterclockwise around the circle $x^2 + y^2 = 1$.

5. Use the method of Illustration 3 to evaluate the following line integral by first finding a curve along which the integral is easier to evaluate and has the same value:

$$\int_C \frac{y^3}{(x^2+y^2)^2} \, dx - \frac{xy^2}{(x^2+y^2)^2} \, dy,$$

where C is the ellipse $x^2 + 3y^2 = 7$, oriented clockwise.

6. Let u and v be functions that have first-order partial derivatives continuous on a set R and its boundary C, where R is a set of the type described in the statement of Green's theorem.

(a) Explain why

$$\int_C (uv\mathbf{i} + uv\mathbf{j}) \cdot d\mathbf{P} = \int_R \left[v\left(\frac{\partial u}{\partial x} - \frac{\partial u}{\partial y}\right) + u\left(\frac{\partial v}{\partial x} - \frac{\partial v}{\partial y}\right) \right] dA.$$

(b) Assume in addition that the second-order partial derivatives of u and v are continuous and explain why

$$\frac{1}{2} \int_C \left[\left(v\frac{\partial u}{\partial x} - u\frac{\partial v}{\partial x}\right)\mathbf{i} + \left(u\frac{\partial v}{\partial y} - v\frac{\partial u}{\partial y}\right)\mathbf{j} \right] \cdot d\mathbf{P} = \int_R \left(u\frac{\partial^2 v}{\partial x \, \partial y} - v\frac{\partial^2 u}{\partial x \, \partial y} \right) dA.$$

7. Let R be a bounded set in the (x, y)-plane whose boundary is a simple closed curve that is *piece-wise smooth*—i.e., consists of a finite number of pieces on each of which x' and y' are continuous. Explain why $\mathbf{n}$ might be called the *unit outer normal* if

$$\mathbf{n}(t) = \frac{y'(t)\mathbf{i} - x'(t)\mathbf{j}}{\{[x'(t)]^2 + [y'(t)]^2\}^{1/2}}.$$

8. For $\mathbf{n}$ as defined in problem 7, show that if $\mathbf{F}$ is continuous then

$$\int_C \mathbf{F} \cdot \mathbf{n} \, ds = \int_R \nabla \cdot \mathbf{F} \, dA.$$

9. For $\mathbf{n}$ as defined in problem 7, show that each of the following is true when u and v have continuous second-order partial derivatives,

$\nabla^2 f$ denotes $\partial^2 f/\partial x^2 + \partial^2 f/\partial y^2$, and $\partial f/\partial n$ denotes the directional derivative of f in the direction of $\mathbf{n}$.

(a) $\displaystyle \int_C v \frac{\partial u}{\partial n}\, ds = \int_C v\left[\frac{\partial u}{\partial x} y'(t) - \frac{\partial u}{\partial y} x'(t)\right] dt = \int_R (v\nabla^2 u + \nabla u \cdot \nabla v)\, dA.$

(b) $\displaystyle \int_C \left(v\frac{\partial u}{\partial n} - u\frac{\partial v}{\partial n}\right) ds = \int_R (v\nabla^2 u - u\nabla^2 v)\, dA.$

10. Use the notation of problems 7 and 9 and show that if $\nabla^2 u = 0$ in R, then $\int_C \partial u/\partial n\, ds = 0$.

11. Prove the following, given that C is a rectifiable curve. (a) [inf (outer sums for C)] $= 0$. [*Hint:* Show that if $\mathbf{P}_1, \mathbf{P}_2, \cdots, \mathbf{P}_{n+1}$ are chosen so that for each k the length of the arc between $\mathbf{P}_k$ and $\mathbf{P}_{k+1}$ is between ε and 2ε, then the union of circles with radii 2ε and centers at $\mathbf{P}_k$ for some k contains C and has area less than $(4\pi\varepsilon^2)$(length of C)/ε or $(4\pi\varepsilon)$(length of C).] (b) C has area and the area of C is zero. [*Note:* It then follows from problem 11, page 133, that a bounded region R has area if its boundary is a rectifiable curve.]

9-6. SOME APPLICATIONS OF GREEN'S THEOREM

We shall now discuss two useful applications of Green's theorem. These applications involve line integrals $\int (L\mathbf{i} + M\mathbf{j})\cdot d\mathbf{P}$, such that $\partial M/\partial x - \partial L/\partial y$ is everywhere 1 or everywhere 0. We shall consider first the case that $\partial M/\partial x - \partial L/\partial y = 1$. In this case, the conclusion of Green's theorem can be written as

$$\int_C (L\mathbf{i} + M\mathbf{j})\cdot d\mathbf{P} = \int_R dA.$$

That is, the line integral around C is the area of the region bounded by C. The condition that $\partial M/\partial x - \partial L/\partial y = 1$ can be satisfied in various ways. For example, we might have $M = x$ and $L = 0$, or $M = 0$ and $L = -y$, or $M = \frac{1}{2}x$ and $L = -\frac{1}{2}y$. Thus, the area of a region R whose boundary C consists of a finite number of positively oriented simple closed curves can be computed by using any one of the following integrals:

$$(\text{area of } R) = \int_C x\, dy = -\int_C y\, dx = \tfrac{1}{2}\int_C x\, dy - y\, dx.$$

ILLUSTRATION 1. The ellipse $x^2/a^2 + y^2/b^2 = 1$ has parametric equations $x = a \cos t$ and $y = b \sin t$, for $0 \leq t \leq 2\pi$. Therefore, the area of the ellipse is given by any of the following:

$$\int x \, dy = \int_0^{2\pi} (a \cos t)(b \cos t \, dt) = ab \int_0^{2\pi} \cos^2 t \, dt = \pi ab,$$

$$\int -y \, dx = \int_0^{2\pi} (-b \sin t)(-a \sin t \, dt) = ab \int_0^{2\pi} \sin^2 t \, dt = \pi ab,$$

$$\tfrac{1}{2} \int x \, dy - y \, dx = \tfrac{1}{2} ab \int_0^{2\pi} dt = \pi ab.$$

ILLUSTRATION 2. Let us evaluate the area of the triangular set T of Fig. 9-25 by using $\int (-y) \, dx$. Between successive vertices, this line integral is the area of a trapezoid (or the negative of the area of a trapezoid). For example,

$$\int_{(x_1, y_1)}^{(x_2, y_2)} (-y) \, dx = \tfrac{1}{2}(x_1 - x_2)(y_1 + y_2).$$

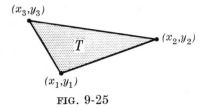

$$(x_3, y_3)$$
$$T$$
$$(x_2, y_2)$$
$$(x_1, y_1)$$

FIG. 9-25

Evaluated around the entire boundary of T, the line integral is equal to

$$\text{(area of } T) = \tfrac{1}{2}(x_1 - x_2)(y_1 + y_2)$$
$$+ \tfrac{1}{2}(x_2 - x_3)(y_2 + y_3) + \tfrac{1}{2}(x_3 - x_1)(y_3 + y_1).$$

We can use $\int x \, dy$ in a similar way to obtain

$$\text{(area of } T) = \tfrac{1}{2}(x_1 + x_2)(y_2 - y_1)$$
$$+ \tfrac{1}{2}(x_2 + x_3)(y_3 - y_2) + \tfrac{1}{2}(x_3 + x_1)(y_1 - y_3).$$

The average of these two expressions is $\int \tfrac{1}{2}(x \, dy - y \, dx)$ or

$$\text{(area of } T) = \tfrac{1}{2}(x_1 y_2 - x_2 y_1) + \tfrac{1}{2}(x_2 y_3 - x_3 y_2) + \tfrac{1}{2}(x_3 y_1 - x_1 y_3).$$

This area is also equal to

$$|\tfrac{1}{2}[(x_2 - x_1)\mathbf{i} + (y_2 - y_1)\mathbf{j}] \times [(x_3 - x_1)\mathbf{i} + (y_3 - y_1)\mathbf{j}]|,$$

or

$$\tfrac{1}{2}[(x_2 - x_1)(y_3 - y_1) - (y_2 - y_1)(x_3 - x_1)],$$

as would follow from Theorem 7-3.1.

We shall now study the condition $\partial M/\partial x - \partial L/\partial y = 0$. To help keep the overall logical development straight in mind, we shall list several related properties that line integrals may have. These are stated for two dimensions, though some have already been discussed for three dimensions and the others have analogies in three dimensions which will be discussed in the next two sections. We shall confine our study to open sets R in the (x, y)-plane that are connected and therefore have the property that any two points can be connected by a polygonal path in R [see problem 15, page 61], and we shall assume that the vector function $\mathbf{F}$ is continuous in R.

(A) $\int_{C_1} \mathbf{F} \cdot d\mathbf{P} = \int_{C_2} \mathbf{F} \cdot d\mathbf{P}$ if C_1 and C_2 are polygonal curves with the same end points.

(B) There exists a (potential) function Φ such that $\mathbf{F} = \nabla\Phi$.

(C) $\int_{C_1} \mathbf{F} \cdot d\mathbf{P} = \int_{C_2} \mathbf{F} \cdot d\mathbf{P}$ if C_1 and C_2 are rectifiable curves with the same end points.

(D) $\mathbf{F}$ is conservative; i.e., $\int_C \mathbf{F} \cdot d\mathbf{P} = 0$ if C is any rectifiable closed curve.

(E) For a moving particle, the sum of the kinetic and the potential energy is constant.

(F) $\mathbf{F} = L\mathbf{i} + M\mathbf{j}$, where $\partial M/\partial x = \partial L/\partial y$.

It follows from Theorem 9-4.1 that (A) $\Rightarrow$ (B), and from Theorem 9-4.2 that (B) $\Rightarrow$ (C). It is easy to show that (C) $\Rightarrow$ (D) [see the introductory discussion of Section 9-4]. Similarly, (D) $\Rightarrow$ (A). Therefore, we can conclude that (A) *through* (D) *are all equivalent.* To give meaning to (E), we must assume that a potential function Φ exists. Then we can define the *potential energy* at $\mathbf{P}$ of a particle whose mass is m as the value at $\mathbf{P}$ of $-m\Phi$. We know that the work done on a moving particle by a conservative force field is equal to the change in kinetic energy [see problem 8, page 455]; hence (D) $\Rightarrow$ (E). Since (E) is not a meaningful statement unless $\mathbf{F}$ has a potential function we might also say that (E) $\Rightarrow$ (D). Now let us consider (F). The following theorem shows that (D) ⇒ (F) if $\partial M/\partial x$ and $\partial L/\partial y$ are continuous. However, we shall see later that (F) *can be true and* (D) *false* if the set R is not "simply connected."

THEOREM 9-6.1. Suppose $\mathbf{F} = L\mathbf{i} + M\mathbf{j}$ is a vector function continuous on a connected open two-dimensional set R. If the partial derivatives $\partial L/\partial y$ and $\partial M/\partial x$ are continuous at each point of R and if $\mathbf{F}$ is a conservative force field, then $\partial L/\partial y = \partial M/\partial x$.

FIRST PROOF OF THEOREM 9-6.1.   Since (B) and (D) are equivalent there is a function Φ such that

$$\mathbf{F} = \nabla\Phi = \frac{\partial\Phi}{\partial x}\mathbf{i} + \frac{\partial\Phi}{\partial y}\mathbf{j}.$$

Therefore, $\partial\Phi/\partial x = L$ and $\partial\Phi/\partial y = M$. If $\partial L/\partial y$ and $\partial M/\partial x$ exist and are continuous in a neighborhood of a point (x_0, y_0), then it follows from Theorem 6-4.1 that

$$\frac{\partial^2\Phi}{\partial x\,\partial y} = \frac{\partial^2\Phi}{\partial y\,\partial x} \quad \text{or} \quad \frac{\partial M}{\partial x} = \frac{\partial L}{\partial y}.$$

The conclusion of Green's theorem is

$$\int_C (L\mathbf{i} + M\mathbf{j})\cdot d\mathbf{P} = \int_R \left(\frac{\partial M}{\partial x} - \frac{\partial L}{\partial y}\right) dA. \tag{9-41}$$

It might seem intuitively obvious that if the left member of this equation is zero for all closed rectifiable curves C, then the integrand of the right member must be zero. This would give an alternative proof of Theorem 9-6.1. A careful argument of this type can easily be given as follows.

SECOND PROOF OF THEOREM 9-6.1.   Suppose there is a point (x_0, y_0) at which $\partial M/\partial x - \partial L/\partial y$ is continuous, but is not zero. Then there is a disk D with center at (x_0, y_0) whose boundary is a circle C small enough so that $\partial M/\partial x - \partial L/\partial y$ is nonzero and has the same sign at all points of D. Then

$$\int_D \left(\frac{\partial M}{\partial x} - \frac{\partial L}{\partial y}\right) dA \neq 0.$$

Because of Eq. (9-41), this is not possible if $\int_C (L\mathbf{i} + M\mathbf{j})\cdot d\mathbf{P} = 0$.

Now we wish to consider the possibility of showing that (F) $\Rightarrow$ (D). We cannot obtain a strict converse of Theorem 9-6.1, since we cannot apply (9-41) to a simple closed curve C unless we know that C is the boundary of a set on which the conditions of Green's theorem are satisfied. For example, if $L = -y/(x^2+y^2)$ and $M = x/(x^2+y^2)$, then

$$\frac{\partial L}{\partial y} = \frac{\partial M}{\partial x} = \frac{y^2-x^2}{(x^2+y^2)^2} \quad \text{and} \quad \frac{\partial L}{\partial y} - \frac{\partial M}{\partial x} = 0.$$

However, we have seen that $\int_C L\,dx + M\,dy = 2\pi$ if C is a circle with center at the origin [Illustration 3 of Section 9-5]. In this case, Eq. (9-41) is not valid, since $(0, 0)$ is not in the domain of $\partial M/\partial x$ or $\partial L/\partial y$. This example shows that (F) $\Rightarrow$ (D) is not true in general. To avoid the difficulty illustrated by this example, we shall use only sets that are "simply connected" in the sense of the definition to follow. Intuitively, such sets do not have any "holes." It is customary to say that a set S is *simply connected* if, given any point in S and any closed curve in S, it is possible to continuously deform the curve into the point without leaving S. However, for open plane sets it is possible to give a definition of simple connectedness that is equivalent to this definition and is easier for us to use. Moreover, by giving the definition in this form, we shall not have to define the concept of "continuous deformation"— a concept which is better left to a topology course.

DEFINITION 9-6.1. A *simply connected* open plane set is an open plane set R with the following two properties:
  (i) R is connected.
  (ii) The interior of each simple closed curve in R is contained in R.

THEOREM 9-6.2. A force field $L\mathbf{i} + M\mathbf{j}$ is conservative if its domain R is a simply connected open set, $\partial M/\partial x$ and $\partial L/\partial y$ are continuous on R, and

$$\frac{\partial M}{\partial x} = \frac{\partial L}{\partial y} \tag{9-42}$$

at each point of R.

PROOF. Since (A) $\Rightarrow$ (D), all we need to show is that

$$\int_{C_1} (L\mathbf{i} + M\mathbf{j}) \cdot d\mathbf{P} = \int_{C_2} (L\mathbf{i} + M\mathbf{j}) \cdot d\mathbf{P}, \tag{9-43}$$

whenever C_1 and C_2 are two polygonal curves in R with the same initial and terminal points. Suppose first that C_1 and C_2 have no points in common except the end points. Since R is simply connected, the set bounded by C_1 and C_2 is contained in R; hence, it follows from equality (9-42) and Green's theorem that (9-43) is true [see Fig. 9-26]. However, C_1 and C_2 may intersect at points other than end points. As shown in Fig. 9-27, it is then possible to divide C_1 into n consecutive pieces, and C_2 into n consecutive pieces, such that corresponding pieces are either coincident and oriented in the same direction, or else the two pieces together form the boundary of a set contained in R—with one piece positively oriented (i.e., directed counterclockwise around the set) and the other piece negatively oriented. If the two pieces form the boundary of a set contained in R, then the line integral around the entire boundary in the positive direction is zero, so that the integrals over the two pieces are equal (one is traversed in the negative direction as one moves around the boundary in the positive direction). Thus, since the line integral has the same values over corresponding pieces of C_1 and C_2, Eq. (9-43) is true.

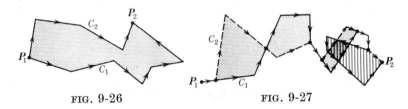

FIG. 9-26   FIG. 9-27

We shall now discuss some physical concepts for which Green's theorem is useful. Suppose that a vector function $\mathbf{v} = v_1\mathbf{i} + v_2\mathbf{j}$ is called "velocity" and is thought of as being the velocity of a fluid of unit thickness that is flowing over the (x, y)-plane. We shall also assume that the flow is steady (i.e., $\mathbf{v}$ is independent of time), and that the velocity is parallel to the (x, y)-plane. Then the line integral,

$$\int_C \mathbf{v} \cdot d\mathbf{P} = \int_R \left(\frac{\partial v_2}{\partial x} - \frac{\partial v_1}{\partial y} \right) dA, \qquad (9\text{-}44)$$

is said to be the *circulation* of $\mathbf{v}$ along C. Since $\int_C \mathbf{v} \cdot d\mathbf{P} = \int_C v_T \, ds$, where v_T is the tangential component of $\mathbf{v}$, the circulation around C is equal to the product of the length of C and the average value of the tangential component of velocity. If the right member of Eq. (9-44) is divided by the area of R, we obtain the mean value of $\partial v_2/\partial x - \partial v_1/\partial y$. The expression $(\partial v_2/\partial x - \partial v_1/\partial y)\mathbf{k}$, where $\mathbf{v}$ is a two-dimensional vector equal to $v_1\mathbf{i} + v_2\mathbf{j}$, is called the *curl* of $\mathbf{v}$ and is denoted by

$$\nabla \times \mathbf{v} = \left(\frac{\partial}{\partial x}\mathbf{i} + \frac{\partial}{\partial y}\mathbf{j} \right) \times \mathbf{v}.$$

The expression $\partial v_2/\partial x - \partial v_1/\partial y$ is called the *circulation density* of $\mathbf{v}$. It follows from (9-44) that *the circulation of $\mathbf{v}$ around the boundary of R is equal to the product of the mean value of the circulation density of $\mathbf{v}$ and the area of R.* The vector $\mathbf{v}$ is said to be *irrotational* in R if $\nabla \times \mathbf{v}$ is zero at all points of R. If R is open and simply connected, then it follows from Theorems 9-6.1 and 9-6.2 that $\mathbf{v}$ is irrotational if and only if the circulation is zero around each closed rectifiable curve.

For the fluid flow of the preceding discussion, let us consider the line integral

$$\int_C (v_1 \, dy - v_2 \, dx) = \int_R \left(\frac{\partial v_1}{\partial x} + \frac{\partial v_2}{\partial y} \right) dA, \qquad (9\text{-}45)$$

and assume that C can be approximated by simple closed polygonal curves. We choose points $\mathbf{P}_1, \mathbf{P}_2, \cdots, \mathbf{P}_{n+1} = \mathbf{P}_1$ around C such that the polygon obtained by joining these points in succession with line segments is a simple closed curve, and we let

$$\Delta_i \mathbf{P} = \mathbf{P}_{i+1} - \mathbf{P}_i = (\Delta_i x)\mathbf{i} + (\Delta_i y)\mathbf{j}.$$

Then

$$v_1 \Delta_i y - v_2 \Delta_i x = \pm |\mathbf{v} \times \Delta_i \mathbf{P}|,$$

where the sign is $+$ or $-$ according to whether the directed angle from $\mathbf{v}$ to $\Delta_i \mathbf{P}$ is between 0 and π or between $-\pi$ and 0. Thus, the absolute value of $v_1 \Delta_i y - v_2 \Delta_i x$ is equal to the product of $\mathbf{v}$ and the component of $\Delta_i \mathbf{P}$ perpendicular to $\mathbf{v}$ [see Fig. 9-28], and is positive or negative according to whether $\mathbf{v}$ points out from the interior of the polygonal curve or points into the interior. Therefore, it is reasonable to say that the net rate of flow of fluid out of R is given by either member of Eq. (9-45). This implies that the net rate of flow out of R is equal to

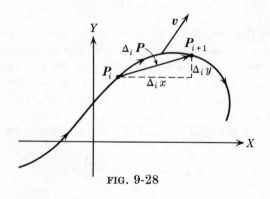

FIG. 9-28

the product of the mean value of $\partial v_1/\partial x + \partial v_2/\partial y$ and the area of R. The term $\partial v_1/\partial x + \partial v_2/\partial y$ is called the *divergence* of $\mathbf{v}$ and is written as

$$\nabla \cdot \mathbf{v} = \left(\frac{\partial}{\partial x}\,\mathbf{i} + \frac{\partial}{\partial y}\,\mathbf{j}\right) \cdot \mathbf{v}.$$

If R is open and simply connected, then $\nabla \cdot \mathbf{v}$ is zero at all points of R if and only if there is zero net flow out of any region bounded by a simple closed polygonal curve.

PROBLEMS

1. Let C be a rectifiable simple closed curve.　Explain why the area of the set bounded by C is equal to $\int_C (y^2 - y)\,dx + (2xy)\,dy$.

2. Let R be the set bounded by the graph of $|x|^{\frac{2}{3}} + |y|^{\frac{2}{3}} = a^{\frac{2}{3}}$.　Use the parametric equations $x = a\cos^3\theta$, $y = a\sin^3\theta$ to determine the area of R.

3. (a) Explain why the graph of the parametric equations

$$x = A\cos(\alpha + t) + C, \quad y = B\sin t + D$$

is an ellipse. (**b**) Determine the area of this ellipse.

4. Let S be the set bounded by the rays $\theta = \theta_1$, $\theta = \theta_2$, and the curve $r = f(\theta)$, where $f(\theta) > 0$.　Evaluate $\frac{1}{2}\int x\,dy - y\,dx$ around the boundary of S, using r as a parameter along the rays and θ as a parameter along the graph of $r = f(\theta)$.

5. In each case, show that the line integral is independent of the curve used to join the points indicated.　Evaluate the integral along a convenient curve.

(**a**) $\displaystyle\int_{(1,0)}^{(X,Y)} (2xy)\,dx + (x^2 - y^2)\,dy$. 　　(**b**) $\displaystyle\int_{(1,1)}^{(X,Y)} (\sin y)\,dx + (x\cos y)\,dy$.

6. For each of the following, check whether the line integral is zero around closed curves.　Evaluate the integral, but if possible first replace the specified curve by one along which the integral is easier to evaluate or use a potential function.

(**a**) $\displaystyle\int_{(0,1)}^{(1,0)} (2xye^{x^2y})\,dx + (x^2e^{x^2y})\,dy$ 　along　$y + x^2 = 1$.

(**b**) $\displaystyle\int_C (2xy^4 + 2x)\,dx + (4x^2y^3)\,dy$; C the ellipse $x^2 + 4y^2 = 16$.

(**c**) $\displaystyle\int_{(0,2)}^{(3,0)} [\sinh(2x + 3y) + 2x\cosh(2x + 3y)]\,dx + [3x\cosh(2x + 3y)]\,dy$

along the graph of $4x^2 - 10x + 3y = 6$.

7. For each of the following, determine the circulation around the curve C and the rate of flow out of the set bounded by C. Let C be oriented counterclockwise.

(a) $\mathbf{v} = y^2\mathbf{i} + (2xy+x)\mathbf{j}$; C is the circle $x^2+y^2 = 4$.

(b) $\mathbf{v} = (3x^2y)\mathbf{i} + x^3\mathbf{j}$; C is the triangle with vertices $(0, 0)$, $(5, 0)$, $(5, 5)$.

(c) $\mathbf{v} = -(2x^3y)\mathbf{i} + (3x^2y^2+1)\mathbf{j}$; C is the square with vertices $(0, 0)$, $(2, 0)$, $(2, 2)$, $(0, 2)$.

8. (a) Show that if R is a simply connected open set not containing the origin, then the value of $\int_P^Q (x^2+y^2)^{-1}(-y\,dx+x\,dy)$ does not depend on the curve used to join P to Q. (b) Let R be the set whose boundary consists of the piece of the x-axis between $(12\pi, 0)$ and $(16\pi, 0)$, and the graphs in polar coordinates of $r = 3\theta$ and $r = 4\theta$ for $0 \leq \theta \leq 4\pi$. Determine the value of the line integral of part (a) along a curve in R joining $(0, 6)$ to $(44, 0)$.

9. Let C be a rectifiable simple closed curve that does not pass through the origin. Explain why

$$\int_C \left[\ln(x^2+y^2) + \frac{2x^2}{x^2+y^2} \right] dx + \frac{2xy}{x^2+y^2}\,dy = 0.$$

10. Let L and M be functions such that $\partial M/\partial x = \partial L/\partial y$ and all of L, M, $\partial M/\partial x$, and $\partial L/\partial y$ are continuous except possibly at the origin and at $(5, 0)$. Also suppose that the line integrals of $L\mathbf{i} + M\mathbf{j}$ counterclockwise around the circles $x^2+y^2 =1$ and $(x-5)^2+y^2 = 2$ are equal, respectively, to -3 and 5. If $\int_{(1,0)}^{(0,1)} (L\mathbf{i}+M\mathbf{j})\cdot d\mathbf{P} = 7$ when evaluated along a straight line, determine all values of this integral along rectifiable curves from $(1, 0)$ to $(0, 1)$.

11. Suppose that L, M, $\partial M/\partial x$ and $\partial L/\partial y$ are continuous except possibly at the points $(\pm 2, 0)$ and $(0, 2)$. Also suppose that $\partial M/\partial x = \partial L/\partial y$ except possibly at these points. Let C_1, C_2, and C_3 be the curves indicated in Fig. 9-29 and suppose that the line integrals of

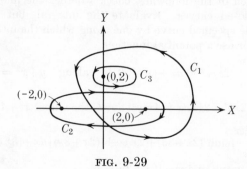

FIG. 9-29

$Li + Mj$ around these curves are equal, respectively, to 2, -1, and 5. Determine the value of the integral of $Li + Mj$ around (**a**) the circle $(x-2)^2 + y^2 = 1$, oriented counterclockwise; (b) the circle $x^2 + y^2 = 9$, oriented counterclockwise.

12. Let **F** be a vector-valued function with the properties that **F** is irrotational and the divergence of **F** is zero at all points of an open set R. Show that

$$\frac{\partial M}{\partial x} = \frac{\partial L}{\partial y} \quad \text{and} \quad \frac{\partial M}{\partial y} = -\frac{\partial L}{\partial x},$$

where $\mathbf{F} = Li + Mj$. These are called the *Cauchy-Riemann equations*. Show that if L and M satisfy these equations, then L and M both satisfy Laplace's equation:

$$\frac{\partial^2 L}{\partial x^2} + \frac{\partial^2 L}{\partial y^2} = 0, \qquad \frac{\partial^2 M}{\partial x^2} + \frac{\partial^2 M}{\partial y^2} = 0.$$

13. A function that satisfies Laplace's equation is said to be *harmonic*. If L and M satisfy the Cauchy-Riemann equations [problem 12], then L is said to be *conjugate* to M. (a) Explain why M is conjugate to $-L$ if L is conjugate to M. (b) Show that if M is harmonic in a simply connected open set R, then L is conjugate to M if

$$L(x, y) = \int_{(x_0, y_0)}^{(x,y)} -\frac{\partial M}{\partial y} \, dx + \frac{\partial M}{\partial x} \, dy.$$

14. Prove that $\nabla \cdot \mathbf{v}$ and $\nabla \times \mathbf{v}$ are independent of the particular rectangular coordinate system used to define them. [*Hint:* Use Eqs. (9-44) and (9-45).]

9-7. STOKES' THEOREM

It will be recalled that for line integrals around a rectifiable simple closed curve, Green's theorem expresses a relation between the line integral and a certain double integral over the interior region bounded by the curve. We shall consider two different ways of generalizing this to three dimensions. One generalization, the *divergence theorem*, will be discussed in the next section. The other, called *Stokes' theorem*, which we shall now consider, relates a surface integral to a line integral around the edge of the surface.

With Green's theorem we assumed that the boundary curve is positively oriented, meaning intuitively that the interior remains on the left as a point moves around the boundary. For a surface in three-dimensions, the meaning of "left side of a curve" depends on which side is thought of as being the positive side of the surface. Of course, this decision cannot be made for one-sided surfaces. Some such surfaces will be described at the end of this section. For a smooth surface element S, the vector

$$\mathbf{n} = \frac{J_1\mathbf{i}+J_2\mathbf{j}+J_3\mathbf{k}}{(J_1^2+J_2^2+J_3^2)^{\frac{1}{2}}} = \frac{(\partial\mathbf{P}/\partial u)\times(\partial\mathbf{P}/\partial v)}{|(\partial\mathbf{P}/\partial u)\times(\partial\mathbf{P}/\partial v)|} \tag{9-46}$$

is a unit vector perpendicular to S. We say that the *positive side of a smooth surface element* is the side toward which this vector $\mathbf{n}$ points when its initial point is on the surface. If the smooth surface element S is described by parametric equations

$$\begin{cases} x = f(u, v), \\ y = g(u, v), \\ z = h(u, v), \end{cases}$$

then a small square D_0 in the (u, v)-plane corresponds to a piece S_0 of S that is approximately a parallelogram [see Fig. 9-30]. We can map D_0 onto the projection X_0 of S_0 into the (x, y)-plane by using the transformation described by

$$\begin{cases} x = f(u, v), \\ y = g(u, v). \end{cases}$$

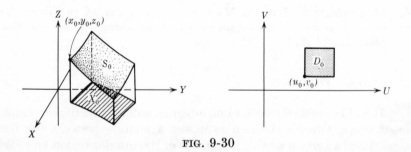

FIG. 9-30

This transformation can be approximated for points near (u_0, v_0) by using the linear transformation

$$\begin{cases} \Delta x = \left(\dfrac{\partial f}{\partial u}\right)\Delta u + \left(\dfrac{\partial f}{\partial v}\right)\Delta v, \\ \Delta y = \left(\dfrac{\partial g}{\partial u}\right)\Delta u + \left(\dfrac{\partial g}{\partial v}\right)\Delta v. \end{cases}$$

The determinant of the matrix of this linear transformation is the Jacobian J_3 [see Eqs. (9-15)]. Therefore, this transformation changes the orientation of D_0 if and only if J_3 is negative. That is, the boundary of X_0 is positively oriented if and only if J_3 is positive, or if and only if the vector **n** defined by (9-46) points upward from the (x, y)-plane. Similar discussions can be given of the other projections; hence, we can conclude that if D_0 is positively oriented in the sense that the interior remains on the left, then S_0 is positively oriented in the same sense. Since S and D can be broken up into small chunks of this type, we can conclude that the same statement can be made for them. This intuitive discussion is adequate for most applications. For Stokes' theorem, *positive orientation of the edge of S is defined as corresponding to positive orientation of the boundary of D.* Therefore, the foregoing discussion serves only to help our intuition and is not needed for the formal theorem itself.

THEOREM 9-7.1 (STOKES' THEOREM). Suppose that a smooth surface element S is described by parametric equations such that the first-order partial derivatives of x, y, and z are continuous on an open set that contains the plane set $\bar{D}$ whose image is S, and the mixed second-order partial derivatives of x, y, and z are continuous at all points of $\bar{D}$. If **F** is a function whose components have partial derivatives of the first order that are continuous at all points of S and **n** is the unit normal defined by (9-46), then

$$\int_S (\boldsymbol{\nabla} \times \mathbf{F}) \cdot \mathbf{n} \, d\sigma = \int_C \mathbf{F} \cdot d\mathbf{P}, \qquad (9\text{-}47)$$

where C is the edge of S.

The vector $\boldsymbol{\nabla} \times \mathbf{F}$ is called the *curl* of **F** and is defined as follows:

$$\boldsymbol{\nabla} \times (L\mathbf{i} + M\mathbf{j} + N\mathbf{k}) = \begin{vmatrix} \mathbf{i} & \mathbf{j} & \mathbf{k} \\ \dfrac{\partial}{\partial x} & \dfrac{\partial}{\partial y} & \dfrac{\partial}{\partial z} \\ L & M & N \end{vmatrix}$$

$$= \left(\frac{\partial N}{\partial y} - \frac{\partial M}{\partial z}\right)\mathbf{i} + \left(\frac{\partial L}{\partial z} - \frac{\partial N}{\partial x}\right)\mathbf{j} + \left(\frac{\partial M}{\partial x} - \frac{\partial L}{\partial y}\right)\mathbf{k}.$$

It follows from Eq. (9-27) that we can write Eq. (9-47) as

$$\int_D (\boldsymbol{\nabla} \times \mathbf{F}) \cdot \left(\frac{\partial \mathbf{P}}{\partial u} \times \frac{\partial \mathbf{P}}{\partial v}\right) dA = \int_C \mathbf{F} \cdot d\mathbf{P}, \qquad (9\text{-}48)$$

where D is the interior of the set $\bar{D}$ that is mapped by **P** onto S.

ILLUSTRATION 1. Suppose that S is the first-octant part of the sphere shown in Fig. 9-31, $\mathbf{n}$ is the unit vector perpendicular to S and pointing outward, and ϕ and θ denote parameters for S, with

$$\mathbf{P}(\phi, \theta) = (a \sin \phi \cos \theta)\mathbf{i} + (a \sin \phi \sin \theta)\mathbf{j} + (a \cos \phi)\mathbf{k}.$$

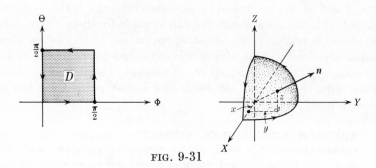

FIG. 9-31

When we use (9-46) to determine $\mathbf{n}$, we can change $\mathbf{n}$ by the factor -1 if we interchange the parameters. With the order (ϕ, θ), we have

$$\frac{\partial \mathbf{P}}{\partial \phi} \times \frac{\partial \mathbf{P}}{\partial \theta} = \begin{vmatrix} \mathbf{i} & \mathbf{j} & \mathbf{k} \\ a \cos \phi \cos \theta & a \cos \phi \sin \theta & -a \sin \phi \\ -a \sin \phi \sin \theta & a \sin \phi \cos \theta & 0 \end{vmatrix}.$$

Since the coefficient of $\mathbf{k}$ in this expression is positive for ϕ and θ in the interval $(0, \tfrac{1}{2}\pi)$, we can see that the correct order has been chosen for ϕ and θ. In particular, if

$$\mathbf{F} = (y+z)\mathbf{i} + (z+x)\mathbf{j} + (x+z)\mathbf{k},$$

then $\nabla \times \mathbf{F} = -\mathbf{i}$ and we have

$$\int_D (\nabla \times \mathbf{F}) \cdot \left(\frac{\partial \mathbf{P}}{\partial \phi} \times \frac{\partial \mathbf{P}}{\partial \theta}\right) dA = \int_D (-a^2 \sin^2 \phi \cos \theta) \, dA$$

$$= \int_0^{\pi/2} \int_0^{\pi/2} (-a^2 \sin^2 \phi \cos \theta) \, d\theta \, d\phi$$

$$= \int_0^{\pi/2} (-a^2 \sin^2 \phi) \, d\phi = -\tfrac{1}{4}\pi a^2.$$

The boundary of S consists of three quarter-circles, and $\mathbf{P}(\phi, \theta)$ traces the boundary in the direction indicated in Fig. 9-31 as (ϕ, θ) runs around the boundary of D. For the quarter-circle in the (x, y)-plane, we have

$$\int \mathbf{F} \cdot d\mathbf{P} = \int y\, dx + x\, dy = a^2 \int_0^{\pi/2} (-\sin^2 \theta + \cos^2 \theta)\, d\theta = 0,$$

where $x = a \cos \theta$ and $y = a \sin \theta$. For the other two pieces, we have

$$\int \mathbf{F} \cdot d\mathbf{P} = \int z\, dy + z\, dz$$

$$= \int_{\pi/2}^0 (+a^2 \cos^2 \phi)\, d\phi + \int_0^a z\, dz = -\tfrac{1}{4}\pi a^2 + \tfrac{1}{2}a^2,$$

$$\int \mathbf{F} \cdot d\mathbf{P} = \int (x+z)\, dz + z\, dx$$

$$= \int_a^0 z\, dz + \int_0^{\pi/2} a^2(-\sin^2 \phi + \cos^2 \phi)\, d\phi = -\tfrac{1}{2}a^2.$$

By adding these, we see that $\int \mathbf{F} \cdot d\mathbf{P}$ around the edge of S is equal to $-\tfrac{1}{4}\pi a^2$, and is therefore equal to the integral of $\mathbf{F}$ over S.

Before giving a proof of Stokes' theorem, we shall try to make the theorem clearer by considering a special case.   If S is in the (x, y)-plane and $\mathbf{F} = L\mathbf{i} + M\mathbf{j} + N\mathbf{k}$, then

$$\int_C \mathbf{F} \cdot d\mathbf{P} = \int_C (L\mathbf{i} + M\mathbf{j}) \cdot d\mathbf{P},$$

and

$$\int_S (\mathbf{\nabla} \times \mathbf{F}) \cdot \mathbf{n}\, d\sigma = \int_D (\mathbf{\nabla} \times \mathbf{F}) \cdot \begin{vmatrix} \mathbf{i} & \mathbf{j} & \mathbf{k} \\ \partial x/\partial u & \partial y/\partial u & 0 \\ \partial x/\partial v & \partial y/\partial v & 0 \end{vmatrix} dA$$

$$= \int\int_D \left(\frac{\partial M}{\partial x} - \frac{\partial L}{\partial y} \right) J_3\, du\, dv = \int\int_S \left(\frac{\partial M}{\partial x} - \frac{\partial L}{\partial y} \right)(\pm dx\, dy),$$

where the sign is $+$ or $-$ according to whether $\mathbf{n} = \mathbf{k}$ or $\mathbf{n} = -\mathbf{k}$—i.e., according to whether J_3 is positive or negative.   Also, the positive orientation of C is as shown in Fig. 9-32 if and only if J_3 is positive. Therefore, in this case, Eq. (9-47) follows directly from Green's theorem [Theorem 9-5.1].

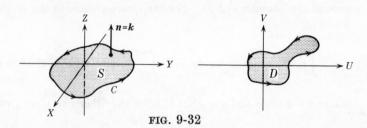

FIG. 9-32

PROOF OF STOKES' THEOREM. Suppose we have a smooth surface element S and a vector-valued function $\mathbf{F}$ that satisfy the conditions of Stokes' theorem. To prove (9-47), we start by working with $\int_C \mathbf{F} \cdot d\mathbf{P}$, where C is the edge of S. If t is a parameter for the boundary Γ of the set $\bar{D}$ in the (u, v)-plane corresponding to S [see Fig. 9-33], with $a \leq t \leq b$, then t is to be used as a parameter for C, with $x = x[u(t), v(t)]$, and similar expressions for y and z. From (9-3), page 425, we have

$$\int_C \mathbf{F} \cdot d\mathbf{P} = \lim_{\delta \to 0} \sum_{i=1}^{n} \mathbf{F}(\tau_i) \cdot (\mathbf{i} \, \Delta_i x + \mathbf{j} \, \Delta_i y + \mathbf{k} \, \Delta_i z), \qquad (9\text{-}49)$$

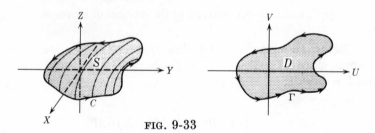

FIG. 9-33

where δ is the fineness of the partition $\{a = t_1, t_2, \cdots, t_{n+1} = b\}$ of $[a, b]$ and $\Delta_i x = x[u(t_{i+1}), v(t_{i+1})] - x[u(t_i), v(t_i)]$, with similar expressions for $\Delta_i y$ and $\Delta_i z$. The set $\bar{D}$ is contained in an open set U on which the first-order partial derivatives of x, y, and z are continuous. Each point of $\bar{D}$ is the center of an open disk with the property that the disk with the same center and twice the radius is contained in U. Since $\bar{D}$ is compact, there is a finite collection of such disks whose union contains $\bar{D}$. If δ is the radius of the smallest disk in this collection, then all chords of Γ with length less than δ are contained in U. Therefore, it follows from Taylor's theorem [Section 6-5] that

$$\Delta_i x = \frac{\partial x}{\partial u} \Delta_i u + \frac{\partial x}{\partial v} \Delta_i v, \quad \Delta_i y = \frac{\partial y}{\partial u} \Delta_i u + \frac{\partial y}{\partial v} \Delta_i v,$$

$$\Delta_i z = \frac{\partial z}{\partial u} \Delta_i u + \frac{\partial z}{\partial v} \Delta_i v,$$

if the partial derivatives are evaluated at suitable points on the chord joining $[u(t_i), v(t_i)]$ and $[u(t_{i+1}), v(t_{i+1})]$. With these expressions for $\Delta_i x$, $\Delta_i y$, and $\Delta_i z$ substituted in Eq. (9-49), we have

$$\int_C \mathbf{F} \cdot d\mathbf{P} = \lim_{\delta \to 0} \sum_{i=1}^{n} \left[\mathbf{F}(\tau_i) \cdot \left(\frac{\partial x}{\partial u} \mathbf{i} + \frac{\partial y}{\partial u} \mathbf{j} + \frac{\partial z}{\partial u} \mathbf{k} \right) \Delta_i u \right.$$
$$\left. + \mathbf{F}(\tau_i) \cdot \left(\frac{\partial x}{\partial v} \mathbf{i} + \frac{\partial y}{\partial v} \mathbf{j} + \frac{\partial z}{\partial v} \mathbf{k} \right) \Delta_i v \right].$$

It can be shown† that in the ith term of this sum we can evaluate $\mathbf{F}$ and all partial derivatives at the point corresponding to t_i and then use (9-3) again to obtain

$$\int_C \mathbf{F} \cdot d\mathbf{P} = \int_\Gamma \left[\left(\mathbf{F} \cdot \frac{\partial \mathbf{P}}{\partial u} \right) \mathbf{i} + \left(\mathbf{F} \cdot \frac{\partial \mathbf{P}}{\partial v} \right) \mathbf{j} \right] \cdot d\mathbf{P}.$$

Then we apply Green's theorem [Theorem 9-5.1] to the last integral, noting that the two mixed second-order partial derivatives of $\mathbf{P}$ are equal, since x, y, and z have continuous mixed second-order partial derivatives. Thus,

$$\int_C \mathbf{F} \cdot d\mathbf{P} = \int_D \left(\frac{\partial \mathbf{F}}{\partial u} \cdot \frac{\partial \mathbf{P}}{\partial v} - \frac{\partial \mathbf{F}}{\partial v} \cdot \frac{\partial \mathbf{P}}{\partial u} \right) dA. \tag{9-50}$$

Now, working with the other member of Eq. (9-47), we obtain

$$\int_S (\mathbf{\nabla} \times \mathbf{F}) \cdot \mathbf{n} \, d\sigma = \int_D (\mathbf{\nabla} \times \mathbf{F}) \cdot \left(\frac{\partial \mathbf{P}}{\partial u} \times \frac{\partial \mathbf{P}}{\partial v} \right) dA. \tag{9-51}$$

We can use some vector identities to manipulate the integrand, treating $\mathbf{\nabla}$ as if it were an ordinary vector rather than an operator. This is permissible, since the identities we use can be proved by writing all vectors in terms of components, and then expanding and comparing terms. The only precaution to be taken is to keep $\mathbf{\nabla}$ always to the left of $\mathbf{F}$ and to let the indicated differentiations be performed on $\mathbf{F}$ eventually, *with $\partial \mathbf{P}/\partial u$ and $\partial \mathbf{P}/\partial v$ treated as constants.* First, we can use Theorem 7-3.4, and then the vector identity $\mathbf{a} \times (\mathbf{b} \times \mathbf{c}) = (\mathbf{a} \cdot \mathbf{c}) \mathbf{b} - (\mathbf{a} \cdot \mathbf{b}) \mathbf{c}$ [see problem 9, page 334], to write

$$(\mathbf{\nabla} \times \mathbf{F}) \cdot \left(\frac{\partial \mathbf{P}}{\partial u} \times \frac{\partial \mathbf{P}}{\partial v} \right) = \mathbf{\nabla} \cdot \left[\mathbf{F} \times \left(\frac{\partial \mathbf{P}}{\partial u} \times \frac{\partial \mathbf{P}}{\partial v} \right) \right]$$
$$= \mathbf{\nabla} \cdot \left[\left(\mathbf{F} \cdot \frac{\partial \mathbf{P}}{\partial v} \right) \frac{\partial \mathbf{P}}{\partial u} - \left(\mathbf{F} \cdot \frac{\partial \mathbf{P}}{\partial u} \right) \frac{\partial \mathbf{P}}{\partial v} \right]. \tag{9-52}$$

---

† The difficulties are similar to those encountered in the proof of Theorem 9-4.2 and will not be repeated here.

Now we observe that $\nabla \cdot (\partial \mathbf{P}/\partial u)$ and $\nabla \cdot (\partial \mathbf{P}/\partial v)$ are operators that can be expanded as follows:

$$\nabla \cdot \frac{\partial \mathbf{P}}{\partial u} = \frac{\partial}{\partial x}\frac{\partial x}{\partial u} + \frac{\partial}{\partial y}\frac{\partial y}{\partial u} + \frac{\partial}{\partial z}\frac{\partial z}{\partial u},$$

$$\nabla \cdot \frac{\partial \mathbf{P}}{\partial v} = \frac{\partial}{\partial x}\frac{\partial x}{\partial v} + \frac{\partial}{\partial y}\frac{\partial y}{\partial v} + \frac{\partial}{\partial z}\frac{\partial z}{\partial v}.$$

These are "chain-rule operators" that differentiate with respect to u and v, respectively. They operate on $\mathbf{F} \cdot (\partial \mathbf{P}/\partial v)$ and $\mathbf{F} \cdot (\partial \mathbf{P}/\partial u)$, respectively, with $\partial \mathbf{P}/\partial v$ and $\partial \mathbf{P}/\partial u$ treated as constants. Hence, they produce $(\partial \mathbf{F}/\partial u) \cdot (\partial \mathbf{P}/\partial v)$ and $(\partial \mathbf{F}/\partial v) \cdot (\partial \mathbf{P}/\partial u)$, and we can write (9-52) as

$$(\nabla \times \mathbf{F}) \cdot \left(\frac{\partial \mathbf{P}}{\partial u} \times \frac{\partial \mathbf{P}}{\partial v}\right) = \frac{\partial \mathbf{F}}{\partial u} \cdot \frac{\partial \mathbf{P}}{\partial v} - \frac{\partial \mathbf{F}}{\partial v} \cdot \frac{\partial \mathbf{P}}{\partial u}.$$

Now, we can substitute in (9-51) and use (9-50) to conclude that Eq. (9-47) is true.

DEFINITION 9-7.1. A *surface* is a connected set S that can be represented as the union of a finite number of surface elements in such a way that
   (i) if two surface elements intersect, their intersection is the union of a finite number of curves along their edges, none of which is a single point;
   (ii) no curve that contains more than one point belongs to the edge of more than two surface elements.
The *edge* of a surface is the union of all curves whose interior points belong to the edge of exactly one surface element. The surface is *orientable* if an orientation can be chosen for the edges of each of the surface elements so that
   (iii) a curve that belongs to two surface elements has opposite orientations in the two cases.

The first five surfaces in Fig. 9-34 are orientable surfaces. The last surface is nonorientable and is called a *Möbius band*.

If an orientable surface can be represented as the union of a finite number of smooth surface elements such that the conditions of Stokes' theorem are satisfied on each surface element, then Stokes' theorem applies to the entire surface. To show this, we have merely to add corresponding members of (9-47) for each surface element and note that line integrals over curves that are on the edges of two surface elements are evaluated twice in opposite directions and cancel.

Stokes' theorem will now be used to generalize the conditions for existence of a potential function that we derived for functions defined in a plane [Theorems 9-6.1 and 9-6.2].

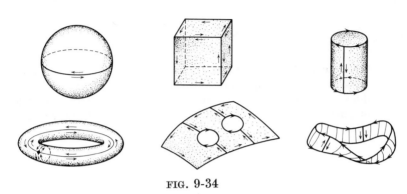

FIG. 9-34

DEFINITION 9-7.2. A *simply connected* open three-dimensional set is an open three-dimensional set R with the following properties: (1) R is connected; (2) any simple closed polygonal curve contained in R is the edge of an orientable surface composed of triangular surface elements contained in R.†

It is not difficult to prove that an open set R is simply connected if it is convex—that is, if any two points of R can be joined by a line segment contained in R. We leave the details to the student.

The use of requirement (2) of Definition 9-7.2 in proving Theorem 9-7.2 is much like the corresponding part of the proof of Theorem 9-6.2. That is, we need to show that if C_1 and C_2 are two polygonal curves in R with the same initial and terminal points, then it is possible to divide C_1 and C_2 into the same number of consecutive pieces in such a way that corresponding pieces are either coincident and oriented in the same direction, or else the two pieces together form the boundary of a surface contained in R that is the union of triangles contained in R.

THEOREM 9-7.2. If R is a simply connected open set and $\mathbf{F}$ is a vector whose partial derivatives exist and are continuous on R, then $\nabla \times \mathbf{F} = \mathbf{0}$ at all points of R if and only if $\mathbf{F}$ is the gradient of some function Φ (called a *potential function* of $\mathbf{F}$).

---

† It is customary to say that a *simply connected* set is a set S such that, given any point in S and any closed curve in S, it is possible to continuously deform the curve into the point without leaving S. For open sets, this is equivalent to Definition 9-7.2. Moreover, giving Definition 9-7.2 removes the necessity of defining the concept of "continuous deformation," which is better left to a topology course.

We shall omit the proof of this theorem, since it is so much like the proofs of Theorems 9-6.1 and 9-6.2. For example, if $\nabla \times \mathbf{F} = \mathbf{0}$ at all points of R, then we can choose a particular point (x_0, y_0, z_0) of R and let

$$\Phi(x, y, z) = \int_{(x_0, y_0, z_0)}^{(x,y,z)} \mathbf{F} \cdot d\mathbf{P}.$$

ILLUSTRATION 2. Suppose that a vector-valued function $\mathbf{v}$ is called velocity and is thought of as being the velocity of an incompressible fluid. Also assume that the flow is steady—i.e., that $\mathbf{v}$ is independent of time. For a closed curve C that is the edge of a surface S, the line integral

$$\int_C \mathbf{v} \cdot d\mathbf{P} = \int_S (\nabla \times \mathbf{v}) \cdot \mathbf{n} \, d\sigma \tag{9-53}$$

is said to be the circulation of $\mathbf{v}$ along C. Since $\int_C \mathbf{v} \cdot d\mathbf{P} = \int_C v_T \, ds$, where v_T is the tangential component of $\mathbf{v}$, the circulation around C is equal to the product of the length of C and the average value of the tangential component of $\mathbf{v}$. If the right member of Eq. (9-53) is divided by the area of S, we obtain the mean value over S of $(\nabla \times \mathbf{v}) \cdot \mathbf{n}$. If S is a plane set, then the circulation around C is equal to the product of the area of S and the mean value of the component of $\nabla \times \mathbf{v}$ perpendicular to the plane of S. The vector $\mathbf{v}$ is said to be *irrotational* in R if $\nabla \times \mathbf{v}$ is zero at all points of R. If R is open and simply connected, then it follows from Theorems 9-7.2 and 9-4.2 that $\mathbf{v}$ is irrotational if and only if the circulation is zero around each simple closed rectifiable curve.

PROBLEMS

1. For each of the following, use Stokes' theorem to evaluate $\int_C \mathbf{F} \cdot d\mathbf{P}$, where C is the intersection of the cylinder $x^2 + y^2 = 4$ with the plane indicated, and C is oriented counterclockwise as viewed from the positive z-axis.

   (a) $\mathbf{F} = (xz - z)\mathbf{j} + (xy + y)\mathbf{k}$; $2x + 3y = 7z$.

   (b) $\mathbf{F} = (yze^{xy})\mathbf{i} + xz(1 + e^{xy})\mathbf{j} + e^{xy}\mathbf{k}$; $2x + 3y + z = 5$.

   (c) $\mathbf{F} = x\mathbf{i} + xz\mathbf{j} + y\mathbf{k}$; $x + z = 2$.

2. For each of the following, evaluate the line integral explicitly. Check by using Stokes' theorem.

   (a) $\int_C (2y\mathbf{i} - 2x\mathbf{j} + z^2x\mathbf{k}) \cdot d\mathbf{P}$; $\mathbf{P}(t) = (\cos t)\mathbf{i} + (\sin t)\mathbf{j} + 5\mathbf{k}$; $0 \leq t \leq 2\pi$.

(b) $\int_C z \, dx + x \, dy + y^2 \, dz$; C the triangle with successive vertices $(3, 0, 0)$, $(0, 1, 0)$, $(0, 0, 2)$.

(c) $\int_C [(yz)\mathbf{i} + (xz^2 - 3y)\mathbf{j} - (xy)\mathbf{k}] \cdot d\mathbf{P}$; $\mathbf{P}(t) = (\cos t)\mathbf{i} + (\sin t)\mathbf{j} + (\cos t)\mathbf{k}$; $0 \leq t \leq 2\pi$.

3. For each of the following, use Stokes' theorem to evaluate the line integral.

(a) $\int_C [(y + z)\mathbf{i} + (z + x)\mathbf{j} + (x + y)\mathbf{k}] \cdot d\mathbf{P}$, where C is the boundary of the first-octant part of the graph of $x^2 + y^2 + z^2 = 4$ and C is oriented counterclockwise as viewed from the origin.

(b) $\int_C [z^2\mathbf{i} + 2x\mathbf{j} + (2xz + y)\mathbf{k}] \cdot d\mathbf{P}$, where C is the closed curve composed of line segments with successive vertices $(0, 0, 0)$, $(2, 0, 3)$, $(0, 0, 3)$, $(0, 4, 3)$, $(0, 4, 0)$, $(0, 0, 0)$.

4. Let C be the circle $x^2 + y^2 = 1$ in the (x, y)-plane and let C be oriented counterclockwise as viewed from the positive z-axis. Use Stokes' theorem cautiously to evaluate the integral

$$\int_C \left[\left(-\frac{\sin x^2 y}{x^2} + 2y \cos x^2 y \right)\mathbf{i} + (x + x \cos x^2 y)\mathbf{j} + \ln (x^2 + y^2)\mathbf{k} \right] \cdot d\mathbf{P}.$$

5. For each of the following integrals, the curve C is the common edge of two surfaces S_1 and S_2, and C is oriented counterclockwise as viewed from the positive direction on the coordinate axis that is perpendicular to S_1. Evaluate the line integral around C by using Stokes' theorem and one of the surfaces. Check by using the other surface.

(a) $\int_C [(3x^2 \sin y)\mathbf{i} + (x^3 \cos y + x)\mathbf{j} + z\mathbf{k}] \cdot d\mathbf{P}$; S_1 the disk $x^2 + y^2 \leq 1$ in the (x, y)-plane; S_2 the hemisphere $z = (1 - x^2 - y^2)^{1/2}$.

(b) $\int_C [(z^2 + ye^{x^2} + 2x^2ye^{x^2})\mathbf{i} + (xe^{x^2} + y)\mathbf{j} + (2x)\mathbf{k}] \cdot d\mathbf{P}$; S_1 the square with vertices $(0, 1, 0)$, $(1, 1, 0)$, $(1, 1, 1)$, $(0, 1, 1)$; S_2 the surface of the unit cube in the first octant with one vertex at $(0, 0, 0)$ and the face S_1 deleted.

6. Let S be a surface bounded by a curve C such that Stokes' theorem is applicable. Show that, if $\mathbf{a}$ is a constant vector, then

$$\int_S \mathbf{a} \cdot \mathbf{n} \, d\sigma = \frac{1}{2} \int_C (\mathbf{a} \times \mathbf{P}) \cdot d\mathbf{P}.$$

7. Let S be a surface bounded by a curve C such that Stokes' theorem is applicable. Show that, if u and v have continuous first-order partial derivatives and the mixed second-order partial derivatives of v are continuous on S, then

$$\int_C [u(\nabla v)] \cdot d\mathbf{P} = \int_S (\nabla u \times \nabla v) \cdot \mathbf{n} \, d\sigma.$$

8. For each of the following, show that $\nabla \times \mathbf{F} = \mathbf{0}$ and determine by inspection or otherwise a potential function of $\mathbf{F}$. Then use Theorem 9-4.2 to evaluate $\int_C \mathbf{F} \cdot d\mathbf{P}$ over a curve joining the points indicated.

(*a*) $\mathbf{F} = (yz)\mathbf{i} + (zx)\mathbf{j} + (xy)\mathbf{k}$, from $(1, 2, 3)$ to $(3, 1, 4)$.

(*b*) $\mathbf{F} = (yz \sinh xy)\mathbf{i} + (xz \sinh xy)\mathbf{j} + (\cosh xy)\mathbf{k}$, from $(3, 0, 2)$ to $(7, 5, 0)$.

(c) $\mathbf{F} = (2xy)\mathbf{i} + (x^2 + \ln z)\mathbf{j} + (y/z)\mathbf{k}$, from $(1, 2, e)$ to $(3, 4, e^2)$.

9. For each of the following, verify that $\nabla \times \mathbf{F} = \mathbf{0}$ everywhere and evaluate a line integral to determine a potential function of $\mathbf{F}$. Start the line integral at $(0, 0, 0)$.

(*a*) $\mathbf{F} = (2xyz)\mathbf{i} + (x^2z)\mathbf{j} + (x^2y)\mathbf{k}$.

(*b*) $\mathbf{F} = (x^2 + y^2 + z^2)(x\mathbf{i} + y\mathbf{j} + z\mathbf{k})$.

10. Find a potential function Φ for $\mathbf{F}$ that is valid when $x > 0$, where

$$\mathbf{F} = \frac{(y-z)(yz-x^2)\mathbf{i} + x(x^2+z^2)\mathbf{j} - x(x^2+y^2)\mathbf{k}}{(x^2+y^2)(x^2+z^2)}.$$

Do this by letting

$$\Phi(x, y, z) = \int_{(1,1,1)}^{(x,y,z)} \mathbf{F} \cdot d\mathbf{P}.$$

11. For $\mathbf{F}$ of problem 10, evaluate $\int_C \mathbf{F} \cdot d\mathbf{P}$, where in each case the parametric equations of C are given. Explain why not all answers are zero, although $\nabla \times \mathbf{F} = \mathbf{0}$ except when $x^2 + y^2 = 0$ or $x^2 + z^2 = 0$.

(*a*) $x = \cos t$, $y = \sin t$, $z = -\sin t$; $\quad 0 \leq t \leq 2\pi$.

(*b*) $x = \cos t$, $y = \sin t$, $z = \sin t$; $\quad 0 \leq t \leq 2\pi$.

(*c*) $x = \cos t$, $y = 1$, $z = \sin t$; $\quad 0 \leq t \leq 2\pi$.

12. Show that e^{xyz} is a potential function of the vector-valued function

$$\mathbf{F} = e^{xyz}[(yz)\mathbf{i} + (zx)\mathbf{j} + (xy)\mathbf{k}],$$

but that there is no point (x_0, y_0, z_0) such that

$$e^{xyz} = \int_{(x_0,y_0,z_0)}^{(x,y,z)} \mathbf{F} \cdot d\mathbf{P}.$$

13. One end of a long tube is fastened to one side of a flat plate along a circle, with the interior of the circle deleted. The other end is fastened to the other side of the plate along a circle, with the interior of the circle deleted. Explain why the resulting surface is nonorientable.

14. The cube in Fig. 9-35 has a quarter of the left and right faces and half the top deleted. A rectangle congruent to half of a face is attached

in the interior as indicated. Explain why this is a nonorientable surface.

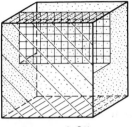

FIG. 9-35

15. Let $\mathbf{F}$ be a vector-valued function whose value is the same at all points. Show that it is impossible to place a Möbius band so that $\int_C \mathbf{F} \cdot d\mathbf{P} \neq 0$, where C is the "edge" of the band. [*Note:* $\nabla \times \mathbf{F} = \mathbf{0}$, so this would follow from Stokes' theorem, if it were applicable.]

16.* A *closed surface* is a surface in the sense of Definition 9-7.1, with the property that, for each surface element of S, the edge of this surface element is the union of pieces of the edges of other surface elements. Show that, if S is closed and orientable and if each of the surface elements of S has the properties needed for Stokes' theorem to be applicable, then

$$\int_S (\nabla \times \mathbf{F}) \cdot \mathbf{n} \, dA = 0,$$

provided only that the first-order partial derivatives of $\mathbf{F}$ exist and are continuous at all points of S, and $\mathbf{n}$ is chosen so that a curve that belongs to the edges of two surface elements has opposite orientations in the two cases.

9-8. THE DIVERGENCE THEOREM

Stokes' theorem was a generalization of Green's theorem from two to three dimensions. The divergence theorem is another type of generalization of Green's theorem to three dimensions. It states a relationship between a certain triple integral over a three-dimensional set bounded by a surface S, and a surface integral over S.

Just as Green's theorem was easy to establish for a rectangle, the divergence theorem is easy to establish for a rectangular parallelepiped.

Suppose we evaluate $\int (\partial L/\partial x)\, dV$ over the solid parallelepiped T of Fig. 9-36. We have

$$\int_T \frac{\partial L}{\partial x}\, dV = \int_{z_0}^{z_0+c} \int_{y_0}^{y_0+b} \int_{x_0}^{x_0+a} \frac{\partial L}{\partial x}\, dx\, dy\, dz$$

$$= \int_{z_0}^{z_0+c} \int_{y_0}^{y_0+b} [L(x_0+a, y, z) - L(x_0, y, z)]\, dy\, dz$$

$$= \int_S (L\mathbf{i}\cdot\mathbf{n})\, d\sigma,$$

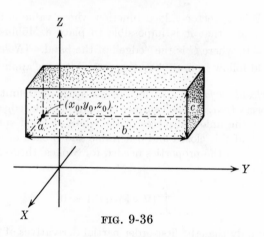

FIG. 9-36

where S is the entire surface of the parallelepiped and $\mathbf{n}$ is perpendicular to S and directed outward. After computing similar expressions for the integrals of $\partial M/\partial y$ and $\partial N/\partial z$, we can add corresponding members of these equalities to obtain

$$\int_S (L\mathbf{i} + M\mathbf{j} + N\mathbf{k})\cdot\mathbf{n}\, d\sigma = \int_T \left(\frac{\partial L}{\partial x} + \frac{\partial M}{\partial y} + \frac{\partial N}{\partial z}\right) dV.$$

If we let $\mathbf{F} = L\mathbf{i} + M\mathbf{j} + N\mathbf{k}$, this equality can be written as

$$\int_S (\mathbf{F}\cdot\mathbf{n})\, d\sigma = \int_T (\nabla\cdot\mathbf{F})\, dV. \qquad (9\text{-}54)$$

ILLUSTRATION. If T is the unit cube in the first octant with one vertex at the origin and S is the boundary of T, then

$$\int_S [(x+7)\mathbf{i} + 2y\mathbf{j} + (3z+1)\mathbf{k}] \cdot \mathbf{n} \, d\sigma$$

$$= \int_0^1 \int_0^1 -dx \, dy + \int_0^1 \int_0^1 4 \, dx \, dy + \int_0^1 \int_0^1 -7 \, dy \, dz + \int_0^1 \int_0^1 8 \, dy \, dz$$

$$+ \int_0^1 \int_0^1 2 \, dz \, dx = 6.$$

This should be equal to the following integral over T:

$$\int_T \mathbf{\nabla} \cdot [(x+7)\mathbf{i} + 2y\mathbf{j} + (3z+1)\mathbf{k}] \, dV = \int_T 6 \, dV = 6.$$

Now let us form a union U of parallelepipeds, each parallelepiped having a face in common with at least one other parallelepiped. If we add the left members of Eq. (9-54) for each parallelepiped, then the integral over a face belonging to two different parallelepipeds is evaluated twice, with $\mathbf{n}$ directed oppositely in the two cases. Therefore, the sum is simply the integral over the surface of U. Clearly, the sum of the right members of (9-54) for all parallelepipeds in U is equal to the integral of $\mathbf{\nabla} \cdot \mathbf{F}$ over U. This provides intuitive support for the following theorem.

THEOREM 9-8.1 (DIVERGENCE THEOREM†). Suppose R is a bounded set in three dimensions whose boundary is a surface S composed of a finite number of smooth surface elements. Also suppose that $\mathbf{n}$ is the exterior normal of S and that $\mathbf{F}$ is a vector-valued function whose components have continuous first-order partial derivatives at all points of R and its boundary. Then $\int_S (\mathbf{F} \cdot \mathbf{n}) \, d\sigma = \int_R (\mathbf{\nabla} \cdot \mathbf{F}) \, dV$.

A general proof of the divergence theorem might be modeled after the proof of Green's theorem. As yet, we have proved only the restricted case of the divergence theorem for which R is the union of rectangular parallelepipeds. We shall now use similar techniques to establish a more general result. First, let us consider a set R whose boundary consists of two smooth surface elements, S_1 and S_2, as shown

---

† Also called *Gauss' theorem*, *Green's theorem in space*, and *Ostrogradski's theorem*.

in Fig. 9-37. We shall assume that S_1 and S_2 have parametric equations,

$$\begin{cases} x = x, \\ y = y, \\ z = h(x, y), \end{cases} \qquad \begin{cases} x = x, \\ y = y, \\ z = k(x, y), \end{cases}$$

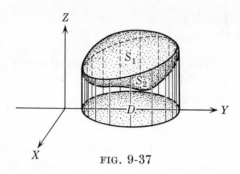

FIG. 9-37

where $h(x, y) \leq k(x, y)$ for all (x, y) in the common domain of h and k. Similarly to the preceding discussion of the rectangular parallelepiped case, we have

$$\int_R \frac{\partial N}{\partial z} \, dV = \int\!\!\int\!\!\int_R \frac{\partial N}{\partial z} \, dz \, dx \, dy$$

$$= \int\!\!\int_D \{N[x, y, k(x, y)] - N[x, y, h(x, y)]\} \, dx \, dy$$

$$= \int_{S_1} (N\mathbf{k}\cdot\mathbf{n}) \, d\sigma + \int_{S_2} (N\mathbf{k}\cdot\mathbf{n}) \, d\sigma = \int_S (N\mathbf{k}\cdot\mathbf{n}) \, d\sigma.$$

Thus, if a set R with boundary surface S can be divided into a finite number of pieces like the one of Fig. 9-37, then for a function N whose partial derivative with respect to z is continuous we have

$$\int_S (N\mathbf{k}\cdot\mathbf{n}) \, d\sigma = \int_R [\boldsymbol{\nabla}\cdot(N\mathbf{k})] \, dV.$$

This argument can be used with each of the other coordinate planes and shows that the conclusion of the divergence theorem is true if R can be divided into a finite number of pieces each of which has the relation to each coordinate plane illustrated in Fig. 9-37 for the (x, y)-plane.

We defined an *irrotational vector-valued function* as a vector-valued function $\mathbf{F}$ such that $\nabla \times \mathbf{F} = \mathbf{0}$ at all points of the domain of $\mathbf{F}$. We have seen [Theorem 9-7.2] that if R is a simply connected open set and $\mathbf{F}$ is irrotational on R, then there is a (scalar) potential function Φ such that $\mathbf{F}$ is the gradient of Φ; that is, $\mathbf{F} = \nabla\Phi$.

Now we shall say that a *solenoidal vector-valued function* is a vector-valued function $\mathbf{F}$ such that $\nabla \cdot \mathbf{F} = 0$ at all points of the domain of $\mathbf{F}$. It is easy to verify that $\mathbf{F}$ is solenoidal if there is a vector function $\mathbf{W}$ such that $\mathbf{F}$ is the curl of $\mathbf{W}$ and the mixed second-order partial derivatives of the components of $\mathbf{W}$ are continuous [problem 6(b)]. Such a function $\mathbf{W}$ is said to be a *vector potential* of $\mathbf{F}$. The following theorem shows that the converse is true in a restricted sense [also see problem 11].

THEOREM 9-8.2. Suppose $\mathbf{F}$ is a vector-valued function whose components have continuous first-order partial derivatives in a convex open set R. If $\nabla \cdot \mathbf{F} = 0$ at all points of R, then there is a vector-valued function $\mathbf{W}$ such that $\nabla \times \mathbf{W} = \mathbf{F}$.

PROOF. Suppose that (x_0, y_0, z_0) is a fixed point of R and that functions $\overline{\mathbf{F}}$ and $\overline{\mathbf{P}}$ are defined by

$$\overline{\mathbf{F}}(x, y, z, t) = \mathbf{F}[x_0 + t(x - x_0), y_0 + t(y - y_0), z_0 + t(z - z_0)],$$

$$\overline{\mathbf{P}}(x, y, z) = (x - x_0)\mathbf{i} + (y - y_0)\mathbf{j} + (z - z_0)\mathbf{k}.$$

We first establish the following useful equality:

$$t \frac{\partial \overline{\mathbf{F}}}{\partial t} = (\overline{\mathbf{P}} \cdot \nabla)\overline{\mathbf{F}}. \tag{9-55}$$

The proof of this equality uses the chain rule for partial differentiation applied to vector-valued functions and is as follows:

$$\begin{aligned}
(\overline{\mathbf{P}} \cdot \nabla)\overline{\mathbf{F}} = &\ (x - x_0) \cdot t\mathbf{F}_1[x_0 + t(x - x_0), y_0 + t(y - y_0), z_0 + t(z - z_0)] \\
&+ (y - y_0) \cdot t\mathbf{F}_2[x_0 + t(x - x_0), y_0 + t(y - y_0), z_0 + t(z - z_0)] \\
&+ (z - z_0) \cdot t\mathbf{F}_3[x_0 + t(x - x_0), y_0 + t(y - y_0), z_0 + t(z - z_0)].
\end{aligned}$$

Now factoring t from the right member of this equality, we note that we have left precisely $\partial\overline{\mathbf{F}}/\partial t$.

Since Eq. (9-55) is proved, we can use it and

$$\mathbf{F}(x, y, z) = \overline{\mathbf{F}}(x, y, z, 1) = \int_0^1 \frac{\partial t^2 \overline{\mathbf{F}}}{\partial t}\, dt$$

to write

$$F(x, y, z) = \int_0^1 [2t\overline{F} + t(\overline{P} \cdot \nabla)\overline{F}] \, dt = \int_0^1 [2\overline{F} + (\overline{P} \cdot \nabla)\overline{F}]t \, dt. \quad (9\text{-}56)$$

It follows from the rule for differentiating products that

$$\nabla \times (\overline{F} \times \overline{P}) = [\nabla \times (\overline{F} \times \overline{P})]_{P \text{ constant}} + [\nabla \times (\overline{F} \times \overline{P})]_{F \text{ constant}}. \quad (9\text{-}57)$$

Since the value of $\nabla \cdot \overline{F}$ at (x, y, z, t) is equal to the product of t and the value of $\nabla \cdot F$ at $[x_0 + t(x - x_0), \ y_0 + t(y - y_0), \ z_0 + t(z - z_0)]$, and $\nabla \cdot F$ is zero everywhere in R, we have $\nabla \cdot \overline{F} = 0$. From this, (9-57), and the vector identity $\mathbf{a} \times (\mathbf{b} \times \mathbf{c}) = (\mathbf{a} \cdot \mathbf{c})\mathbf{b} - (\mathbf{a} \cdot \mathbf{b})\mathbf{c}$ [see problem 9 page 334], it follows that

$$\nabla \times (\overline{F} \times \overline{P}) = [(\overline{P} \cdot \nabla)\overline{F} - (\nabla \cdot \overline{F})\overline{P}] + [(\nabla \cdot \overline{P})\overline{F} - (\overline{F} \cdot \nabla)\overline{P}]$$
$$= (\overline{P} \cdot \nabla)\overline{F} + 3\overline{F} - \overline{F} = (\overline{P} \cdot \nabla)\overline{F} + 2\overline{F}.$$

Therefore, (9-56) can be written as $F(x, y, z) = \int_0^1 \nabla \times (\overline{F} \times \overline{P})t \, dt$. It follows from this and Theorem 6-3.1 that $F = \nabla \times W$ if

$$W(x, y, z) = \int_0^1 [\overline{F} \times (t\overline{P})] \, dt. \quad (9\text{-}58)$$

We shall discuss some important physical heuristics. Suppose we think of $\mathbf{v}$ as the velocity of a fluid. Then $\int_S (\mathbf{v} \cdot \mathbf{n}) \, d\sigma$ can be interpreted as being the rate of flow of fluid out of the region R whose boundary is S. Since

$$\int_S (\mathbf{v} \cdot \mathbf{n}) \, d\sigma = \int_R (\nabla \cdot \mathbf{v}) \, dV,$$

the product of the volume of R and the mean value over R of the divergence of $\mathbf{v}$ is equal to the rate of flow of fluid out of R. Thus, the divergence of $\mathbf{v}$ is a measure of the rate at which the fluid is expanding, i.e., diverging, per unit volume. This is the reason for applying the name "divergence" to $\nabla \cdot \mathbf{v}$. In fact, a proof of the divergence theorem can be based on these ideas.

PROBLEMS

1. For each of the following, let $\mathbf{n}$ be the exterior normal and evaluate the surface integral explicitly. Check by using the divergence theorem.

(a) $\int_S (x\mathbf{i} + y^2\mathbf{j} - \mathbf{k}) \cdot \mathbf{n} \, d\sigma$, where S is the cube with vertices $(\pm 1, \pm 1, \pm 1)$.

(b) $\int_S (3x\mathbf{i} - y\mathbf{j} - z\mathbf{k}) \cdot \mathbf{n} \, d\sigma$, where S is the graph of $x^2 + y^2 + z^2 = 9$.

2. For each of the following, use the divergence theorem to evaluate the surface integral. Let **n** be the exterior normal.

(a) $\int_S (x^2\mathbf{i}+y^2\mathbf{j}+z^2\mathbf{k})\cdot\mathbf{n}\,d\sigma$, where S is the surface of the unit cube in the first octant with one vertex at $(0, 0, 0)$.

(b) $\int_S (x\mathbf{i}-y\mathbf{j}-z\mathbf{k})\cdot\mathbf{n}\,d\sigma$, where S is the graph of $x^2+(y-2)^2 +(z+1)^2 = 3$.

(c) $\int_S (x^2z\mathbf{i}+y^4z^3\mathbf{j}+z\mathbf{k})\cdot\mathbf{n}\,d\sigma$, where S is the surface of the solid cylinder bounded by $x^2+y^2 =1$ and the two planes, $z = 0$ and $z =1$.

3. Let $\mathbf{P} = x\mathbf{i}+y\mathbf{j}+z\mathbf{k}$. Show that $(\mathbf{F}\cdot\boldsymbol{\nabla})\mathbf{P} = \mathbf{F}$ for all $\mathbf{F}$.

4. Let $\mathbf{F}$ and h be vector-valued and scalar-valued functions, respectively, whose first-order partial derivatives are continuous. Also let $\mathbf{P} = x\mathbf{i}+y\mathbf{j}+z\mathbf{k}$ and suppose that x, y, and z are differentiable functions of a parameter t. Explain why

(a) $\dfrac{dh}{dt} = \left(\dfrac{d\mathbf{P}}{dt}\cdot\boldsymbol{\nabla}\right) h;$ (b) $\dfrac{d\mathbf{F}}{dt} = \left(\dfrac{d\mathbf{P}}{dt}\cdot\boldsymbol{\nabla}\right)\mathbf{F}.$

5. Let $\mathbf{F}$ and $\mathbf{G}$ be vector-valued functions and h be a scalar-valued function whose first-order partial derivatives exist. Explain why

(a) $\boldsymbol{\nabla}\cdot(h\mathbf{F}) = (h\boldsymbol{\nabla})\cdot\mathbf{F}+(\mathbf{F}\cdot\boldsymbol{\nabla})h;$

(b) $\boldsymbol{\nabla}\times(h\mathbf{F}) = (h\boldsymbol{\nabla})\times\mathbf{F}-(\mathbf{F}\times\boldsymbol{\nabla})h;$

(c) $\boldsymbol{\nabla}\cdot(\mathbf{F}\times\mathbf{G}) = \mathbf{G}\cdot(\boldsymbol{\nabla}\times\mathbf{F})-\mathbf{F}\cdot(\boldsymbol{\nabla}\times\mathbf{G});$

(d) $\boldsymbol{\nabla}\times(\mathbf{F}\times\mathbf{G}) = [\mathbf{F}(\boldsymbol{\nabla}\cdot\mathbf{G})-(\mathbf{F}\cdot\boldsymbol{\nabla})\mathbf{G}]+[(\mathbf{G}\cdot\boldsymbol{\nabla})\mathbf{F}-\mathbf{G}(\boldsymbol{\nabla}\cdot\mathbf{F})].$

6. Show that if Φ and the components of $\mathbf{F}$ have continuous second-order partial derivatives, then (a) $\boldsymbol{\nabla}\times(\boldsymbol{\nabla}\Phi) = \mathbf{0}$; (b) $\boldsymbol{\nabla}\cdot(\boldsymbol{\nabla}\times\mathbf{F}) = 0$.

7. Let R be a bounded set in three dimensions whose boundary is a surface S composed of a finite number of smooth surface elements. Let **n** be the exterior normal of S. Show that

(a) $\int_S (x\mathbf{i})\cdot\mathbf{n}\,d\sigma = \int_S (y\mathbf{j})\cdot\mathbf{n}\,d\sigma = \int_S (z\mathbf{k})\cdot\mathbf{n}\,d\sigma = $ volume of R;

(b) $\int_S \mathbf{P}\cdot\mathbf{n}\,d\sigma = 3$(volume of R).

8. Use problem 7(a) to determine the volume of a rectangular parallelepiped that has three adjacent edges of lengths a, b, and c.

9. Use problem 7(b) to determine the volume of a sphere of radius r, given that the area of the surface of the sphere is $4\pi r^2$.

10. Let R be a bounded set in three-space whose boundary is a surface S composed of a finite number of smooth surface elements. Let **n** be the exterior normal of S. Show that if the origin is not in $R \cup S$, then

(a) $\displaystyle\int_S \frac{\mathbf{P}\cdot\mathbf{n}}{|\mathbf{P}|}\,dA = 2\int_R \frac{1}{|\mathbf{P}|}\,dV;$ (b) $\displaystyle\int_S \frac{\mathbf{P}\cdot\mathbf{n}}{|\mathbf{P}|^2}\,dA = \int_R \frac{1}{|\mathbf{P}|^2}\,dV.$

11. Let $\mathbf{F} = \mathbf{P}|\mathbf{P}|^{-3}$ at all points except $(0, 0, 0)$. Show that (a) $\nabla \cdot \mathbf{F} = 0$ at all points except $(0, 0, 0)$; (b) $\int_S \mathbf{F} \cdot \mathbf{n} \, d\sigma = 4\pi$ if S is the graph of $x^2 + y^2 + z^2 = a^2$ and $\mathbf{n}$ is the exterior normal; (c) there is no number a and vector-valued function $\mathbf{W}$ such that $\mathbf{F} = \nabla \times \mathbf{W}$ at all points outside the sphere $x^2 + y^2 + z^2 = a^2$ [see problem 16, Section 9-7].

12. Let S be a union of smooth surface elements. Also assume that S does not contain the origin and that each ray from the origin intersects S in at most one point. Let S_1 be the set of points on the unit sphere that are on rays containing a point of S. Then the area of S_1 is called the *solid angle* subtended at the origin by S. Show that this solid angle is equal to

$$\int_S \frac{\mathbf{P} \cdot \mathbf{n}}{|\mathbf{P}|^3} \, d\sigma.$$

13. For each of the following, show that $\mathbf{F}$ is solenoidal and use Eq. (9-58) to determine a vector potential of $\mathbf{F}$. Use $(0, 0, 0)$ as (x_0, y_0, z_0).

    (*a*) $\mathbf{F} = \mathbf{i} + (xy)\mathbf{j} - (xz)\mathbf{k}$.   (b) $\mathbf{F} = x^2\mathbf{i} + (x^2y - 2xy)\mathbf{j} - (x^2z)\mathbf{k}$.

14. For each of the following, show that $\mathbf{F}$ is solenoidal and use Eq. (9-58) to determine a vector potential of $\mathbf{F}$.

    (*a*) $\mathbf{F} = (x^3z - 2xyz)\mathbf{i} + (xy - 3x^2yz)\mathbf{j} + (yz^2 - xz)\mathbf{k}$.

    (*b*) $\mathbf{F} = (z - y)\mathbf{i} + (x - z)\mathbf{j} + (y - x)\mathbf{k}$.

15. For any function f, let $\partial f/\partial n$ denote the directional derivative of f in the direction of the vector $\mathbf{n}$. The following are called *Green's formulas*. In each case, R is a three-dimensional set and S is its boundary. Assuming that u, v, R, and S are such that the divergence theorem is applicable, prove these formulas.

    (a) $\displaystyle\int_S \frac{\partial u}{\partial n} \, d\sigma = \int_R \nabla^2 u \, dV.$

    (b) $\displaystyle\int_S u \frac{\partial v}{\partial n} \, d\sigma = \int_R (u\nabla^2 v + \nabla u \cdot \nabla v) \, dV.$

    (c) $\displaystyle\int_S \left(u \frac{\partial v}{\partial n} - v \frac{\partial u}{\partial n} \right) d\sigma = \int_R (u\nabla^2 v - v\nabla^2 u) \, dV.$

16. Using the same conventions as for problem 15, prove that, if a vector field $\mathbf{F}$ is both irrotational and solenoidal in a simply connected open set, then $\mathbf{F}$ has a scalar potential Φ and this potential is harmonic—i.e., satisfies Laplace's equation, $\nabla^2\Phi = 0$.

ORTHOGONAL
FUNCTIONS AND
FOURIER SERIES

10-1. VECTOR SPACES AND ORTHONORMAL SETS

In Chapter 8, we generalized the concept of vectors to include vectors in R^n. In this chapter, we shall be interested primarily in function spaces that have a scalar product. Such spaces, as well as the spaces R^n, are examples of what are usually called *vector spaces* or *linear spaces*. For the most part, we shall use specific function spaces. However, some of our discussion can be given in general. This will be done in this section in order to give the reader a clear picture of some of the basic concepts we need before we use these concepts in specialized situations.

DEFINITION 10-1.1. A *(real) vector space*† is a set V with which there are associated two functions, Σ and Π, which with V satisfy the following axioms:

V_1: The range of Σ is contained in V and the domain is the set of all ordered pairs $(\mathbf{x}, \mathbf{y})$ of members of V. Also, if $\sum (\mathbf{x}, \mathbf{y})$ is denoted by $\mathbf{x}+\mathbf{y}$, then, for all members $\mathbf{x}$, $\mathbf{y}$, and $\mathbf{z}$ of V,

  (i) $\mathbf{x}+\mathbf{y} = \mathbf{y}+\mathbf{x}$;   (Commutative law)
  (ii) $\mathbf{x}+(\mathbf{y}+\mathbf{z}) = (\mathbf{x}+\mathbf{y})+\mathbf{z}$.   (Associative law)

V_2: There is a member of V, that we shall denote by $\mathbf{0}$, which has the property that $\mathbf{x}+\mathbf{0} = \mathbf{x}$ for all $\mathbf{x}$ in V.

V_3: For any member $\mathbf{x}$ of V, there is a member, that we shall denote by $-\mathbf{x}$, which has the property that $\mathbf{x}+(-\mathbf{x}) = \mathbf{0}$.

---

† Or *linear space*.

and

V_4: The range of Π is contained in V and the domain is the set of all ordered pairs $(t, \mathbf{x})$ for which t is a real number and $\mathbf{x} \in V$. Also, if we denote $\Pi(t, \mathbf{x})$ by $t \cdot \mathbf{x}$ or $t\mathbf{x}$, then, for any real numbers a and b and any members $\mathbf{x}$ and $\mathbf{y}$ of V, we have

(i) $(a+b)\mathbf{x} = a\mathbf{x} + b\mathbf{x}$;   (Left distributive law)
(ii) $a(\mathbf{x}+\mathbf{y}) = a\mathbf{x} + a\mathbf{y}$;   (Right distributive law)
(iii) $(ab)\mathbf{x} = a(b\mathbf{x})$;
(iv) $1 \cdot \mathbf{x} = \mathbf{x}$.

Axiom V_2 requires that a vector space V contain a "zero vector," which has the property that $\mathbf{x} + \mathbf{0} = \mathbf{x}$ for all $\mathbf{x}$. It also is true that $0 \cdot \mathbf{x} = \mathbf{0}$ for all vectors $\mathbf{x}$ in V. To show this, we first use (i) of axiom V_4 to obtain

$$0 \cdot \mathbf{x} + 0 \cdot \mathbf{x} = (0+0) \cdot \mathbf{x} = 0 \cdot \mathbf{x}. \tag{10-1}$$

It follows from V_3 that there is a vector $-(0 \cdot \mathbf{x})$ for which

$$0 \cdot \mathbf{x} + [-(0 \cdot \mathbf{x})] = \mathbf{0}.$$

Adding $-(0 \cdot \mathbf{x})$ to the first and last members of (10-1), we obtain

$$(0 \cdot \mathbf{x} + 0 \cdot \mathbf{x}) + [-(0 \cdot \mathbf{x})] = (0 \cdot \mathbf{x}) + [-(0 \cdot \mathbf{x})] = \mathbf{0}.$$

Now it follows from this equality and the associative law that

$$0 \cdot \mathbf{x} + \{0 \cdot \mathbf{x} + [-(0 \cdot \mathbf{x})]\} = \mathbf{0},$$

or $0 \cdot \mathbf{x} + \mathbf{0} = \mathbf{0}$. Using V_2, we then obtain $0 \cdot \mathbf{x} = \mathbf{0}$.

DEFINITION 10-1.2. A *scalar product*† for a vector space V is a function P whose domain is the set of all ordered pairs $(\mathbf{x}, \mathbf{y})$ of members of V, whose range is contained in the set of all real numbers, and which satisfies the following for all numbers t and all members $\mathbf{x}$, $\mathbf{y}$, and $\mathbf{z}$ of V:

(a) $P(\mathbf{x}, \mathbf{y}) = P(\mathbf{y}, \mathbf{x})$;
(b) $P(\mathbf{x}+\mathbf{y}, \mathbf{z}) = P(\mathbf{x}, \mathbf{z}) + P(\mathbf{y}, \mathbf{z})$;
(c) $P(t\mathbf{x}, \mathbf{y}) = t \cdot P(\mathbf{x}, \mathbf{y})$;
(d) $P(\mathbf{x}, \mathbf{x}) > 0$ if $\mathbf{x} \neq \mathbf{0}$.

---

† Often the scalar product is called the *inner product*.

We leave it for the student to use (a) through (d) and prove that

(e) $P(\mathbf{x}, \mathbf{y} + \mathbf{z}) = P(\mathbf{x}, \mathbf{y}) + P(\mathbf{x}, \mathbf{z})$;

(f) $P(\mathbf{x}, t\mathbf{y}) = t \cdot P(\mathbf{x}, \mathbf{y})$;

(g) $P(\mathbf{0}, \mathbf{0}) = 0$.

For general vector spaces, it is customary to abbreviate $P(\mathbf{x}, \mathbf{y})$ as $(\mathbf{x}, \mathbf{y})$. It should be recalled that we used the symbol $\mathbf{x} \cdot \mathbf{y}$ for the scalar product of members $\mathbf{x}$ and $\mathbf{y}$ of R^n. The student should check that R^n is a vector space and that the scalar product of Definition 8-5.1 satisfies (a) through (d) of Definition 10-1.2.

DEFINITION 10-1.3. The *norm* of a vector $\mathbf{x}$ is the number $\sqrt{(\mathbf{x}, \mathbf{x})}$. We shall denote the norm of $\mathbf{x}$ by $\|\mathbf{x}\|$.

Often a norm is defined for a vector space without a scalar product. One then assumes that the norm has all the properties listed in the next theorem, except property (10-4). Such spaces are very interesting and have been studied and used a great deal. However, we shall use only vector spaces that have scalar products. Hereafter, whenever a vector space is used, we assume it has a scalar product. Also, whenever objects are called vectors, it is to be understood that they are members of a vector space with an inner product.

THEOREM 10-1.1. For any number t and any vectors $\mathbf{x}$ and $\mathbf{y}$,

$$\|\mathbf{0}\| = 0 \text{ and } \|\mathbf{x}\| > 0 \text{ if } \mathbf{x} \neq \mathbf{0}, \tag{10-2}$$

$$\|t\mathbf{x}\| = |t|\, \|\mathbf{x}\|, \tag{10-3}$$

$$|(\mathbf{x}, \mathbf{y})| \leq \|\mathbf{x}\|\, \|\mathbf{y}\|, \quad \text{(Schwarz's inequality)} \tag{10-4}$$

$$\|\mathbf{x} + \mathbf{y}\| \leq \|\mathbf{x}\| + \|\mathbf{y}\|. \quad \text{(Triangle inequality)} \tag{10-5}$$

PROOF. Property (10-2) follows directly from (d) and (g). To prove (10-3), we use (c) and (f) as follows:

$$\|t\mathbf{x}\| = (t\mathbf{x}, t\mathbf{x})^{1/2} = [t(\mathbf{x}, t\mathbf{x})]^{1/2} = [t^2(\mathbf{x}, \mathbf{x})]^{1/2}$$
$$= [t^2 \|\mathbf{x}\|^2]^{1/2} = |t|\, \|\mathbf{x}\|.$$

For (10-4), we first write

$$\|\mathbf{x} + t\mathbf{y}\|^2 = (\mathbf{x} + t\mathbf{y}, \mathbf{x} + t\mathbf{y}) = (\mathbf{x}, \mathbf{x}) + 2t(\mathbf{x}, \mathbf{y}) + t^2(\mathbf{y}, \mathbf{y})$$
$$= \|\mathbf{x}\|^2 + 2t(\mathbf{x}, \mathbf{y}) + t^2 \|\mathbf{y}\|^2. \tag{10-6}$$

Since $\|\mathbf{x}+t\mathbf{y}\|^2 \geqq 0$, it follows that

$$\|\mathbf{x}\|^2\|\mathbf{y}\|^2 + 2t\|\mathbf{y}\|^2(\mathbf{x},\mathbf{y}) + t^2\|\mathbf{y}\|^4 \geqq 0.$$

Now we obtain $\|\mathbf{x}\|^2\|\mathbf{y}\|^2 - (\mathbf{x},\mathbf{y})^2 \geqq 0$ by letting t be a number for which $t\|\mathbf{y}\|^2 = -(\mathbf{x},\mathbf{y})$. To prove (10-5), we use (10-6) with $t = 1$, and(10-4), to obtain

$$\|\mathbf{x}+\mathbf{y}\|^2 = \|\mathbf{x}\|^2 + 2(\mathbf{x},\mathbf{y}) + \|\mathbf{y}\|^2 \leqq \|\mathbf{x}\|^2 + 2\|\mathbf{x}\|\ \|\mathbf{y}\| + \|\mathbf{y}\|^2$$

$$= (\|\mathbf{x}\| + \|\mathbf{y}\|)^2.$$

This implies (10-5).

DEFINITION 10-1.4. Two *orthogonal vectors* are two vectors $\mathbf{x}$ and $\mathbf{y}$ such that $(\mathbf{x},\mathbf{y}) = 0$. An *orthogonal set* of vectors is a set of vectors for which $\mathbf{x}$ and $\mathbf{y}$ are orthogonal if $\mathbf{x}$ and $\mathbf{y}$ are different members of the set. An *orthonormal set* of vectors is an orthogonal set for which each member has unit norm.

ILLUSTRATION. Let V be the set of all polynomials. The set V is a vector space if the sum of two polynomials, and the product of a polynomial and a real number, are defined in the usual way. If f and g both belong to V, we shall define (f,g) by

$$(f,g) = \int_0^1 f(t)g(t)\, dt.$$

It is easy to verify that (a) through (d) of Definition 10-1.2 are satisfied. We then have

$$\|f\| = \left\{ \int_0^1 [f(t)]^2\, dt \right\}^{\frac{1}{2}}.$$

The polynomials 1 and $x - \frac{1}{2}$ are orthogonal, since $\int_0^1 1 \cdot (t - \frac{1}{2})\, dt = 0$. Since $\int_0^1 (t - \frac{1}{2})^2\, dt = \frac{1}{12}$, the set $\{1, \sqrt{12}\,(x - \frac{1}{2})\}$ is an orthonormal set.

Suppose $\{\mathbf{e}_1, \mathbf{e}_2, \cdots, \mathbf{e}_n\}$ is an orthonormal set in a vector space. Then it follows from the definition of norm, and repeated use of (b) and (e), that

$$\left\| \sum_1^n a_i\mathbf{e}_i \right\|^2 = \left(\sum_1^n a_i\mathbf{e}_i, \sum_1^n a_j\mathbf{e}_j \right) = \sum_{i,j=1}^n (a_i\mathbf{e}_i, a_j\mathbf{e}_j).$$

Then it follows from (c) and (f) that the last sum is equal to $\sum a_i a_j(\mathbf{e}_i, \mathbf{e}_j)$. Since $(\mathbf{e}_i, \mathbf{e}_j) = 0$ if $i \neq j$ and $(\mathbf{e}_i, \mathbf{e}_i) = 1$ for all i, we have

$$\left\| \sum_1^n a_i \mathbf{e}_i \right\|^2 = \sum_1^n a_i^2. \tag{10-7}$$

This corresponds to a familiar fact for R^3, that

$$\| a\mathbf{i} + b\mathbf{j} + c\mathbf{k} \| = a^2 + b^2 + c^2.$$

The next definition is motivated by the fact that, for example, the component a of a vector $\mathbf{x} = a\mathbf{i} + b\mathbf{j} + c\mathbf{k}$ in R^3 is equal to $\mathbf{x} \cdot \mathbf{i}$. The theorems that follow also are generalizations of theorems about vectors in R^3.

DEFINITION 10-1.5. For an orthonormal set $\{\mathbf{e}_1, \mathbf{e}_2, \cdots\}$ and a vector $\mathbf{x}$, the number $(\mathbf{x}, \mathbf{e}_i)$ is the *component* of $\mathbf{x}$ that corresponds to the unit vector $\mathbf{e}_i$.

THEOREM 10-1.2. Suppose $\{\mathbf{e}_1, \mathbf{e}_2, \cdots, \mathbf{e}_n\}$ is a finite orthonormal set in a vector space V and $\mathbf{x}$ is a member of V. Then $\| \mathbf{x} - \sum_1^n a_i \mathbf{e}_i \|$ has its smallest value, for all possible choices of the numbers $\{a_i\}$, if and only if $a_i = (\mathbf{x}, \mathbf{e}_i)$ for each i. Moreover, this smallest value is

$$\left\| \mathbf{x} - \sum_1^n (\mathbf{x}, \mathbf{e}_i)\mathbf{e}_i \right\| = \left[\|\mathbf{x}\|^2 - \sum_1^n (\mathbf{x}, \mathbf{e}_i)^2 \right]^{\frac{1}{2}}. \tag{10-8}$$

PROOF. We first use properties of the scalar product, Eq. (10-7), and finally "completing of squares," to obtain

$$\left\| \mathbf{x} - \sum_1^n a_i \mathbf{e}_i \right\|^2 = \left(\mathbf{x} - \sum_1^n a_i \mathbf{e}_i, \ \mathbf{x} - \sum_1^n a_i \mathbf{e}_i \right)$$

$$= (\mathbf{x}, \mathbf{x}) - 2\left(\mathbf{x}, \ \sum_1^n a_i \mathbf{e}_i \right) + \left(\sum_1^n a_i \mathbf{e}_i, \ \sum_1^n a_i \mathbf{e}_i \right)$$

$$= \|\mathbf{x}\|^2 - 2\sum_1^n a_i(\mathbf{x}, \mathbf{e}_i) + \sum_1^n a_i^2$$

$$= \|\mathbf{x}\|^2 - \sum_1^n (\mathbf{x}, \mathbf{e}_i)^2 + \sum_1^n [a_i - (\mathbf{x}, \mathbf{e}_i)]^2.$$

The conclusions of the theorem follow directly from this equality, since the smallest value of the last member is the value when $a_i = (\mathbf{x}, \mathbf{e}_i)$ for each i, so that all terms in the last sum are zero.

For any orthonormal sequence $\{e_i\}$ and any vector x, it follows from (10-8) that $\|x\|^2 = \sum_1^n (x, e_i)^2 + \|x - \sum_1^n (x, e_i)e_i\|^2$ for all n. Therefore,

$$\sum_1^{+\infty} (x, e_i)^2 \leqq \|x\|^2. \qquad \text{(Bessel's inequality)} \qquad (10\text{-}9)$$

The preceding theorem can be described as meaning that when we attempt to represent a vector x in terms of members of an orthonormal set, the representation $\sum a_i e_i$ is best, in the sense that $\|x - \sum a_i e_i\|$ is least, when the a_i's are components of x. Then, $\|x - \sum a_i e_i\|^2$ is the difference between the square of the norm of x and the sum of the squares of the components of x. However, it often is difficult to establish for a particular vector space that we have "enough" vectors in an orthonormal set so that each x can be "represented" in terms of such vectors. Intuitively, an orthonormal set has "enough" members if it is complete in the sense of the next definition. The next theorem explains the meaning of this definition in several ways.

Before stating this definition and theorem, we must first make an important observation. For some vector spaces, it is possible for an orthonormal set to have more than a countable number of members. However, for an orthonormal set $\{e_i\}$ and a vector x, there are at most a countably infinite number of vectors e_i with $(x, e_i) \neq 0$. To see this, for each positive integer n we let

$$S_n = \left\{ e_i : |(x, e_i)| > \frac{1}{n} \right\}.$$

Then it follows from the fact that the bracketed expression in (10-8) is not negative that each S_n is a finite set. Since $\cup S_n$ is the set of all e_i with $(x, e_i) \neq 0$, this set is countable. The equality in the next definition is well defined, since the set of x with $(x, e_i) \neq 0$ is finite or countably infinite and the series converges absolutely.

DEFINITION 10-1.6. A *complete* orthonormal set for a vector space V is an orthonormal set with the property that, for each member x of V,

$$\|x\|^2 = \sum (x, e_i)^2, \qquad \text{(Parseval's equality)} \qquad (10\text{-}10)$$

where the sum is for all members e_i of the orthonormal set.

THEOREM 10-1.3. Each of the following is a necessary and sufficient condition for an orthonormal sequence $\{e_i\}$ in a vector space V to be complete:

(a) $\lim_{n \to +\infty} \|\mathbf{x} - \sum_1^n (\mathbf{x}, \mathbf{e}_i)\mathbf{e}_i\| = 0$ if $\mathbf{x} \in V$.

(b) For any positive number ε and any member $\mathbf{x}$ of V, there is a finite set of numbers $\{a_1, \cdots, a_n\}$ such that

$$\left\|\mathbf{x} - \sum_1^n a_i\mathbf{e}_i\right\| < \varepsilon.$$

PROOF. It follows from Eq. (10-8) and Eq. (10-10) that condition (a) is satisfied by every complete orthonormal sequence. Also, (a) clearly implies (b). We shall complete the proof by showing that an orthonormal sequence that satisfies (b) also satisfies (10-10) and therefore is complete. To do this, we note that if (b) is satisfied for particular numbers $\varepsilon > 0$, n, and $a_1, \cdots, a_n$, then it follows from Theorem 10-1.2 that

$$0 \leqq \|\mathbf{x}\|^2 - \sum_1^p (\mathbf{x}, \mathbf{e}_i)^2 < \varepsilon^2 \text{ if } p > n.$$

This implies (10-10).

THEOREM 10-1.4. If $\{\mathbf{e}_i\}$ is a complete orthonormal set in a vector space V, then

(c) $\mathbf{w} = \mathbf{0}$ if $\mathbf{w}$ is orthogonal to each $\mathbf{e}_i$;

(d) $\mathbf{x} = \mathbf{y}$ if $(\mathbf{x}, \mathbf{e}_i) = (\mathbf{y}, \mathbf{e}_i)$ for each i.†

PROOF. To prove (c), we merely use (10-10) to write $\|\mathbf{w}\|^2 = \sum (\mathbf{w}, \mathbf{e}_i)^2$. If $\mathbf{w}$ is orthogonal to each $\mathbf{e}_i$, this implies that $\|\mathbf{w}\| = 0$. Now (d) follows easily from (c). We merely observe that if $(\mathbf{x}, \mathbf{e}_i) = (\mathbf{y}, \mathbf{e}_i)$, then $(\mathbf{x} - \mathbf{y}, \mathbf{e}_i) = 0$ and $\mathbf{x} - \mathbf{y}$ is orthogonal to $\mathbf{e}_i$.

We might describe (c) of Theorem 10-1.4 as stating that if an orthonormal set is complete, then it cannot be enlarged by adjoining another vector of unit length that is orthogonal to each of the given members. Condition (d) can be described as stating that if an orthonormal set is complete, then each vector is determined when its components are specified. That is, two different vectors cannot have the same components. The orthonormal set $\{\mathbf{i}, \mathbf{j}\}$ in R^3 is not complete, since the vectors $2\mathbf{i} + 3\mathbf{j}$ and $2\mathbf{i} + 3\mathbf{j} + 4\mathbf{k}$ both have the components 2 and 3 with respect to this orthonormal set.

---

† Conditions (c) and (d) also are sufficient conditions for $\{\mathbf{e}_i\}$ to be complete, provided the vector space is complete in the sense that all Cauchy sequences are convergent; that is, provided there is a vector $\mathbf{x}$ such that $\lim_{n \to +\infty} \|\mathbf{x} - \mathbf{x}_n\| = 0$ if $\{\mathbf{x}_n\}$ is a sequence for which $\lim_{m,n \to +\infty} \|\mathbf{x}_m - \mathbf{x}_n\| = 0$. We do not wish to discuss complete spaces at present, since most of the examples we shall discuss, other than the finite-dimensional spaces R^n, are not complete. Moreover, we shall not be able to enlarge these spaces to be complete until we have generalized the theory of Riemann integration [see Theorems 11-4.4 and 11-4.5].

PROBLEMS

1. Prove that $(\mathbf{0}, \mathbf{x}) = 0$ for all vectors $\mathbf{x}$.

2. Let $\mathbf{x}$ be a member of a vector space. Show that $-\mathbf{x} = (-1)\mathbf{x}$.

3. Let t be a scalar and $\mathbf{x}$ a member of a vector space. Show that $t\mathbf{x} = \mathbf{0}$ only if $t = 0$ or $\mathbf{x} = \mathbf{0}$.

4. A subset S of a vector space V satisfies axioms V_1 and V_4 if and only if $\mathbf{x}+\mathbf{y}$ and $t\mathbf{x}$ belong to S whenever $\mathbf{x}$ and $\mathbf{y}$ are members of S and t is a scalar. If S satisfies axioms V_1 and V_4, then it follows from $\mathbf{0} = 0 \cdot \mathbf{x}$ and $-\mathbf{x} = (-1)\mathbf{x}$ [problem 1] that S satisfies axioms V_2 and V_3. For R^3, determine for each of the following whether the subset S is a vector space if S contains those vectors (u_1, u_2, u_3) that satisfy the stated condition.

(**a**) $u_1 = 0$.

(**d**) At least one of u_1 or u_3 is zero.

(**b**) $u_1 + u_3 = 0$.

(e) $2u_1 - u_2 + 5u_3 = 0$ and $u_1 = u_3$.

(**c**) $u_1 + u_3 = 1$.

(f) u_1 is a rational number.

5. For each of the following, let S be the subset of the vector space of polynomials which consists of those polynomials that satisfy the stated condition. Determine whether S is a vector space.

(**a**) u has degree 5.

(c) $u(3) \geq 0$.

(**b**) $2u(0) = 3u(2)$.

(d) u has degree one and $u(1) = 0$.

6. None of the following is a vector space. In each case, determine which of the axioms for a vector space are not satisfied. [Determine which parts of V_1 and V_4 are not satisfied.]

(**a**) V is the set of ordered pairs of real numbers with
$(u_1, u_2) + (v_1, v_2) = (u_1 + v_1, u_2 + v_2)$ and $t(u_1, u_2) = (tu_1, 0)$.

(**b**) V is the set of ordered pairs of real numbers with
$(u_1, u_2) + (v_1, v_2) = (u_1, u_2 + v_2)$ and $t(u_1, u_2) = (u_1, tu_2)$.

(c) V is the set of ordered pairs of real numbers with
$(u_1, u_2) + (v_1, v_2) = (u_1 + v_1, u_2 + v_2)$, $-(u_1, u_2) = (-u_1, -u_2)$,

and

$$t(u_1, u_2) = (2tu_1, 2tu_2).$$

7. Find a polynomial p of degree 2 such that $\{1, \sqrt{12}\,(x - \tfrac{1}{2}), p\}$ is an orthonormal set in the vector space of polynomials, with $(f, g) = \int_0^1 f(t)g(t)\,dt$.

8. Prove that an orthonormal set is linearly independent [see page 396].

9.* Let $\{x_1, x_2, \cdots\}$ be a sequence in a vector space. Show that $\{w_1, w_2, \cdots\}$ is an orthogonal set if $w_1 = x_1$ and

$$w_n = x_n - \sum_{i=1}^{n-1} \frac{(x_n, w_i)}{\|w_i\|^2} w_i, \quad n = 2, 3, \cdots.$$

[*Note:* This is called the *Gram-Schmidt* process.]

10. In each case, use the Gram-Schmidt process of problem 9 to derive an orthogonal set from the given subset of R^4.

(*a*) $\{(2, -2, 0, 4), (2, 0, 4, 2), (6, 0, 3, 0)\}$.

(b) $\{(9, 0, 3, 6), (7, 0, -1, 4), (2, 5, -16, -9)\}$.

11. Let V be the vector space of polynomials, with the scalar product of polynomials f and g defined as $\int_{-1}^{+1} f(t)g(t)\,dt$. In each case, use the Gram-Schmidt process of problem 9 to replace the given set by an orthogonal set.

(*a*) $\{5x, 1+x, x^2\}$.   (b) $\{6, x^2, 3+x+7x^2, x^3\}$.

12. Let V be the vector space of continuous functions on an interval $[a, b]$, with

$$(f, g) = \int_a^b f(t)g(t)\,dt.$$

Suppose $\{f_1, f_2, \cdots\}$ is a complete orthonormal sequence.

(a) Explain why $\lim_{n \to +\infty} \int_a^b [g(x) - \sum_1^n (g, f_n)f_n(x)]^2 \, dx = 0$ for all g in V.

(b) Prove that $g(x) = \lim_{n \to +\infty} \sum_1^n (g, f_n)f_n(x)$ for all x in $[a, b]$, if g is a function for which the series converges uniformly.

13.* Let V be the vector space of problem 12 and let $\{f_n\}$ be an orthonormal sequence in V.

(a) Suppose there is a member g of V such that $\sum (g, f_n)f_n(x)$ converges uniformly on $[a, b]$, but there is an x for which the sum is not $g(x)$. Explain why $\{f_n\}$ is not complete. Also prove that $(h, f_n) = 0$ for all n, if h is defined by

$$h(x) = g(x) - \sum (g, f_n)f_n(x) \text{ for all } x.$$

(b) Prove that if $\{f_n\}$ is complete and $\sum a_n f_n$ converges uniformly to ϕ on $[a, b]$, then $a_n = (\phi, f_n)$ for all n.

14. Let V be the vector space of all functions on $[0, 1]$ with only a finite number of nonzero values. Define (f, g) as $\sum f(t_i)g(t_i)$, where the sum is for all numbers t_i for which $f(t_i)g(t_i) \neq 0$. Describe a complete orthonormal set and prove that it is not countable.

10-2. LEGENDRE POLYNOMIALS

Throughout this chapter, we shall understand that an integrable function is a function whose integral exists, either as the Riemann integral of Definition 3-4.4 or as an improper integral [see Section 3-7]. We know that if f and g are continuous on $[a, b]$, then

$$\int_a^b [f(x) - g(x)]^2 \, dx = 0$$

if and only if $f(x) = g(x)$ for all x in $[a, b]$ [see problem 7, page 145]. However, this is not true of discontinuous functions. We shall define "$f = g$ on $[a, b]$" to mean that $f(x) = g(x)$ for all x in $[a, b]$ except for a set of measure zero.† Then $f = g$ on $[a, b]$ if

$$\int_a^b |f(x) - g(x)| \, dx = 0 \quad \text{or} \quad \int_a^b [f(x) - g(x)]^2 \, dx = 0$$

[see problem 11, page 167]. Also, if $f = g$ on $[a, b]$, then

$$\int_a^b |f(x) - g(x)| \, dx$$

either does not exist or is zero, and $\int_a^b [f(x) - g(x)]^2 \, dx$ either does not exist or is zero [see problem 12, page 167]. Clearly, the relation "$f = g$ on $[a, b]$" is an equivalence relation. Also, the sum of equivalence classes F and G can be defined uniquely as the equivalence class that contains $f + g$, where $f \in F$ and $g \in G$.

Hereafter, we shall seldom use the language of equivalence classes. However, when studying vector spaces of functions, we shall understand that a function is to be thought of as a symbol or representative that designates a particular equivalence class.

DEFINITION 10-2.1. For an interval $[a, b]$, the vector space $L^2_{[a,b]}$ is the set of equivalence classes of functions f such that f and f^2 are integrable on $[a, b]$. If f and g are members of equivalence classes F and G, respectively, then the *scalar product* of F and G is

$$(F, G) = \int_a^b f(x)g(x) \, dx. \tag{10-11}$$

---

† Hereafter, we shall use "almost everywhere" or "a.e." to mean "for all . . . except for a set of measure zero."

This definition of scalar product for $L^2_{[a,b]}$ is not meaningful unless the value of the scalar product is independent of the representatives chosen. That is, we must show that

$$\int_a^b [f_1(x)g_1(x) - f_2(x)g_2(x)]\, dx = 0,$$

whenever $f_1 = f_2$ and $g_1 = g_2$ on $[a, b]$. If $f_1 = f_2$ and $g_1 = g_2$ on $[a, b]$, then $f_1 g_1 = f_2 g_2$ on $[a, b]$. Thus, the desired equality follows as soon as we know that fg is integrable whenever f and g belong to equivalence classes in $L^2_{[a,b]}$ [see problem 12, page 167]. This is property (2) of the next paragraph.

Most of the properties of vector spaces and scalar products can be verified easily for $L^2_{[a,b]}$. We shall discuss two nontrivial facts that need verification: (1) $f + g$ is a member of $L^2_{[a,b]}$ if f and g are members; (2) fg is integrable if f and g are members of $L^2_{[a,b]}$. If both f and g are bounded on $[a, b]$, then both f and g are continuous almost everywhere [see Theorem 3-5.2] and each of $f + g$, $(f + g)^2$, and fg is continuous almost everywhere. Therefore, each of these functions is integrable and (1) and (2) are satisfied. Assuming the student verifies the remaining axioms, we know now that the subset of $L^2_{[a,b]}$ whose members are bounded is a vector space with a scalar product. Now suppose one or both of f and g is not bounded. Integrability of $f + g$ still follows easily from integrability of f and g [see problem 13, page 167]. For positive numbers k, we define f_k by $f_k(x) = f(x)$ if $|f(x)| \leq k$, $f_k(x) = k$ if $f(x) > k$, and $f_k(x) = -k$ if $f(x) < -k$, with a similar definition of g_k. Since the triangle inequality (10-5) can be used for bounded functions, we have

$$\int_a^b [f_k(x) + g_k(x)]^2\, dx \leq \left\{ \left[\int_a^b f_k(x)^2\, dx \right]^{1/2} + \left[\int_a^b g_k(x)^2\, dx \right]^{1/2} \right\}^2.$$

Integrability of f^2 and g^2 implies the right member of this inequality is bounded as k increases. Therefore, $(f + g)^2$ is integrable. Since f^2 and g^2 are integrable, it follows from the definition of improper integral on page 163 that $\frac{1}{2}(f + g)^2 - \frac{1}{2}(f^2 + g^2)$ is integrable. Therefore, fg is integrable.

In this section, we shall use Legendre polynomials to obtain a complete orthonormal sequence for $L^2_{[-1,+1]}$. In the next section, we shall use trigonometric functions to obtain complete orthonormal sequences using arbitrary bounded intervals. For the study of completeness, it is useful first to establish some results about approximation of integrable functions by polygonal functions and of continuous functions by polynomials. This will make the investigation of completeness for Legendre polynomials particularly easy.

THEOREM 10-2.1. Suppose f is integrable on the interval $[a, b]$. Then for any positive number ε,

(i) if $|f|$ is integrable on $[a, b]$, there is a polygonal function θ such that

$$\int_a^b |f(x) - \theta(x)| \, dx < \varepsilon; \qquad (10\text{-}12)$$

(ii) if f^2 is integrable on $[a, b]$, then $|f|$ is integrable and there is a polygonal function ϕ such that

$$\int_a^b |f(x) - \phi(x)| \, dx < \varepsilon \quad \text{and} \quad \int_a^b [f(x) - \phi(x)]^2 \, dx < \varepsilon. \quad (10\text{-}13)$$

PROOF. Suppose f and $|f|$ are integrable on $[a, b]$ and that $\varepsilon > 0$. The integral of $|f|$ is the area under the graph of $|f|$. Therefore, it follows from Theorem 3-7.1 that there is a positive number k such that

$$\int_a^b [|f(x)| - |f_k(x)|] \, dx < \frac{\varepsilon}{2}, \qquad (10\text{-}14)$$

where $f_k(x) = f(x)$ if $|f(x)| \leq k$, $f_k(x) = k$ if $f(x) > k$, and $f_k(x) = -k$ if $f(x) < -k$. We can write (10-14) as

$$\int_a^b |f(x) - f_k(x)| \, dx < \frac{\varepsilon}{2}. \qquad (10\text{-}15)$$

Whichever concept of improper integral discussed in Section 3-7 is used, integrability of f_k follows from integrability of f. Therefore, there is a partition $\{a = x_1, x_2, \cdots, x_{n+1} = b\}$ of $[a, b]$ such that

$$\left| \int_a^b f_k(x) \, dx - \sum_{i=1}^n f_k(\xi_i)(x_{i+1} - x_i) \right| < \frac{\varepsilon}{2},$$

if $\xi_i \in [x_i, x_{i+1}]$ for each i. If θ is the polygonal function whose graph consists of straight line segments joining the points $(x_i, f_k(x_i))$ successively, then the graphs of both f_k and θ in the interval $[x_i, x_{i+1}]$ are in a rectangle with width $x_{i+1} - x_i$ and altitude equal to the difference between sup $\{f_k(t): t \in [x_i, x_{i+1}]\}$ and inf $\{f_k(t): t \in [x_i, x_{i+1}]\}$.   Since the sum of the areas of these rectangles is not larger than $\frac{1}{2}\varepsilon$, we have

$$\int_a^b |f_k(x) - \theta(x)| \, dx \le \frac{\varepsilon}{2}. \tag{10-16}$$

This and (10-15) imply (10-12).

To prove (ii), we use the inequality $(u-v)^2 \le u^2 - v^2$ when $u \ge v \ge 0$ or $u \le v \le 0$, and integrability of f^2, to obtain a positive number K such that

$$\int_a^b [f(x) - f_K(x)]^2 \, dx \le \int_a^b [f(x)^2 - f_K(x)^2] \, dx$$

$$< \inf\left\{\frac{\varepsilon^2}{16(b-a)}, \frac{\varepsilon}{4}\right\}, \tag{10-17}$$

where $f_K(x) = f(x)$ if $|f(x)| \le K$, $f_K(x) = K$ if $f(x) > K$, and $f_K(x) = -K$ if $f(x) < -K$.   Observe that $\int_a^b |f(x) - f_K(x)| \, dx$ is not greater than $\frac{1}{4}\varepsilon + \beta$, where $\frac{1}{4}\varepsilon$ is greater than the area of the region under the graph of $|f(x) - f_K(x)|$ and under the line $y = \frac{1}{4}\varepsilon/(b-a)$, and β is the area of the region under the graph of $|f(x) - f_K(x)|$ and above the line $y = \frac{1}{4}\varepsilon/(b-a)$. Also,

$$|f(x) - f_K(x)| \le \frac{4(b-a)}{\varepsilon} |f(x) - f_K(x)|^2$$

if

$$|f(x) - f_K(x)| \ge \frac{\varepsilon}{4(b-a)}.$$

Therefore,

$$\int_a^b |f(x) - f_K(x)| \, dx \le \frac{\varepsilon}{4} + \frac{4(b-a)}{\varepsilon} \int_a^b [f(x) - f_K(x)]^2 \, dx < \frac{\varepsilon}{2}. \tag{10-18}$$

By the same method used to obtain (10-16), it follows there is a polygonal function ϕ such that $|\phi(x)| \le K$ for all x, and

$$\int_a^b |f_K(x) - \phi(x)| \, dx < \inf\left\{\frac{\varepsilon}{8K}, \frac{\varepsilon}{2}\right\}. \tag{10-19}$$

Since $[f_K(x) - \phi(x)]^2 \le 2K|f_K(x) - \phi(x)|$, we then have

$$\int_a^b [f_K(x) - \phi(x)]^2 \, dx \le 2K \int_a^b |f_K(x) - \phi(x)| \, dx < \frac{\varepsilon}{4}. \tag{10-20}$$

The first inequality in (10-13) follows from (10-18) and (10-19). The second inequality follows from (10-17), (10-20), and the triangle inequality:

$$\left\{ \int_a^b [f(x) - \phi(x)]^2 \, dx \right\}^{1/2} \leq \left\{ \int_a^b [f(x) - f_K(x)]^2 \, dx \right\}^{1/2}$$

$$+ \left\{ \int_a^b [f_K(x) - \phi(x)]^2 \, dx \right\}^{1/2} < \varepsilon^{1/2}.$$

In preparation for the next theorem, we shall prove the following lemma.

LEMMA. For any bounded interval $[a, b]$ and any numbers c, ξ, and $\varepsilon > 0$, there is a polynomial p such that

$$|[c|x - \xi| - p(x)]| < \varepsilon \quad \text{if} \quad x \in [a, b]. \tag{10-21}$$

PROOF. The series $\sum_2^{+\infty} 1 \cdot 3 \cdot 5 \cdots (2n - 3)/(2^n n!)$ converges. To show this, we note that if a_n denotes the nth term of this series, then

$$\frac{a_n}{a_{n-1}} = \frac{2n - 1}{2n + 2} = 1 - \frac{3}{2n + 2} = 1 - \frac{\pi(n)}{n},$$

where $\pi(n) = \frac{3}{2}n/(n + 1) > \frac{9}{8}$ if $n > 3$. Convergence then follows from Ratio Test III, page 179. Now it follows from Weierstrass' test for uniform convergence [page 215] that the series,

$$S(x) = 1 - \tfrac{1}{2}(1 - x^2) - \frac{1}{2^2 2!}(1 - x^2)^2 - \frac{1 \cdot 3}{2^3 3!}(1 - x^2)^3$$

$$- \cdots - \frac{1 \cdot 3 \cdot 5 \cdots (2n - 5)}{2^{n-1}(n - 1)!}(1 - x^2)^{n-1} - \cdots,$$

converges uniformly on the closed interval $[-\sqrt{2}, \sqrt{2}]$. We can apply Taylor's theorem to $(1 - z)^{1/2}$ with $|z| < 1$ and obtain [see problem 10, page 189]

$$S(x) = [1 - (1 - x^2)]^{1/2} = |x| \quad \text{if} \quad |1 - x^2| < 1.$$

Since both S and $|x|$ are continuous on the closed interval $[-\sqrt{2}, \sqrt{2}]$, we have

$$S(x) = |x| \quad \text{if} \quad |x| \leq \sqrt{2}.$$

Therefore, for any positive number η, there is a polynomial q that is a partial sum of the series for S and has the property that

$$|[|x| - q(x)]| < \eta \text{ if } |x| \leq \sqrt{2}.$$

To obtain (10-21), we choose a positive number k to be specified later and let $x = k(t - \xi)$. Then

$$\left| \left[c|t - \xi| - \frac{c}{k} q[k(t - \xi)] \right] \right| < \frac{|c|\eta}{k} \text{ if } |t - \xi| \leq \frac{\sqrt{2}}{k}.$$

Now (10-21) is satisfied with $p(x) = (c/k)q[k(x - \xi)]$, if we choose k so that $[a, b] \subset [\xi - (\sqrt{2}/k), \xi + (\sqrt{2}/k)]$ and then let $\eta = k\varepsilon/|c|$.

THEOREM 10-2.2 (WEIERSTRASS' APPROXIMATION THEOREM). If f is continuous on the closed interval $[a, b]$, then for any positive number ε there exists a polynomial p such that†

$$|f(x) - p(x)| < \varepsilon \text{ if } x \in [a, b]. \tag{10-22}$$

PROOF. We know that if f is continuous on $[a, b]$, then f is uniformly continuous on $[a, b]$. Therefore, there is a polygonal function θ such that

$$|f(x) - \theta(x)| < \frac{\varepsilon}{2} \text{ if } x \in [a, b]. \tag{10-23}$$

To show this, we can choose a partition $\{a = x_1, x_2, \cdots, x_{n+1} = b\}$ of $[a, b]$ fine enough that $|f(r) - f(s)| < \frac{1}{2}\varepsilon$ if both r and s are in $[x_i, x_{i+1}]$ for some i. Then θ can be the polygonal curve that joins successively the points $(x_i, f(x_i))$. It will be left for the student [problem 16] to prove that there are numbers c_i such that

$$\theta(x) = \sum_{i=1}^{n+1} c_i |x - x_i| \text{ if } x \in [a, b].$$

It follows from the lemma that for each i there is a polynomial p_i such that

$$|[c_i |x - x_i| - p_i(x)]| < \frac{\varepsilon}{2(n+1)} \text{ if } x \in [a, b].$$

---

† This theorem often is described by saying that "every continuous function can be 'uniformly approximated' by a polynomial."

This implies that $|\theta(x) - p(x)| < \frac{1}{2}\varepsilon$, where $p = \sum p_i$. We can then use (10-23) to obtain

$$|f(x) - p(x)| \leq |f(x) - \theta(x)| + |\theta(x) - p(x)| < \varepsilon \text{ if } x \in [a, b].$$

We are now prepared to study completeness of orthonormal sets whose members are polynomials. The next theorem gives a very useful general criterion for completeness.

THEOREM 10-2.3. Suppose $\{p_0, p_1, \cdots\}$ is a sequence of polynomials that is an orthonormal sequence in $L^2_{[a,b]}$. If the degree of p_k is k for every k, then $\{p_0, p_1, \cdots\}$ is complete.

PROOF. Suppose p is an arbitrary polynomial. If the degree of p is n, then there is a number a_n such that the degree of $p - a_n p_n$ is $n-1$ or less, a number a_{n-1} such that the degree of $p - a_n p_n - a_{n-1}p_{n-1}$ is $n-2$ or less, etc. Thus, there are numbers $a_0, a_1, \cdots, a_n$ such that $p = \sum_0^n a_k p_k$. It then follows from Theorem 10-2.1 and Theorem 10-2.2 that, for any member f of $L^2_{[a,b]}$, there is a polynomial p such that

$$\int_a^b [f(x) - p(x)]^2 \, dx < \varepsilon^2.$$

Therefore, if n and $a_0, a_1, \cdots, a_n$ are chosen so that $p = \sum_0^n a_k p_k$, then

$$\int_a^b \left[f(x) - \sum_0^n a_k p_k(x) \right]^2 dx < \varepsilon^2 \quad \text{or} \quad \left\| f - \sum_0^n a_k p_k \right\| < \varepsilon.$$

Completeness of the sequence $\{p_0, p_1, \cdots\}$ now follows from (b) of Theorem 10-1.3.

We could find orthogonal polynomials by using the Gram-Schmidt process [see problem 9, page 505]. However, for the interval $[-1, +1]$ it is much more efficient to discover orthogonal polynomials by using *Legendre's differential equation,*

$$(1 - x^2)y'' - 2xy' + \lambda(\lambda + 1)y = 0, \quad \lambda \geq 0.$$

Let us consider the problem of finding all polynomial solutions of such equations. To do this, we use a substitution of type

$$y(x) = \sum_0^{+\infty} a_n x^n,$$

where only a finite number of coefficients are nonzero.   Then

$$y'(x) = \sum_{1}^{+\infty} na_n x^{n-1}, \qquad y''(x) = \sum_{2}^{+\infty} n(n-1)a_n x^{n-2},$$

and substitution in the differential equation gives

$$\sum_{2}^{+\infty} n(n-1)a_n x^{n-2} - \sum_{2}^{+\infty} n(n-1)a_n x^n - \sum_{1}^{+\infty} 2na_n x^n + \sum_{0}^{+\infty} \lambda(\lambda+1)a_n x^n = 0.$$

This can be written as

$$\sum_{0}^{+\infty} (n+2)(n+1)a_{n+2} x^n - \sum_{0}^{+\infty} n(n-1)a_n x^n$$

$$- \sum_{0}^{+\infty} 2na_n x^n + \sum_{0}^{+\infty} \lambda(\lambda+1)a_n x^n = 0,$$

or

$$\sum_{0}^{+\infty} [(n+2)(n+1)a_{n+2} - (n^2+n-\lambda^2-\lambda)a_n]x^n = 0.$$

Therefore,

$$(n+2)(n+1)a_{n+2} - [n^2+n-\lambda^2-\lambda]a_n = 0 \quad \text{for} \quad n \geq 0.$$

After factoring the bracket in the left member and dividing by $(n+2)(n+1)$, we have

$$a_{n+2} = -\frac{(\lambda-n)(n+\lambda+1)}{(n+2)(n+1)} a_n \quad \text{for} \quad n \geq 0.$$

The coefficients for even n are determined from a_0, those for odd n from a_1.   These coefficients can be computed successively, to obtain

$$y = a_0\left[1 - \frac{\lambda(\lambda+1)}{2!} x^2 + \frac{\lambda(\lambda-2)(\lambda+1)(\lambda+3)}{4!} x^4 - \cdots\right]$$

$$+ a_1\left[x - \frac{(\lambda-1)(\lambda+2)}{3!} x^3 + \frac{(\lambda-1)(\lambda-3)(\lambda+2)(\lambda+4)}{5!} x^5 - \cdots\right].$$

$$(10\text{-}24)$$

This is a polynomial if and only if $a_1 = 0$ and λ is a nonnegative even integer, or $a_0 = 0$ and λ is a positive odd integer. When a_0 and a_1 are given values such that this polynomial has the value 1 when $x = 1$, the polynomial is a *Legendre polynomial*. Since Eq. (10-24) gives all polynomial solutions of Legendre's differential equation, it follows that the Legendre polynomial P_n is the only polynomial solution of Legendre's differential equation (with $\lambda = n$) which has the value 1 when $x = 1$. The following are the first six Legendre polynomials:

$$P_0(x) = 1, \qquad\qquad P_3(x) = \tfrac{5}{2}x^3 - \tfrac{3}{2}x,$$

$$P_1(x) = x, \qquad\qquad P_4(x) = \tfrac{35}{8}x^4 - \tfrac{15}{4}x^2 + \tfrac{3}{8},$$

$$P_2(x) = \tfrac{3}{2}x^2 - \tfrac{1}{2}, \qquad\qquad P_5(x) = \tfrac{63}{8}x^5 - \tfrac{35}{4}x^3 + \tfrac{15}{8}x.$$

THEOREM 10-2.4. If P_m and P_n are different Legendre polynomials, then

$$\int_{-1}^{+1} P_m(x)P_n(x)\, dx = 0.$$

PROOF. Legendre's differential equation can be written in the form

$$D_x[(1-x^2)y'] + \lambda(\lambda+1)y = 0. \tag{10-25}$$

Therefore, for any Legendre polynomial P_n, we have

$$n(n+1)P_n(x) = -D_x[(1-x^2)P_n'(x)].$$

First we use this equality and then integration by parts to obtain

$$n(n+1)\int_{-1}^{+1} P_m(x)P_n(x)\, dx = -\int_{-1}^{+1} P_m(x)\cdot D_x[(1-x^2)P_n'(x)]\, dx$$

$$= \left[-(1-x^2)P_m(x)P_n'(x) \right]_{-1}^{+1} + \int_{-1}^{+1} (1-x^2)P_m'(x)P_n'(x)\, dx,$$

and

$$n(n+1)\int_{-1}^{+1} P_m(x)P_n(x)\, dx = \int_{-1}^{+1} (1-x^2)P_m'(x)P_n'(x)\, dx.$$

Similarly,

$$m(m+1)\int_{-1}^{+1} P_m(x)P_n(x)\, dx = \int_{-1}^{+1} (1-x^2)P_m'(x)P_n'(x)\, dx.$$

It follows from these two equalities that

$$[n(n+1) - m(m+1)] \int_{-1}^{+1} P_m(x)P_n(x)\, dx = 0.$$

Since $m \neq n$, we must have

$$\int_{-1}^{+1} P_m(x)P_n(x)\, dx = 0.$$

It follows from Theorems 10-2.3 and 10-2.4 that the sequence $\{P_0/\|P_0\|,\ P_1/\|P_1\|,\ \cdots\}$ is complete and orthogonal. Therefore, from (a) of Theorem 10-1.3, we have

$$\lim_{n \to +\infty} \int_{-1}^{+1} \left[f(x) - \sum_{k=0}^{n} c_k P_k(x) \right]^2 dx = 0, \quad f \in L_{[-1,\, +1]}^2, \quad (10\text{-}26)$$

if

$$c_k \|P_k\| = \int_{-1}^{+1} f(x) [P_k(x)/\|P_k\|]\, dx,$$

or

$$c_k = \|P_k\|^{-2} \int_{-1}^{+1} f(x) P_k(x)\, dx.$$

It is customary to say that the series $\sum c_k P_k$ *converges in the mean (of order two)* to f.

To determine the value of $\|P_n\|$ in general, it is useful to introduce the function

$$W(x, h) = \frac{1}{(1 - 2xh + h^2)^{1/2}}.$$

If $|t| \leq \frac{1}{2}$ and $|h| \leq \frac{1}{2}$, then $|2th + h^2| < 1$ and the binomial expansion of $[1 - (2th + h^2)]^{-1/2}$ is valid [see problem 10, page 189]. Moreover, if this series is written as $\sum a_{k,n} t^k h^n$, then all terms are nonnegative when t and h are positive. It follows that the order of terms is immaterial and the series converges uniformly for $|t| \leq \frac{1}{2}$ and $|h| \leq \frac{1}{2}$, both as a power series in t and as a power series in h. For the series

$$W(x, h) = \frac{1}{(1 - 2xh + h^2)^{1/2}} = \sum A_{k,n} x^k h^n, \quad (10\text{-}27)$$

we have $A_{k,n} = \pm a_{k,n}$ for each k and n. Therefore, this series converges uniformly for $|x| \leq \frac{1}{2}$ and $|h| \leq \frac{1}{2}$, so that as a power series in either x or h it can be differentiated term-by-term repeatedly for $|t| < \frac{1}{2}$ and $|h| < \frac{1}{2}$. Let us write (10-27) as

$$W(x, h) = \sum F_n(x) h^n. \tag{10-28}$$

Since $A_{k,n} = 0$ if $k > n$, it follows that the degree of F_n is not greater than n. Since $W(1, h) = \sum h^n$, we have $F_n(1) = 1$. Therefore, if F_n satisfies Legendre's differential equation with $\lambda = n$, then we must have $F_n = P_n$. By formal calculation,

$$(1 - x^2)\frac{\partial^2 W}{\partial x^2} - 2x \frac{\partial W}{\partial x} + h \frac{\partial^2 (hW)}{\partial h^2} = 0.$$

The coefficient of h^n in the left member of this equality is zero for each n, so that

$$(1 - x^2) F_n''(x) - 2x F_n'(x) + n(n+1) F_n(x) = 0 \quad \text{for all} \quad n.$$

Now with $F_n = P_n$, it follows from (10-28) and Theorem 10-2.4 that

$$\int_{-1}^{+1} W^2(x, h)\, dx = \sum_{m,n=1}^{+\infty} \left[\int_{-1}^{+1} P_m(x) P_n(x)\, dx \right] h^{m+n}$$

$$= \sum_{n=1}^{+\infty} \left[\int_{-1}^{+1} P_n^2(x)\, dx \right] h^{2n}.$$

By direct integration,

$$\int_{-1}^{+1} W^2(x, h)\, dx = \int_{-1}^{+1} \frac{1}{1 - 2xh + h^2}\, dx$$

$$= \frac{\ln(1+h) - \ln(1-h)}{h} = \sum \frac{2}{2n+1} h^{2n}.$$

Therefore, we can conclude that

$$\|P_n\| = \left[\int_{-1}^{+1} P_n^2(x)\, dx \right]^{1/2} = \left[\frac{2}{2n+1} \right]^{1/2}. \tag{10-29}$$

ILLUSTRATION. Let $f(x) = 5x^3 - 6x^2 + 3$. Then

$$f = a_0 \frac{P_0}{\|P_0\|} + a_1 \frac{P_1}{\|P_1\|} + a_2 \frac{P_2}{\|P_2\|} + a_3 \frac{P_3}{\|P_3\|}$$

$$= \frac{1}{\sqrt{2}} a_0 P_0 + \sqrt{\frac{3}{2}} a_1 P_1 + \sqrt{\frac{5}{2}} a_2 P_2 + \sqrt{\frac{7}{2}} a_3 P_3,$$

where

$$a_0 = \left(f, \frac{P_0}{\|P_0\|} \right) = \int_{-1}^{+1} (5x^3 - 6x^2 + 3) \frac{1}{\sqrt{2}} \, dx = \sqrt{2},$$

$$a_1 = \left(f, \frac{P_1}{\|P_1\|} \right) = \int_{-1}^{+1} (5x^3 - 6x^2 + 3) \frac{x}{\sqrt{\frac{2}{3}}} \, dx = \sqrt{6},$$

$$a_2 = \left(f, \frac{P_2}{\|P_2\|} \right) = \int_{-1}^{+1} (5x^3 - 6x^2 + 3) \frac{\frac{3}{2}x^2 - \frac{1}{2}}{\sqrt{\frac{2}{5}}} \, dx = -4\sqrt{\frac{2}{5}},$$

$$a_3 = \left(f, \frac{P_3}{\|P_3\|} \right) = \int_{-1}^{+1} (5x^3 - 6x^2 + 3) \frac{\frac{5}{2}x^3 - \frac{3}{2}x}{\sqrt{\frac{2}{7}}} \, dx = 2\sqrt{\frac{2}{7}},$$

so that $f = P_0 + 3P_1 - 4P_2 + 2P_3$.

PROBLEMS

1. In each case, determine a_0, a_1, and a_2 if $\sum_0^{+\infty} a_n P_n$ is the representation of the given function using Legendre polynomials.

(a) $x + 6x^2$. (b) $63x^5 - 20x^3 - 9x^2 + 3$.

2. In each case, determine a_0, a_1, and a_2 if $\sum_0^{+\infty} a_n P_n$ is the representation of the given function using Legendre polynomials. Sketch $\sum_0^2 a_n P_n$ on the interval $[-1, +1]$.

(a) e^x. (b) $\sin x$.

3. Determine P_7.

4. (a) Prove that $\{f_n\}$ is a sequence of orthogonal polynomials on $[a, b]$ if f_n is defined for $n \geq 0$ by

$$f_n(x) = P_n\left(\frac{2x - a - b}{b - a} \right).$$

(b) Evaluate $\|f_n\|$ for the sequence of part (a).

5. (a) For the function W used in the proof of (10-29), verify that

$$(1-2xh+h^2)\frac{\partial W}{\partial h}+(h-x)W = 0.$$

(b) Use part (a) to show that

$$(n+1)P_{n+1}(x)-(2n+1)xP_n(x)+nP_{n-1}(x) = 0.$$

6. By methods similar to those of problem 5, show that

(a) $P'_{n+1}(x)-xP'_n(x) = (n+1)P_n(x)$;

(b) $xP'_n(x)-P'_{n-1}(x) = nP_n(x)$.

7. Use problem 6 to show that

(a) $P'_{n+1}(x)-P'_{n-1}(x) = (2n+1)P_n(x)$;

(b) $(x^2-1)P'_n(x) = nxP_n(x)-nP_{n-1}(x)$.

8. Let $\{v_1, v_2, \cdots, v_n\}$ be a set of vectors and suppose that v_i is orthogonal to v_j whenever $i \neq j$. Let w be in the linear span of $\{v_1, v_2, \cdots, v_n\}$ and orthogonal to each of $v_1, v_2, \cdots, v_{n-1}$. Show that there is a scalar α such that $w = \alpha v_n$.

9. For $L^2_{[-1,+1]}$, show that, if

$$f(x) = \frac{1}{2^n n!}\frac{d^n}{dx^n}(x^2-1)^n,$$

then (a) f is a polynomial of degree n such that $f(1) =1$; (b) f is orthogonal to all polynomials of degree less than n; (c) $f = P_n$. [*Hint:* Use problem 8. This formula for P_n is called *Rodrigues' formula*.]

10. Suppose $|f|$ is bounded on the interval $[a, b]$. Explain why $|f|$ is integrable if and only if f^2 is integrable.

11. Suppose f and $|f|$ are integrable on $[-\infty, +\infty]$. Show that, if $\varepsilon > 0$, then there is a polygonal function θ such that

$$\int_{-\infty}^{+\infty} |f(x) - \theta(x)| \, dx < \varepsilon.$$

[*Hint:* Choose θ to be zero outside a suitable bounded interval.]

12. Suppose f and f^2 are integrable on $[-\infty, +\infty]$. Show that, if $\varepsilon > 0$, then there is a polygonal function ϕ such that

$$\int_{-\infty}^{+\infty} [f(x) - \phi(x)]^2 \, dx < \varepsilon.$$

13. Give an example to show that integrability of $|f|$ on $[-\infty, +\infty]$ does not follow from integrability of f^2 on $[-\infty, +\infty]$.

14. Show that an orthonormal sequence $\{f_1, f_2, \cdots\}$ in $L^2_{[-1,+1]}$ is complete if $\sum_1^{+\infty}(g, f_n)f_n(x)$ converges uniformly to $g(x)$ whenever g is a polynomial.

15. Suppose that $x_1 < x_2 < x_3$. Show that for any number y_2 there are numbers c_1, c_2, and c_3 such that, if

$$\theta(x) = c_1|x - x_1| + c_2|x - x_2| + c_3|x - x_3|,$$

then $\theta(x_2) = y_2$ and $\theta(x) = 0$ if $x \leqq x_1$ or if $x \geqq x_3$.

16. Suppose the graph of θ is a polygonal curve. Use problem 15 to show that there is an integer n and numbers $c_1, \cdots, c_n$, and $x_1, \cdots, x_n$, such that

$$\theta(x) = \sum_1^n c_i|x - x_i| \quad \text{for all} \quad x.$$

10-3. FOURIER SERIES

Although the theory of Fourier series now is accepted as a part of the general theory of orthogonal functions, Fourier's contemporaries were very skeptical when he stated in 1807 that any integrable function could be represented over the interval $[-L, L]$ by a series of sines and cosines of type

$$\frac{a_0}{2} + \sum_1^{+\infty} \left(a_n \cos \frac{n\pi x}{L} + b_n \sin \frac{n\pi x}{L} \right).$$

Fourier did not prove this, but he did a great deal of work with special cases and with methods of using trigonometric series in applied problems. As a result, the trigonometric series associated with a function is called the *Fourier series* of the function.

As early as the middle of the eighteenth century, d'Alembert, Euler, and Bernoulli had realized that the solution of the differential equation of a vibrating string seemed to involve representing rather general functions by trigonometric series. But the possibility of doing this seemed absurd. In 1755, Daniel Bernoulli claimed in a memoir that it could be done, but he was neither able to prove it nor able to convince other mathematicians. Twenty-two years later, Euler determined what the coefficients would be if such a representation were possible [see Eqs. (10-34) and (10-35)]. Finally, in 1829, Dirichlet proved one of the first convergence theorems.

Probably the slow development of the theory of trigonometric series was partly a result of the narrow concept of a function then generally accepted, whereby a function was considered to be defined on an interval only if it were given by a single "formula." The difficulties seem amazing in view of the ease with which convergence theorems now can be established, as in this and the next section. Fourier series have become an indispensable tool in the study of periodic phenomena in physics and engineering. The study of Fourier series has led to many important mathematical problems and theories. As a result, much of the development of modern mathematics has been influenced by the theory of trigonometric series.

THEOREM 10-3.1. For $L^2_{[-\pi,\pi]}$, the following is an orthonormal sequence:†

$$\left\{ \frac{1}{\sqrt{2\pi}}, \frac{\cos x}{\sqrt{\pi}}, \frac{\sin x}{\sqrt{\pi}}, \cdots, \frac{\cos nx}{\sqrt{\pi}}, \frac{\sin nx}{\sqrt{\pi}}, \cdots \right\}. \qquad (10\text{-}30)$$

PROOF. We first recall the trigonometric identities:

$$\sin A \cos B = \tfrac{1}{2}[\sin (A+B) + \sin (A-B)],$$
$$\sin A \sin B = \tfrac{1}{2}[\cos (A-B) - \cos (A+B)],$$
$$\cos A \cos B = \tfrac{1}{2}[\cos (A+B) + \cos (A-B)].$$

From these, it is easy to show for integers m and n that

$$\int_{-\pi}^{\pi} \sin mx \cos nx \, dx = \tfrac{1}{2} \int_{-\pi}^{\pi} [\sin (m+n)x + \sin (m-n)x] \, dx = 0; \qquad (10\text{-}31)$$

$$\int_{-\pi}^{\pi} \sin mx \sin nx \, dx = \begin{cases} 0 & \text{if } m \neq n, \\ \pi & \text{if } m = n; \end{cases} \qquad (10\text{-}32)$$

$$\int_{-\pi}^{\pi} \cos mx \cos nx \, dx = \begin{cases} 0 & \text{if } m \neq n, \\ \pi & \text{if } m = n \neq 0, \\ 2\pi & \text{if } m = n = 0. \end{cases} \qquad (10\text{-}33)$$

These equalities imply that (10-30) is an orthonormal sequence.

DEFINITION 10-3.1. For the interval $[-\pi, \pi]$, the *Fourier coefficients* of a function f are the numbers

$$a_n = \frac{1}{\pi} \int_{-\pi}^{\pi} f(s) \cos ns \, ds, \quad n = 0, 1, \cdots; \qquad (10\text{-}34)$$

$$b_n = \frac{1}{\pi} \int_{-\pi}^{\pi} f(s) \sin ns \, ds, \quad n = 1, 2, \cdots; \qquad (10\text{-}35)$$

---

† This also is true for any number a and $L^2_{[a, 2\pi+a]}$. For simplicity, we shall use the interval $[-\pi, \pi]$. The student might check that $[-\pi, \pi]$ could be replaced by $[a, 2\pi+a]$ throughout the first part of this section.

provided all these integrals exist. The *Fourier series* of a function for which these integrals exist is the trigonometric series,

$$\tfrac{1}{2}a_0 + \sum_{n=1}^{+\infty} (a_n \cos nx + b_n \sin nx).$$

All that we demand of a function in order for it to have a Fourier series is that the integrals in (10-34) and (10-35) all exist. We do not demand that the series converge in any sense. Theorem 10-3.4 gives us an important condition for uniform convergence that will be used in proving completeness for the sequence (10-30). Other convergence theorems will be studied in the next section.

THEOREM 10-3.2. If a trigonometric series,

$$\tfrac{1}{2}a_0 + \sum_{n=1}^{+\infty} (a_n \cos nx + b_n \sin nx),$$

converges uniformly on $[-\pi, \pi]$, then it is the Fourier series of its sum.

PROOF. If the sum of the trigonometric series is $S(x)$, we integrate the series $S(x) \cos nx$ and $S(x) \sin nx$ term-by-term. It follows from (10-31) through (10-33) that we get

$$\int_{-\pi}^{\pi} S(x) \cos nx \, dx = \int_{-\pi}^{\pi} a_n \cos^2 nx \, dx = \pi a_n, \text{ if } n \geqq 0;$$

$$\int_{-\pi}^{\pi} S(x) \sin nx \, dx = \int_{-\pi}^{\pi} b_n \sin^2 nx \, dx = \pi b_n, \text{ if } n \geqq 1.$$

Thus, a_n and b_n are given by formulas (10-34) and (10-35), with f replaced by S, so that the given trigonometric series is the Fourier series of S.

We might say that this theorem indicates that the Fourier series is a good choice of a trigonometric series to represent a function. The Fourier coefficients are those that would result if we use (10-30) as an orthonormal sequence. Therefore, it follows from Theorem 10-1.2 that a partial sum of the Fourier series for f is a best mean-square approximation for f, in the sense that

$$\int_{-\pi}^{\pi} \left\{ f(x) - \left[\tfrac{1}{2}a_0 + \sum_{k=1}^{n} (a_k \cos kx + b_k \sin kx) \right] \right\}^2 dx$$

is least when the a's and b's are the Fourier coefficients. The next lemma is a strong indication of completeness, but unfortunately gives only a necessary condition [see (d) of Theorem 10-1.4].

THEOREM 10-3.3. If a trigonometric series,

$$\tfrac{1}{2}a_0 + \sum_{n=1}^{+\infty} (a_n \cos nx + b_n \sin nx),$$

converges uniformly on $[-\pi, \pi]$, then it is the Fourier series of exactly one continuous function.†

PROOF. Suppose two functions are continuous and have the same Fourier series. Then their difference, ϕ, has the property that all coefficients in its Fourier series are zero. We shall use a proof by contradiction to show that ϕ is zero. Suppose ϕ is not identically zero. Then there is no loss of generality in assuming there is a number ξ with $\phi(\xi) > 0$. Since ϕ is continuous, we can take ξ to be an interior point of $[-\pi, \pi]$. Then it follows from continuity of ϕ that there is a positive number δ such that $[\xi - \delta, \xi + \delta] \subset [-\pi, \pi]$ and

$$\phi(x) > \tfrac{1}{2}\phi(\xi) \quad \text{if} \quad x \in [\xi - \delta, \xi + \delta]. \tag{10-36}$$

Now let $t_n(x) = [1 + \cos (x - \xi)]^n$ if $n \geqq 1$. Since $\sin x$ and $\cos x$ can be expressed as $\tfrac{1}{2}(e^{ix} - e^{-ix})/i$ and $\tfrac{1}{2}(e^{ix} + e^{-ix})$, respectively, the functions $\sin^n x$ and $\cos^n x$ can be expressed as finite linear combinations of $\cos kx$ and $\sin kx$ with $0 \leqq k \leqq n$. Therefore, this also is true of t_n. Then we must have $\int_{-\pi}^{\pi} \phi(x)t_n(x)\, dx = 0$ for all n, since all Fourier coefficients of ϕ are zero. We shall obtain our contradiction by showing there is an n such that $\int_{-\pi}^{\pi} \phi(x)t_n(x)\, dx \neq 0$. Let M be an upper bound for $|\phi|$ on $[-\pi, \pi]$ and let

$$\alpha = 1 + \cos \delta, \qquad \beta = 1 + \cos \tfrac{1}{2}\delta.$$

Then $0 < \alpha < \beta$ and

$$|\phi(x)|[1 + \cos (x - \xi)]^n \leqq \alpha^n M \quad \text{if} \quad x \in [-\pi, \xi - \delta] \cup [\xi + \delta, \pi],$$

$$\phi(x)[1 + \cos (x - \xi)]^n \geqq 0 \quad \text{if} \quad x \in [\xi - \delta, \xi - \tfrac{1}{2}\delta] \cup [\xi + \tfrac{1}{2}\delta, \xi + \delta],$$

$$\phi(x)[1 + \cos (x - \xi)]^n \geqq \tfrac{1}{2}\beta^n\phi(\xi) \quad \text{if} \quad x \in [\xi - \tfrac{1}{2}\delta, \xi + \tfrac{1}{2}\delta].$$

---

† When we have proved that sequence (10-30) is complete, then we will know that a trigonometric series is the Fourier series of at most one member of $L^2_{[-\pi,\pi]}$ [see Theorem 10-1.4 (d), page 503, and Theorem 10-3.5, page 526].

Therefore,

$$\int_{-\pi}^{\pi} \phi(x)t_n(x)\, dx \geqq \left\{ \int_{-\pi}^{\xi-\delta} \phi(x)t_n(x)\, dx + \int_{\xi+\delta}^{\pi} \phi(x)t_n(x)\, dx \right\}$$

$$+ \int_{\xi-\frac12\delta}^{\xi+\frac12\delta} \phi(x)t_n(x)\, dx$$

$$> -2\pi M\alpha^n + \tfrac12 \delta\phi(\xi)\beta^n,$$

and $\int_{-\pi}^{\pi} \phi(x)t_n(x)\, dx > 0$ if n is large enough that

$$\left(\frac{\beta}{\alpha}\right)^n > \frac{2\pi M}{\tfrac12 \delta\phi(\xi)}.$$

THEOREM 10-3.4. Suppose f is a function such that $f(-\pi) = f(\pi)$, f is continuous and piecewise differentiable on $[-\pi, \pi]$,† and f' and $(f')^2$ are integrable on $[-\pi, \pi]$. Then the Fourier series of f converges uniformly on $[-\pi, \pi]$ and its sum is f. Moreover, the Fourier series of f' is the series obtained by term-by-term differentiation of the Fourier series of f.

PROOF. Since $(f')^2$ is integrable on $[-\pi, \pi]$, the function $|f'|$ is integrable and $f'g$ is integrable for any continuous function g [see problem 10, page 167]. Therefore, we can use integration by parts with (10-34) and (10-35) to obtain

$$a_n = \frac{1}{\pi}\int_{-\pi}^{\pi} f(x)\cos nx\, dx = \left[\frac{f(x)\sin nx}{n\pi}\right]_{-\pi}^{\pi} - \frac{1}{n\pi}\int_{-\pi}^{\pi} f'(x)\sin nx\, dx$$

$$= -\frac{1}{n\pi}\int_{-\pi}^{\pi} f'(x)\sin nx\, dx,$$

$$b_n = \frac{1}{\pi}\int_{-\pi}^{\pi} f(x)\sin nx\, dx = \left[-\frac{f(x)\cos nx}{n\pi}\right]_{-\pi}^{\pi} + \frac{1}{n\pi}\int_{-\pi}^{\pi} f'(x)\cos nx\, dx$$

$$= \frac{1}{n\pi}\int_{-\pi}^{\pi} f'(x)\cos nx\, dx.$$

These equations give the Fourier series of f as

$$\tfrac12 a_0 + \sum_{n=1}^{+\infty} \left\{ \left[\frac{-1}{n\pi}\int_{-\pi}^{\pi} f'(t)\sin nt\, dt\right]\cos nx \right.$$

$$\left. + \left[\frac{1}{n\pi}\int_{-\pi}^{\pi} f'(t)\cos nt\, dt\right]\sin nx \right\}.$$

---

† Being *piecewise differentiable* means that f is differentiable except at a finite number of points and at these points f has both a right and a left derivative.

Term-by-term differentiation gives us the Fourier series of f', except that the constant term is zero. However, it should be zero, since $\int_{-\pi}^{\pi} f'(t)\, dt = f(\pi) - f(-\pi) = 0.$†

We shall now have need for Schwarz's inequality,

$$\left| \sum_{n=1}^{p} c_n d_n \right| \leq \left[\sum_{n=1}^{p} |c_n|^2 \right]^{1/2} \left[\sum_{n=1}^{p} |d_n|^2 \right]^{1/2}. \tag{10-37}$$

This can be proved for p finite in the same way that inequality (7-7) was proved, and then extended to include the case $p = +\infty$. Uniform convergence of the Fourier series of f will follow from Weierstrass' test for uniform convergence [page 215] if we show that $\sum (|a_n| + |b_n|)$ is convergent. From Schwarz's inequality, we have

$$\sum_{n=1}^{p} (|a_n| + |b_n|) = \sum_{n=1}^{p} \left[|na_n| \frac{1}{n} + |nb_n| \frac{1}{n} \right]$$

$$\leq \left[\sum_{n=1}^{p} (na_n)^2 + (nb_n)^2 \right]^{1/2} \left[\sum_{n=1}^{p} \frac{1}{n^2} \right]^{1/2}.$$

Since the Fourier coefficients of f' are na_n and nb_n, for $n \geq 1$, it now follows from Theorem 10–3.1 and Bessel's inequality (10-9) that

$$\sum_{n=1}^{p} (|a_n| + |b_n|) \leq \left[\frac{1}{\pi} \int_{-\pi}^{\pi} (f')^2 \, dx \right]^{1/2} \left[\sum_{n=1}^{+\infty} \frac{1}{n^2} \right]^{1/2}. \tag{10-38}$$

Therefore $\sum (|a_n| + |b_n|)$ is convergent and the Fourier series of f is uniformly convergent. Suppose the sum is S. Then it follows from Theorem 10-3.2 that the Fourier series of f is the Fourier series of S. Now we can use Theorem 10-3.3 to conclude that $f = S$.

ILLUSTRATION 1. Suppose we define a function f by $f(x) = 0$ if $x \leq 0$ and $f(x) = 1 - \cos 2x$ if $x > 0$. Then f' is continuous everywhere and $f(-\pi) = f(\pi) = 0$. By Theorem 10-3.4, the Fourier series of f converges uniformly to f on $[-\pi, \pi]$. We obtain

$$a_0 = \frac{1}{\pi} \int_0^{\pi} (1 - \cos 2x) \, dx = 1,$$

$$a_n = \frac{1}{\pi} \int_0^{\pi} (1 - \cos 2x) \cos nx \, dx$$

$$= \frac{1}{\pi} \int_0^{\pi} [\cos nx - \tfrac{1}{2} \cos (n+2)x - \tfrac{1}{2} \cos (n-2)x] \, dx.$$

---

† Note that the series for f' need not be convergent.

Thus, $a_2 = -\frac{1}{2}$ and $a_n = 0$ if n is not 0 or 2.   For all n,

$$b_{2n} = \frac{1}{\pi} \int_0^\pi (1 - \cos 2x) \sin 2nx \, dx$$

$$= \frac{1}{\pi} \int_0^\pi [\sin 2nx - \tfrac{1}{2} \sin (2n+2)x - \tfrac{1}{2} \sin (2n-2)x] \, dx = 0,$$

$$b_{2n-1} = \frac{1}{\pi} \int_0^\pi (1 - \cos 2x) \sin (2n-1)x \, dx$$

$$= \frac{1}{\pi} \int_0^\pi [\sin (2n-1)x - \tfrac{1}{2} \sin (2n+1)x - \tfrac{1}{2} \sin (2n-3)x] \, dx$$

$$= \frac{1}{\pi} \left[\frac{2}{2n-1} - \frac{1}{2n+1} - \frac{1}{2n-3} \right] = -\frac{8}{\pi(2n-3)(2n-1)(2n+1)}.$$

Figure 10-1 shows the graphs of f and the sum of the first three terms of the Fourier series of f,

$$\frac{1}{2} + \frac{8}{3\pi} \sin x - \frac{1}{2} \cos 2x.$$

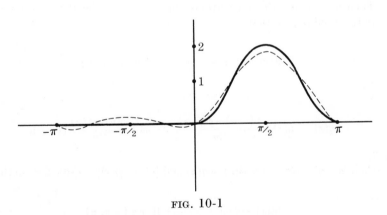

FIG. 10-1

We know now that there is a rather large class of functions whose Fourier series converges uniformly to the function; namely, those functions f for which $f(-\pi) = f(\pi)$ and f is continuous and piecewise differentiable on $[-\pi, \pi]$, with f' and $(f')^2$ integrable on $[-\pi, \pi]$.   This can be used to show that sequence (10-30) is complete.   Roughly, the technique is to show that functions of this type can be used to approximate arbitrary members of $L^2_{[-\pi,\pi]}$.

THEOREM 10-3.5. For the space $L^2_{[-\pi,\,\pi]}$, the orthonormal sequence,

$$\left\{ \frac{1}{\sqrt{2\pi}}, \frac{\cos x}{\sqrt{\pi}}, \frac{\sin x}{\sqrt{\pi}}, \ldots, \frac{\cos nx}{\sqrt{\pi}}, \frac{\sin nx}{\sqrt{\pi}}, \ldots \right\}, \tag{10-39}$$

is complete.

PROOF. We shall use the criterion for completeness given in (b) of Theorem 10-1.3. Thus, we shall show that, for any member f of $L^2_{[-\pi,\,\pi]}$ and any positive number ε, there is a finite trigonometric series t such that

$$\left\{ \int_{-\pi}^{\pi} [f(x) - t(x)]^2 \, dx \right\}^{\frac{1}{2}} < \varepsilon. \tag{10-40}$$

From Theorem 10-2.1, we know there is a polygonal function ϕ that satisfies the following inequality. Clearly, we can require that ϕ also satisfy $\phi(-\pi) = \phi(\pi)$.

$$\left\{ \int_{-\pi}^{\pi} [f(x) - \phi(x)]^2 \, dx \right\}^{\frac{1}{2}} < \frac{\varepsilon}{2}. \tag{10-41}$$

Then we can use the Weierstrass approximation theorem to obtain a polynomial p such that

$$|\phi(x) - p(x)| < \frac{\varepsilon}{12\sqrt{2\pi}} \text{ if } x \in [-\pi, \pi].$$

If

$$q(x) = p(x) + \frac{p(-\pi) - \phi(-\pi)}{2\pi}(x - \pi) + \frac{\phi(\pi) - p(\pi)}{2\pi}(x + \pi),$$

then $q(-\pi) = \phi(-\pi) = \phi(\pi) = q(\pi)$ and $|q(x) - p(x)| < \varepsilon/(6\sqrt{2\pi})$, so that

$$|\phi(x) - q(x)| < \frac{\varepsilon}{4\sqrt{2\pi}} \text{ if } x \in [-\pi, \pi].$$

Since q is a polynomial with $q(-\pi) = q(\pi)$, it follows from Theorem 10-3.4 that there is a finite trignometric sum t such that $|q(x) - t(x)| < \varepsilon/(4\sqrt{2\pi})$ and therefore

$$|\phi(x) - t(x)| < \frac{\varepsilon}{2\sqrt{2\pi}} \text{ if } x \in [-\pi, \pi].$$

From this, $\left\{\int_{-\pi}^{\pi} [\phi(x) - t(x)]^2 \, dx\right\}^{1/2} < \frac{1}{2}\varepsilon.$ Now (10-40) follows from this inequality, inequality (10-41), and the triangle inequality:

$$\left\{\int_{-\pi}^{\pi} [f(x) - t(x)]^2 \, dx\right\}^{1/2}$$
$$\leq \left\{\int_{-\pi}^{\pi} [f(x) - \phi(x)]^2 \, dx\right\}^{1/2} + \left\{\int_{-\pi}^{\pi} [\phi(x) - t(x)]^2 \, dx\right\}^{1/2}.$$

For any complete orthonormal sequence $\{\phi_n\}$ in $L^2_{[a,b]}$, it follows from Parseval's equality that, for members f and g of $L^2_{[a,b]}$,

$$\int_a^b [f(x) - g(x)]^2 \, dx = \sum_{n=1}^{+\infty} \left\{\int_a^b [f(x) - g(x)]\phi_n(x) \, dx\right\}^2$$
$$= \sum_{n=1}^{+\infty} (a_n - b_n)^2,$$

where $a_n = \int_a^b f(x)\phi_n(x) \, dx$ and $b_n = \int_a^b g(x)\phi_n(x) \, dx.$ Since Parseval's equality gives us

$$\int_a^b f^2(x) \, dx = \sum_{n=1}^{+\infty} a_n^2 \quad \text{and} \quad \int_a^b g^2(x) \, dx = \sum_{n=1}^{+\infty} b_n^2,$$

it follows that

$$\int_a^b f(x)g(x) \, dx = \sum_{n=1}^{+\infty} a_n b_n.$$

This gives a natural generalization of the usual formula for the scalar product of vectors in R^3. Moreover, by letting $g = 1$, we obtain the surprising result:

THEOREM 10-3.6. Suppose $\{\phi_n\}$ is a complete orthonormal sequence in $L^2_{[a,b]}$ and that $\sum a_n \phi_n$ is the corresponding expansion of a member f of $L^2_{[a,b]}$. Then it is legitimate to integrate this series term-by-term on $[a, b]$, in the sense that

$$\int_a^b f(x) \, dx = \sum_{n=1}^{+\infty} a_n \left[\int_a^b \phi_n(x) \, dx\right].$$

This theorem may seem very strange, since we know nothing about pointwise convergence, let alone uniform convergence, of $\sum a_n \phi_n$. Since (10-39) is complete, we know that *any* Fourier series on

$[-\pi, \pi]$ can be integrated term-by-term on $[-\pi, \pi]$. One must be very cautious about differentiating Fourier series. For example, the series $\sum (\sin nx)/n$ converges for all x and converges uniformly on any closed interval that does not contain an even multiple of π, but the differentiated series, $\sum \cos nx$, diverges for all x.

Now that we know (10-39) is complete, it follows from (d) of Theorem 10-1.4 that a trigonometric series is the Fourier series of at most one member of $L^2_{[-\pi, \pi]}$. This is a generalization of Theorem 10-3.3. Also, we know from (a) of Theorem 10-1.3 that, if $f \in L^2_{[-\pi, \pi]}$, then the Fourier series of f *converges in the mean* to f. That is,

$$\lim_{n \to +\infty} \int_{-\pi}^{\pi} \left\{ f(x) - \left[\tfrac{1}{2}a_0 + \sum_{k=1}^{n} (a_k \cos kx + b_k \sin kx) \right] \right\}^2 dx = 0.$$

$$(10\text{-}42)$$

Also, we can write Parseval's equality (10-10) for Fourier series as

$$\int_{-\pi}^{\pi} f^2(x)\, dx = \pi \left[\tfrac{1}{2}a_0^2 + \sum_{n=1}^{+\infty} (a_n^2 + b_n^2) \right]. \qquad \text{(Parseval's equality)}$$

$$(10\text{-}43)$$

To specialize Parseval's equality of Definition 10-1.6 and obtain (10-43), we use the orthonormal sequence (10-39) and the equalities:

$$\sqrt{\frac{\pi}{2}}\, a_0 = \int_{-\pi}^{\pi} f(x)\, \frac{1}{\sqrt{2\pi}}\, dx, \quad \sqrt{\pi}\, a_n = \int_{-\pi}^{\pi} f(x)\, \frac{\cos nx}{\sqrt{\pi}}\, dx,$$

$$\sqrt{\pi}\, b_n = \int_{-\pi}^{\pi} f(x)\, \frac{\sin nx}{\sqrt{\pi}}\, dx.$$

The next theorem is included here, because it follows directly from Parseval's equality if $f \in L^2_{[-\pi, \pi]}$ and r is restricted to integral values. However, in the next section we shall need this theorem for functions with only f and $|f|$ integrable. Therefore, we use a different method of proof. This method does not depend on r being an integer.

THEOREM 10-3.7 (RIEMANN-LEBESGUE LEMMA). If f and $|f|$ are integrable on $[a, b]$, then

$$\lim_{r \to +\infty} \int_{a}^{b} f(x) \sin rx\, dx = \lim_{r \to +\infty} \int_{a}^{b} f(x) \cos rx\, dx = 0.$$

PROOF. Let ε be an arbitrary positive number. From (i) of Theorem 10-2.1 and the Weierstrass approximation theorem [Theorem 10-2.2], it follows that there is a polynomial p such that

$$\int_a^b |f(x) - p(x)| \, dx < \frac{\varepsilon}{2}.$$

If we use repeated integration by parts to evaluate $\int_a^b p(x) \sin rx \, dx$, then each term of the answer has a factor r^{-k} for some positive integer k. Therefore, $\lim_{r \to +\infty} \int_a^b p(x) \sin rx \, dx = 0$, and there is a number N such that

$$\left| \int_a^b p(x) \sin rx \, dx \right| < \frac{\varepsilon}{2} \text{ if } r > N.$$

Since

$$\left| \int_a^b [f(x) \sin rx - p(x) \sin rx] \, dx \right| \leq \int_a^b |f(x) - p(x)| \, dx < \tfrac{1}{2}\varepsilon,$$

it now follows that

$$\left| \int_a^b f(x) \sin rx \, dx \right| < \varepsilon \text{ if } r > N.$$

Therefore, $\lim_{r \to +\infty} \int_a^b f(x) \sin rx \, dx = 0$. Similarly,

$$\lim_{r \to +\infty} \int_a^b f(x) \cos rx \, dx = 0.$$

As yet, we have considered only Fourier series for the interval $[-\pi, \pi]$. We shall now enlarge the theory by considering other intervals.

For an interval $[c, c + 2\pi]$, all of the preceding theory can be translated directly. For such an interval, a function f has the Fourier series

$$\tfrac{1}{2}a_0 + \sum_{n=1}^{+\infty} (a_n \cos nx + b_n \sin nx),$$

where

$$a_n = \frac{1}{\pi} \int_c^{c+2\pi} f(t) \cos nt \, dt, \tag{10-44}$$

$$b_n = \frac{1}{\pi} \int_c^{c+2\pi} f(t) \sin nt \, dt.$$

If the domain of f is the set of real numbers and f is periodic with period 2π, then formulas (10-44) give the same Fourier coefficients as formulas (10-34) and (10-35). Otherwise, the Fourier series can be used to represent f in the interval $[c, c+2\pi]$, and the periodic extension of f outside this interval.

An *even* function on an interval $[-c, c]$ is a function θ such that $\theta(x) = \theta(-x)$ if $|x| \leq c$. An *odd* function is a function ϕ such that $\phi(-x) = -\phi(x)$ if $|x| \leq c$. The product of two even functions and the product of two odd functions is even. The product of an odd and an even function is odd. Also,

$$\int_{-c}^{c} \phi(x)\, dx = 0, \quad \phi \text{ odd}; \qquad \int_{-c}^{c} \theta(x)\, dx = 2 \int_{-c}^{c} \theta(x)\, dx, \quad \theta \text{ even}.$$

$$(10\text{-}45)$$

Now suppose f is even in the interval $[-\pi, \pi]$. Then $f(x) \cos nx$ is even and $f(x) \sin nx$ is odd. Using (10-45), we obtain

$$a_n = \frac{2}{\pi} \int_0^{\pi} f(x) \cos nx\, dx, \quad b_n = 0.$$

DEFINITION 10-3.2. For the interval $[0, \pi]$, the *Fourier cosine series* of a function f is the series

$$\tfrac{1}{2}a_0 + \sum_{n=1}^{+\infty} a_n \cos nx, \quad \text{where} \quad a_n = \frac{2}{\pi} \int_0^{\pi} f(t) \cos nt\, dt. \quad (10\text{-}46)$$

The Fourier cosine series of f for the interval $[0, \pi]$ is the Fourier series for the interval $[-\pi, \pi]$ of the even function θ defined by $\theta(x) = f(|x|)$ if $x \in [-\pi, \pi]$.

DEFINITION 10-3.3. For the interval $[0, \pi]$, the *Fourier sine series* of a function f is the series

$$\sum_{n=1}^{+\infty} b_n \sin nx, \quad \text{where} \quad b_n = \frac{2}{\pi} \int_0^{\pi} f(t) \sin nt\, dt. \quad (10\text{-}47)$$

The Fourier sine series of f for the interval $[0, \pi]$ is the Fourier series for the interval $[-\pi, \pi]$ of the odd function ϕ defined by $\phi(x) = f(x)$ if $x > 0$, $\phi(0) = 0$, and $\phi(x) = -f(-x)$ if $x < 0$.

DEFINITION 10-3.4. For the interval $[-\ell, \ell]$, the *Fourier coefficients* of a function g are the numbers

$$a_n = \frac{1}{\ell} \int_{-\ell}^{\ell} g(t) \cos \frac{n\pi t}{\ell}\, dt, \quad n = 0, 1, \cdots; \qquad (10\text{-}48)$$

$$b_n = \frac{1}{\ell} \int_{-\ell}^{\ell} g(t) \sin \frac{n\pi t}{\ell}\, dt, \quad n = 1, 2, \cdots; \qquad (10\text{-}49)$$

provided all these integrals exist. The *Fourier series* of a function for which these integrals exist is the trigonometric series

$$\tfrac{1}{2}a_0 + \sum_{n=1}^{+\infty} \left(a_n \cos \frac{n\pi x}{\ell} + b_n \sin \frac{n\pi x}{\ell} \right).$$

It is easy to see that the change made to shift from Definition 10-3.1 and the interval $[-\pi, \pi]$ to Definition 10-3.4 and the interval $[-\ell, \ell]$ is merely a change in scale. Specifically, we can let $s = \pi t/\ell$ and obtain Eqs. (10-48) and (10-49) from (10-34) and (10-35) by defining f as a function for which

$$g(x) = f\left(\frac{\pi x}{\ell}\right), \qquad x \in [-\ell, \ell].$$

A similar change in scale can be made for the cosine and sine series. This yields the following definition:

DEFINITION 10-3.5. For the interval $[0, \ell]$, the *Fourier cosine series* of a function g is the series

$$\tfrac{1}{2}a_0 + \sum_{n=1}^{+\infty} a_n \cos \frac{n\pi x}{\ell}, \quad \text{where} \quad a_n = \frac{2}{\ell} \int_0^\ell g(t) \cos \frac{n\pi t}{\ell} \, dt. \quad (10\text{-}50)$$

The *Fourier sine series* is the series

$$\sum_{n=1}^{+\infty} b_n \sin \frac{n\pi x}{\ell}, \quad \text{where} \quad b_n = \frac{2}{\ell} \int_0^\ell g(t) \sin \frac{n\pi t}{\ell} \, dt. \quad (10\text{-}51)$$

ILLUSTRATION 2. Suppose we wish to determine the Fourier sine series on $[0, 2\pi]$ of the function f for which $f(x) = 1$ if $x \geqq 0$. Then

$$b_n = \frac{1}{\pi} \int_0^{2\pi} \sin \frac{nt}{2} \, dt = \left[-\frac{2}{n\pi} \cos \frac{nt}{2} \right]_0^{2\pi} = \frac{2}{n\pi} (1 - \cos n\pi).$$

Thus, the Fourier sine series is

$$\sum_{n=1}^{+\infty} b_n \sin \frac{nx}{2} = \frac{4}{\pi} \left(\sin \frac{x}{2} + \tfrac{1}{3} \sin \frac{3x}{2} + \tfrac{1}{5} \sin \frac{5x}{2} + \cdots \right).$$

PROBLEMS

1. In each case, find the Fourier series of the given function for the interval $[-\pi, \pi]$.

    (*a*) $f(x) = \cos^2 3x$ if $-\pi < x < \pi$.

    (*b*) $f(x) = -1$ if $x < 0$, $f(0) = 0$, $f(x) = +1$ if $x > 0$.

    (*c*) $f(x) = \frac{1}{2}\pi + x$ if $-\pi \leqq x \leqq 0$, $f(x) = \frac{1}{2}\pi - x$ if $0 < x \leqq \pi$.

    (*d*) $f(x) = x$ for all x.

    (*e*) $f(x) = x^2$ for all x.

    (*f*) $f(x) = x(\pi - x)(\pi + x)$ for all x.

2. Prove that the Fourier sine series of $\cos x$ on $[0, \pi]$ is

$$\frac{8}{\pi} \sum_{n=1}^{+\infty} \frac{n \sin 2nx}{4n^2 - 1}.$$

3. Prove that the Fourier cosine series of $\sin x$ on $[0, \pi]$ is

$$\frac{2}{\pi} - \frac{4}{\pi} \sum_{n=1}^{+\infty} \frac{1}{4n^2 - 1} \cos 2nx.$$

4. Prove that

$$\frac{\pi}{4} \cos x + \frac{x}{2} - \frac{\pi}{4} = \sum_{n=1}^{+\infty} \frac{\sin 2nx}{(2n-1)(2n)(2n+1)} \quad \text{if} \quad 0 \leq x \leq \pi.$$

*5.** Prove that the Fourier cosine and the Fourier sine series of $x(\pi - x)$ on $[0, \pi]$ are

$$\frac{\pi^2}{6} - \left(\frac{\cos 2x}{1^2} + \frac{\cos 4x}{2^2} + \frac{\cos 6x}{3^2} + \cdots\right),$$

$$\frac{8}{\pi} \left(\frac{\sin x}{1^3} + \frac{\sin 3x}{3^3} + \frac{\sin 5x}{5^3} + \frac{\sin 7x}{7^3} + \cdots\right).$$

6. Use Theorems 10-3.2 and 10-3.3, and the series of problems 2 through 5, to prove that

  (a) $\sum_1^{+\infty} \frac{1}{n^2} = \frac{\pi^2}{6}$,   (e) $\sum_1^{+\infty} \frac{1}{(2n-1)^4} = \frac{\pi^4}{96}$,

  (b) $\sum_1^{+\infty} \frac{(-1)^{n-1}}{n^2} = \frac{\pi^2}{12}$,   (f) $\frac{1}{2} = \frac{1}{1\cdot3} + \frac{1}{3\cdot5} + \frac{1}{5\cdot7} + \cdots$,

  (c) $\sum_1^{+\infty} \frac{1}{(2n-1)^2} = \frac{\pi^2}{8}$,   (g) $\frac{\pi}{4\sqrt{2}} - \frac{1}{2} = \frac{1}{3\cdot5} - \frac{1}{7\cdot9} + \frac{1}{11\cdot13} - \cdots$,

  (d) $\sum_1^{+\infty} \frac{(-1)^{n-1}}{(2n-1)^3} = \frac{\pi^3}{32}$,   (h) $\frac{\pi}{8}(\sqrt{2}-1) = \frac{1}{1\cdot2\cdot3} - \frac{1}{5\cdot6\cdot7}$

$$+ \frac{1}{9\cdot10\cdot11} - \cdots.$$

7. Suppose $f \in L^2_{[-\ell,\ell)}$. For the Fourier series of f on $[-\ell, \ell]$, prove Parseval's equality:

$$\int_{-\ell}^{\ell} f^2(x)\, dx = \ell \left[\frac{a_0^2}{2} + \sum_{n=1}^{+\infty} (a_n^2 + b_n^2) \right].$$

8. In each case, use Parseval's equality and problems or answers to problems of this section to prove the given equality.

(a) $\dfrac{\pi^2}{6} = \displaystyle\sum_{n=1}^{+\infty} n^{-2}.$ (d) $\dfrac{\pi^4}{96} = \displaystyle\sum_{n=1}^{+\infty} (2n-1)^{-4}.$

(b) $\dfrac{\pi^2}{8} = \displaystyle\sum_{n=1}^{+\infty} (2n-1)^{-2}.$ (e) $\dfrac{\pi^6}{945} = \displaystyle\sum_{n=1}^{+\infty} n^{-6}.$

(c) $\dfrac{\pi^4}{90} = \displaystyle\sum_{n=1}^{+\infty} n^{-4}.$ (f) $\dfrac{\pi^6}{960} = \displaystyle\sum_{n=1}^{+\infty} (2n-1)^{-6}.$

(g) $\dfrac{\pi^2 - 8}{16} = \dfrac{1}{1^2 \cdot 3^2} + \dfrac{1}{3^2 \cdot 5^2} + \dfrac{1}{5^2 \cdot 7^2} + \dfrac{1}{7^2 \cdot 9^2} + \cdots.$

9. In each case, find the Fourier sine series of f on $[0, 8]$.

(a) $f(x) = 1 + \sin \pi x, \quad 0 \le x \le 8.$

(b) $f(x) = x, \quad 0 \le x \le 4; \quad f(x) = 8 - x, \quad 4 \le x \le 8.$

10. In each case, find the Fourier series of f on $[0, 2]$.

(a) $f(x) = \sin(\pi x + \tfrac{1}{3}\pi), \quad 0 \le x \le 2.$

(b) $f(x) = 2x + 1, \quad 0 \le x \le 2.$

(c) $f(x) = x^2, \quad 0 \le x \le 2.$

11. For a function ϕ with domain $[-\pi, \pi]$, let ϕ_* be the periodic extension of ϕ defined by $\phi_*(x + 2n\pi) = \phi(x)$ if $x \in [-\pi, \pi)$. Determine what conclusions can be made about the Fourier coefficients of a function ϕ that has the stated property.

(a) $\phi(-x) = -\phi(x), \quad |x| < \pi.$

(b) $\phi_*(\pi - x) = \phi_*(x), \quad$ all $x.$

(c) $\phi_*(-x) = \phi_*(x) = \phi_*(\tfrac{1}{2}\pi - x), \quad$ all $x.$

(d) $\phi(x + \pi) = \phi(x), \quad -\pi < x < 0.$

(e) $\phi(x + \tfrac{1}{2}\pi) = \phi(x), \quad -\pi < x < \tfrac{1}{2}\pi.$

(f) $\phi(x + \tfrac{2}{3}\pi) = \phi(x), \quad -\pi < x < \tfrac{1}{3}\pi.$

(g) $\phi(x + \tfrac{1}{3}\pi) = \phi(x), \quad -\pi < x < \tfrac{2}{3}\pi.$

(h) ϕ is continuous at 0 and $\phi(x) = \phi(2x) \quad$ if $\quad |x| < \tfrac{1}{2}\pi.$

12. Suppose $f(x) = 0$ if $-\pi < x < 0$. Show that, if

$$\tfrac{1}{2}a_0 + \sum_{n=1}^{+\infty} (a_n \cos nx + b_n \sin nx)$$

is the Fourier series of f on the interval $[-\pi, \pi]$, then the Fourier cosine series and the Fourier sine series of f on the interval $[0, \pi]$ are, respectively,

$$a_0 + \sum_{n=1}^{+\infty} 2a_n \cos nx \quad \text{and} \quad \sum_{n=1}^{+\infty} 2b_n \sin nx.$$

13. Suppose f is a function for which f'' is bounded and integrable on $[-\pi, \pi]$ and $f(-\pi) = f(\pi)$.

(a) Prove that there is a number M such that, for all Fourier coefficients $\{a_n\}$ and $\{b_n\}$ of f,

$$|a_n| \leq Mn^{-2} \quad \text{and} \quad |b_n| \leq Mn^{-2}.$$

(b) Explain how the conclusion of part (a) can be strengthened, if we also know that f''' is bounded and integrable on $[-\pi, \pi]$ and that

$$f'(-\pi) = f'(\pi).$$

14. (a) Show that there are numbers A, B, and C such that

$$f(x) = A + B \cos x + C \sin x, \quad x \in [-\pi, \pi],$$

if and only if the domains of all derivatives of f contain the interval $[-\pi, \pi]$, $f^{[k]}(-\pi) = f^{[k]}(\pi)$ for all $k \geq 0$, and there is a number M that is an upper bound of $|f^{[k]}|$ for infinitely many values of k. (b) What conclusion can be reached if we replace the last hypothesis in part (a) by the hypothesis that there exists a number M such that $2^k M$ is an upper bound of $|f^{[k]}|$ for infinitely many values of k?

15. Suppose f and $|f|$ are integrable on $[-\pi, \pi]$. Prove each of the following.

(a) $\lim_{n \to +\infty} a_n = \lim_{n \to +\infty} b_n = 0$, where the a_n's and b_n's are the Fourier coefficients of f.

(b) If f^2 is not integrable on $[-\pi, \pi]$, then

$$\lim_{n \to +\infty} \tfrac{1}{2}a_0^2 + \sum_{k=1}^{n} (a_k^2 + b_k^2) = +\infty.$$

16. (a) Use an identity from problem 9, page 222, to show that

$$\sum_{k=1}^{n} \frac{\sin kx}{k} = \int_0^x \left(\sum_{k=1}^{n} \cos kt \right) dt = \tfrac{1}{2} \int_0^x \left[\frac{\sin (n+\tfrac{1}{2})t}{\sin \tfrac{1}{2}t} - 1 \right] dt.$$

(b) Prove that, for all x,

$$\left| \sum_{k=1}^{n} \frac{\sin kx}{k} \right| \leq \frac{\pi}{2} + \tfrac{1}{2} \int_0^{\pi/(n+1/2)} \frac{\sin (n+\tfrac{1}{2})t}{\sin \tfrac{1}{2}t} \, dt$$

$$\leq \frac{\pi}{2} + \tfrac{1}{2} \int_0^{\pi/(n+1/2)} \frac{(n+\tfrac{1}{2})t}{\tfrac{1}{3}t} \, dt = 2\pi.$$

10-4.   POINTWISE CONVERGENCE

In order to establish conditions for convergence of a Fourier series at a particular point, we shall obtain an integral representation for the partial sums.   For a function f and the interval $[-\pi, \pi]$, we have

$$s_n(x) = \tfrac{1}{2}a_0 + \sum_{k=1}^{n-1} (a_k \cos kx + b_k \sin kx)$$

$$= \frac{1}{2\pi} \int_{-\pi}^{\pi} f(t)\, dt + \sum_{k=1}^{n-1} \left\{ \left[\frac{1}{\pi} \int_{-\pi}^{\pi} f(t) \cos kt\, dt \right] \cos kx \right.$$

$$\left. + \left[\frac{1}{\pi} \int_{-\pi}^{\pi} f(t) \sin kt\, dt \right] \sin kx \right\}$$

$$= \frac{1}{\pi} \int_{-\pi}^{\pi} f(t) \left[\tfrac{1}{2} + \sum_{k=1}^{n-1} (\cos kt \cos kx + \sin kt \sin kx) \right] dt$$

$$= \frac{1}{\pi} \int_{-\pi}^{\pi} f(t) \left[\tfrac{1}{2} + \sum_{k=1}^{n-1} \cos k(t - x) \right] dt.$$

Now we use the identity $\tfrac{1}{2} + \sum_{1}^{n-1} \cos ks = [\sin(n - \tfrac{1}{2})s]/[2 \sin \tfrac{1}{2}s]$ [see problem 9, page 222] to obtain

$$s_n(x) = \frac{1}{\pi} \int_{-\pi}^{\pi} f(t) \frac{\sin(n - \tfrac{1}{2})(t - x)}{2 \sin \tfrac{1}{2}(t - x)}\, dt.$$

Now let f_* be the periodic extension of f defined by $f_*(x + 2k\pi) = f(x)$ if $x \in [-\pi, \pi)$ and k is an integer.   Then we can replace f by f_* and use the fact that the integrand has period 2π to obtain the first of the following equalities.   Changes of variables give the other equalities.

$$s_n(x) = \frac{1}{\pi} \int_{-\pi + x}^{\pi + x} f_*(t) \frac{\sin(n - \tfrac{1}{2})(t - x)}{2 \sin \tfrac{1}{2}(t - x)}\, dt$$

$$= \frac{1}{\pi} \int_{-\pi}^{\pi} f_*(x + t) \frac{\sin(n - \tfrac{1}{2})t}{2 \sin \tfrac{1}{2}t}\, dt \qquad (10\text{-}52)$$

$$= \frac{1}{\pi} \int_{-\frac{1}{2}\pi}^{\frac{1}{2}\pi} f_*(x + 2t) \frac{\sin(2n - 1)t}{\sin t}\, dt.$$

Finally, we can write the last integral as the sum of integrals over $[-\tfrac{1}{2}\pi, 0]$ and $[0, \tfrac{1}{2}\pi]$ and change the sign of the variable of integration in the first of these integrals, to obtain

$$s_n(x) = \frac{2}{\pi} \int_{0}^{\frac{1}{2}\pi} \frac{f_*(x + 2t) + f_*(x - 2t)}{2} \frac{\sin(2n - 1)t}{\sin t}\, dt. \qquad (10\text{-}53)$$

We know that if $f \in L^2_{[-\pi,\pi]}$, then the Fourier series of f converges in the mean to f. This is true even if f is discontinuous. If f is continuous and $f(-\pi) = f(\pi)$, then from the Weierstrass approximation theorem we know that f can be approximated uniformly by a polynomial p on $[-\pi, \pi]$, with $p(-\pi) = p(\pi)$. From Theorem 10-3.4, we know that the Fourier series of p converges uniformly to p on $[-\pi, \pi]$. Thus, a continuous function with $f(\pi) = f(-\pi)$ can be approximated uniformly on $[-\pi, \pi]$ by a trigonometric sum. However, many continuous functions have Fourier series that diverge at many points [see Theorem 10-4.5]. We have seen that the Fourier coefficients are "best" in the sense of mean-square approximation. The next two theorems show that we can obtain good theorems about pointwise convergence if the Fourier coefficients are multiplied by suitable "convergence factors." For applications, see pages 562, 567, and 568.

DEFINITION 10-4.1. A *Cesàro summable* series is a series $\sum c_n$ for which the following limit exists:

$$\lim_{n \to +\infty} \frac{s_1 + s_2 + \cdots + s_n}{n},$$

where s_n denotes $\sum_1^n c_k$. The *Cesàro sum* of a Cesàro summable series is this limit.

THEOREM 10-4.1 (FEJÉR). Suppose f and $|f|$ are integrable on $[-\pi, \pi]$. Let f_* be the periodic extension of f for which $f_*(x + 2k\pi) = f(x)$ if $x \in [-\pi, \pi)$ and k is an integer. Also suppose that x is a number for which the following limit exists:

$$F(x) = \lim_{h \to 0+} \frac{f_*(x+h) + f_*(x-h)}{2}. \tag{10-54}$$

Then the Fourier series of f is Cesàro summable at x and the Cesàro sum is $F(x)$. If f_* is continuous at all points of a closed interval $[a, b]$, then the sequence $\{(s_1 + \cdots + s_n)/n\}$ converges uniformly to f_* on $[a, b]$.

PROOF. If we denote $(s_1 + s_2 + \cdots + s_n)/n$ by σ_n, then it follows from Eq. (10-53) and a trigonometric identity [see problem 10, page 223] that

$$\sigma_n(x) = \frac{2}{\pi} \int_0^{\frac{1}{2}\pi} \frac{f_*(x+2t) + f_*(x-2t)}{2} \left[\frac{\sin t + \sin 3t + \cdots + \sin(2n-1)t}{n \sin t} \right] dt$$

$$= \frac{2}{\pi n} \int_0^{\frac{1}{2}\pi} \frac{f_*(x+2t) + f_*(x-2t)}{2} \left(\frac{\sin nt}{\sin t} \right)^2 dt. \tag{10-55}$$

Now we note that the constant function 1 has a simple Fourier series, namely, 1. Therefore, for this function, $\sigma_n(x) = 1$ for all n and it follows from (10-55) that

$$1 = \frac{2}{\pi n} \int_0^{\frac{1}{2}\pi} \left(\frac{\sin nt}{\sin t}\right)^2 dt. \tag{10-56}$$

We can use this equality and (10-55) to conclude that, if x is a number for which the limit $F(x)$ in (10-54) exists, then

$$\sigma_n(x) - F(x) = \frac{2}{\pi n} \int_0^{\frac{1}{2}\pi} \left[\frac{f_*(x+2t) + f_*(x-2t)}{2} - F(x)\right] \left(\frac{\sin nt}{\sin t}\right)^2 dt.$$

To show that this expression approaches zero as n increases, we let ε be an arbitrary positive number and choose a positive number $\delta < \frac{1}{2}\pi$ such that

$$\left|\frac{f_*(x+2t) + f_*(x-2t)}{2} - F(x)\right| < \frac{\varepsilon}{2} \text{ if } 0 < t \le \delta. \tag{10-57}$$

Then we have

$$|\sigma_n(x) - F(x)| < \frac{\varepsilon}{\pi n} \int_0^{\delta} \left(\frac{\sin nt}{\sin t}\right)^2 dt$$
$$+ \frac{2}{\pi n \sin^2 \delta} \int_{\delta}^{\frac{1}{2}\pi} \left|\frac{f_*(x+2t) + f_*(x-2t)}{2} - F(x)\right| dt.$$

From (10-56), the first integral is less than $\frac{1}{2}\pi n$. The second integral is not larger than $\int_{-\pi}^{\pi} |f(t)| \, dt + \frac{1}{2}\pi |F(x)|$. Therefore,

$$|\sigma_n(x) - F(x)| < \frac{\varepsilon}{2} + \frac{2}{\pi n \sin^2 \delta} \left[\int_{-\pi}^{\pi} |f(t)| \, dt + \frac{1}{2}\pi |F(x)|\right].$$

With $N = 4\left[\int_{-\pi}^{\pi} |f(t)| \, dt + \frac{1}{2}\pi |F(x)|\right] / [\varepsilon \pi \sin^2 \delta]$, we have

$$|\sigma_n(x) - F(x)| < \varepsilon \text{ if } n > N. \tag{10-58}$$

Therefore, $\lim \sigma_n(x) = F(x)$. In other words, the Fourier series of f is Cesàro summable at x and the Cesàro sum is $F(x)$. If f_* is continuous at each point of $[a, b]$, then the number δ of (10-57) can be the same for all x in $[a, b]$ [see problem 16, page 77]. Also, $|f_*|$ is then bounded on $[a, b]$ and we can replace $|F(x)|$ in the definition of N by an upper bound of $|f_*|$. Then (10-58) is valid on $[a; b]$. Thus, $\sigma_n \to F$ uniformly on $[a, b]$.

The possibility of other methods of summability of series is suggested by the following identity for a series $\sum c_k$:

$$\sigma_n = \frac{s_1 + s_2 + \cdots + s_n}{n}$$

$$= 1 \cdot c_1 + \left(1 - \frac{1}{n}\right)c_2 + \left(1 - \frac{2}{n}\right)c_3 + \cdots + \left(1 - \frac{n-1}{n}\right)c_n.$$

The coefficient of c_k, $1 - (k-1)/n$, is called a *convergence factor*. If we let $p_k(n) = 1 - (k-1)/n$ when $k \le n+1$ and $p_k(n) = 0$ when $k \ge n+1$, then

$$\sigma_n = \sum_{k=1}^{+\infty} p_k(n)c_k.$$

We might consider the possibility of using other types of convergence factors. For example, we shall see that the convergence factors defined by $p_k(r) = r^k$ are very useful. More generally, we shall consider sequences of nonnegative functions $\{p_k\}$ which have the property that there is a system of stages S for which $\lim_S p_k(r) = 1$ for all k. Also, we shall demand that the sequence be *monotone decreasing* and *convex* on some stage A. This means that, if $r \in A$, then

$$p_k(r) \ge p_{k+1}(r)$$

and

$$p_k(r) - 2p_{k+1}(r) + p_{k+2}(r) \ge 0 \quad \text{for all} \quad k$$

[also see problem 12]. For example, if $p_k(r) = r^k$ and $0 \le r < 1$, then $r^k - r^{k+1} \ge 0$ and

$$r^k - 2r^{k+1} + r^{k+2} = r^k(1-r)^2 \ge 0 \quad \text{for all} \quad k.$$

LEMMA. Suppose $\{p_k\}$ is a sequence of functions for which there is a system of stages S such that $\lim_S p_k(r) = 1$ for each k. Also suppose there is a stage A such that, if $r \in A$, then $p_k(r) \ge 0$ for each k, the sequence $\{p_k(r)\}$ is monotone decreasing and convex, and

$$\lim_{n \to +\infty} [p_n(r) \cdot \ln n] = 0. \tag{10-59}$$

If $\sum c_k$ is Cesàro summable and its Cesàro sum is C, and if there are numbers M and K such that $|c_1 + \cdots + c_k| \leq M \cdot \ln k$ for all $k > K$, then $\sum p_k(r)c_k$ is convergent if $r \in A$. Moreover,

$$\lim_S \sum_{k=1}^{+\infty} p_k(r)c_k = C \qquad (10\text{-}60)$$

PROOF. Let s_n denote the nth partial sum of $\sum c_k$ and let $\sigma_n = (\sum_1^n s_k)/n$. The following is a formal identity:

$$\begin{aligned}
\sum_{k=1}^{n} p_k(r)c_k &= [p_1(r) - p_2(r)]s_1 + [p_2(r) - p_3(r)]s_2 + \cdots \\
&\quad + [p_{n-1}(r) - p_n(r)]s_{n-1} + p_n(r)s_n \\
&= [p_1(r) - 2p_2(r) + p_3(r)]\sigma_1 + 2[p_2(r) - 2p_3(r) + p_4(r)]\sigma_2 + \cdots \\
&\quad + (n-2)[p_{n-2}(r) - 2p_{n-1}(r) + p_n(r)]\sigma_{n-2} \\
&\quad + (n-1)[p_{n-1}(r) - p_n(r)]\sigma_{n-1} + p_n(r)s_n. \qquad (10\text{-}61)
\end{aligned}$$

It follows from (10-59) and the inequality $|s_k| \leq M \cdot \ln k$, if $k > K$, that

$$\lim_{n \to +\infty} p_n(r)s_n = 0. \qquad (10\text{-}62)$$

Since $\{p_k\}$ is monotone decreasing and nonnegative on A, the series $S = \sum [p_n(r) - p_{n+1}(r)]$ is convergent and its terms are nonnegative. Since $\{p_k\}$ is convex, the terms of S are monotone decreasing. Therefore, $\lim_{n \to +\infty} (n-1)[p_{n-1}(r) - p_n(r)] = 0$ [see problem 9(b), page 182]. Since $\lim \sigma_n$ exists, it follows that $|\sigma_n|$ is bounded and that

$$\lim_{n \to +\infty} n - 1[p_{n-1}(r) - p_n(r)]\sigma_{n-1} = 0. \qquad (10\text{-}63)$$

The series $\sum n[p_n(r) - 2p_{n+1}(r) + p_{n+2}(r)]\sigma_n$ is absolutely convergent, since $|\sigma_n|$ is bounded and $\sum n[p_n(r) - 2p_{n+1}(r) + p_{n+2}(r)]$ is a series of nonnegative terms with sum $p_1(r)$.† Thus, it follows from (10-61), (10-62), and (10-63) that the following series are convergent and equal:

$$\sum_{k=1}^{+\infty} p_k(r)c_k = \sum_{n=1}^{+\infty} n[p_n(r) - 2p_{n+1}(r) + p_{n+2}(r)]\sigma_n.$$

---

† The nth partial sum is $p_1(r) - (n+1)[p_{n+1}(r) - p_{n+2}(r)] - p_{n+2}(r)$, which approaches $p_1(r)$ as $n \to +\infty$.

Since we could replace the sequence $\{p_k(r)\}$ by $\{p_k(r)/[\sup\{1,\ p_1(r)\}]\}$, there is no loss of generality in assuming that $p_1(r) = 1$ if $r \in A$. Then we have

$$\left| C - \sum_{k=1}^{+\infty} p_k(r)c_k \right| = \left| \sum_{n=1}^{+\infty} n[p_n(r) - 2p_{n+1}(r) + p_{n+2}(r)](C - \sigma_n) \right|$$

$$\leqq \left| \sum_{n=1}^{N-1} n[p_n(r) - 2p_{n+1}(r) + p_{n+2}(r)](C - \sigma_n) \right|$$

$$+ \left| \sum_{n=N}^{+\infty} n[p_n(r) - 2p_{n+1}(r) + p_{n+2}(r)](C - \sigma_n) \right|$$

$$\leqq \left| \sum_{n=1}^{N-1} n[p_n(r) - 2p_{n+1}(r) + p_{n+2}(r)](C - \sigma_n) \right|$$

$$+ \left\{ N[p_N(r) - p_{N+1}(r)] \right.$$

$$\left. + \sum_{n=N+1}^{+\infty} [p_n(r) - p_{n+1}(r)] \right\} \cdot \sup\{|C - \sigma_n| : n \geqq N\}.$$

$$(10\text{-}64)$$

Now suppose that, for an arbitrary positive number ε, we choose N large enough that $|C - \sigma_n| < \frac{1}{2}\varepsilon$ if $n \geqq N$. Then the second term of the last member of (10-64) is less than $\frac{1}{2}\varepsilon N[p_N(r) - p_{N+1}(r)] + \frac{1}{2}\varepsilon$. Since $\lim_S p_k(r) = 1$ for all k, there is a stage $B \subset A$ such that the last member of (10-64) is less than ε if $r \in B$. Then it follows from (10-64) that

$$\left| C - \sum_{k=1}^{+\infty} p_k(r)c_k \right| < \varepsilon \text{ if } r \in B.$$

This proves that $\lim_S \sum p_k(r)c_k = C$.

THEOREM 10-4.2. Suppose $\{p_k\}$ is a sequence of functions for which there is a system of stages S such that $\lim_S p_k(r) = 1$ for each k. Also suppose there is a stage A such that, if $r \in A$, then $p_k(r) \geqq 0$ for each k, the sequence $\{p_k(r)\}$ is monotone decreasing and convex, and $\lim_{n \to +\infty} [p_n(r) \cdot (\ln n)] = 0$. If f satisfies the hypothesis of Fejér's theorem, and $\{a_k\}$ and $\{b_k\}$ are the Fourier coefficients of f, then

$$F(x) = \lim_S \left[\frac{1}{2}a_0 p_1(r) + \sum_{k=1}^{+\infty} p_{k+1}(r)(a_k \cos kx + b_k \sin kx) \right], \qquad (10\text{-}65)$$

where

$$F(x) = \lim_{h \to 0+} \frac{f_*(x+h) - f_*(x-h)}{2}. \tag{10-66}$$

If f_* is continuous at all points of a closed interval $[a, b]$, then the bracketed expression in (10-65) converges uniformly to f_* on $[a, b]$.

PROOF. Equality (10-65) follows directly from Fejér's theorem and the preceding lemma, provided we show that there are numbers M and K such that $|s_n(x)| < M \cdot \ln n$ for all $n > K$, where s_n is the nth partial sum of the Fourier series of f. To do this, we use Eq. (10-53). Because of (10-66), there is a positive number $\delta < \frac{1}{2}\pi$ and a positive number E for which

$$\left| \frac{f_*(x+2t) + f_*(x-2t)}{2} \right| < E \text{ if } 0 < t \leq \delta. \tag{10-67}$$

Also, $|[\sin(2n-1)t]/(\sin t)| < 2n-1$ if $0 < t \leq \pi/(2n-1)$. We suppose n is large enough that $\pi/(2n-1) < \delta$. Then from (10-53) we obtain

$$|s_n(x)| \leq 2E + \frac{2E}{\pi} \int_{\pi/(2n-1)}^{\delta} \left| \frac{\sin(2n-1)t}{\sin t} \right| dt$$

$$+ \frac{1}{\pi \sin \delta} \int_{\delta}^{1/2 \pi} |f_*(x+2t) + f_*(x-2t)| \, dt.$$

Since $\sin t > \frac{1}{2}t$ if $0 < t < \frac{1}{2}\pi$, the first integral is increased if the integrand is replaced by $2/t$. The second integral is less than $\int_{-\pi}^{\pi} |f(t)| \, dt$. Therefore,

$$|s_n(x)| \leq 2E + \frac{4E}{\pi} \left[\ln\left(n - \frac{1}{2}\right) - \ln \frac{\pi}{2\delta} \right] + \frac{1}{\pi \sin \delta} \int_{-\pi}^{\pi} |f(t)| \, dt.$$

We can choose M large enough that the right side of this inequality is less than $M \cdot \ln n$ for all $n > 1$.

If f_* is continuous at each point of $[a, b]$, then from Fejér's theorem we know that $\sigma_n(x)$ converges uniformly to $f_*(x)$ on $[a, b]$. To adapt the lemma, we first observe that, after stating inequality (10-64) for our present situation, we could choose N so that

$$|C - \sigma_n(x)| < \tfrac{1}{2}\varepsilon \text{ if } x \in [a, b] \text{ and } n \geq N.$$

Then the second term of the last member of (10-64) is less than $\frac{1}{2}\varepsilon N[p_N(r) - p_{N+1}(r)] + \frac{1}{2}\varepsilon$ if $n \geq N$ and $x \in [a, b]$. Since we have

$\lim_S p_k(r) = 1$, there is a stage $B \subset A$ such that the last member of (10-64) is less than ε. Then

$$\left| C - \left[\tfrac{1}{2}a_0 p_1(r) + \sum_{k=1}^{+\infty} p_{k+1}(r)(a_k \cos kx + b_k \sin kx) \right] \right| < \varepsilon \quad \text{if } r \in B.$$

We shall now investigate ordinary point-wise convergence of a Fourier series. The results are not nearly as satisfactory as Fejér's theorem and Theorem 10-4.2, but we shall obtain several sufficient conditions for convergence. The next theorem is a *localization theorem*. It has the amazing implication that, except for integrability of f and $|f|$, the convergence of a Fourier series at a particular point x depends only on the nature of f in "arbitrarily small" neighborhoods of x.

THEOREM 10-4.3. Suppose f and $|f|$ are integrable on $[-\pi, \pi]$. Let f_* be the periodic extension of f for which $f_*(x + 2k\pi) = f(x)$ if $x \in [-\pi, \pi)$ and k is an integer. Then the Fourier series of f converges at a point x if and only if there is a positive number δ for which the following limit exists:

$$\lim_{n \to +\infty} \frac{2}{\pi} \int_0^\delta \frac{f_*(x + 2t) + f_*(x - 2t)}{2} \frac{\sin (2n-1)t \, dt}{t}. \tag{10-68}$$

If this limit exists, its value is the sum of the Fourier series.

PROOF. For a positive number $\eta < \tfrac{1}{2}\pi$, it follows from the Riemann-Lebesgue lemma [Theorem 10-3.7] that

$$\lim_{n \to +\infty} \int_\eta^{\frac{1}{2}\pi} \frac{f_*(x + 2t) + f_*(x - 2t)}{2} \frac{\sin (2n-1)t}{\sin t} \, dt = 0.$$

This and Eq. (10-53) imply that

$$\lim_{n \to +\infty} s_n(x) = \lim_{n \to +\infty} \frac{2}{\pi} \int_0^\eta \frac{f_*(x + 2t) + f_*(x - 2t)}{2} \frac{\sin (2n-1)t}{\sin t} \, dt, \tag{10-69}$$

where one limit exists if and only if the other exists. Since

$$\lim_{t \to 0} \left(\frac{1}{\sin t} - \frac{1}{t} \right) = \lim_{t \to 0} \frac{t - \sin t}{t \sin t} = 0,$$

it follows from the Riemann-Lebesgue lemma that we can replace $\sin t$ by t in (10-69). After doing this, it follows from the Riemann-Lebesgue lemma that we can replace η by an unrestricted positive number δ.

In order to state one of our sufficient conditions for convergence of a Fourier series, we need the next definition.

DEFINITION 10-4.2.   The *total variation* of a function f on an interval $[a, b]$ is the number

$$\sup \left\{ \sum_{i=1}^{n} |f(x_{i+1}) - f(x_i)| : \{x_1, \cdots, x_{n+1}\} \text{ is a partition of } [a, b] \right\}.$$

A *function of bounded variation* on an interval $[a, b]$ is a function f whose total variation on $[a, b]$ is not $+\infty$.

If f is monotone on $[a, b]$, then the total variation of f on $[a, b]$ is $|f(b) - f(a)|$. The crucial fact we shall need about functions of bounded variation is that a function of bounded variation is the difference of two monotone increasing functions. Specifically, suppose f is of bounded variation on $[a, b]$ and let p and q be defined on $[a, b]$ by

$$p(x) = \tfrac{1}{2} V_f(a, x) + \tfrac{1}{2} f(x), \qquad q(x) = \tfrac{1}{2} V_f(a, x) - \tfrac{1}{2} f(x),$$

where $V_f(a, x)$ is the total variation of f on $[a, x]$. Clearly, $p(x) - q(x) = f(x)$. To show p and q are monotone increasing, we use the equalities

$$p(s) - p(r) = \tfrac{1}{2} V_f(r, s) + \tfrac{1}{2}[f(s) - f(r)],$$

$$q(s) - q(r) = \tfrac{1}{2} V_f(r, s) - \tfrac{1}{2}[f(s) - f(r)], \quad a \leqq r < s \leqq b.$$

These follow from the equality $V_f(a, s) = V_f(a, r) + V_f(r, s)$ [see problem 15]. Since $|f(s) - f(r)| \leqq V(r, s)$, we see that $p(s) \geqq p(r)$ and $q(s) \geqq q(r)$.

In the next theorem, conditions (a) and (b) are closely related, and conditions (c), (d), and (e) are closely related. However, these two groups of conditions are essentially different. In fact, it is possible for a function to satisfy both (a) and (b) but none of (c), (d), or (e) [see problem 18]; and it is possible to satisfy all of (c), (d), and (e) but neither (a) nor (b) [see problem 16].

THEOREM 10-4.4.   Suppose f and $|f|$ are integrable on $[-\pi, \pi]$. Let f_* be the periodic extension of f for which $f_*(x + 2k\pi) = f(x)$ if $x \in [-\pi, \pi)$ and k is an integer. If x is a number for which at least one of the following conditions is satisfied, then the Fourier series of f is convergent at x, both the right and left limits of f_* at x exist, and the sum of the Fourier series is $\tfrac{1}{2}[f_*(x+) + f_*(x-)]$.

(a) There is a neighborhood W of x such that f is bounded on W and f is monotone on each of the sets $W \cap (x, +\infty)$ and $W \cap (-\infty, x)$.

(b) (*Jordan*) There is a neighborhood of x on which f_* is of bounded variation.

(c) (*Dini*) Both of the limits $f_*(x+)$ and $f_*(x-)$ exist and there is a positive number δ such that the following function is integrable on $[-\delta, \delta]$:

$$\left| \frac{f_*(x+2t)-f_*(x+)}{t} + \frac{f_*(x-2t)-f_*(x-)}{t} \right|.$$

(d) Both of the limits $f_*(x+)$ and $f_*(x-)$ exist and there are positive numbers δ and M such that, if $0 < t \leq \delta$, then

$$|f_*(x+2t)-f_*(x+)| < Mt \quad \text{and} \quad |f_*(x-2t)-f_*(x-)| < Mt.$$

(e) f_* is differentiable on the right and on the left at x.

PROOF. From Illustration 3 of Section 6-3, $\int_0^{+\infty} (\sin t)/t \, dt = \frac{1}{2}\pi$. Therefore, for any positive number δ,

$$\lim_{n \to +\infty} \frac{2}{\pi} \int_0^{\delta} \frac{\sin (2n-1)t}{t} \, dt = \lim_{n \to +\infty} \frac{2}{\pi} \int_0^{(2n-1)\delta} \frac{\sin t}{t} \, dt = 1. \quad (10\text{-}70)$$

Suppose the right and left limits of f_* exist at x. Then we subtract from expression (10-68) the product of $\frac{1}{2}[f_*(x+)+f_*(x-)]$ and the first member of (10-70). This shows that it follows from Theorem 10-4.3 that the sum of the Fourier series is $\frac{1}{2}[f_*(x+)+f_*(x-)]$ if and only if there is a positive number δ for which

$$\lim_{n \to +\infty} \int_0^{\delta} \left[\frac{f_*(x+2t)-f_*(x+)}{t} + \frac{f_*(x-2t)-f_*(x-)}{t} \right] \sin (2n-1)t \, dt = 0.$$

$$(10\text{-}71)$$

Thus, we must prove that if any one of (a) through (e) is satisfied at x, then the left and right limits of f_* exist at x and Eq. (10-71) is valid for some positive number δ.

Suppose first that (a) is satisfied at x. Then there is a positive number δ such that f_* is bounded on $[x-\delta, x+\delta]$ and f_* is monotone on $[x-\delta, x)$ and on $(x, x+\delta]$. This implies that both $f_*(x+)$ and $f_*(x-)$ exist. To establish (10-71), we first choose an arbitrary positive number ε and then choose a positive number η such that $\eta < \delta$ and

$$|f_*(x+2\eta)-f_*(x+)| < \frac{\varepsilon}{3\pi}.$$

Now we study the equality

$$\int_0^\delta \frac{f_*(x+2t)-f_*(x+)}{t} \sin(2n-1)t \, dt = A(n)+B(n)+C(n),$$

where

$$A(n) = \int_0^\eta \frac{f_*(x+2t)-f_*(x+2\eta)}{t} \sin(2n-1)t \, dt,$$

$$B(n) = [f_*(x+2\eta)-f_*(x+)] \int_0^\eta \frac{\sin(2n-1)t}{t} \, dt,$$

and

$$C(n) = \int_\eta^\delta \frac{f_*(x+2t)-f_*(x+)}{t} \sin(2n-1)t \, dt.$$

Since $[f_*(x+2t)-f_*(x+2\eta)]/t$ does not change sign and its absolute value is monotone decreasing for $0 < t \leq \eta$, we have, when $\pi/(2n-1) < \eta$,

$$|A(n)| \leq \int_0^{\pi/(2n-1)} \left| \frac{f_*(x+2t)-f_*(x+2\eta)}{t} \right| \sin(2n-1)t \, dt$$

$$< \frac{\varepsilon}{3\pi} \int_0^{\pi/(2n-1)} \frac{\sin(2n-1)t}{t} \, dt < \frac{\varepsilon}{3}.$$

Similarly,

$$|B(n)| < \frac{\varepsilon}{3\pi} \int_0^{\pi/(2n-1)} \frac{\sin(2n-1)t}{t} \, dt < \frac{\varepsilon}{3}.$$

From the Riemann-Lebesgue lemma, there is an N such that $|C(n)| < \frac{1}{3}\varepsilon$ if $n > N$. Thus, for any positive number ε, there is an N such that

$$\left| \int_0^\delta \frac{f_*(x+2t)-f_*(x+)}{t} \sin(2n-1)t \, dt \right| < \varepsilon \quad \text{if} \quad n > N.$$

Since $\int_0^\delta \{[f_*(x-2t)-f_*(x-)]/t\} \sin(2n-1)t \, dt$ can be treated similarly, we see that (10-71) is satisfied.

If f satisfies condition (b), then $f = p - q$, where p and q are monotone on a neighborhood of x. Thus, no additional proof is needed for case (b). Since (e) implies (d) implies (c), we can complete the proof of the theorem by considering case (c). This case involves only a direct application of the Riemann-Lebesgue lemma since, if (c) is satisfied for x, then there is a positive number δ for which the bracketed expression in Eq. (10-71) is absolutely integrable.

ILLUSTRATION. Let f be defined by $f(x) = 0$ if $-\pi \leq x < 0$ and $f(x) = 1$ if $0 \leq x \leq \pi$. Then the Fourier series of f on $[-\pi, \pi]$ is

$$\frac{1}{2} + \frac{2}{\pi} \left(\frac{\sin x}{1} + \frac{\sin 3x}{3} + \frac{\sin 5x}{5} + \cdots \right).$$

Since $\frac{1}{2}[f(0+) + f(0-)] = \frac{1}{2}$, the sum of the series is $\frac{1}{2}$ when $x = 0$. Similarly, $\frac{1}{2}[f_*(\pi+) + f_*(\pi-)] = \frac{1}{2}$ and the sum is $\frac{1}{2}$ when $x = \pi$. Since $\frac{1}{2}[f(\frac{1}{2}\pi+) + f(\frac{1}{2}\pi-)] = f(\frac{1}{2}\pi) = 1$, we have

$$1 = \frac{1}{2} + \frac{2}{\pi} \left(\frac{1}{1} - \frac{1}{3} + \frac{1}{5} - \frac{1}{7} + \cdots \right) \quad \text{or} \quad \frac{\pi}{4} = \frac{1}{1} - \frac{1}{3} + \frac{1}{5} - \frac{1}{7} + \cdots.$$

We saw that the Fourier series of a continuous function is uniformly Cesàro summable if $f(-\pi) = f(\pi)$ [Theorem 10-4.1]. To show that this theorem fails badly for ordinary convergence, we prove the next theorem. This theorem gives the existence of many continuous functions whose Fourier series diverge on a preassigned countable set, e.g., the set of rational numbers. In fact, such a continuous function can be chosen so that the reason the Fourier series diverges at a rational point is that the partial sums are not bounded. This is the next theorem.

THEOREM 10-4.5. Suppose $\{r_1, r_2, \cdots\}$ is a sequence of numbers in the interval $[-\pi, \pi]$. Then there exists a continuous function f such that $f(-\pi) = f(\pi)$ and, for each r_k and any positive numbers M and N, there exists an $n > N$ such that $s_n(r_k) > M$.

PROOF. From the equality of $\sum_1^n \sin(2k-1)x$ and $(\sin^2 nx)/(\sin x)$ [see problem 10, page 223], we obtain

$$\int_0^{\frac{1}{2}\pi} \frac{\sin^2 (2n-1)t}{\sin t} \, dt = 1 + \frac{1}{3} + \frac{1}{5} + \cdots + \frac{1}{4n-3}$$

$$> \frac{1}{2} \int_1^{4n-1} \frac{1}{t} \, dt = \frac{1}{2} \ln (4n-1).$$

If f has period 2π and $f(x) = \sin(n-\frac{1}{2})|x-r|$ when $x \in [r-\pi, r+\pi)$, then from (10-53) and the preceding inequality we have

$$s_n(r) = \frac{2}{\pi} \int_0^{\frac{1}{2}\pi} \frac{\sin^2 (2n-1)t}{\sin t} \, dt > \frac{1}{\pi} \ln (4n-1). \tag{10-72}$$

Now we choose a sequence $\{\rho_n\}$ such that each r_k occurs infinitely often as a member of this sequence. For example, we might let

$$\{\rho_n\} = \{r_1; r_1, r_2; r_1, r_2, r_3; \cdots; r_1, r_2, \cdots, r_n; r_1, \cdots\}.$$

Then we use induction to choose a sequence of integers $\{p_n\}$ and a sequence of continuous functions $\{f_n\}$ such that:

(i) $|f_n(x)| \leqq 2^{-n}$ for all n and all x,

(ii) $f_n(-\pi) = f_n(\pi)$ for all n,

(iii) $s_{p_n}(\rho_n) \geqq n$, where s_{p_n} is the p_nth partial sum of the Fourier series for $\sum_1^{+\infty} f_n$.

If we satisfy (i) and (ii), then it follows from the Weierstrass test for uniform convergence [page 215] that $\sum_1^{+\infty} f_n$ converges uniformly to a continuous function f for which $f(-\pi) = f(\pi)$. Since each r_k occurs infinitely often in $\{\rho_n\}$, it will follow from (iii) that, for any r_k and any numbers M and N, there exists an $n > N$ such that $s_n(r_k) > M$.

To choose $\{p_n\}$ and $\{f_n\}$, we first define f_1 as periodic with period 2π and with

$$f_1(x) = \mu_1 \sin (p_1 - \tfrac{1}{2})|x - \rho_1| \quad \text{when } x \in [\rho_1 - \pi, \rho_1 + \pi),$$

where $\mu_1 = \tfrac{1}{2}$ and (10-72) is used to choose p_1 large enough that

$$\frac{2}{\pi} \int_0^{\frac{1}{2}\pi} f_1(\rho_1 + 2t) \frac{\sin (2p_1 - 1)t}{\sin t} \, dt > 1. \tag{10-73}$$

Then we choose μ_2 and p_2 and define f_2 as periodic with period 2π and with

$$f_2(x) = \mu_2 \sin (p_2 - \tfrac{1}{2})|x - \rho_2| \quad \text{when } x \in [\rho_2 - \pi, \rho_2 + \pi).$$

We first choose μ_2 less than $\tfrac{1}{4}$ and small enough that (10-73) is satisfied with f_1 replaced by $f_1 + f_2$, whatever the choice of p_2. Then we choose p_2 large enough that

$$\frac{2}{\pi} \int_0^{\frac{1}{2}\pi} [f_1(\rho_2 + 2t) + f_2(\rho_2 + 2t)] \frac{\sin (2p_2 - 1)t}{\sin t} \, dt > 2. \tag{10-74}$$

This can be done by using the convergence of the Fourier series of f_1 at ρ_2 and inequality (10-72), since we can choose p_2 large enough that the contribution of f_1 in (10-74) is nearly $f_1(\rho_2)$ and the contribution of f_2 is as large as needed. We choose μ_3 and p_3 and define f_3 as periodic with period 2π and with

$$f_3(x) = \mu_3 \sin (p_3 - \tfrac{1}{2})|x - \rho_3| \quad \text{when } x \in [\rho_3 - \pi, \rho_3 + \pi).$$

We first choose μ_3 less than $\frac{1}{8}$ and small enough that (10-73) and (10-74) are satisfied with f_1 and f_1+f_2 replaced by $f_1+f_2+f_3$, whatever the choice of p_3. Then we use (10-72) to choose p_3 large enough that

$$\frac{2}{\pi} \int_0^{\frac{1}{2}\pi} [f_1(\rho_3+2t)+f_2(\rho_3+2t)+f_3(\rho_3+2t)] \frac{\sin (2p_3-1)t}{\sin t} \, dt > 3.$$

This process can be continued inductively, so that (i) through (iii) are satisfied.

PROBLEMS

1. Suppose f and g are defined by $f(x) = 0$ if $-\pi \leq x < 0$, $f(x) = 1$ if $0 \leq x \leq \pi$, $g(x) = 0$ if $-\pi \leq x < 0$, and $g(x) = x$ if $0 \leq x \leq \pi$. Then the Fourier series of f and g on $[-\pi, \pi]$ are

$$f \leftrightarrow \frac{1}{2} + \frac{2}{\pi} \sum_{n=1}^{+\infty} \frac{\sin (2n-1)x}{2n-1},$$

$$g \leftrightarrow \frac{\pi}{4} - \frac{2}{\pi} \sum_{n=1}^{+\infty} \frac{\cos (2n-1)x}{(2n-1)^2} + \sum_{n=1}^{+\infty} (-1)^{n-1} \frac{\sin nx}{n}.$$

In each case, find the Fourier series of the given function on $[-\pi, \pi]$. Do this by using the series for f and g, series derived from these series, and term-by-term integration when needed and valid.

(**a**) $f(x) = +1$, all x. (**e**) $f(x) = x^2$, all x.

(**b**) $f(x) = -1$, $-\pi \leq x \leq 0$, (**f**) $f(x) = x^3 - \pi^2 x$, all x.
$ f(x) = 1$, $0 < x \leq \pi$.

(**c**) $f(x) = x$, all x. (**g**) $f(x) = x^4 - 2\pi^2 x^2$, all x.

(**d**) $f(x) = 3x - 5$, all x. (**h**) $f(x) = x^4$, all x.

2. In each case, use Theorem 10-4.4 and the answers to problem 1 to prove the given equality.

(a) $\dfrac{3\pi\sqrt{2}}{8} = \dfrac{1}{1}+\dfrac{\sqrt{2}}{2}+\dfrac{1}{3}-\dfrac{1}{5}-\dfrac{\sqrt{2}}{6}-\dfrac{1}{7}+\dfrac{1}{9}+\dfrac{\sqrt{2}}{10}+\dfrac{1}{11}-\cdots.$

(b) $\dfrac{1}{4}\pi\sqrt{2} = \dfrac{1}{1}+\dfrac{1}{3}-\dfrac{1}{5}-\dfrac{1}{7}+\dfrac{1}{9}+\dfrac{1}{11}-\dfrac{1}{13}-\dfrac{1}{15}+\cdots.$

(c) $\dfrac{7\pi^4}{720} = \dfrac{1}{1^4}-\dfrac{1}{2^4}+\dfrac{1}{3^4}-\dfrac{1}{4^4}+\dfrac{1}{5^4}-\dfrac{1}{6^4}+\dfrac{1}{7^4}-\cdots.$

3. Prove that the Fourier series of e^x on $[-\pi, \pi]$ is

$$\frac{2 \sinh \pi}{\pi} \left[\frac{1}{2} + \sum_{n=1}^{+\infty} \frac{(-1)^n}{1+n^2} (\cos nx - n \sin nx) \right].$$

4. Use Theorem 10-4.4 and problem 3 and prove that

$$\frac{1}{2} - \frac{\pi}{2 \sinh \pi} = \frac{1}{1+1^2} - \frac{1}{1+2^2} + \frac{1}{1+3^2} - \cdots,$$

$$\frac{\pi}{2 \tanh \pi} = \frac{1}{2} + \frac{1}{1+1^2} + \frac{1}{1+2^2} + \frac{1}{1+3^2} + \cdots.$$

5. Suppose $\frac{1}{2}a_0 + \sum_1^{+\infty} (a_n \cos nx + b_n \sin nx)$ is the Fourier series for f on $[-\pi, \pi]$. Show that if k is an integer and we use the convention that $b_{-n} = -b_n$, then

(a) the Fourier series on $[-\pi, \pi]$ of $f(x) \cos kx$ is

$$\frac{1}{2}a_k + \sum_{n=1}^{+\infty} [\frac{1}{2}(a_{n+k} + a_{|n-k|}) \cos nx + \frac{1}{2}(b_{n+k} + b_{n-k}) \sin nx];$$

(b) the Fourier series on $[-\pi, \pi]$ of $f(x) \sin kx$ is

$$\frac{1}{2}b_k + \sum_{n=1}^{+\infty} [\frac{1}{2}(b_{n+k} - b_{n-k}) \cos nx + \frac{1}{2}(a_{|n-k|} - a_{n+k}) \sin nx];$$

(c) the Fourier series on $[-\pi, \pi]$ of $f_*(\pi - x)$ is

$$\frac{1}{2}a_0 + \sum_{n=1}^{+\infty} (-1)^n [a_n \cos nx - b_n \sin nx].$$

6. Use the method of problem 5 and the results of other problems to show that, on $[-\pi, \pi]$,

$$x \cos x \longleftrightarrow -\frac{1}{2} \sin x + 2 \sum_{n=2}^{+\infty} (-1)^n \frac{n}{n^2 - 1} \sin nx,$$

$$x^2 \sin x \longleftrightarrow \left(\frac{\pi^2}{3} - \frac{1}{2}\right) \sin x - 8 \sum_{n=2}^{+\infty} (-1)^n \frac{n}{(n^2 - 1)^2} \sin nx.$$

7. (a) Prove that $\ln |2 \sin \frac{1}{2}x| = -\sum_1^{+\infty} n^{-1} \cos nx$ if $x \neq 2k\pi$. [*Hint:* For $n > 0$, use problem 9, page 222, to aid in evaluating a_n after an integration by parts. Then use Illustration 1 of Section 4-3.]

(b) Prove that

$$\ln |2 \cos \frac{1}{2}x| = \sum_1^{+\infty} (-1)^{n-1} n^{-1} \cos nx \quad \text{if} \quad x \neq (2k+1)\pi.$$

8. Prove that if $|x| \leq \pi$ and θ is not an integer, then

$$\cos \theta x = \frac{2\theta \sin \pi\theta}{\pi} \left[\frac{1}{2\theta^2} + \sum_{n=1}^{+\infty} (-1)^n \frac{\cos nx}{\theta^2 - n^2}\right].$$

9. Use problem 8 and prove each of the following in succession.

(a) $\operatorname{ctn} \pi\theta - \dfrac{1}{\pi\theta} = \dfrac{1}{\pi} \left[\displaystyle\sum_{n=1}^{+\infty} \dfrac{-2\theta}{n^2 - \theta^2} \right].$

(b) $\ln \left(\dfrac{\sin \pi \theta x}{\pi x} \right) = \displaystyle\sum_{n=1}^{+\infty} \ln \left(1 - \dfrac{x^2}{n^2} \right).$

(c) $\dfrac{\sin \pi x}{\pi x} = \displaystyle\lim_{n \to +\infty} \left[\left(1 - \dfrac{x^2}{1^2} \right) \left(1 - \dfrac{x^2}{2^2} \right) \left(1 - \dfrac{x^2}{3^2} \right) \cdots \left(1 - \dfrac{x^2}{n^2} \right) \right].$

(d) $\dfrac{\pi}{2} = \displaystyle\lim_{n \to +\infty} \left[\dfrac{2^2 \cdot 4^2 \cdot 6^2 \cdot 8^2 \cdots (2n)^2}{1^2 \cdot 3^2 \cdot 5^2 \cdots (2n-1)^2 (2n+1)} \right].$

10. Prove each of the following:

(a) $\displaystyle\int_0^{1/2 \pi} \dfrac{\cos 2kt \sin^2 nt}{\sin^2 t} \, dt = \dfrac{n\pi}{2}$ if $n \geqq k.$

(b) $\displaystyle\int_0^{1/2 \pi} \dfrac{\sin 2kt \sin^2 nt}{\sin^2 t} \, dt = 0$ if $n \geqq k.$

11. Suppose $\{p_k\}$ is a sequence of functions for which there is a system of stages S such that $\lim_S p_k(r) = 1$ for each k. Also, suppose there is a stage A such that, if $r \in A$, then $p_k(r) \geqq 0$, the sequence $\{p_k(r)\}$ is monotone decreasing, and $\lim_{n \to +\infty} p_n(r) = 0$. Prove that, if $\sum c_n$ is convergent, then

$$\lim_S \left[\sum_{n=1}^{+\infty} p_n(r)c_n \right] = \sum_{n=1}^{+\infty} c_n.$$

12. Suppose $f''(x) \geqq 0$ if $x > 0$. Prove that the sequence $\{f(k): k = 1, 2, \cdots\}$ is convex.

13. Prove that $\lim_{x \to a+} f(x)$ exists if f is of bounded variation on $[a, b]$.

14. Prove that f is of bounded variation on $[a, b]$ if the domain of f' contains $[a, b]$ and f' is bounded on $[a, b]$.

15. Suppose $a < b < c$ and f is of bounded variation on $[a, c]$. Prove that $V_f(a, c) = V_f(a, b) + V_f(b, c)$.

16. Give an example of a continuous function whose domain is the interval $[-\pi, \pi]$, which is differentiable at $x = 0$, and which is *not* of bounded variation in any neighborhood of 0.

17. Give an example of a continuous function whose domain is the interval $[0, \pi]$, which is of bounded variation on $[0, \pi]$, and which is *not* differentiable on the right at 0.

18. Let $f(0) = 0$ and $f(t) = 1/(\ln t)$ if $0 < t < 1$. Show that f is monotone and of bounded variation on $[0, \frac{1}{2}]$, but that $|f(t)/t|$ is not integrable on $[0, \delta]$ for any positive number δ.

10-5.   THE ONE-DIMENSIONAL WAVE EQUATION

The *one-dimensional wave equation* is the equation

$$\frac{\partial^2 u}{\partial t^2} = c^2 \frac{\partial^2 u}{\partial x^2}. \tag{10-75}$$

The two-dimensional and three-dimensional wave equations are obtained by replacing $\partial^2 u/\partial x^2$ by $\partial^2 u/\partial x^2 + \partial^2 u/\partial y^2$ and by $\partial^2 u/\partial x^2 + \partial^2 u/\partial y^2 + \partial^2 u/\partial z^2$, respectively. Such wave equations have applications in the study of many types of waves, such as sound waves, waves in elastic material, and electric and electromagnetic waves.

A solution of Eq. (10-75) has the property that the result of two differentiations with respect to x differs from the result of two differentiations with respect to t only in the factor c^2. This suggests that we let

$$u(x, t) = \Theta(x + ct) + \Phi(x - ct). \tag{10-76}$$

For such a function u, we have

$$\frac{\partial u}{\partial x} = \Theta'(x + ct) + \Phi'(x - ct), \qquad \frac{\partial u}{\partial t} = c \cdot \Theta'(x + ct) - c \cdot \Phi'(x - ct);$$

$$\frac{\partial^2 u}{\partial x^2} = \Theta''(x + ct) + \Phi''(x - ct), \qquad \frac{\partial^2 u}{\partial t^2} = c^2 \cdot \Theta''(x + ct) + c^2 \cdot \Phi''(x - ct),$$

from which it follows that u is a solution of Eq. (10-75) at all points (x, t) such that Θ is twice-differentiable at $x + ct$ and Φ is twice-differentiable at $x - ct$.

Now suppose $c > 0$ and that u is a function that satisfies Eq. (10-75) and has continuous second-order partial derivatives at all points (x, t) for which $\alpha < x < \beta$, $0 \leq t < (x - \alpha)/c$, and $0 \leq t < (\beta - x)/c$, where α can be $-\infty$ and β can be $+\infty$. We shall show there are functions Θ and Φ that satisfy (10-76) when $\alpha < x < \beta$, $0 \leq t < (x - \alpha)/c$, and $0 \leq t < (\beta - x)/c$. To do this, the substitutions $r = x + ct$ and $s = x - ct$ are useful. The conditions on x and t become the conditions $\alpha < s \leq r < \beta$. If we let v be the function defined by

$$v(r, s) = u\left(\frac{r + s}{2}, \frac{r - s}{2c}\right) = u(x, t),$$

then we can use the chain rule of partial differentiation to obtain

$$\frac{\partial u}{\partial t} = \frac{\partial v}{\partial r}\frac{\partial r}{\partial t} + \frac{\partial v}{\partial s}\frac{\partial s}{\partial t} = c\frac{\partial v}{\partial r} - c\frac{\partial v}{\partial s},$$

$$\frac{\partial^2 u}{\partial t^2} = \frac{\partial}{\partial r}\left(c\frac{\partial v}{\partial r} - c\frac{\partial v}{\partial s}\right)\frac{\partial r}{\partial t} + \frac{\partial}{\partial s}\left(c\frac{\partial v}{\partial r} - c\frac{\partial v}{\partial s}\right)\frac{\partial s}{\partial t}$$

$$= c^2\frac{\partial^2 v}{\partial r^2} - 2c^2\frac{\partial^2 v}{\partial r\,\partial s} + c^2\frac{\partial^2 v}{\partial s^2}.$$

Similarly,

$$\frac{\partial^2 u}{\partial x^2} = \frac{\partial^2 v}{\partial r^2} + 2\frac{\partial^2 v}{\partial r\,\partial s} + \frac{\partial^2 v}{\partial s^2}.$$

It follows from the last two equations that $\partial^2 u/\partial t^2 = c^2(\partial^2 u/\partial x^2)$ if and only if

$$\frac{\partial^2 v}{\partial r\,\partial s} = 0 \quad\text{or}\quad \frac{\partial}{\partial r}\left(\frac{\partial v}{\partial s}\right) = 0.$$

It follows from this equation that, for each value of s, $\partial v/\partial s$ has the same value for all r. That is, there is a function ϕ such that

$$\frac{\partial v}{\partial s} = \phi(s).$$

It then follows that there is a function Θ such that

$$v(r, s) = \Theta(r) + \Phi(s) \quad\text{or}\quad u(x, t) = \Theta(x + ct) + \Phi(x - ct),$$

where Φ is an antiderivative of ϕ.

A vibrating string gives one of the simplest applications of the preceding discussion. Suppose a vibrating string is constrained so that its ends either are fixed or move along vertical lines. Also suppose that, when the string is at rest along a horizontal line, the mass per unit length of the string is a constant ρ. We shall let $y(x, t)$ be the function whose graph for a particular value of t is the curve described by the string at time t. Also, we shall make the simplifying assumptions that all points of the string move along vertical lines, that the tensile forces are large enough that the mass of the segment PP^* can be neglected when deriving Eq. (10-78), and that the tensile forces are tangential.

If we can then show that y is a solution of the one-dimensional wave equation, then we might expect the motion to be described approximately by a solution of the one-dimensional wave equation, if the vibration is not too violent.   Suppose that ϕ and $\phi + \Delta\phi$ are the angles of inclination of the tangent lines at the end points of the segment PP^* of the string shown in Fig. 10-2, and that T and T^* are the magnitudes of the tensile forces at these points.   The horizontal component of the tensile force is constant, since there is no horizontal motion.   Therefore,

$$T \cos \phi = T^* \cos (\phi + \Delta\phi) = H, \qquad (10\text{-}77)$$

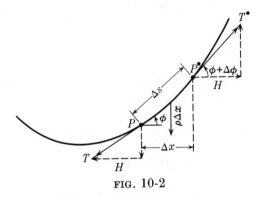

FIG. 10-2

where H is a function only of t.   The rest-length of the segment PP^* is Δx, so that from Newton's law, $F = ma$, we have

$$T^* \sin (\phi + \Delta\phi) - T \sin \phi = \rho \, \Delta x \, \frac{\partial^2 y}{\partial t^2}. \qquad (10\text{-}78)$$

Using (10-77) to eliminate T and T^*, we obtain

$$\frac{\partial^2 y}{\partial t^2} = \frac{H}{\rho} \frac{\tan (\phi + \Delta\phi) - \tan \phi}{\Delta x}.$$

Since $\tan \phi = \partial y / \partial x$, we can let $\Delta x \to 0$ and have

$$\frac{\partial^2 y}{\partial t^2} = c^2 \frac{\partial^2 y}{\partial x^2}, \quad \text{where} \quad c^2 = \frac{H}{\rho}. \qquad (10\text{-}79)$$

In applications, we shall assume that the vibrations are small enough that H is approximately constant.   Now suppose that an elastic string is stretched between the points a and b of Fig. 10-3.   At time $t = 0$, it is distorted so that the vertical displacement at a point x is equal to the value at x of some given function f. We shall let c^2 in Eq. (10-75) be H/ρ and Θ and Φ be the functions in Eq. (10-76). Then

$$u(x, 0) = \Theta(x) + \Phi(x) = f(x). \tag{10-80}$$

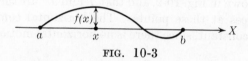

FIG. 10-3

At time $t = 0$, all points of the string are at rest. Since $\partial u/\partial t$, or $c\Theta'(x+ct) - c\Phi'(x-ct)$, is the velocity at time t, we have

$$u_2(x, 0) = c\Theta'(x) - c\Phi'(x) = 0 \quad \text{and} \quad \Theta'(x) - \Phi'(x) = 0.$$

Therefore, there is a number d such that, for all x, $\Theta(x) - \Phi(x) = d$. Since $\Theta(x) + \Phi(x) = f(x)$, we can solve for $\Theta(x)$ and $\Phi(x)$. This gives

$$\Theta(x) = \tfrac{1}{2}f(x) + \tfrac{1}{2}d, \qquad \Phi(x) = \tfrac{1}{2}f(x) - \tfrac{1}{2}d.$$

It follows from this and Eq. (10-76) that

$$u(x, t) = \tfrac{1}{2}[f(x+ct) + f(x-ct)]. \tag{10-81}$$

This gives the value of $u(x, t)$ for values of x and t such that

$$a \leqq x + ct \leqq b \quad \text{and} \quad a \leqq x - ct \leqq b.$$

The determination of other values of u and the application of Eq. (10-81) will be illustrated by an example.

ILLUSTRATION 1. At time $t = 0$, an elastic string is distorted so that it is in the position shown in Fig. 10-4. We shall assume that the density of the string, the tension, and the units of distance and time are such that the constant c in the wave equation is equal to 2. If $f(x)$ is the initial displacement at x, then Eq. (10-81) becomes

$$u(x, t) = \tfrac{1}{2}[f(x+2t) + f(x-2t)]. \tag{10-82}$$

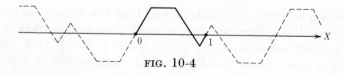

FIG. 10-4

When $x+2t > 1$, or $x-2t < 0$, this equation does not define a value
for u.   To overcome this difficulty, we shall extend the definition of f
as shown in Fig. 10-4, so that

$$f(2t)+f(-2t) = 0 \quad \text{and} \quad f(1+2t)+f(1-2t) = 0$$

for all t.   Then Eq. (10-82) gives a solution of the wave equation which
has the given value $f(x)$ when $t = 0$ and $0 \leq x \leq 1$, and has the
value zero at $x = 0$ and $x = 1$ for all values of t.   The terms $\frac{1}{2}f(x+2t)$
and $\frac{1}{2}f(x-2t)$ represent waves moving to the left and right, respectively,
at the rate of 2 units per unit of time.   These waves and their sum are
sketched in Fig. 10-5 at time $t = \frac{1}{8}$.

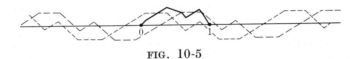

FIG. 10-5

We shall now study the use of Fourier series to obtain solutions
of Eq. (10-75).   The standard procedure is to find all solutions of type
XT, where X is a function only of x and T is a function only of t.
Then such solutions are combined to create other solutions.   If we
substitute XT for u in Eq. (10-75), we obtain

$$XT'' = c^2 X''T, \quad \text{or} \quad \frac{X''}{X} = \frac{1}{c^2}\frac{T''}{T}.$$

Since the first member of the last equality is a function of x alone, and
the second is a function of t alone, it is reasonable that each should be
constant.   Thus, we let

$$\frac{X''}{X} = -\kappa, \qquad \frac{T''}{T} = -\kappa c^2,$$

and obtain for XT:

$$(A \cos \sqrt{\kappa}\, x + B \sin \sqrt{\kappa}\, x)(C \cos \sqrt{\kappa}\, ct + D \sin \sqrt{\kappa}\, ct), \quad \text{if} \quad \kappa > 0;$$

$$(A^* \cosh \sqrt{-\kappa}\, x + B^* \sinh \sqrt{-\kappa}\, x)$$
$$\times (C^* \cosh \sqrt{-\kappa}\, ct + D^* \sinh \sqrt{-\kappa}\, ct), \quad \text{if} \quad \kappa < 0;$$

$$(A^{**} + B^{**}x)(C^{**} + D^{**}t), \quad \text{if} \quad \kappa = 0.$$

It is easy to check that each of these is a solution of the one-dimensional wave equation (10-75). Also, any linear combination of these solutions is a solution. Let us suppose we wish to find a particular solution for the case of a string with end points at 0 and ℓ. Then the condition $u(0, t) \equiv 0$ suggests we should take $A = A^* = A^{**} = 0$. Also, the condition $u(\ell, t) = 0$ suggests we should take $B^* = B^{**} = 0$ and let $\sqrt{\kappa}$ be $n\pi/\ell$, with n an integer. Then any finite sum of the following type is a solution of (10-75), with $u(0, t) = u(\ell, t) = 0$ for all t:

$$u(x, t) = \sum \sin \frac{n\pi x}{\ell} \left(C_n \cos \frac{n\pi ct}{\ell} + D_n \sin \frac{n\pi ct}{\ell} \right). \qquad (10\text{-}83)$$

If the initial position and initial velocity are described by functions f and g, so that $u(x, 0) \equiv f(x)$ and $u_2(x, 0) \equiv g(x)$, then we must have

$$f(x) = \sum C_n \sin \frac{n\pi x}{\ell}, \qquad g(x) = \sum \left(\frac{n\pi c D_n}{\ell} \right) \sin \frac{n\pi x}{\ell}. \qquad (10\text{-}84)$$

Usually these conditions cannot be satisfied by a finite sum. This suggests we might use (10-83) as an infinite series, with the coefficients $\{C_n\}$ and $\{D_n\}$ determined so that the series in (10-84) are the Fourier sine series for f and g on $[0, \ell]$. However, except in special circumstances, it is difficult to prove that this actually gives a solution of the one-dimensional wave equation. We shall describe two cases for which it is not difficult: (1) If there is a constant M such that $|C_n| \leq Mn^{-4}$ and $|D_n| \leq Mn^{-4}$ for all n, then the series in (10-83) converges uniformly after two differentiations with respect to either x or t. Then we can use term-by-term differentiation and show by substitution that (10-75) is satisfied. (2) We have shown that if Eq. (10-75) has a solution u whose second-order partial derivatives are continuous, then there are functions Θ and Φ as described in (10-76). Also, for the vibrating-string problem with $g = 0$, we then have Eq. (10-81):

$$u(x, t) = \tfrac{1}{2}[f(x+ct) + f(x-ct)].$$

If the initial position of the string is described by a function f whose Fourier sine series, $\sum C_n \sin n\pi x/\ell$, converges to $f(x)$ for all x, then

$$\tfrac{1}{2}[f(x+ct) + f(x-ct)] = \sum \tfrac{1}{2}C_n \left[\sin \left(\frac{n\pi x}{\ell} + \frac{n\pi ct}{\ell} \right) + \sin \left(\frac{n\pi x}{\ell} - \frac{n\pi ct}{\ell} \right) \right]$$

$$= \sum \sin \frac{n\pi x}{\ell} \left(C_n \cos \frac{n\pi ct}{\ell} \right).$$

Therefore, if $u_2(x, 0) \equiv 0$ and u satisfies (10-75) and has continuous second-order partial derivatives, then (10-83) is a valid formula for u.

ILLUSTRATION 2. Suppose the end points of a string are at 0 and π, and that the initial position and initial velocity are described by

$$f(x) = x(\pi - x) \quad \text{and} \quad g(x) = \sin x.$$

The Fourier sine series of f has been evaluated before [see problem 5, page 532]:

$$f(x) = \frac{8}{\pi} \sum_{n=1}^{+\infty} \frac{\sin (2n-1)x}{(2n-1)^3}$$

The Fourier sine series of g is merely $\sin x$. Therefore, Eq. (10-83) becomes

$$u(x, t) = \sin x \left(\frac{8}{\pi} \cos ct + \frac{1}{c} \sin ct \right) + \frac{8}{\pi} \sum_{n=2}^{+\infty} \frac{\sin (2n-1)x \cos (2n-1)ct}{(2n-1)^3}.$$

Then

$$\frac{\partial^2 u}{\partial x^2} = -\sin x \left(\frac{8}{\pi} \cos ct + \frac{1}{c} \sin ct \right) - \frac{8}{\pi} \sum_{n=2}^{+\infty} \frac{\sin (2n-1)x \cos (2n-1)ct}{2n-1}.$$

The series for $\partial^2 u / \partial t^2$ differs from this only in that each term is multiplied by c^2. Since

$$\sin (2n-1)x \cos (2n-1)ct = \tfrac{1}{2}[\sin (2n-1)(x+ct) + \sin (2n-1)(x-ct)],$$

both of these series converge uniformly on any compact set in the (x, t)-plane that does not contain any points for which $x+ct$ or $x-ct$ is a multiple of π [see problem 10, page 223]. Except at such points, u satisfies the one-dimensional wave equation.

PROBLEMS

1. A certain solution u of the particular wave equation,

$$\frac{\partial^2 u}{\partial t^2} = \frac{1}{4} \frac{\partial^2 u}{\partial x^2},$$

is such that $u(x, 0) = \sin x$ and $u_2(x, 0) = 0$ for $0 \leq x \leq 2\pi$, and $u(0, t) = u(2\pi, t) = 0$ for all t. Show that $u(x, t) = \sin x \cos \tfrac{1}{2}t$.

2. An elastic string is stretched between the points $x = 0$ and $x = 10$ on the x-axis. At time $t = 0$, the string is released from rest. At this

time, the string follows the x-axis from $x = 0$ to $x = 4$, a line of slope $+1$ from $x = 4$ to $x = 6$, the line $y = 2$ from $x = 6$ to $x = 8$, and a line of slope -1 from $x = 8$ to $x = 10$. Assume that the constant c in the wave equation is equal to unity and that the wave equation is applicable. Sketch the path of the string at times $t = 1$, $t = 2$, $t = 5$, and $t = 10$.

3. Suppose a function u has continuous second-order partial derivatives and satisfies the one-dimensional wave equation (10-75) at all points (x, t) for which $\alpha < x < \beta$, $0 \leq t < (x - \alpha)/c$, and $0 \leq t < (\beta - x)/c$. Also suppose that u satisfies the boundary conditions $u(x, 0) = f(x)$ and $u_2(x, 0) = g(x)$ for $\alpha \leq x \leq \beta$. For the functions Θ and Φ in Eq. (10-76), show that, if $\alpha < x < \beta$, $0 \leq t < (x - \alpha)/c$, and $0 \leq t < (\beta - x)/c$, then

(a) $\Theta(x) + \Phi(x) = f(x)$, $\quad \Theta'(x) - \Phi'(x) = \dfrac{1}{c} g(x)$;

(b) $u(x, t) = \dfrac{1}{2} [f(x + ct) + f(x - ct)] + \dfrac{1}{2c} \displaystyle\int_{x - ct}^{x + ct} g(s) \, ds.$

4. Suppose both u and v have continuous second-order partial derivatives and satisfy the one-dimensional wave equation (10-75) at all points (x, t) for which $\alpha < x < \beta$, $0 \leq t < (x - \alpha)/c$, and $0 \leq t < (\beta - x)/c$. Also suppose that

$$u(x, 0) = v(x, 0) \quad \text{and} \quad u_2(x, 0) = v_2(x, 0) \quad \text{if} \quad \alpha < x < \beta.$$

Prove that $u(x, t) = v(x, t)$ when $\alpha < x < \beta$, $0 \leq t < (x - \alpha)/c$, and $0 \leq t < (\beta - x)/c$.

5. In each case, determine the solution of the particular wave equation,

$$\frac{\partial^2 u}{\partial t^2} = \frac{9}{4} \frac{\partial^2 u}{\partial x^2},$$

that has the stated properties.

(a) $u(x, 0) = 2 \sin 2x$ and $u_2(x, 0) = 0$ for all x.

(b) $u(x, 0) = 0$ and $u_2(x, 0) = 3 \sin 2x$ for $0 \leq x \leq 2\pi$; $u(0, t) = u(2\pi, t) = 0$ for $t \geq 0$.

(c) $u(x, 0) = 4x^2 + 5x$ and $u_2(x, 0) = 12x$ for all x.

6. Find the solution of the wave equation $\partial^2 u/\partial t^2 = 9 \cdot \partial^2 u/\partial x^2$ for which $u(0, t) = u(2, t) = 0$ for $t \geq 0$, $u(x, 0) = x(2 - x)$ and $u_2(x, 0) = 0$ for $0 \leq x \leq 2$.

7. Find the solution of the wave equation $\partial^2 u/\partial t^2 = 25 \cdot \partial^2 u/\partial x^2$ for which $u(0, t) = u(\pi, t) = 0$ for all t, $u(x, 0) = x^2 - \pi x$ and $u_2(x, 0) = \sin x$ for $0 \leq x \leq \pi$.

8. Suppose u is defined by

$$u(x, t) = \sum c_n \sin \frac{n \pi x}{\ell} \cos \frac{n \pi c t}{\ell},$$

where the series converges for all x and t. Also, let $u(x, 0) = f(x)$, so that

$$f(x) = \sum c_n \sin \frac{n\pi x}{\ell} \quad \text{for all} \quad x.$$

Prove that $u(x, t) = \frac{1}{2}[f(x+ct)+f(x-ct)]$.

10-6. HEAT CONDUCTION

Experiments indicate that if a thin slab of solid material is homogeneous and the two faces are at temperatures u_1 and u_2, then the instantaneous rate H at which heat passes through a piece of the slab is given approximately by the formula

$$H = -kA \frac{\Delta u}{\Delta x}, \tag{10-85}$$

where A is the area of a face of the piece, $\Delta u = u_2 - u_1$, Δx is the thickness of the slab, and k is a number that does not depend on the size or temperature of the slab and is called the *thermal conductivity* of the material in the slab. If the slab is perpendicular to a line X, then Δx is the difference $x_2 - x_1$ of the value x_2 of x at which the temperature is u_2 and the value x_1 at which the temperature is u_1. As $\Delta x \to 0$, Eq. (10-85) becomes

$$H = -kA \frac{du}{dx}. \tag{10-86}$$

Let us suppose the rod in Fig. 10-6 is insulated except at the ends, and that the temperature at the ends are specified functions of time. Since the rod is insulated, the segment of the rod from a to s loses or gains heat only through the ends. Let $u(x, t)$ be the temperature of the rod at time t at the points of the section of the rod at distance x from the left end. Then the instantaneous rate of increase of heat in the segment $[a, s]$ is equal to

$$kA[u_1(s, t) - u_1(a, t)], \tag{10-87}$$

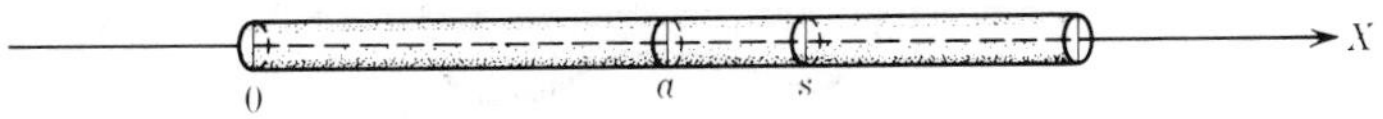

FIG. 10-6

where A is the area of a cross section of the rod. Now let us assume the rod is homogeneous and use the experimental result that the amount of heat which will produce a change from temperature τ to temperature τ' in a piece of the rod is proportional to $\tau' - \tau$ and to the mass of the piece. The constant of proportionality is the *specific heat* of the material. We shall let K denote this constant and $Q(s, t)$ denote the difference between the amount of heat in the segment $[a, s]$ at time t and the amount when the temperature is zero everywhere. Then for a segment of length Δx, there is a point for which the contribution to $Q(s, t)$ is equal to $K(\rho A \, \Delta x)u$, where u is the temperature at this point of the segment and ρ is the density. Therefore,

$$Q(s, t) = K\rho A \int_a^s u(x, t) \, dx. \tag{10-88}$$

By differentiating Eq. (10-88) with respect to t, we see that it follows from (10-87) and (10-88) that

$$K\rho A \int_a^s u_2(x, t) \, dx = kA[u_1(s, t) - u_1(a, t)].$$

Now if we let $c^2 = K\rho/k$ and differentiate each member of this equation with respect to s, we have $u_{11}(s, t) = c^2 u_2(s, t)$. This might also be written as

$$\frac{\partial^2 u}{\partial x^2} = c^2 \frac{\partial u}{\partial t}, \tag{10-89}$$

and is called the *one-dimensional heat equation*.

Now let us consider the flat plate shown in Fig. 10-7. We shall assume the plane sides of the plate are insulated. If the temperature at a point (x, y) at time t is denoted by $u(x, y, t)$, then the instantaneous

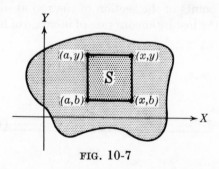

FIG. 10-7

rate at which heat enters the square S through the top edge is equal to $kh \int_a^x u_2(s, y, t) \, ds$, where k is the thermal conductivity and h is the thickness of the plate. With similar expressions for the other edges, the instantaneous rate at which the amount of heat in the square is changing is equal to

$$kh \int_b^y [u_1(x, s, t) - u_1(a, s, t)] \, ds$$

$$+ kh \int_a^x [u_2(s, y, t) - u_2(s, b, t)] \, ds. \quad (10\text{-}90)$$

For $Q(S, t)$ defined as the difference between the amount of heat in S at time t and the amount when the temperature is zero everywhere, (10-90) is equal to

$$\frac{dQ}{dt} = \frac{d}{dt} \int_S K\rho h u(x, y, t) \, dA = K\rho h \int_b^y \left[\int_a^x u_3(x, \dot{y}, t) \, dx \right] dy,$$

where K is the specific heat of the material in the plate. We equate this expression with (10-90) and differentiate with respect to y, and then with respect to x, to obtain

$$k[u_1(x, y, t) - u_1(a, y, t)] + k \int_a^x u_{22}(s, y, t) \, ds = K\rho \int_a^x u_3(x, y, t) \, dx,$$

and

$$ku_{11}(x, y, t) + ku_{22}(x, y, t) = K\rho u_3(x, y, t).$$

With $c^2 = K\rho/k$, we have

$$\frac{\partial^2 u}{\partial x^2} + \frac{\partial^2 u}{\partial y^2} = c^2 \frac{\partial u}{\partial t}. \quad (10\text{-}91)$$

This is the *two-dimensional heat equation*. If $\partial u/\partial t = 0$, then Eq. (10-91) becomes *Laplace's equation* for two dimensions.

To find solutions of the one-dimensional heat equation, we might first find all solutions of type XT, where X is a function only of x and T only of t. Substitution in Eq. (10-89) gives us

$$X''T = c^2 X T' \quad \text{or} \quad \frac{X''}{X} = c^2 \frac{T'}{T}.$$

Solving the equations $X'' = -\kappa X$ and $T' = -\kappa T/c^2$, we obtain for XT

$$(A \cos \sqrt{\kappa}\, x + B \sin \sqrt{\kappa}\, x)e^{-\kappa t/c^2} \quad \text{if} \quad \kappa > 0,$$

$$(A^* \cosh \sqrt{-\kappa}\, x + B^* \sinh \sqrt{-\kappa}\, x)e^{-\kappa t/c^2} \quad \text{if} \quad \kappa < 0,$$

$$A^{**} + B^{**}x \quad \text{if} \quad \kappa = 0.$$

For an insulated rod, we shall assume the ends are kept at a constant temperature. This implies the temperature of the rod is bounded as a function of time, and suggests we discard all solutions with $\kappa < 0$. With the ends of the rod placed at 0 and ℓ on the x-axis, we let $A = 0$ and $\sqrt{\kappa}$ be $n\pi/\ell$ for n an integer. Then the solutions of type

$$e^{-n^2\pi^2 t/(c^2\ell^2)} \sin \frac{n\pi x}{\ell}$$

are zero at both ends of the rod. The solution $A^{**} + B^{**}x$ can be used to give the correct temperature at the ends. That is, we shall investigate series of type

$$u(x, t) = \alpha + \beta x + \sum_{n=1}^{+\infty} b_n e^{-n^2\pi^2 t/(c^2\ell^2)} \sin \frac{n\pi x}{\ell}. \tag{10-92}$$

Suppose the temperature of the rod at time $t = 0$ is described by a function τ. Then we should have

$$\tau(x) = \alpha + \beta x + \sum_{n=1}^{+\infty} b_n \sin \frac{n\pi x}{\ell}. \tag{10-93}$$

We shall choose α and β so that $\alpha + \beta x$ gives the correct temperature at both 0 and ℓ when $t > 0$. Then the rest of the terms should be the Fourier sine series of $\tau(x) - (\alpha + \beta x)$ on $[0, \ell]$. If τ and $|\tau|$ are integrable on $[0, \ell]$, then it follows from the Riemann-Lebesgue lemma [Theorem 10-3.7] that the coefficients $\{b_n\}$ converge to zero and therefore are bounded. In this case, series (10-92) and all its term-by-term derivatives with respect to either x or t converge uniformly, provided a neighborhood of $t = 0$ is excluded. Thus, term-by-term differentiation is valid, except when $t = 0$. By formal substitution, we see that u of (10-92) is a solution of the one-dimensional heat equation, except possibly when $t = 0$. Moreover, for any positive numbers a and t, the sequence $\{e^{-n^2 at}\}$ is monotone decreasing and convex, and

$$\lim_{n \to +\infty} [e^{-n^2 at} \cdot \ln n] = 0.$$

Therefore, it follows from Theorem 10-4.2 that, as $t \to 0$, $u(x, t)$ converges uniformly to $\tau(x)$ on any closed interval on which τ is continuous. This behavior is much better than that of the solution (10-83) of the vibrating-string problem. In that case, discontinuities of f "traveled" back and forth along the string, being at points $k\ell \pm ct$ at time t. For the heat equation, there is an "averaging" effect. Even if the initial temperature distribution is discontinuous, the corresponding solution u is continuous at all points (x, t) with $t > 0$.

ILLUSTRATION 1. Suppose an insulated rod has the uniform temperature $\tau(x) = 50°$. Starting at $t = 0$, one end is kept at $50°$, but the other end is kept at $100°$. With the ends placed at 0 and ℓ on the x-axis, we should have $\alpha + \beta x$ in (10-92) equal to $50 + 50x/\ell$, so that $\alpha + \beta x$ is 50 when $x = 0$ and 100 when $x = \ell$. Then, when $t = 0$ the series $\sum b_n \sin n\pi x/\ell$ in (10-93) should be the Fourier sine series of the function $\tau(x) - (\alpha + \beta x)$, where

$$\tau(x) - (\alpha + \beta x) = -\frac{50x}{\ell} \quad \text{if} \quad 0 \leqq x < \ell, \quad \text{and} \quad \tau(\ell) - (\alpha + \beta \ell) = 0.$$

Thus,

$$b_n = \frac{2}{\ell} \int_0^\ell \left(-\frac{50x}{\ell} \right) \sin \frac{n\pi x}{\ell} \, dx$$

$$= \frac{100}{\ell^2} \left[\frac{x\ell}{n\pi} \cos \frac{n\pi x}{\ell} - \left(\frac{\ell}{n\pi} \right)^2 \sin \frac{n\pi x}{\ell} \right]_0^\ell = (-1)^n \frac{100}{n\pi}.$$

Substituting in (10-92), we obtain

$$u(x, t) = 50 + \frac{50x}{\ell} + \frac{100}{\pi} \sum_{n=1}^{+\infty} (-1)^n \frac{1}{n} e^{-n^2 \pi^2 t/(c^2 \ell^2)} \sin \frac{n\pi x}{\ell}.$$

As $t \to +\infty$, this approaches the "steady-state" solution: $50 + 50x/\ell$.

For the two-dimensional heat equation (10-91), we shall need solutions of type XYT, where X, Y, and T are functions of x, of y, and of t, respectively. Substitution in (10-91) gives

$$X''YT + XY''T = c^2 XYT', \quad \text{or} \quad \frac{X''}{X} + \frac{Y''}{Y} = c^2 \frac{T'}{T},$$

at points where XYT is nonzero. This suggests we let

$$X'' = -\lambda X, \quad Y'' = -\mu Y, \quad \text{and} \quad T' = -\frac{1}{c^2}(\lambda + \mu)T. \quad (10\text{-}94)$$

This gives a large number of possibilities for XYT. Rather than list these we shall consider a particular type of problem and how it might be solved.

ILLUSTRATION 2. Suppose the sides of the plate R shown in Fig. 10-8 are insulated. At time $t = 0$, the temperature distribution is described by a function τ that is continuous at the corners.† We also assume that the temperature at points (x, y) of the edges does not change with time, so it is given as $\tau(x, y)$ at all times. First, we determine the constants in the solution with $\lambda = \mu = 0$; namely,

$$\phi_1(x, y) = \alpha + \beta x + \gamma y + \delta xy.$$

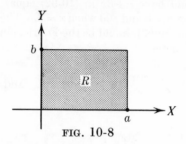

FIG. 10-8

These constants are determined so that ϕ_1 gives the temperature at all corners of R. Then we determine the constants in a sum of solutions with $\lambda + \mu = 0$,

$$\phi_2(x, y) = \sum (A_n e^{n\pi x/b} + B_n e^{-n\pi x/b}) \sin \frac{n\pi y}{b}$$

$$+ \sum (C_n e^{n\pi y/a} + D_n e^{-n\pi y/a}) \sin \frac{n\pi x}{a}, \quad (10\text{-}95)$$

so that on each edge of R this is the Fourier series of $\tau - \phi_1$. To do this, we use the equations

$$\tau(x, 0) - \phi_1(x, 0) = \sum (C_n + D_n) \sin \frac{n\pi x}{a}$$

and

$$\tau(x, b) - \phi_1(x, b) = \sum (C_n e^{n\pi b/a} + D_n e^{-n\pi b/a}) \sin \frac{n\pi x}{a}$$

---

† If τ is not continuous at a corner P, use the average of the two one-sided limits as P is approached along the boundary.

to determine $\{C_n\}$ and $\{D_n\}$. Then we determine $\{A_n\}$ and $\{B_n\}$ by using the equations

$$\tau(0, y) - \phi_1(0, y) = \sum (A_n + B_n) \sin \frac{n\pi y}{b}$$

and

$$\tau(a, y) - \phi_1(a, y) = \sum (A_n e^{n\pi a/b} + B_n e^{-n\pi a/b}) \sin \frac{n\pi y}{b}.$$

We have found the "steady-state" solution: $\phi_1 + \phi_2$. The solution u we are seeking is given by

$$u(x, y, t) = \phi_1(x, y) + \phi_2(x, y)$$
$$+ \sum_{m,n=1}^{+\infty} b_{m,n} \sin \frac{m\pi x}{a} \sin \frac{n\pi y}{b} \exp\left[-\frac{\pi^2}{c^2}\left(\frac{m^2}{a^2} + \frac{n^2}{b^2}\right)t\right] \quad (10\text{-}96)$$

To determine the numbers $\{b_{m,n}\}$, we let $t = 0$ and use the equation

$$\tau(x, y) - \phi_1(x, y) - \phi_2(x, y) = \sum_{m,n=1}^{+\infty} b_{m,n} \sin \frac{m\pi x}{a} \sin \frac{n\pi y}{b}.$$

The trigonometric identities on page 520 can be used to show that the set,

$$\left\{\frac{1}{\sqrt{ab}} \sin \frac{m\pi x}{a} \sin \frac{n\pi y}{b} : m \text{ and } n \text{ positive integers}\right\},$$

is orthonormal on the rectangle R of Fig. 10-8, with the scalar product of functions f and g defined as

$$\int_R f(x, y) g(x, y) \, dA.$$

This set is complete in the space L_R^2 of functions f for which f and $|f|^2$ are integrable on R, but we shall not prove this. From the theory of orthonormal sequences, we have

$$b_{m,n} = \frac{1}{ab} \int_R [f(x, y) - \phi_1(x, y) - \phi_2(x, y)] \sin \frac{m\pi x}{a} \sin \frac{n\pi y}{b} \, dA.$$

For a circular flat plate, it is best to write the two-dimensional heat equation using polar coordinates. It then becomes [see problem 11(b), page 301]

$$\frac{\partial^2 u}{\partial r^2} + \frac{1}{r}\frac{\partial u}{\partial r} + \frac{1}{r^2}\frac{\partial^2 u}{\partial \theta^2} = c^2 \frac{\partial u}{\partial t}.$$

For simplicity, we shall assume the temperature does not change with time, so that $\partial u/\partial t = 0$. Then the heat equation becomes Laplace's equation in polar coordinates:

$$\frac{\partial^2 u}{\partial r^2} + \frac{1}{r}\frac{\partial u}{\partial r} + \frac{1}{r^2}\frac{\partial^2 u}{\partial \theta^2} = 0. \tag{10-97}$$

We shall need solutions of type $R\Theta$, where R and Θ are functions of r and of θ, respectively. Substitution of $R\Theta$ into (10-97) gives us

$$R''\Theta + \frac{1}{r}R'\Theta + \frac{1}{r^2}R\Theta'' = 0.$$

Formal multiplication by $r^2/(R\Theta)$ changes this into

$$r^2\frac{R''}{R} + r\frac{R'}{R} + \frac{\Theta''}{\Theta} = 0.$$

The sum of the first two terms is independent of θ, and also equal to $-\Theta''/\Theta$, which is independent of r. Therefore, we introduce a constant κ and have

$$r^2 R'' + rR' - \kappa R = 0 \quad\text{and}\quad \Theta'' = -\kappa\Theta.$$

We want only solutions that are periodic with period 2π as functions of θ, so we take κ to be n^2 for n a nonnegative integer. The solutions of $r^2 R'' + rR' - \kappa R$ are of type

$$\alpha + \beta \ln r \quad\text{if}\quad \kappa = 0, \qquad Ar^n + Br^{-n} \quad\text{if}\quad \kappa = n^2.$$

Adding the possible values of $R\Theta$ gives us

$$u(r,\,\theta) = \alpha + \beta \ln r + \sum_{n=1}^{+\infty} (A_n r^n + B_n r^{-n})(a_n \cos n\theta + b_n \sin n\theta).$$

$$\tag{10-98}$$

Now suppose a circular plate has the sides insulated and that the unit of distance is chosen so that the radius is 1. Let the origin be placed at the center of the plate and the temperature at the point $(1,\,\theta)$ on the boundary be $\tau(\theta)$. Since the temperature is bounded, the terms in (10-98) that involve $\ln r$ and r^{-n} should be discarded. Then

$$u(r,\,\theta) = \alpha + \sum_{n=1}^{+\infty} r^n(a_n \cos n\theta + b_n \sin n\theta). \tag{10-99}$$

When $r = 1$, we have

$$\tau(\theta) = \alpha + \sum_{n=1}^{+\infty} (a_n \cos n\theta + b_n \sin n\theta).$$

If τ and $|\tau|$ are integrable on $[-\pi, \pi]$, then the coefficients $\{a_n\}$ and $\{b_n\}$ are bounded. In this case, the series (10-99) and all series obtained by term-by-term differentiation with respect to either r or θ converge uniformly on any set of type $\{(r, \theta): 0 \le r \le \mu\}$, where $0 < \mu < 1$. Formal substitution then shows that u as given by (10-99) satisfies Laplace's equation, except possibly when $r = 1$. Moreover, if $0 < r < 1$, then the sequence $\{r^n\}$ is monotone decreasing and convex, and

$$\lim_{n \to +\infty} [r^n \cdot \ln n] = 0.$$

Therefore, it follows from Theorem 10-4.2 that, as $r \to 1-$, $u(r, \theta)$ converges uniformly to $\tau(\theta)$ on any closed interval on which τ is continuous.

When $|\tau|$ is bounded, the solution $u(r, \theta)$ given by (10-99) can be written in "closed form." To show this, we first note that

$$u(r, \theta) = \frac{1}{2\pi} \int_{-\pi}^{\pi} \tau(s) \, ds + \sum_{n=1}^{+\infty} r^n \left\{ \left[\frac{1}{\pi} \int_{-\pi}^{\pi} \tau(s) \cos ns \, ds \right] \cos n\theta \right.$$

$$\left. + \left[\frac{1}{\pi} \int_{-\pi}^{\pi} \tau(s) \sin ns \, ds \right] \sin n\theta \right\}$$

$$= \frac{1}{2\pi} \int_{-\pi}^{\pi} \tau(s) \, ds + \frac{1}{\pi} \sum_{n=1}^{+\infty} r^n \int_{-\pi}^{\pi} \tau(s) \cos n(\theta - s) \, ds. \qquad (10\text{-}100)$$

For $r < 1$, uniform convergence in s of the series $\sum r^n \tau(s) \cos n(\theta - s)$ follows from boundedness of $|\tau|$. This justifies writing

$$u(r, \theta) = \frac{1}{\pi} \int_{-\pi}^{\pi} \tau(s) \left[\frac{1}{2} + \sum_{n=1}^{+\infty} r^n \cos n(\theta - s) \right] ds.$$

To collapse the series in the integrand, we use the identity

$$\frac{1}{2} + \sum_{n=1}^{+\infty} r^n e^{inx} = \frac{1}{2} + \sum_{n=1}^{+\infty} (re^{ix})^n = \frac{1}{2} + \frac{re^{ix}}{1 - re^{ix}} = \frac{1}{2} \left(\frac{1 + re^{ix}}{1 - re^{ix}} \right) \left(\frac{1 - re^{-ix}}{1 - re^{-ix}} \right)$$

$$= \frac{1}{2} \left(\frac{1 + 2ri \sin x - r^2}{1 - 2r \cos x + r^2} \right).$$

Equating real parts gives us

$$\frac{1}{2} + \sum_{n=1}^{+\infty} r^n \cos nx = \frac{1}{2}\left(\frac{1-r^2}{1-2r\cos x + r^2}\right).$$

Thus,

$$u(r,\,\theta) = \frac{1}{2\pi}\int_{-\pi}^{\pi} \tau(s)\left(\frac{1-r^2}{1-2r\cos(\theta-s)+r^2}\right) ds. \qquad (10\text{-}101)$$

This is *Poisson's integral*. We have noted already that, as $r \to 1-$, $u(r,\,\theta) \to \tau(\theta)$ uniformly on any closed interval on which τ is continuous. To obtain (10-101), we assumed that τ is bounded. It should be clear that the next theorem, for the case $|f|$ is bounded, follows from the preceding discussion.

DEFINITION 10-6.1. An *Abel summable series* is an infinite series $\sum a_n$ for which the following limit exists:

$$\lim_{r\to 1-} (ra_1 + r^2 a_2 + r^3 a_3 + \cdots + r^n a_n + \cdots).$$

If this limit exists, it is the *Abel sum* of the series.

THEOREM 10-6.1. Suppose f and $|f|$ are integrable on $[-\pi, \pi]$. Let f_* be the periodic extension of f for which $f_*(\theta + 2k\pi) = f(\theta)$ if $\theta \in [-\pi,\pi)$ and k is an integer, and let θ be a number for which the following limit exists:

$$F(\theta) = \lim_{h\to 0+} \frac{f_*(\theta+h)+f_*(\theta-h)}{2}. \qquad (10\text{-}102)$$

Then the Fourier series of f is Abel summable at θ, the Abel sum is $F(\theta)$, and

$$F(\theta) = \lim_{r\to 1-} \frac{1}{2\pi}\int_{-\pi}^{\pi} f(s)\left(\frac{1-r^2}{1-2r\cos(\theta-s)+r^2}\right) ds. \qquad (10\text{-}103)$$

If f_* is continuous at all points of a closed interval $[a, b]$, then the Fourier series of f is uniformly Abel summable on $[a, b]$ and the Poisson integral in (10-103) converges uniformly on $[a, b]$ to the limit $F(\theta)$ as $r \to 1-$.

PROOF. If $0 < r < 1$, the sequence $\{r^n\}$ is monotone decreasing and convex, $\lim_{r\to 1-} r^n = 1$ for each n, and $\lim_{n\to +\infty} [r^n \cdot \ln n] = 0$. Therefore, it follows from Theorem 10-4.2 that the Fourier series of f is Abel summable and has the Abel sum $F(\theta)$ for any θ such that the limit (10-102) exists. Also, if

$$u(r, \theta) = \tfrac{1}{2}a_0 + \sum_{n=1}^{+\infty} r^n(a_n \cos n\theta + b_n \sin n\theta),$$

where $\{a_n\}$ and $\{b_n\}$ are the Fourier coefficients of f, then $\lim_{r \to 1-} u(r, \theta)$ $= F(\theta)$, uniformly on any closed interval such that f_* is continuous at each point of the interval. It remains to show that $F(\theta)$ also is given by (10-103), uniformly on any closed interval $[a, b]$ such that f_* is continuous at each point of $[a, b]$. When deriving (10-101) from (10-100), we needed $|\tau|$ to be bounded so as to justify term-by-term integration of a certain infinite series. However, we can avoid this assumption as follows. If $a = b$ or if f_* is continuous at each point of $[a, b]$, there are positive numbers K and δ such that

$$|F(\theta)| \leqq K \quad \text{if} \quad \theta \in [a - \delta, b + \delta].$$

For a positive number ε, we then choose $k > K$ so that

$$\int_{-\pi}^{\pi} |f_*(s) - f_k(s)| \, ds < \pi\varepsilon(1 - \cos \delta)^2,$$

where $f_k(s) = f_*(s)$ if $|f_*(s)| \leqq k$, $f_k(s) = k$ if $f_*(s) > k$, and $f_k(s) = -k$ if $f_*(s) < -k$. Then $f_*(s) = f_k(s)$ if $s \in [a - \delta, b + \delta]$ and, from Eq. (10-101) with τ replaced by f_k, we conclude there is a positive number $\rho < 1$ such that

$$\left| F(\theta) - \frac{1}{2\pi} \int_{-\pi}^{\pi} f_k(s) \left[\frac{1 - r^2}{1 - 2r \cos (\theta - s) + r^2} \right] ds \right| < \frac{\varepsilon}{2} \quad \text{if} \quad \rho < r < 1$$

$$(10\text{-}104)$$

and $\theta \in [a, b]$. Since $f_*(s) = f_k(s)$ if s is in any translation of the interval $[a - \delta, b + \delta]$ by a multiple of 2π, and $\cos (\theta - s) < \cos \delta$ otherwise, we have

$$\left| \frac{1}{2\pi} \int_{-\pi}^{\pi} [f_*(s) - f_k(s)] \left[\frac{1 - r^2}{1 - 2r \cos (\theta - s) + r^2} \right] ds \right|$$

$$\leqq \frac{1}{2\pi} \frac{1 - r^2}{1 - 2r \cos \delta + r^2} \int_{-\pi}^{\pi} |f_*(s) - f_k(s)| \, ds$$

$$< \frac{\pi\varepsilon(1 - \cos \delta)^2}{2\pi[(1 - r \cos \delta)^2 + r^2 \sin^2 \delta]} < \frac{\varepsilon}{2},$$

if $\theta \in [a, b]$. If $\rho < r < 1$, this and (10-104) imply that

$$\left| F(\theta) - \frac{1}{2\pi} \int_{-\pi}^{\pi} f_*(s) \left[\frac{1 - r^2}{1 - 2r \cos (\theta - s) + r^2} \right] ds \right| < \varepsilon \quad \text{if} \quad \theta \in [a, b].$$

This proves that the limit in (10-103) is $F(\theta)$ if $F(\theta)$ exists, and the limit is uniform on $[a, b]$ if f_* is continuous on $[a, b]$.

PROBLEMS

1. Find a solution of the heat equation $\frac{1}{3} \partial u / \partial t = \partial^2 u / \partial x^2$ for $t > 0$ and $0 \leq x \leq 2$ which satisfies the boundary conditions $u(0, t) = 20$ and $u(2, t) = 20$ if $t \geq 0$, $u(x, 0) = x + 20$ if $0 \leq x \leq 2$.

2. In each case, find a solution u of the heat equation $\partial^2 u / \partial x^2 = 5 \cdot \partial u / \partial t$ for $t > 0$ and $0 \leq x \leq \pi$ which satisfies the given boundary conditions.

(**a**) $u(0, t) = 0$ and $u(\pi, t) = 100$ if $t \geq 0$, $u(x, 0) = 20$ if $0 < x < \pi$.

(**b**) $u(0, t) = 50$ and $u(\pi, t) = 100$ if $t \geq 0$, $u(x, 0) = 50$ if $0 \leq x < \frac{1}{2}\pi$ and $u(x, 0) = 100$ if $\frac{1}{2}\pi < x \leq \pi$.

3. A rod has ends at 0 and π on the x-axis and its ends are kept at zero temperature. At $t = 0$, the temperature is given by $u(x, 0) = 20x$ if $0 \leq x \leq \frac{1}{2}\pi$ and $u(x, 0) = 20(\pi - x)$ if $\frac{1}{2}\pi \leq x \leq \pi$. Determine the corresponding solution u of the one-dimensional heat equation (10-89) with $c = \frac{1}{2}$.

4. A rectangle has vertices at the points $(0, 0)$, $(3, 0)$, $(0, 5)$, and $(3, 5)$. In each case, determine a solution of the two-dimensional heat equation that satisfies the given conditions for (x, y) in this rectangle, and for which $\partial u / \partial t \equiv 0$.

(**a**) $u(0, y, 0) = 100$, $u(3, y, 0) = 130 - 15y$; $u(x, 0, 0) = 100 + 10x$, $u(x, 5, 0) = 100 - 15x$.

(**b**) $u(x, 0, 0) = u(x, 5, 0) = 10x$, $u(0, y, 0) = \sin \frac{1}{5}\pi y$, $u(3, y, 0) = 30 + e^{3\pi/5} \sin \frac{1}{5}\pi y$.

5. A rectangular plate has vertices at the points $(0, 0)$, $(\pi, 0)$, $(0, \frac{1}{2}\pi)$, and $(\pi, \frac{1}{2}\pi)$. At time $t = 0$, the temperature is given by

$$\tau(x, y) = 50 + 100xy + e^{-2y} \sin 2x + \sin x \sin 4y.$$

Find a solution u of the two-dimensional heat equation (10-91) with $c = 3$ that satisfies this boundary condition.

6. A thin plate is the region between two concentric circles of radii 4 and 7. The plane faces of the plate are insulated. In each case, find the solution of Laplace's equation that has the given boundary values when the centers of the circles are at the origin.

(*a*) The temperature on the inner circle is constantly 100 degrees and the temperature on the outer circle is constantly 50 degrees.

(*b*) The temperature on the inner circle is $20 + \cos\theta$ and the temperature on the outer circle is $20 + 10\cos\theta$.

7. In each case, find a solution of Laplace's equation in the unit disk that satisfies the stated boundary condition.

(*a*) $u(1, \theta) = -50$ if $-\pi < \theta < 0$, $\quad u(1, \theta) = 50$ if $0 < \theta < \pi$.

(*b*) $u(1, \theta) = 0$ if $-\pi < \theta < 0$, $\quad u(1, \theta) = \sin\theta$ if $0 < \theta < \pi$.

(*c*) $u(1, \theta) = \pi\cos\frac{1}{2}\theta$ if $-\pi \leq \theta \leq \pi$.

8. Suppose $u(r, \theta)$ is given by the series (10-99) for $0 \leq r < 1$ and all θ. Also suppose that τ and $|\tau|$ are integrable on $[-\pi, \pi]$ and that $u(1, \theta)$ as given by (10-99) is the Fourier series of τ on $[-\pi, \pi]$. Prove that, if $0 \leq r < 1$, then

$$|u(r, \theta)| \leq \sup\{|\tau(\theta)|\colon -\pi \leq \theta < \pi\}.$$

10-7. FOURIER TRANSFORMS

With mild restrictions on a function, we have seen that the Fourier series on the interval $[-\ell, \ell]$ represents the function on $[-\ell, \ell]$ and represents the periodic extension of f outside this interval. But suppose the domain of the function is the interval $(-\infty, +\infty)$. Then it is impossible to represent the function throughout its domain by a Fourier series, unless the function is periodic. However, in such cases the function may be representable by an integral rather than by an infinite series. We shall start our study of this problem by "stretching" the interval on which the Fourier series represents the function.

Suppose f and $|f|$ are integrable on $(-\infty, +\infty)$. For a positive number ℓ, let us define g by

$$g(x) = f\left(\frac{\ell x}{\pi}\right) \quad \text{for} \quad -\pi \leq x \leq \pi. \tag{10-105}$$

If x is an interior point of $[-\pi, \pi]$ for which one of the conditions (a) through (e) of Theorem 10-4.4 is satisfied for f, then this condition also is satisfied for g at the point $\pi x/\ell$. Moreover, it follows from Theorems 10-4.3 and 10-4.4 that the Fourier series of g converges at $\pi x/\ell$ and the sum of the series is

$$\frac{1}{2}\left[g\left(\frac{\pi x}{\ell}+\right) + g\left(\frac{\pi x}{\ell}-\right)\right]$$

$$= \lim_{n \to +\infty} \frac{1}{\pi}\left[\int_{-\frac{1}{2}\pi(\ell+x)/\ell}^{\frac{1}{2}\pi(\ell-x)/\ell} g\left(\frac{\pi x}{\ell} + 2t\right)\frac{\sin(2n-1)t}{t}\,dt\right].$$

If we make the substitution $2t = \pi s/\ell$ and use (10-105), we get

$$\frac{f(x+)+f(x-)}{2} = \lim_{n \to +\infty} \frac{1}{\pi} \int_{-\ell-x}^{\ell-x} f(x+s) \frac{\sin (n-\frac{1}{2})\pi s/\ell}{s} \, ds.$$

Now we make the substitution $x+s = t$ and use elementary integration to obtain

$$\frac{f(x+)+f(x-)}{2} = \lim_{n \to +\infty} \frac{1}{\pi} \int_{-\ell}^{\ell} f(t) \frac{\sin (n-\frac{1}{2})\pi(t-x)/\ell}{t-x} \, dt$$

$$= \lim_{n \to +\infty} \frac{1}{\pi} \int_{-\ell}^{\ell} \left[\int_{0}^{(n-1/2)\pi/\ell} f(t) \cos u(t-x) \, du \right] dt.$$

Since f and $|f|$ are integrable on $(-\infty, +\infty)$, $|f(t) \cos u(t-x)|$ is integrable over the rectangle involved here. Moreover, this double integral can be evaluated as either of two iterated integrals [see Theorem 5-3.3]. Therefore,

$$\frac{f(x+)+f(x-)}{2} = \lim_{n \to +\infty} \frac{1}{\pi} \int_{0}^{(n-1/2)\pi/\ell} \left[\int_{-\ell}^{\ell} f(t) \cos u(t-x) \, dt \right] du. \tag{10-106}$$

Since $\int_{-\ell}^{\ell} f(t) \cos u(t-x) \, dt$ and $\int_{-\ell}^{\ell} f(t) \sin u(t-x) \, dt$ are even and odd functions of u, respectively, it follows from (10-106) that

$$\frac{f(x+)+f(x-)}{2} = \lim_{n \to +\infty} \frac{1}{2\pi} \int_{-[n-1/2]\pi/\ell}^{[n-1/2]\pi/\ell} \left[\int_{-\ell}^{\ell} f(t) e^{iu(t-x)} \, dt \right] du. \tag{10-107}$$

We shall integrate complex-valued functions only along the real line, so this equality and the ones to follow are easy to interpret: A complex-valued function $f = u + iv$ is integrable if and only if u and v are integrable; if f is integrable, then the integral of f is the integral of u *plus* the product of i and the integral of v.

THEOREM 10-7.1 (FOURIER INTEGRAL THEOREM). Suppose f and $|f|$ are integrable on $(-\infty, +\infty)$. If x is a number for which one of the conditions (a) through (e) of Theorem 10-4.4 is satisfied, then

$$\frac{f(x+)+f(x-)}{2} = \frac{1}{2\pi} \int_{-\infty}^{+\infty} \left[\int_{-\infty}^{+\infty} f(t) e^{iu(t-x)} \, dt \right] du. \tag{10-108}$$

PROOF. It follows from the Riemann-Lebesgue lemma [Theorem 10-3.7] that $\lim_{u \to +\infty} \int_{-\ell}^{\ell} f(t)e^{iu(t-x)} \, dt = 0$. Therefore, there is no need to restrict the limits in the first integral of (10-107) to be of type $\pm (n - \frac{1}{2})\pi/\ell$, and it follows from (10-107) that

$$\frac{f(x+)+f(x-)}{2} = \frac{1}{2\pi} \int_{-\infty}^{+\infty} \left[\int_{-\ell}^{\ell} f(t)e^{iu(t-x)} \, dt \right] du.$$

This equality is valid if $\ell > |x|$, but we must be cautious about letting $\ell \to +\infty$. If $|f(t)e^{iu(t-x)}|$ were integrable over the entire (t, u)-plane, there would be no problem [see Theorem 5-3.3]. But this may not be true. To circumvent this difficulty, we shall do some juggling so that we can change the order of integration for a suitable iterated integral which is equal to the double integral over a region on which

$$|f(t)e^{iu(t-x)}|$$

is integrable. Let ε be an arbitrary positive number, and choose ℓ so that

$$\int_{\ell}^{+\infty} |f(t)| \, dt < \varepsilon, \quad \int_{-\infty}^{-\ell} |f(t)| \, dt < \varepsilon, \quad \text{and} \quad |t-x| > \frac{4}{\pi} \quad \text{if} \quad |t| \geqq \ell. \tag{10-109}$$

Then choose a number A so that

$$\left| \frac{f(x+)+f(x-)}{2} - \frac{1}{2\pi} \int_{-\alpha}^{\alpha} \left[\int_{-\ell}^{\ell} f(t)e^{iu(t-x)} \, dt \right] du \right| < \frac{\varepsilon}{2} \quad \text{if} \quad \alpha > A. \tag{10-110}$$

The double integral of $|f(t)e^{iu(t-x)}|$ over the set of all (t, u) with $|t| \geqq \ell$ and $-\alpha \leqq u \leqq \alpha$ exists. In fact, it is not greater than $2\alpha \int_{-\infty}^{\infty} |f(t)| \, dt$. Therefore, we can use Theorem 5-3.3 to interchange the order of integration in the first of the following iterated integrals, and then use inequalities (10-109), to obtain

$$\left| \int_{-\alpha}^{\alpha} \left[\int_{\ell}^{+\infty} f(t)e^{iu(t-x)} \, dt \right] du \right| = \frac{1}{2\pi} \left| \int_{\ell}^{+\infty} \left[\int_{-\alpha}^{\alpha} f(t)e^{iu(t-x)} \, du \right] dt \right|$$

$$= \frac{1}{\pi} \left| \int_{\ell}^{+\infty} f(t) \frac{\sin \alpha(t-x)}{t-x} \, dt \right|$$

$$\leqq \frac{1}{4} \int_{\ell}^{+\infty} |f(t)| \, dt < \frac{\varepsilon}{4}.$$

Similarly, $|\int_{-\alpha}^{\alpha}[\int_{-\infty}^{\ell} f(t)e^{iu(t-x)}\,dt]\,du| < \frac{1}{4}\varepsilon$. From these inequalities and (10-110), we have

$$\left| \frac{f(x+)+f(x-)}{2} - \frac{1}{2\pi} \int_{-\alpha}^{\alpha} \left[\int_{-\infty}^{\infty} f(t)e^{iu(t-x)}\,dt \right] du \right| < \varepsilon \quad \text{if} \quad \alpha > A.$$

This implies (10-108).

The *Fourier integral* of a function f is the integral

$$f(x) \longleftrightarrow \frac{1}{2\pi} \int_{-\infty}^{+\infty} \left[\int_{-\infty}^{+\infty} f(t)e^{iu(t-x)}\,dt \right] du. \qquad (10\text{-}111)$$

We use $\longleftrightarrow$ instead of $=$, since the integral may be said to *correspond* to f in any case, but need not always equal $f(x)$. Since the imaginary part of (10-111) is zero, we also have the following form of the *Fourier integral*:

$$f(x) \longleftrightarrow \frac{1}{\pi} \int_{0}^{+\infty} \left[\int_{-\infty}^{+\infty} f(t)\cos u(t-x)\,dt \right] du. \qquad (10\text{-}112)$$

If f is an even function, then $f(t) \sin ut$ is odd, $f(t) \cos ut$ is even, and (10-112) becomes

$$f(x) \longleftrightarrow \frac{2}{\pi} \int_{0}^{+\infty} \left[\int_{0}^{+\infty} f(t)\cos ut\,dt \right] \cos ux\,du. \qquad (10\text{-}113)$$

This is the *Fourier cosine integral* of f. If f is odd, then $f(t) \cos ut$ is odd, $f(t) \sin ut$ is even, and (10-112) becomes

$$f(x) \longleftrightarrow \frac{2}{\pi} \int_{0}^{+\infty} \left[\int_{0}^{+\infty} f(t)\sin ut\,dt \right] \sin ux\,du. \qquad (10\text{-}114)$$

This is the *Fourier sine integral* of f.

ILLUSTRATION 1. Let $f(x) = 1$ if $|x| \leq 1$, $f(-1) = f(1) = \frac{1}{2}$, and $f(x) = 0$ if $|x| > 1$. Then f is even and

$$f(x) \longleftrightarrow \frac{2}{\pi} \int_{0}^{+\infty} \left[\int_{0}^{1} \cos ut\,dt \right] \cos ux\,du = \frac{2}{\pi} \int_{0}^{+\infty} \frac{\sin u \cos ux}{u}\,du.$$

Therefore, it follows from the Fourier integral theorem and (10-113) that

$$\int_0^{+\infty} \frac{\sin u \cos ux}{u} \, du = \begin{cases} \frac{1}{2}\pi & \text{if } |x| < 1, \\ \frac{1}{4}\pi & \text{if } |x| = 1, \\ 0 & \text{if } |x| > 1. \end{cases}$$

Integral transforms are very useful in both pure and applied mathematics. They are particularly useful in solving certain types of boundary value problems, differential equations, and integral equations. Some of these transforms are:

Fourier transform: $\dfrac{1}{\sqrt{2\pi}} \displaystyle\int_{-\infty}^{+\infty} f(t)e^{-ixt} \, dt.$

Fourier cosine transform: $\sqrt{\dfrac{2}{\pi}} \displaystyle\int_0^{+\infty} f(t) \cos xt \, dt.$

Fourier sine transform: $\sqrt{\dfrac{2}{\pi}} \displaystyle\int_0^{+\infty} f(t) \sin xt \, dt.$

Suppose f is a continuous function that is equal to its Fourier integral. If g is the Fourier transform of f, then f is not quite the Fourier transform of g. However, it follows from (10-108) that, if

$$g(x) = \frac{1}{\sqrt{2\pi}} \int_{-\infty}^{+\infty} f(t)e^{-ixt} \, dt, \quad \text{then} \quad f(x) = \frac{1}{\sqrt{2\pi}} \int_{-\infty}^{+\infty} g(t)e^{ixt} \, dt.$$

ILLUSTRATION 2. Suppose $f(x) = e^{-|x|}$. Then the Fourier transform of f is

$$g(x) = \frac{1}{\sqrt{2\pi}} \int_{-\infty}^{+\infty} e^{-|t|-ixt} \, dt = \frac{1}{\sqrt{2\pi}} \left[\int_{-\infty}^0 e^{t-ixt} \, dt + \int_0^{+\infty} e^{-t-ixt} \, dt \right]$$

$$= \frac{1}{\sqrt{2\pi}} \left[\frac{1}{1-ix} + \frac{1}{1+ix} \right] = \sqrt{\frac{2}{\pi}} \frac{1}{1+x^2},$$

and

$$\frac{1}{\sqrt{2\pi}} \int_{-\infty}^{+\infty} g(t)e^{ixt} \, dt = \frac{1}{\pi} \int_{-\infty}^{+\infty} \frac{1}{1+t^2} e^{ixt} \, dt = \frac{2}{\pi} \int_0^{+\infty} \frac{\cos xt}{1+t^2} \, dt.$$

Therefore, the following equation is a consequence of the Fourier integral theorem [also see problem 1(b)]:

$$\frac{2}{\pi} \int_0^{+\infty} \frac{\cos xt}{1+t^2} \, dt = e^{-|x|}.$$

Again, suppose f is a continuous function that is equal to its Fourier integral. Also, suppose f is even. If g is the Fourier cosine transform of f, then it follows from (10-113) that f is the Fourier cosine transform of g. There is a similar situation for the Fourier sine transform of odd functions.

ILLUSTRATION 3. Suppose we wish to find a solution u of Laplace's equation,

$$\frac{\partial^2 u}{\partial x^2} + \frac{\partial^2 u}{\partial y^2} = 0,$$

that is bounded for $y \geqq 0$. Also, suppose we are given a function f and we wish to have

$$\lim_{y \to 0+} u(x, y) = f(x).$$

Using Eqs. (10-94) with $\lambda + \mu = 0$, we try solutions of type

$$e^{-ay}(A \cos ax + B \sin ax), \quad a \geqq 0.$$

Thus, we might try to represent u in the form

$$u(x, y) = \int_0^{+\infty} e^{-uy}[A(u) \cos ux + B(u) \sin ux] \, du,$$

where A and B are to be determined so that

$$u(x, 0) = f(x) = \int_0^{+\infty} [A(u) \cos ux + B(u) \sin ux] \, du.$$

Using the Fourier integral theorem in the form

$$\frac{f(x+) + f(x-)}{2} = \frac{1}{\pi} \int_0^{+\infty} \left[\int_{-\infty}^{+\infty} f(t) \cos u(t-x) \, dt \right] du,$$

we see that we might let

$$A(u) \cos ux + B(u) \sin ux = \frac{1}{\pi} \int_{-\infty}^{+\infty} f(t) \cos u(t-x) \, dt,$$

and

$$u(x, y) = \frac{1}{\pi} \int_0^{+\infty} \left[\int_{-\infty}^{+\infty} f(t) \cos u(t-x) \, dt \right] e^{-uy} \, du.$$

If we invert the order of integration and evaluate the inner integral, we obtain

$$u(x, y) = \frac{1}{\pi} \int_{-\infty}^{+\infty} \left[\int_0^{+\infty} e^{-uy} \cos u(t-x) \, du \right] f(t) \, dt$$

$$= \frac{1}{\pi} \int_{-\infty}^{+\infty} \frac{yf(t)}{y^2 + (t-x)^2} \, dt.$$

If f is such that we can differentiate under the integral sign, it is easy to prove that u satisfies Laplace's equation. With suitable restrictions on f, one can prove that $\lim_{y \to 0+} u(x, y) = f(x)$. If, in particular, we have $f(x) = 0$ if $x < 0$, and $f(x) = 1$ if $x > 0$, then

$$u(x, y) = \frac{1}{\pi} \int_0^{+\infty} \frac{y}{y^2 + (t-x)^2} \, dt = \frac{1}{\pi} \left(\frac{\pi}{2} + \tan^{-1} \frac{x}{y} \right).$$

In this case, it is clear that $\lim_{y \to 0+} u(x, y) = f(x)$ if $x \neq 0$, and that $\lim_{y \to 0+} u(0, y) = \frac{1}{2}$. Also, u satisfies Laplace's equation if $y \neq 0$. We might be said to have won by default, since this choice of f does not satisfy the hypotheses of the Fourier integral theorem.

PROBLEMS

1. Prove each of the following, using the Fourier cosine or the Fourier sine integral and the function e^{-ax}.

(a) $\displaystyle\int_0^{+\infty} \frac{u \sin ux}{a^2 + u^2} \, du = \frac{1}{2}\pi e^{-ax}$ if $x > 0$ and $a > 0$.

(b) $\displaystyle\int_0^{+\infty} \frac{\cos ux}{a^2 + u^2} \, du = \frac{\pi}{2a} e^{-a|x|}$ if $a > 0$.

2. Prove that

$$\int_0^{+\infty} \frac{t^3 \sin tx}{t^4 + 4} \, dt = \frac{1}{2}\pi e^{-x} \cos x \quad \text{if} \quad x > 0.$$

3. Prove that

$$\int_0^{+\infty} \frac{\sin \pi t \sin tx}{1 - t^2} \, dt = \begin{cases} \frac{1}{2}\pi \sin x & \text{if} \quad 0 \leq x \leq \pi, \\ 0 & \text{if} \quad x > \pi. \end{cases}$$

4. Prove that

$$\int_0^{+\infty} \frac{\sin xu \cos yu}{u} \, du = \begin{cases} \frac{1}{2}\pi & \text{if } 0 \leq y < x, \\ \frac{1}{4}\pi & \text{if } x = y > 0, \\ 0 & \text{if } 0 \leq x < y. \end{cases}$$

5. In each case, solve the given integral equation.

(a) $\int_0^{+\infty} f(t) \cos tx \, dt = \begin{cases} a - x & \text{if } 0 < x \leq a, \\ 0 & \text{if } x > a. \end{cases}$

(b) $\int_0^{+\infty} f(t) \cos tx \, dt = \begin{cases} 1 - x^2 & \text{if } |x| < 1, \\ 0 & \text{if } |x| > 1. \end{cases}$

(c) $\int_0^{+\infty} f(t) \sin tx \, dt = e^{-ax} \sin bx$ if $x \geq 0$.

6. Let $f(0) = 1$ and $f(x) = (\sin x)/x$ if $x \neq 0$. Prove that this even function is equal to its Fourier cosine integral for all x, even though $|f|$ is not integrable on $[0, +\infty)$. [*Hint:* Use Illustration 1.]

7. Determine the solution to the problem of Illustration 3 when $f(x) = 1$ if $|x| < 1$ and $f(x) = 0$ if $|x| > 1$.

8. Determine the solution to the problem of Illustration 3 when $f(x) = 0$ if $|x| > 1$, $f(x) = x + 1$ if $-1 \leq x \leq 0$, and $f(x) = -x + 1$ if $0 \leq x \leq 1$.

9. Suppose we wish to find a solution of the heat equation,

$$\frac{\partial^2 u}{\partial x^2} = c^2 \frac{\partial u}{\partial t},$$

valid for $t > 0$ and all values of x. Show that it is plausible that a solution with the property that $\lim_{t \to 0+} u(x, t) = f(x)$ might be given by

$$u(x, t) = \frac{1}{\pi} \int_0^{+\infty} \left[\int_{-\infty}^{+\infty} f(s) \cos u(s - x) \, ds \right] e^{-u^2 t/c^2} \, du.$$

10. Show that if the order of integration is changed in problem 9, we obtain

$$u(x, t) = \frac{c}{2\sqrt{\pi t}} \int_{-\infty}^{+\infty} f(s) e^{-c^2(s-x)^2/(4t)} \, ds.$$

11. Find the solution of the wave equation of problem 9 for which $f(x) = e^{-c^2 x^2}$ for all x. [*Hint:* Use Illustration 3 of Section 8-2.]

11

MEASURE AND
INTEGRATION

11-1. MEASURE

The fundamental concepts of the theory of measure and integration will be studied first for measures on algebras of sets. The purpose will be to discuss the main principles involved in the introduction of the theory and some of the basic theorems, without the camouflage of details. In this and the next three sections, the theory will be very general. Following this, it will be specialized to Lebesgue measure and integration in R^n.

DEFINITION 11-1.1. An *algebra* (or *Boolean algebra*) of subsets of a set T is a collection $\mathscr{B}$ of subsets of T with the property that $R \cup S$ and $\sim R$ belong to $\mathscr{B}$ whenever R and S belong to $\mathscr{B}$. A *σ-algebra* is an algebra $\mathscr{B}$ for which $\bigcup_1^{+\infty} S_n$ belongs to $\mathscr{B}$ whenever each S_n belongs to $\mathscr{B}$.

If a set R is a member of an algebra $\mathscr{B}$, then $R \cup \sim R = T$ belongs to $\mathscr{B}$. Also, $\sim T = \Phi$, so that Φ belongs to $\mathscr{B}$. If both R and S belong to $\mathscr{B}$, then it follows from the equalities,

$$R \cap S = \sim[(\sim R) \cup (\sim S)] \quad \text{and} \quad R - S = R \cap (\sim S),$$

that $R \cap S$ and $R - S$ belong to $\mathscr{B}$. If $\mathscr{B}$ is a σ-algebra, then it follows from

$$\bigcap_{n=1}^{+\infty} S_n = S_1 - \bigcup_{n=1}^{+\infty} (S_1 - S_n)$$

that $\bigcap_1^{+\infty} S_n$ belongs to $\mathscr{B}$ if each S_n belongs to $\mathscr{B}$.

For any set T, the set of all subsets of T is a σ-algebra. However, we shall often use σ-algebras that are not of this type. The proof of the next theorem describes how a smallest algebra and a smallest σ-algebra can be determined to satisfy the requirement that they contain certain prescribed sets.

THEOREM 11-1.1. Given a collection $\mathscr{C}$ of subsets of a set T, there is a smallest algebra $\mathscr{B}$ of subsets of T that contains $\mathscr{C}$, and a smallest σ-algebra $\mathscr{B}^*$ of subsets of T that contains $\mathscr{C}$.

PROOF. We note first that the collection of all subsets of T is a σ-algebra that contains $\mathscr{C}$. Then we can let $\mathscr{B}$ be the intersection of all algebras that contain $\mathscr{C}$, and $\mathscr{B}^*$ be the intersection of all σ-algebras that contain $\mathscr{C}$. If R and S belong to $\mathscr{B}$, then both R and S belong to every algebra that contains $\mathscr{C}$. This implies that $R \cup S$ and $\sim R$ belong to every algebra that contains $\mathscr{C}$. Thus, $\mathscr{B}$ is an algebra. Similarly, it follows that $\mathscr{B}^*$ is a σ-algebra.

DEFINITION 11-1.2. A *measure* on an algebra $\mathscr{B}$ is a function whose domain is $\mathscr{B}$, whose range is contained in the set of nonnegative extended real numbers, and which is *additive* in the sense that

$$m(R \cup S) = m(R) + m(S)$$

whenever R and S belong to $\mathscr{B}$ and $R \cap S = \Phi$. A *countably additive measure* on a σ-algebra $\mathscr{B}^*$ is a measure m with the property that, if each S_n belongs to $\mathscr{B}^*$ and $S_i \cap S_j = \Phi$ whenever $i \neq j$, then

$$m\left(\bigcup_{n=1}^{+\infty} S_n\right) = \sum_{n=1}^{+\infty} m(S_n). \tag{11-1}$$

It should be emphasized that the measure of a set may be $+\infty$. In particular, the set X of the next theorem may have infinite measure.

THEOREM 11-1.2. Suppose m is a countably additive measure on a σ-algebra $\mathscr{B}$. If $\{X_n\}$ is a sequence of members of $\mathscr{B}$ for which $X_n \subset X_{n+1}$ for all n, then

$$\lim_{n \to +\infty} m(X_n) = m(X), \quad \text{where} \quad X = \bigcup_{n=1}^{+\infty} X_n. \tag{11-2}$$

If $\{V_n\}$ is a sequence of members of $\mathscr{B}$ for which $V_n \supset V_{n+1}$ for all n and $m(V_1) < +\infty$, then

$$\lim_{n \to +\infty} m(V_n) = m(V), \quad \text{where} \quad V = \bigcap_{n=1}^{+\infty} V_n. \tag{11-3}$$

PROOF. We introduce the sequence $\{Y_n\}$ for which $Y_1 = X_1$ and $Y_n = X_n - X_{n-1}$ if $n > 1$. Then $Y_i \cap Y_j = \Phi$ whenever $i \neq j$. Also, $X_n = \bigcup_1^n Y_k$ and $X = \bigcup_1^{+\infty} Y_k$. Therefore,

$$m(X_n) = \sum_{k=1}^n m(Y_k) \quad \text{and} \quad m(X) = \sum_{k=1}^{+\infty} m(Y_k).$$

Equation (11-2) follows from these equalities. Now let $W_n = V_1 - V_n$ if $n > 1$. Then $W_n \subset W_{n+1}$ and it follows from (11-2) that

$$\lim_{n \to +\infty} m(W_n) = m(W), \quad \text{where} \quad W = \bigcup_{n=2}^{+\infty} W_n.$$

However, $m(W_n) = m(V_1) - m(V_n)$ [see problem 3(b)] and

$$W = \bigcup_2^{+\infty} (V_1 - V_n) = V_1 - V,$$

so that

$$\lim_{n \to +\infty} m(W_n) = m(V_1) - \lim_{n \to +\infty} m(V_n)$$

and

$$m(W) = m(V_1) - m(V).$$

Thus, $\lim_{n \to +\infty} m(V_n) = m(V)$.

PROBLEMS

1. Let $\mathscr{C}$ be the collection of all one-member sets of real numbers. Describe the smallest algebra and the smallest σ-algebra that contain $\mathscr{C}$.

2. Suppose m is a measure on an algebra $\mathscr{B}$ and that there is a set S for which $m(S) \neq +\infty$. Prove that $m(\Phi) = 0$.

3. Suppose m is a measure on an algebra $\mathscr{B}$ of subsets of a set T and that R and S are members of $\mathscr{B}$. Prove each of the following.

  (a) $m(R) \leqq m(S)$ if $R \subset S$.

  (b) $m(R - S) = m(R) - m(S)$ if $S \subset R$ and $m(S) \neq +\infty$.

  (c) $m(R \cup S) = m(R) + m(S) - m(R \cap S)$ if $m(R \cap S) \neq +\infty$.

4. Suppose m is a measure on an algebra $\mathscr{B}$ of subsets of a set T and that $S_1, S_2, \cdots, S_n$ are members of $\mathscr{B}$. Prove that, if $m(S_i \cap S_j) = 0$ whenever $i \neq j$, then

$$m(S_1 \cup S_2 \cup \cdots \cup S_n) = \sum_{k=1}^{n} m(S_k).$$

5. Suppose $\mathscr{B}$ is a σ-algebra and m is a measure defined on $\mathscr{B}$. Prove each of the following.

(a) $m(\bigcup_1^{+\infty} A_n) \geq \sum_1^{+\infty} m(A_n)$, if each A_n belongs to B and $m(A_i \cap A_j) = 0$ whenever $i \neq j$. [*Note:* Problems 7(b) and 8 provide cases for which we can have $m(\bigcup_1^{+\infty} A_n) > \sum_1^{+\infty} m(A_n)$.]

(b) $m(\bigcup_1^{+\infty} A_n) \leq \sum_1^{+\infty} m(A_n)$ if each A_n belongs to B and m is *countably additive*.

6. In each case, let $\mathscr{B}$ be the σ-algebra of all subsets of the reals and determine whether m is additive and whether m is countably additive.

(a) For the rational numbers $\{r_n\}$ arranged as a sequence, $m(S) = \sum_1^{+\infty} 2^{-n}\varepsilon_n(S)$, where $\varepsilon_n(S) = +1$ if $r_n \in S$ and $\varepsilon_n(S) = 0$ if $r_n \notin S$.

(b) $m(S)$ is the number of integers that belong to S, if S contains a finite number of integers; $m(S) = +\infty$ otherwise.

(c) $m(S)$ is the number of members of S if S is finite and $m(S) = +\infty$ if S is not finite.

(d) $m(\Phi) = 0$, $m(S) = 1$ if $S \neq \Phi$ and S is finite, and $m(S) = +\infty$ if S is not finite.

(e) $m(S) = \sup \{$inner sums for $S\}$ [see Definition 3-2.1].

7. In each case, determine whether $\mathscr{B}$ is an algebra, whether $\mathscr{B}$ is a σ-algebra, whether m is additive, and whether m is countably additive.

(a) Members of $\mathscr{B}$ are finite unions of disjoint intervals on the real line. If $S = \bigcup_1^n I_k$, where $I_r \cap I_s = \Phi$ if $r \neq s$, then $m(S)$ is the sum of the lengths of these intervals.

(b*) $\mathscr{B}$ is the set of all subsets of the positive integers for which $m(S)$ exists, with

$$m(S) = \lim_{p \to +\infty} \frac{\varepsilon_1(S) + \cdots + \varepsilon_p(S)}{p},$$

where $\varepsilon_k(S) = 1$ if $k \in S$ and $\varepsilon_k(S) = 0$ if $k \notin S$.

8. Let $\mathscr{B}$ be the σ-algebra of all subsets of the set of positive integers and let m be a function defined on $\mathscr{B}$ for which $m(A) = 0$ if A is finite and for which there is an infinite set B with $m(B) \neq 0$. Prove that m is not countably additive. [*Note:* We might let $m(B) = +\infty$ for all infinite sets. However, it is possible for m to be additive, nonzero for some sets, and never infinite. But some principle such as Zorn's lemma is needed to prove this.]

9. For the σ-algebra of all sets of positive integers, let $m(S)$ be the number of members of S if S is finite and $m(S) = +\infty$ if S is infinite. For each positive integer n, let $V_n = \{k \colon k \geqq n\}$. Prove that

$$\lim_{n \to +\infty} m(V_n) \neq m\left(\bigcap_1^{+\infty} V_n\right)$$

and explain why this does not contradict Theorem 11-1.2.

11-2. MEASURABLE FUNCTIONS

Not all functions defined on an interval are Riemann integrable. In fact, a bounded function f defined on a bounded interval is Riemann integrable if and only if the set of points of discontinuity of f is of measure zero. Similarly, we should expect that some restriction must be made when developing a theory of general integration. A function must be measurable in the following sense if it is to be integrable, although not all measurable functions are integrable. A measure may have infinite values. Similarly, throughout this chapter we shall understand that the range of a real-valued function is contained in the set of extended real numbers and may include $+\infty$ or $-\infty$.

DEFINITION 11-2.1. Suppose m is a measure on an algebra $\mathscr{B}$ of subsets of a set T. A *measurable function* with respect to m is an extended-real-valued function f whose domain is a measurable subset of T and which has the property that $\{x \colon f(x) = +\infty\} \in \mathscr{B}$, $\{x \colon f(x) = -\infty\} \in \mathscr{B}$, and $\{x \colon f(x) \in [a, b)\} \in \mathscr{B}$ whenever a and b are ordinary real numbers and $a < b$.

If m is countably additive, much more can be said about functions that are measurable with respect to m. Some of these facts are given in the next three theorems.

THEOREM 11-2.1. Suppose m is a countably additive measure on a σ-algebra $\mathscr{B}$. Then each of the following is a necessary and sufficient condition for f to be measurable with respect to m.

  (i) $\{x \colon f(x) < a\} \in \mathscr{B}$ for all ordinary real numbers a.
  (ii) $\{x \colon f(x) > a\} \in \mathscr{B}$ for all ordinary real numbers a.
  (iii) $\{x \colon f(x) \geqq a\} \in \mathscr{B}$ for all ordinary real numbers a.
  (iv) $\{x \colon f(x) \in (a, b)\} \in \mathscr{B}$ and $\{x \colon f(x) = +\infty\} \in \mathscr{B}$ if a and b are ordinary real numbers and $a < b$.
  (v) $\{x \colon f(x) \in [a, b]\} \in \mathscr{B}$ if $-\infty < a < b \leqq +\infty$.
  (vi) $\{x \colon f(x) \leqq a\} \in \mathscr{B}$ for all ordinary real numbers a.
  (vii) $\{x \colon f(x) \in (a, b]\} \in \mathscr{B}$ if $-\infty < a < b \leqq +\infty$.

PROOF. Since $\mathscr{B}$ is a σ-algebra, $\mathscr{B}$ contains all countable unions and countable intersections of members of $\mathscr{B}$. Therefore, to prove that sets (i) through (v) are measurable if f is measurable, we need only observe that each of these sets can be built using countable unions or countable intersections of inverse images of half-open intervals of type $[a, b)$. For example, $\{x: f(x) < a\}$ is the union of $\{x: f(x) = -\infty\}$ and all inverse images of sets of type $[n, a)$, where n is an integer less than a; if $b \neq +\infty$, $\{x: f(x) \in [a, b]\}$ is the intersection of inverse images of sets of type $[a, b + 1/n)$, where n is a positive integer. Also, each set of type (vi) is the complement of a set of type (ii), and each set of type (vii) is a countable union of sets of type (v). Thus, each set in (i) through (vii) belongs to $\mathscr{B}$ if f is measurable.

To complete the proof, for each of (i) through (vii) we must show that f is measurable if $\mathscr{B}$ contains all sets of that particular type. We shall discuss one case and leave the rest for the student [problem 3]. If each set of type $\{x: f(x) < a\}$ belongs to $\mathscr{B}$, then $\{x: f(x) = -\infty\}$ is $\{x: f(x) < -n\}$ and belongs to $\mathscr{B}$. Also, complements of sets in $\mathscr{B}$ belong to $\mathscr{B}$. Therefore, $\mathscr{B}$ contains all sets of type $\{x: f(x) \geq a\}$. Therefore, $\{x: f(x) = +\infty\} = \bigcap_1^{+\infty} \{x: f(x) \geq n\} \in \mathscr{B}$. Also, if $a < b$, then

$$\{x: f(x) \in [a, b)\} = \{x: f(x) < b\} \cap \{x: f(x) \geq a\},$$

so that all sets of type $\{x: f(x) \in [a, b)\}$ belong to $\mathscr{B}$ and f is measurable.

THEOREM 11-2.2. Suppose m is a countably additive measure on a σ-algebra B and that f and g are measurable with respect to m. Then $cf, f^+, f^-, f+g, |f|$, and fg are measurable.

PROOF. If $c = 0$, measurability of cf follows from the fact that the inverse image of $[a, b)$ is Φ or T, according to whether $0 \in [a, b)$ or $0 \notin [a, b)$. If $c \neq 0$, measurability of cf follows from (i) and (ii) of Theorem 11-2.1, since

$$\{x: cf(x) < a\} = \left\{x: f(x) < \frac{a}{c}\right\} \quad \text{if} \quad c > 0,$$

$$\{x: cf(x) < a\} = \left\{x: f(x) > \frac{a}{c}\right\} \quad \text{if} \quad c < 0.$$

Measurability of f^+ follows from (i) of Theorem 11-2.1 and the equalities $\{x: f^+(x) < a\} = \Phi$ if $a \leq 0$,

$$\{x: f^+(x) < a\} = \{x: f(x) < a\} \quad \text{if} \quad a > 0.$$

Measurability of f^- is proved similarly. Measurability of $f+g$ follows from (i) of Theorem 11-2.1 and the equality

$$\{x: f(x) + g(x) < a\} = \bigcup_{n=1}^{+\infty} \{x: f(x) < a + r_n\} \cap \{x: g(x) < -r_n\},$$

where $\{r_n\}$ is the set of rational numbers arranged as a sequence. Then measurability of $|f|$ follows from the equality $|f| = f^+ + f^-$. To prove fg is measurable, we first note that measurability of f^2 follows from measurability of $|f|$ and (i) of Theorem 11-2.1, because of the equalities

$$\{x: f^2(x) < a\} = \Phi \quad \text{if} \quad a \leq 0,$$

$$\{x: f^2(x) < a\} = \{x: |f(x)| < \sqrt{a}\} \quad \text{if} \quad a > 0.$$

Now measurability of fg follows from the fact that fg is equal to $\frac{1}{2}[(f+g)^2 - f^2 - g^2]$.

The next theorem describes more ways in which measurable functions can be derived from measurable functions. For this theorem, we need the following definition.

DEFINITION 11-2.2. The *limit superior* and the *limit inferior* of a sequence of functions $\{f_n\}$ with a common domain are the functions defined by the equations

$$\limsup_{n \to +\infty} f_n(x) = \inf_{n \geq 1} [\sup \{f_k(x): k \geq n\}],$$

$$\liminf_{n \to +\infty} f_n(x) = \sup_{n \geq 1} [\inf \{f_k(x): k \geq n\}].$$

THEOREM 11-2.3. Suppose m is a countably additive measure on a σ-algebra $\mathscr{B}$ of subsets of a set T and that each of the functions $\{f_n\}$ is measurable and has domain T. Then all of the functions $\sup \{f_n\}$, $\inf \{f_n\}$, $\limsup \{f_n\}$, and $\liminf \{f_n\}$ are measurable. Also, F is measurable if F is defined by $F(x) = \lim_{n \to +\infty} f_n(x)$ for all x for which this limit exists.

PROOF. If g is defined by $g(x) = \sup \{f_n(x)\}$, then

$$\{x: g(x) > a\} = \bigcup_{n=1}^{+\infty} \{x: f_n(x) > a\}.$$

Thus, g is measurable. A similar argument shows that $\inf \{f_n\}$ is measurable. Since

$$\limsup f_n(x) = \inf_{n \geq 1} [\sup \{f_k(x): k \geq n\}],$$

it follows that $\limsup \{f_n\}$ is measurable. The proof for $\liminf \{f_n\}$ is similar. Now let W be the set of x for which $\lim f_n(x)$ exists. Since the function h, defined by

$$h(x) = \limsup f_n(x) - \liminf f_n(x),$$

is measurable, and $W = \{x: h(x) = 0\}$ [see problem 7], the set W is measurable. Then measurability of F follows from the equality

$$\{x: F(x) < a\} = W \cap \left[\bigcup_{n=1}^{+\infty} \bigcap_{k=n}^{+\infty} \{x: f_k(x) < a\} \right].$$

PROBLEMS

1. Suppose f is a measurable function and $f = g$ a.e.† Prove that g is measurable.

2. Suppose m is a countably additive measure on a σ-algebra $\mathscr{B}$ of subsets of a set T and that f is a measurable function whose domain T. In each case, prove without using Theorem 11-2.1 that the given set is measurable.

(a) $\{x: f(x) > a\}$.   (b) $\{x: f(x) \geqq a\}$.

(c) $\{x: f(x) \in (a, b)\}$,   where $a < b$.

3. Suppose m is a countably additive measure on a σ-algebra $\mathscr{B}$ of subsets of a set T and that f is a real-valued function whose domain is a measurable subset of T. In each case, prove that f is measurable if $\mathscr{B}$ contains all sets of the type described for a and b ordinary real numbers except that b may be $+\infty$ in cases (d) and (f).

(a) $\{x: f(x) > a\}$.   (d) $\{x: f(x) \in [a, b]\}$.

(b) $\{x: f(x) \geqq a\}$.   (e) $\{x: f(x) \leqq a\}$.

(c) $\{x: f(x) \in (a, b)\}$ and   (f) $\{x: f(x) \in (a, b]\}$.
$\{x: f(x) = +\infty\}$.

4. Prove that if f and g are measurable with respect to a countably additive measure, then f/g is measurable if $f(x)/g(x)$ is defined to be zero whenever $g(x) = 0$.

5. Prove that $\limsup f_n(x)$ and $\liminf f_n(x)$ as described in Definition 11-2.2 are equal, respectively, to

$$\lim_{n \to +\infty} \left[\sup \{f_k(x): k \geqq n\} \right] \quad \text{and} \quad \lim_{n \to +\infty} \left[\inf \{f_k(x): k \geqq n\} \right].$$

6. Prove that $\limsup f_n(x)$ and $\liminf f_n(x)$ as described in Definition 11-2.2 are equal, respectively, to the largest and smallest cluster points of the sequence $\{f_k(x): k \geqq 1\}$ in the extended real number system. [A *cluster point* of a sequence is a point p such that each neighborhood of p contains infinitely many terms of the sequence.]

---

† "Except on a set of measure zero" will often be replaced by "almost everywhere" or "a.e."

7. Use problem 6 and prove that $\lim_{n \to +\infty} f_n(x)$ exists if and only if $\lim \sup f_n(x) = \lim \inf f_n(x)$.

8.* Prove that any open set of real numbers can be expressed as a union of disjoint open intervals in exactly one way. [*Hint:* For each x in an open set G, let I_x be the union of all open intervals that are contained in G and contain x.]

9. The class of *Borel sets* is the smallest σ-algebra of sets of real numbers that contains all intervals. Prove each of the following.

(a) All open sets and all closed sets are Borel sets. [*Hint:* Use problem 8.]

(b) If f is measurable with respect to a countably additive measure defined on a σ-algebra of subsets of a set T, then for any Borel set B the set $\{x: f(x) \in B\}$ is measurable. [*Hint:* Show that the collection of all sets A for which $\{x: f(x) \in A\}$ is measurable contains all intervals and is a σ-algebra of sets of real numbers.]

11-3. GENERAL INTEGRATION

We shall give two equivalent definitions of an integral for non-negative measurable functions. From these, it should be clear that it would be very unnatural to attempt to define an integral for a non-measurable function. It is useful to introduce the following definition.

DEFINITION 11-3.1. A *simple function* is a function whose range is a finite set of ordinary real numbers.

If m is a measure on an algebra of subsets of a set T, then it is easy to see that a simple function s with domain T and range $\{p_1, p_2, \cdots, p_n\}$ is measurable with respect to m if and only if $\{x: f(x) = p_i\}$ is measurable for each i.

DEFINITION 11-3.2. Suppose m is a measure on an algebra $\mathscr{B}$ of subsets of a set T. Let s be a measurable simple function with domain T and let $\{q_1, \cdots, q_n\}$ be the nonzero members of the range of s. Then the *integral* of s is

$$\int_T s \, dm = \sum_{i=1}^{n} q_i \cdot m\{x: s(x) = q_i\}, \tag{11-4}$$

provided this sum is meaningful.

A measurable simple function s has an integral unless the right member of (11-4) contains a term equal to $+\infty$ and a term equal to $-\infty$.

Thus, all nonnegative measurable simple functions have integrals. In fact, a simple function has an integral if and only if at least one of the sets $\{x: f(x) > 0\}$ and $\{x: f(x) < 0\}$ has finite measure.

DEFINITION 11-3.3. Suppose m is a measure on an algebra of subsets of a set T. The *integral of a nonnegative measurable function* f is equal to the least upper bound of the set of all numbers $\int_T s \, dm$, where s is a measurable simple function with $s(x) \leqq f(x)$ on T. The *integral of a measurable function* f is

$$\int_T f \, dm = \int_T f^+ \, dm - \int_T f^- \, dm,$$

provided not both $\int_T f^+ \, dm$ and $\int_T f^- \, dm$ are $+\infty$.†

This definition of the integral of a nonnegative measurable function often can be used directly. However, the next theorem gives an alternate formula for the integral that sometimes is more useful. Both have the advantage that there is no need for the function to be bounded or for T to be bounded. Thus, improper integrals need not be treated separately. We have not restricted the measure of T to being finite nor have we assumed that f is bounded. In fact, the range of f is in the extended real number system.

THEOREM 11-3.1. If m is a measure on an algebra of subsets of a set T and f is a nonnegative measurable function, then

$$\int_T f \, dm = \sup \left[\sum_{i=1}^{n-1} y_i \cdot m\{x: f(x) \in [y_i, y_{i+1})\} + y_n \cdot m\{x: y_n \leqq f(x)\} \right],$$

(11-5)

where the sup is for all finite sequences $\{y_i\}$ with $0 < y_1 < \cdots < y_n$.

PROOF. Let f be a nonnegative measurable function. For an arbitrary sequence $\{y_i\}$ with $0 < y_1 < \cdots < y_n$, we define a simple function s by letting $s(x) = y_n$ if $y_n \leqq f(x)$, and $s(x) = y_i$ if $y_i \leqq f(x) < y_{i+1}$ and $1 \leqq i \leqq n-1$. Then we have

$$\sum_{i=1}^{n-1} y_i \cdot m\{x: f(x) \in [y_i, y_{i+1})\} + y_n \cdot m\{x: y_n \leqq f(x)\} = \int_T s \, dm.$$

---

† Often an *integrable function* is defined to be a function that has an integral which is not $+\infty$ or $-\infty$. Then a function can have an integral and not be integrable. To avoid this semantic conflict, we shall not use the concept of "integrable function," leaving the reader free to use whatever definition he wishes.

Thus, $\int_T f\, dm$ is not less than the right member of Eq. (11-5). Now suppose σ is a measurable simple function with $\sigma(x) \leq f(x)$ on T. Let $\{0, y_1, \cdots, y_n\}$ be a set that contains the range of σ, with $0 < y_1 < \cdots < y_n$. We let

$$S_{in} = \{x: \sigma(x) = y_i\} \cap \{x: y_n \leq f(x)\},$$

$$S_{ij} = \{x: \sigma(x) = y_i\} \cap \{x: f(x) \in [y_j, y_{j+1})\}$$

if $j < n$. Since $\sigma(x) \leq f(x)$, we have $S_{ij} = \Phi$ if $i > j$. Then

$$\int_T \sigma\, dm = \sum_{i=1}^n y_i \cdot m\{x: \sigma(x) = y_i\} = \sum_{i \leq j} y_i \cdot m(S_{ij}), \qquad (11\text{-}6)$$

since $\{x: \sigma(x) = y_i\} = \bigcup_{k=i}^n S_{ik}$. Also, $\{x: f(x) \in [y_i, y_{i+1})\} \supset \bigcup_{k=1}^i S_{ki}$, so that

$$\sum_{i=1}^{n-1} y_i \cdot m\{x: f(x) \in [y_i, y_{i+1})\} + y_n \cdot m\{x: y_n \leq f(x)\}$$

$$\geq \sum_{j \leq i} y_j \cdot m(S_{ji}) = \sum_{i \leq j} y_j \cdot m(S_{ij}). \qquad (11\text{-}7)$$

Since $y_i \leq y_j$ if $i \leq j$, it follows from (11-6) and (11-7) that

$$\int_T \sigma\, dm \leq \sum_{i=1}^{n-1} y_i \cdot m\{x: f(x) \in [y_i, y_{i+1})\} + y_n \cdot m\{x: y_n \leq f(x)\}.$$

Thus, $\int_T f\, dm$ is not larger than the right member of Eq. (11-5) and Eq. (11-5) is valid.

It is important to note that the use of y_i rather than y_{i+1} as a factor in (11-5) is crucial, unless $m(T) \neq +\infty$ [see problems 2 and 3]. We shall now state and prove some theorems analogous to properties of the Riemann integrals discussed in Chapters 3 and 5. In each case, f and g are assumed to be measurable with respect to a countably additive measure on a σ-algebra of subsets of a set T.

THEOREM 11-3.2. If $m(T) = 0$, then $\int_T f\, dm = 0$ for all measurable functions f.

PROOF. This follows directly from Theorem 11-3.1, since all sums of the type used in (11-5) are zero for both f^+ and f^-.

THEOREM 11-3.3.   If $\int_T f\,dm$ exists, then for all ordinary real numbers c

$$\int_T cf\,dm = c\int_T f\,dm.$$

PROOF.   Since $\int_T f\,dm$ exists, not both f^+ and f^- have infinite integrals. Also, it follows from Theorem 11-3.1 that

$$\int_T (cf)^+\,dm = c\int_T f^+\,dm$$

and

$$\int_T (cf)^-\,dm = c\int_T f^-\,dm, \quad \text{if} \quad c > 0;$$

$$\int_T (cf)^+\,dm = (-c)\int_T f^-\,dm$$

and

$$\int_T (cf)^-\,dm = (-c)\int_T f^+\,dm, \quad \text{if} \quad c < 0.$$

Thus, not both $\int_T (cf)^+\,dm$ and $\int_T (cf)^-\,dm$ are $+\infty$, so $\int_T cf\,dm$ exists and

$$\int_T cf\,dm = \int_T (cf)^+\,dm - \int_T (cf)^-\,dm$$

$$= c\int_T f^+\,dm - c\int_T f^-\,dm = c\int_T f\,dm.$$

THEOREM 11-3.4.   Suppose $m(R \cap S) = 0$, both $\int_R f\,dm$ and $\int_S f\,dm$ exist, and it is not true that one of these integrals is $+\infty$ and the other is $-\infty$.   Then

$$\int_R f\,dm + \int_S f\,dm = \int_{R \cup S} f\,dm.$$

PROOF.   We must prove that

$$\left[\int_R f^+\,dm - \int_R f^-\,dm\right] + \left[\int_S f^+\,dm - \int_S f^-\,dm\right]$$

$$= \int_{R \cup S} f^+\,dm - \int_{R \cup S} f^-\,dm. \quad (11\text{-}8)$$

To do this, we shall use Theorem 11-3.1 and write

$$\int_X f^+ \, dm = \sup \left\{ \sum_{i=1}^{n-1} y_i \cdot m[X \cap \{x: f(x) \in [y_i, y_{i+1})\}] \right.$$

$$\left. + y_n \cdot m[X \cap \{x: y_n \leq f(x)\}] \right\},$$

where the sup is for all finite sequences $\{y_i\}$ with $0 < y_1 < \cdots < y_n$. Since $m[(R \cup S) \cap A] = m[R \cap A] + m[S \cap A]$ for all $A \subset T$, we can let X be successively $R \cup S$, R, and S, to obtain

$$\int_{R \cup S} f^+ \, dm = \int_R f^+ \, dm + \int_S f^+ \, dm. \tag{11-9}$$

Similarly,

$$\int_{R \cup S} f^- \, dm = \int_R f^- \, dm + \int_S f^- \, dm. \tag{11-10}$$

Since it is not true that one of $\int_R f \, dm$ and $\int_S f \, dm$ is $+\infty$ and the other is $-\infty$, not both (11-9) and (11-10) are $+\infty$ and we can subtract to obtain (11-8).

THEOREM 11-3.5. If $f(x) \leq g(x)$ on T and both $\int_T f \, dm$ and $\int_T g \, dm$ exist, then

$$\int_T f \, dm \leq \int_T g \, dm.$$

PROOF. Since any simple function s with $s(x) \leq f^+(x)$ on T also satisfies $s(x) \leq g^+(x)$ on T, we have

$$\int_T f^+ \, dm \leq \int_T g^+ \, dm.$$

Similarly, $-\int_T f^- \, dm \leq -\int_T g^- \, dm$. Corresponding members of these inequalities can be added to complete the proof.

THEOREM 11-3.6. If $\int_T f \, dm$ exists, then

$$\left| \int_T f \, dm \right| \leq \int_T |f| \, dm \leq \sup \{|f(x)|: x \in T\} \cdot m(T). \tag{11-11}$$

PROOF. Note first that measurability of $|f|$ follows from measurability of f [Theorem 11-2.2]. Since any simple function s with $s(x) \leq f^+(x)$ on T also has the property that $s(x) \leq |f(x)|$ on T, it follows that

$\int_T f^+ \, dm \leqq \int_T |f| \, dm$. Similarly, $\int_T f^- \, dm \leqq \int_T |f| \, dm$. Then it follows from the equation

$$\int_T f \, dm = \int_T f^+ \, dm - \int_T f^- \, dm$$

that $|\int_T f \, dm| \leqq \int_T |f| \, dm$. The second inequality in (11-11) follows directly from Theorem 11-3.1.

THEOREM 11-3.7. If $\int_T f \, dm$ and $\int_T g \, dm$ both exist and it is not true that one is $+\infty$ and the other is $-\infty$, then

$$\int_T (f+g) \, dm = \int_T f \, dm + \int_T g \, dm.$$

PROOF. First, let us see why the theorem is true for simple functions. Suppose s_1 and s_2 are measurable simple functions for which it is not true that one of $\int_T s_1 \, dm$ and $\int_T s_2 \, dm$ is $+\infty$ and the other is $-\infty$. Let $\{y_1, \cdots, y_m\}$ and $\{z_1, \cdots, z_n\}$ be the nonzero members of the ranges of s_1 and s_2, respectively, and

$$A_{ij} = \{x \colon s_1(x) = y_i \text{ and } s_2(x) = z_j\}, \quad 0 \leqq i \leqq m, \quad 0 \leqq j \leqq n,$$

where $y_0 = z_0 = 0$. Then

$$\int_T s_1 \, dm = \sum_{i=1}^m y_i \cdot m\left(\bigcup_{j=0}^n A_{ij}\right) = \sum\nolimits^* y_i \cdot m(A_{ij}),$$

$$\int_T s_2 \, dm = \sum_{j=1}^n z_j \cdot m\left(\bigcup_{i=0}^m A_{ij}\right) = \sum\nolimits^* z_j \cdot m(A_{ij}),$$

and

$$\int_T (s_1+s_2) \, dm = \sum\nolimits^* (y_i+z_j) \cdot m(A_{ij}),$$

where $\sum^*$ denotes the sum over all pairs (i, j) with not both i and j zero. Thus, Theorem 11-3.7 is valid for simple functions.

To complete the proof of Theorem 11-3.7, we shall use Theorem 11-3.4 after proving Theorem 11-3.7 separately for each of the following sets, which are pair-wise disjoint and whose union is T:

$$S_1 = \{x \colon f(x) \geqq 0 \text{ and } g(x) \geqq 0\},$$

$$S_2 = \{x \colon f(x) < 0 \text{ and } g(x) < 0\},$$

$$S_3 = \{x \colon f(x) \geqq 0 \text{ and } g(x) < 0 \text{ and } (f+g)(x) \geqq 0\},$$

$$S_4 = \{x \colon f(x) \geqq 0 \text{ and } g(x) < 0 \text{ and } (f+g)(x) < 0\},$$

$$S_5 = \{x \colon f(x) < 0 \text{ and } g(x) \geqq 0 \text{ and } (f+g)(x) \geqq 0\},$$

$$S_6 = \{x \colon f(x) < 0 \text{ and } g(x) \geqq 0 \text{ and } (f+g)(x) < 0\}.$$

To prove Theorem 11-3.7 for $T = S_1$ is equivalent to proving it for the case f and g are nonnegative. To do this, we note first that if σ_1 and σ_2 are measurable simple functions with $\sigma_1(x) \leq f(x)$ and $\sigma_2(x) \leq g(x)$ for all x in T, then $\sigma_1(x) + \sigma_2(x) \leq (f+g)(x)$. Therefore,

$$\int_T (f+g)\, dm \geq \sup\left\{\int_T (\sigma_1 + \sigma_2)\, dm\right\}$$

$$= \sup\left\{\int_T \sigma_1\, dm + \int_T \sigma_2\, dm\right\} = \int_T f\, dm + \int_T g\, dm,$$

$$(11\text{-}12)$$

where the sup's are for all measurable simple functions σ_1 and σ_2 with $\sigma_1(x) \leq f(x)$ and $\sigma_2(x) \leq g(x)$ on T. If the equality in (11-12) is not valid, then there is a measurable simple function s with $s(x) \leq (f+g)(x)$ on T and which is such that the strict inequality holds with $f+g$ replaced by s. Then it follows from Theorem 11-3.4 that there is a set R on which s has a constant value α and

$$\int_R \alpha\, dm > \int_R f\, dm + \int_R g\, dm.$$

Whether or not $m(R) = +\infty$, there is a positive number $\varepsilon < \alpha$ such that

$$\int_R (\alpha - \varepsilon)\, dm > \int_R f\, dm + \int_R g\, dm. \qquad (11\text{-}13)$$

Now we choose a sequence $0 < y_1 < \cdots < y_n = \alpha$, with $|y_{i+1} - y_i| < \varepsilon$ for all i. Let σ be defined by $\sigma(x) = y_i$ if $f(x) \in [y_i, y_{i+1})$ and $\sigma(x) = \alpha$ if $y_n \leq f(x)$. Then σ is a measurable simple function with $\sigma(x) \leq f(x)$ on R, so that $\int_R f\, dm \geq \int_R \sigma\, dm$. If $x \in R$ and $f(x) < y_n$, then $\sigma(x) + \varepsilon > f(x)$; if $x \in R$ and $y_n \leq f(x)$, then $\alpha - \varepsilon - \sigma(x) < 0$. This and $\alpha \leq (f+g)(x)$ imply $\alpha - \varepsilon - \sigma(x) \leq g(x)$ on R and

$$\int_R g\, dm \geq \int_R (\alpha - \varepsilon - \sigma)\, dm. \qquad (11\text{-}14)$$

But from (11-13),

$$\int_R g\, dm < \int_R (\alpha - \varepsilon)\, dm - \int_R f\, dm$$

$$\leq \int_R (\alpha - \varepsilon)\, dm - \int_R \sigma\, dm = \int_R (\alpha - \varepsilon - \sigma)\, dm.$$

This contradicts (11-14) and completes the proof of the case $T = S_1$.

The case $T = S_2$ reduces to the case $T = S_1$ if f and g are replaced by $-f$ and $-g$. The case $T = S_3$ can be treated by proving first that $\int_{S_3} (f+g)\, dm$ exists and then noting that

$$\int_{S_3} (-g)\, dm + \int_{S_3} (f+g)\, dm = \int_{S_3} f\, dm$$

follows from the case $T = S_1$. Similarly, the case $T = S_4$ can be proved by using $\int f\, dm + \int -(f+g)\, dm = \int -g\, dm$. The cases $T = S_5$ and $T = S_6$ are similar.

PROBLEMS

1. Suppose m is a measure on an algebra of subsets of a set T. Prove each of the following.

   (a) $\int_T f\, dm = 0$ if $f = 0$ a.e. on T.

   (b) $f = 0$ a.e. on T if $\int_T |f|\, dM = 0$.

2. Suppose m is a measure on an algebra of subsets of a set T and that f is a measurable function whose range is contained in the set of ordinary real numbers. Prove each of the following.

   (a) There is a sequence of simple functions $\{s_n\}$ for which $\lim s_n(x) = f(x)$ if $x \in T$.

   (b) If f is nonnegative on T, then each s_n of part (a) can be nonnegative with $s_n(x) \leq s_{n+1}(x)$ for all x in T.

   (c) If f is bounded on T, then the sequence $\{s_n\}$ of part (a) can be chosen so as to converge uniformly to f on T.

3. Suppose m is a measure on an algebra of subsets of a set T, that $m(T) \neq +\infty$, and that f is nonnegative, measurable, and bounded with upper bound M. Prove that

$$\int_T f\, dm = \lim_S \sum_{i=1}^{n} \eta_i \cdot m\{x: f(x) \in [y_i, y_{i+1})\},$$

where S is a system of stages for which a stage is determined by a positive number δ and is the set of all partitions with selection $(\{y_1, y_2, \cdots, y_{n+1}\}, \{\eta_1, \cdots, \eta_n\})$ for which $0 = y_1 < y_2 < \cdots < y_{n+1} = M$, $|y_{i+1} - y_i| < \delta$, and $\eta_i \in [y_i, y_{i+1})$ for all i.

4. Suppose a measure m is defined on the collection of all subsets of the set R of real numbers by letting $m(S)$ be the number of positive integers

belonging to S. Let $f(0) = 0$ and $f(x) = x^{-2}$ if $x \neq 0$. Prove the following.

(a) $\int_R f \, dm = \sum_{n=1}^{+\infty} n^{-2}$.

(b) The right member of Eq. (11-5) is $+\infty$ if the factor y_i is replaced by y_{i+1}.

5. Suppose m is a countably additive measure on a σ-algebra $\mathscr{B}$ of subsets of a set T. Prove that

$$\int_E f \, dm = \lim_{n \to +\infty} \int_{E_n} f \, dm,$$

if f is measurable and nonnegative, $\bigcup_1^{+\infty} E_n = E$, and, for all n, $E_n \subset E_{n+1}$ and $E_n \in \mathscr{B}$.

6. Let m be a countably additive measure on a σ-algebra of subsets of a set T. For a nonnegative measurable function f and a positive number M, let f_M be the function for which $f_M(x)$ is the smaller of $f(x)$ and M if $x \in T$. Prove that

$$\int_T f \, dm = \lim_{M \to +\infty} \int_T f_M \, dm.$$

7. Suppose that f is nonnegative on T and $\int_T f \, dm < +\infty$. Prove that

(a*) $\lim_{t \to +\infty} t \cdot m\{x : f(x) \geq t\} = 0$.   (b) $\lim_{t \to 0+} t \cdot m\{x : f(x) \geq t\} = 0$.

8. Suppose that f is measurable and $|\int_T f \, dm| \neq +\infty$. Prove that for any $\varepsilon > 0$ there is a $\delta > 0$ such that

$$\int_E |f| \, dm < \varepsilon,$$

if E is a measurable subset of T with $m(E) < \delta$. [*Note:* Also see problem 9, page 167, and problem 6, page 259.]

11-4. CONVERGENCE THEOREMS AND COMPLETENESS

In this section, we shall generalize our previous theorems about term-by-term integration of sequences and series [Theorems 4-8.1 and 4-8.4]. Then we shall introduce the concept of complete vector space and prove that the spaces L_T^2 are complete, using this concept to describe complete orthonormal sets [Theorem 11-4.4].

THEOREM 11-4.1 (MONOTONE CONVERGENCE THEOREM). Suppose m is a countably additive measure on a σ-algebra of subsets of a set T. If $\{f_n\}$ is a monotone increasing sequence of nonnegative measurable functions, then

$$\int_T F \, dm = \lim_{n \to +\infty} \int_T f_n \, dm \quad \text{if} \quad \lim_{n \to +\infty} f_n(x) = F(x) \quad \text{a.e. on } T.$$

PROOF. Measurability of F follows from Theorem 11-2.3. Since $\{f_n\}$ is monotone increasing, we have $f_n(x) \leq F(x)$ a.e. on T. Then it follows from Theorem 11-3.5 that the sequence $\{\int_T f_n \, dm\}$ is monotone increasing and has a limit, and that

$$\int_T F \, dm \geq \lim_{n \to +\infty} \int_T f_n \, dm. \tag{11-15}$$

Now let s be a simple function for which $s(x) \leq F(x)$ a.e. on T, and let θ be a positive number with $\theta < 1$. For each n, let

$$T_n = \{x : f_n(x) \geq \theta \cdot s(x)\}.$$

Then $T_n \subset T_{n+1}$ for all n, and $\bigcup_1^{+\infty} T_n$ differs from T by a set of measure zero. Also,

$$\int_T f_n \, dm \geq \int_{T_n} f_n \, dm \geq \theta \int_{T_n} s \, dm. \tag{11-16}$$

Since the range of s is a finite set of ordinary real numbers, it follows from Theorem 11-1.2 and the fact that $\bigcup_1^{+\infty} T_n$ differs from T by a set of measure zero, that

$$\lim_{n \to +\infty} \int_{T_n} s \, dm = \int_T s \, dm.$$

This and (11-16) imply

$$\lim_{n \to +\infty} \int_T f_n \, dm \geq \theta \int_T s \, dm.$$

Since θ was an arbitrary positive number with $\theta < 1$ and $\int_T F \, dm$ is equal to the sup of $\int_T s \, dm$ for simple functions s with $s(x) \leq F(x)$ a.e. on T, we have

$$\lim_{n \to +\infty} \int_T f_n \, dm \geq \int_T F \, dm.$$

This and (11-15) give the desired conclusion.

The assumption in Theorem 11-4.1 that $\{f_n\}$ be a monotone increasing sequence of nonnegative functions enabled us to obtain the conclusion of the theorem without assuming either that T has finite measure or that the sequence is bounded. It is important to realize that in this case $\lim \int_T f_n \, dm$ may be $+\infty$. In the next theorem, we assume that $m(T) < +\infty$ and that the sequence $\{f_n\}$ is bounded. Then the sequence need not be monotone and the functions need not be nonnegative. Moreover, in this case $\lim \int_T f_n \, dm$ is finite.

LEMMA. Suppose m is a countably additive measure on a σ-algebra of subsets of a set T and that $m(T) < +\infty$. Also suppose that $\{f_n\}$ is a sequence of measurable functions and that

$$\lim_{n \to +\infty} f_n(x) = F(x) \quad \text{a.e. on } T.$$

Then for any positive numbers ε and δ, there is a measurable set A with $m(A) < \delta$ and an integer N such that

$$|F(x) - f_n(x)| < \varepsilon \quad \text{if} \quad n > N \quad \text{and} \quad x \notin A.$$

PROOF. It follows from Theorem 11-2.3 that F is measurable. Then each of the following sets is measurable:

$$E_k = \{x : x \in T \text{ and } |F(x) - f_k(x)| \geq \varepsilon\}.$$

Now let

$$W_n = \bigcup_{k=n}^{+\infty} E_k = \{x : x \in T \text{ and } |F(x) - f_k(x)| \geq \varepsilon \text{ for some } k \geq n\}.$$

Since each E_k is measurable, the set W_n is measurable for every n. Also, $W_n \supset W_{n+1}$. Therefore, it follows from Theorem 11-1.2 that $\bigcap_1^{+\infty} W_n = W$ is measurable and

$$m(W) = \lim_{n \to +\infty} m(W_n).$$

Since $\lim f_n(x) = F(x)$ a.e., we have $m(W) = 0$. Therefore, there is an N for which $m(W_N) < \delta$. Then

$$|F(x) - f_n(x)| < \varepsilon \quad \text{if} \quad n > N \quad \text{and} \quad x \notin W_n.$$

THEOREM 11-4.2 (BOUNDED CONVERGENCE THEOREM). Suppose m is a countably additive measure on a σ-algebra of subsets of a set T with $m(T) < +\infty$. If $\{f_n\}$ is a sequence of measurable functions for which there is a number M such that $|f_n(x)| \leq M$ for all n and all x in T, then

$$\int_T F \, dm = \lim_{n \to +\infty} \int_T f_n \, dm \quad \text{if} \quad \lim_{n \to +\infty} f_n(x) = F(x) \quad \text{a.e. on } T.$$

PROOF. Measurability of F follows from Theorem 11-2.3. From the lemma, there is an integer N and a measurable set A such that $m(A) < \varepsilon/(4M)$ and

$$|F(x) - f_n(x)| < \frac{\varepsilon}{2 \cdot m(T)} \quad \text{if} \quad x \notin A.$$

Note that $|F(x) - f_n(x)| \leq 2M$ except on a set of measure zero on which $\lim f_n(x) \neq F(x)$. Then

$$\left| \int_T F \, dm - \int_T f_n \, dm \right| = \left| \int_T (F - f_n) \, dm \right| \leq \int_T |F - f_n| \, dm$$

$$= \int_{T-A} |F - f_n| \, dm + \int_A |F - f_n| \, dm$$

$$\leq \frac{\varepsilon}{2 \cdot m(T)} \, m(T - A) + 2M \cdot m(A) \leq \frac{\varepsilon}{2} + \frac{\varepsilon}{2} = \varepsilon.$$

Therefore, $\lim \int_T f_n \, dm = \int_T F \, dm$.

The next theorem is stronger than the bounded convergence theorem in the sense that boundedness of the sequence $\{f_n\}$ is replaced by the hypothesis that there is a nonnegative measurable function g with $|f(x)| \leq g(x)$ a.e. and $\int_T g \, dm < +\infty$.

THEOREM 11.4.3 (LEBESGUE CONVERGENCE THEOREM). Suppose m is a countably additive measure on a σ-algebra of subsets of a set T and that g is nonnegative and measurable with $\int_T g \, dm < +\infty$. If $\{f_n\}$ is a sequence of measurable functions such that $|f_n(x)| \leq g(x)$ on T, then

$$\int_T F \, dm = \lim_{n \to +\infty} \int_T f_n \, dm \quad \text{if} \quad \lim_{n \to +\infty} f_n(x) = F(x) \quad \text{a.e. on } T.$$

PROOF. Measurability of F follows from Theorem 11-2.3. Since $\int_T g \, dm < +\infty$, for an arbitrary positive number ε there is an increasing sequence $y_1 > 0, y_2, \cdots, y_k$ of positive numbers such that

$$\int_T g \, dm < \frac{\varepsilon}{3} + \sum_{i=1}^{k-1} y_i \cdot m\{x : g(x) \in [y_i, y_{i+1})\} \tag{11-17}$$

[see Theorem 11-3.1 and problem 7(a), page 595]. For $1 \leq i < k$, let $A_i = \{x : g(x) \in [y_i, y_{i+1})\}$, and let $A = \bigcup_1^{k-1} A_i$. Then $m(A_i) < +\infty$ for each i and

$$|f_n(x)| \leq g(x) < y_{i+1} \quad \text{if} \quad x \in A_i,$$

so that it follows from the bounded convergence theorem that

$$\int_{A_i} F\,dm = \lim_{n \to +\infty} \int_{A_i} f_n\,dm \quad \text{if} \quad 1 \le i < k.$$

Thus, there is an integer N such that

$$\left| \int_{A_i} F\,dm - \int_{A_i} f_n\,dm \right| < \frac{\varepsilon}{3k} \quad \text{if} \quad 1 \le i < k \quad \text{and} \quad n > N.$$

Also, (11-17) implies that $\int_{\sim A} g\,dm < \varepsilon/3$. This and $|f_n(x)| \le g(x)$ imply

$$\left| \int_{\sim A} f_n\,dm \right| < \frac{\varepsilon}{3} \quad \text{for all} \quad n, \qquad \left| \int_{\sim A} F\,dm \right| < \frac{\varepsilon}{3}.$$

Combining inequalities we have established, we obtain

$$\left| \int_T F\,dm - \int_T f_n\,dm \right| \le \sum_{i=1}^{k-1} \left| \int_{A_i} F\,dm - \int_{A_i} f_n\,dm \right|$$

$$+ \left| \int_{\sim A} F\,dm - \int_{\sim A} f_n\,dm \right| < \frac{\varepsilon}{3} + \frac{2\varepsilon}{3} = \varepsilon.$$

Therefore, $\lim_n \int_T f_n\,dm = \int_T F\,dm$.

If m is a countably additive measure on a σ-algebra of subsets of a set T, then we can define L_T^2 to be the set of equivalence classes of measurable functions f for which $\int_T f^2\,dm < +\infty$. The discussion of pages 506 and 507 for Riemann integration on an interval can be restated with essentially no change, so it will not be repeated here. However, we are now prepared to prove completeness of L_T^2 and apply this to obtain a new and elegant characterization of complete orthogonal sequences. This is not possible for L^2-spaces defined using Riemann integration. In fact, this is one of the most important reasons for studying the concept of countably additive measures and the resulting integrals, especially the Lebesgue measure of Section 11-6.

DEFINITION 11-4.1. A *complete vector space* is a vector space V with the property that all Cauchy sequences are convergent; that is, if $\{\mathbf{v}_n\}$ is a sequence of vectors for which $\lim_{m,n \to +\infty} \|\mathbf{v}_m - \mathbf{v}_n\| = 0$, then there is a vector $\mathbf{v}$ such that

$$\lim_{n \to +\infty} \|\mathbf{v} - \mathbf{v}_n\| = 0.$$

THEOREM 11-4.4 (RIESZ-FISCHER). For any countably additive measure on a σ-algebra of subsets of a set T, the corresponding vector space L_T^2 is complete.

PROOF. We must show that if

$$\lim_{j,k \to +\infty} \int_T (f_j - f_k)^2 \, dm = 0, \tag{11-18}$$

where each f_k is measurable and $\int_T f_k^2 \, dm < +\infty$, then there is a measurable function F such that $\int_T F^2 \, dm < +\infty$ and

$$\lim_{p \to +\infty} \int_T (F - f_p)^2 \, dm = 0.$$

If the sequence $\{f_n\}$ satisfies (11-18), then there is a subsequence $\{f_{n_k}\}$ such that

$$\sum_{k=1}^{+\infty} \left[\int_T (f_{n_k} - f_{n_{k+1}})^2 \, dm \right] = \sigma < +\infty.$$

Define a function g by

$$g(x) = |f_{n_1}(x)| + \sum_{k=1}^{+\infty} |f_{n_{k+1}}(x) - f_{n_k}(x)|. \tag{11-19}$$

Then it follows from the fact that

$$|\sum x_i|^2 \leqq 2 \sum x_i^2 \quad \text{for all numbers} \quad \{x_i\}, \tag{11-20}$$

that

$$\int_T g^2 \, dm \leqq 2 \int_T (f_{n_1})^2 \, dm + 2\sigma,$$

so that $\int_T g^2 \, dm < +\infty$. Therefore, there is a set E such that $m(E) = 0$ and $g(x) < +\infty$ if $x \notin E$. Because of convergence of the series (11-19) when $x \notin E$, we can define F by letting

$$F(x) = f_{n_1}(x) + \sum_{k=1}^{+\infty} [f_{n_{k+1}}(x) - f_{n_k}(x)] = \lim_{k \to +\infty} f_{n_k}(x) \quad \text{if} \quad x \notin E,$$

and $F(x) = 0$ if $x \in E$. Since

$$|F(x) - f_{n_k}(x)|^2 \leqq \left[\sum_{r=1}^{+\infty} |f_{n_{r+1}}(x) - f_{n_r}(x)| \right]^2 \leqq [g(x)]^2 \quad \text{a.e.,}$$

and $\lim [F(x)-f_{n_k}(x)]^2 = 0$ a.e., it follows from the Lebesgue convergence theorem that

$$\lim_{k \to +\infty} \int_T [F-f_{n_k}]^2 \, dm = 0.$$

Then it follows from this equality, Eq. (11-18), and inequality (11-20), that

$$\lim_{p \to +\infty} \int_T [F-f_p]^2 \, dm = \lim_{k,p \to +\infty} \int_T [(F-f_{n_k})+(f_{n_k}-f_p)]^2 \, dm$$

$$\leqq 2 \cdot \lim_{k \to +\infty} \int_T (F-f_{n_k})^2 \, dm$$

$$+2 \cdot \lim_{k,p \to +\infty} \int_T (f_{n_k}-f_p)^2 \, dm = 0.$$

To complete the proof, we must show that $\int_T F^2 \, dm < +\infty$. This we do by using (11-20) to establish, for any particular k,

$$\int_T F^2 \, dm \leqq 2 \int_T (F-f_{n_k})^2 \, dm + 2 \int_T f_{n_k}^2 \, dm.$$

We have used several criteria for an orthonormal set to be complete [see Definition 10-1.6 and Theorem 10-1.3]. We can now establish the criteria stated in the next theorem. One can describe this theorem as stating that an orthonormal set $\{e_i\}$ in a *complete* vector space is complete if and only if $\{e_i\}$ is not a proper subset of some other orthonormal set.

THEOREM 11-4.5. Each of the following is a necessary and sufficient condition for an orthonormal set $\{e_i\}$ in a complete vector space V to be complete.

    (i) $\mathbf{w} = \mathbf{0}$ if $\mathbf{w}$ is orthogonal to each e_i.
    (ii) $\mathbf{x} = \mathbf{y}$ if $(\mathbf{x}, e_i) = (\mathbf{y}, e_i)$ for each i.

PROOF. We know already that (i) and (ii) are satisfied if $\{e_i\}$ is complete [see Theorem 10-1.4]. Suppose now that $\{e_i\}$ is an orthonormal set in a complete vector space V, but that $\{e_i\}$ is not complete. Then from (a) of Theorem 10-1.3, there is a member $\mathbf{x}$ of V such that

$$\lim_{n \to +\infty} \left\| \mathbf{x} - \sum_{i=1}^{n} (\mathbf{x}, e_i)e_i \right\| \neq 0.$$

Bessel's inequality (10-9) implies $\sum_1^{+\infty} (\mathbf{x}, \mathbf{e}_i)^2 \leq \|\mathbf{x}\|^2 < +\infty$. Then we have

$$\lim_{m \to +\infty} \left\| \sum_{i=m+1}^{m+n} (\mathbf{x}, \mathbf{e}_i)\mathbf{e}_i \right\| = \lim_{m \to +\infty} \left[\sum_{i=m+1}^{m+n} (\mathbf{x}, \mathbf{e}_i)^2 \right]^{\frac{1}{2}} = 0,$$

so that it follows from completeness of V that $\sum_1^{+\infty} (\mathbf{x}, \mathbf{e}_i)\mathbf{e}_i$ is convergent. Now we let

$$\mathbf{w} = \mathbf{x} - \sum_{i=1}^{+\infty} (\mathbf{x}, \mathbf{e}_i)\mathbf{e}_i.$$

Then $\mathbf{w}$ is orthogonal to each $\mathbf{e}_i$ and $\mathbf{w} \neq \mathbf{0}$, so (i) is not satisfied. Also, $\mathbf{0}$ and $\mathbf{w}$ have the property that $(\mathbf{0}, \mathbf{e}_i) = (\mathbf{w}, \mathbf{e}_i)$ for each i, so that (ii) is not satisfied.

PROBLEMS

1. Let $\{f_n\}$ be a sequence of measurable functions and C be the set of all x for which $\lim_{n \to +\infty} f_n(x)$ exists and is not $+\infty$ or $-\infty$. Explain why C is measurable.

2. Let $f_n(x) = 1/n$ if $|x| \leq n$ and $f_n(x) = 0$ if $|x| > n$. Prove that

$$\int_{-\infty}^{+\infty} f_n(x)\, dx = 2 \quad \text{and} \quad \int_{-\infty}^{+\infty} [\lim_{n \to +\infty} f_n(x)]\, dx = 0,$$

where the integrals are improper Riemann integrals. Explain why this is consistent with the monotone convergence theorem.

3. Let $f_n(x) = 1$ if $x \in [n, n+1]$ and $f_n(x) = 0$ otherwise. Determine a function F such that $\lim_{n \to +\infty} f_n(x) = F(x)$ and prove that

$$\int_{-\infty}^{+\infty} f_n(x)\, dx = 1 \quad \text{and} \quad \int_{-\infty}^{+\infty} F(x)\, dx = 0,$$

where the integrals are improper Riemann integrals. For each of Theorems 11-4.1, 11-4.2, and 11-4.3, explain why this does not contradict that theorem.

4. Let functions $\{f_n\}$ and F have domains the set of positive integers, with $F(k) = 1$ for all k, $f_n(k) = 1$ if $k < n$, and $f_n(k) = 0$ if $k \geq n$. Prove the following and explain why this does not contradict the monotone convergence theorem.

(a) $\lim_{n \to +\infty} f_n(k) = F(k)$ for all k.

(b) For m the measure of problem 7(b), page 582, $\int f_n\, dm = 0$ for all n, and $\int F\, dm = 1$.

5. Let m be a countably additive measure on a σ-algebra of subsets of a set T and $\{f_n\}$ be a sequence of nonnegative measurable functions on T such that $f_n \to f$ a.e. on T and

$$\lim_{n \to +\infty} \int_T f_n \, dm = \int_T f \, dm < +\infty.$$

Prove that $\int_E f \, dm = \lim_{n \to +\infty} \int_E f_n \, dm$ if E is a measurable subset of T.

6. Let S be the system of stages for which A is a stage if and only if there is a finite subset α of the interval $[0, 1]$ for which A is the set of all finite subsets of $[0, 1]$ that contain α. For each finite subset α of $[0, 1]$, let $f_\alpha(x) = 1$ if $x \in \alpha$ and $f_\alpha(x) = 0$ if $x \notin \alpha$. Let $f(x) = 1$ if $x \in [0, 1]$. Prove each of the following.

(a) $\lim_S f_\alpha(x) = f(x)$ if $x \in [0, 1]$.

(b) The set $\{f_\alpha\}$ is increasing in the sense that $f_\alpha(x) \leqq f_\beta(x)$ if $\alpha \subset \beta$.

(c) $\lim_S \int_0^1 f_\alpha(x) \, dx \neq \int_0^1 f(x) \, dx$.   [*Note:* This indicates the importance of using *ordinary* sequences when stating the monotone convergence theorem.]

7. Suppose the functions $\{f_n\}$ are measurable on a set T, that $m(T) < +\infty$, and that $\lim f_n(x) = F(x)$ a.e. on T.

(a) Prove that for any positive numbers ρ and r there is a subset A of T with $m(A) < r$ and a positive number N such that

$$|F(x) - f_n(x)| < \rho \quad \text{if} \quad n > N \quad \text{and} \quad x \notin A.$$

[*Hint:* Let $A_n = \bigcup_{k=n}^{+\infty} \{x: |F(x) - f_k(x)| > \rho\}$ and note that $m(\bigcap_1^{+\infty} A_n) = 0$.]

(b) Prove that for any $\delta > 0$ there is a subset E of T with $m(E) < \delta$ such that $\{f_n\}$ converges uniformly to f on $T - E$.

8. Prove that if $f \in L_T^2$ and g is bounded and measurable on T, then $fg \in L_T^2$.

9. Prove that if $\lim_{p \to +\infty} \int_T (F - f_p)^2 \, dm = \lim_{p \to +\infty} \int_T (G - f_p)^2 \, dm = 0$ and $f_p \in L_T^2$ for each p, then $F(x) = G(x)$ a.e. on T.

10. Let $\{f_n\}$ be a sequence of functions with domain $[0, 1]$ defined by letting $f_n(x)$ be 1 or 0 according to whether $x \in I_{p,k}$ or $x \notin I_{p,k}$, where p and k are integers for which $n = p + 2^k$ with $0 \leq p < 2^k$, and $I_{p,k}$ is the closed interval $[2^{-k} p, 2^{-k}(p+1)]$ and $0 \leq p \leq 2^{k-1}$.   Show that

$$\lim_{m,n \to +\infty} \int_0^1 [f_m(x) - f_n(x)]^2 \, dx = 0,$$

but there is no x for which $\lim f_n(x)$ exists.   Explain why this does not contradict Theorem 11-4.4.

11. Suppose m is a countably additive measure on a σ-algebra of subsets of a set T, and that $\{f_n\}$ is a sequence of measurable functions for which $\int_T |f_k| \, dm < +\infty$ for each k and

$$\lim_{j,k \to +\infty} \int_T |f_j - f_k| \, dm = 0.$$

Prove that there is a measurable function F such that

$$\lim_{p \to +\infty} \int_T |F - f_p| \, dm = 0.$$

12. Suppose $\{e_i\}$ is an orthonormal set in a vector space V. Prove that each member of V is orthogonal to all but a countable number of members of e_i.

11-5. LEBESGUE MEASURABLE SETS

Before defining Lebesgue measure, we shall generalize the concepts of length, area, and volume discussed in Sections 3-1, 3-2, and 5-1. For simplicity, we shall call an n-dimensional rectangular parallelepiped [Definition 8-5.2] an n-D interval. Thus an n-D *interval* is a subset I of R^n for which there is a vector $\mathbf{u}$ and pair-wise orthogonal vectors $\mathbf{v}_1, \cdots, \mathbf{v}_n$ such that I either is the set of all vectors

$$\mathbf{u} + \alpha_1 \mathbf{v}_1 + \alpha_2 \mathbf{v}_2 + \cdots + \alpha_n \mathbf{v}_n, \quad \text{with} \quad 0 \leqq \alpha_i \leqq 1 \quad \text{for all} \quad i,$$

$$(11\text{-}21)$$

or the set of vectors described by (11-21), with any or all of the $\leqq$ signs replaced by $<$. The interval is *closed* if and only if all the signs are $\leqq$; it is *open* if and only if all the signs are $<$. The vectors $\mathbf{v}_1, \cdots, \mathbf{v}_n$ are *adjacent edges* of I.

We shall give only a brief summary of facts about n-D inner and outer sums and n-D content, since the proofs are analogous to those for length, area, and volume. As before, we shall say that two intervals *overlap* if and only if some interior point of one of the intervals belongs to the other. An interior point is a point as described in (11-21), with $0 < \alpha_i < 1$ for all i.

DEFINITION 11-5.1. Suppose B is a set of points in R^n and $\{I_1, \cdots, I_k\}$ is a set of intervals, no two of which overlap and each of which is contained in B. Also suppose $a_i^1, \cdots, a_i^n$ are the lengths of adjacent edges of I_i. Then $\sum_{i=1}^k a_i^1 a_i^2 \cdots a_i^n$ is an n-D *inner sum* for the set B.

DEFINITION 11-5.2. Suppose B is a set of points in R^n and $\{I_1, \cdots, I_k\}$ is a set of intervals whose union contains B. Also suppose $a_i^1, \cdots, a_i^n$ are the lengths of adjacent edges of I_i. Then $\sum_{i=1}^{k} a_i^1 a_i^2 \cdots a_i^n$ is an *n-D outer sum* for the set B.

DEFINITION 11-5.3. A *set of points with n-D content* is a set of points in R^n for which there exists at least one *n-D* outer sum, and

$$\sup \{\text{inner sums}\} = \inf \{\text{outer sums}\}.$$

The *n-D content* of a set B having *n-D* content is the common value of $\sup \{\text{inner sums}\}$ and $\inf \{\text{outer sums}\}$. It will be denoted by $c(B)$.

For the facts about length, area, and volume, there are corresponding facts about content that can be proved by similar methods. Some of these facts will be listed as I, II, III, IV, and Theorem 11-5.1.

I. If B is a bounded set of points in R^n and s_* and s^* are inner and outer sums for B, then $s_* \leqq s^*$.

II. If A and B are sets that have content, then $A \cap B$, $B - A$, and $A \cup B$ have content. If $A \cap B = \Phi$, then the content of $A \cup B$ is the sum of the contents of A and B.

III. If $A \subset B$ and A and B have content, then $c(A) \leqq c(B)$.

IV. The content of an interval with adjacent edges of length $a_1, \cdots, a_n$ is equal to $a_1 a_2 \cdots a_n$.

DEFINITION 11-5.4. A *system of intervals* with *mesh* σ is a set of non-overlapping intervals whose union is R^n, for which σ is the least upper bound of lengths of edges of these intervals, and there is a positive lower bound for these lengths.

THEOREM 11-5.1. For a bounded set B in R^n, each of the following is a necessary and sufficient condition for B to have content.

   (i) For each positive number ε, there exist inner and outer sums s_* and s^* for B such that $s^* - s_* < \varepsilon$.

  (ii) For each positive number ε, there is a positive number δ such that, if s_* and s^* are the inner and outer sums determined by a system of intervals with mesh less than δ, then $s^* - s_* < \varepsilon$.

 (iii) For each positive number ε, there are sets A and C that have *n-D* content and have the properties that $A \subset B \subset C$ and the content of $C - A$ is less than ε.

The set of all subsets of R^n with content is not an algebra, since R^n itself does not have content. This is not a serious defect. In fact, we could choose a bounded set T with content. Then the set of all subsets of T with content is an algebra. However, we cannot obtain a σ-algebra in this way, since the union of a countable number of sets with content need not have content. For example, the set of rational points in the interval $[0, 1]$ does not have length (1-D content). Similarly, the set of points (x, y) with x rational and $|x| \leq 1$ and $|y| \leq 1$ does not have area (2-D content), although it is the union of a countable number of line segments with zero area. Our task is to enlarge the collection of sets with content to obtain a σ-algebra on which we can define a countably additive measure.

We shall see that there are many ways in which Lebesgue measure is analogous to content. We shall use such an analogy with (iii) of Theorem 11-5.1 to introduce Lebesgue measure. However, let us first consider an example that illustrates how (iii) might be modified.

ILLUSTRATION. Let $B = [0, 1] - \bigcup_{k=1}^{+\infty} S_k$, where S_1 is the open interval of length 2^{-2} centered in the interval $[0, 1]$ and, in general, S_n has length 2^{-n-1} and is the union of 2^{n-1} equal intervals centered in the 2^{n-1} intervals whose union is the set $[0, 1] - \bigcup_1^{n-1} S_k$ [also see problem 7, page 126]. For each n, we see that all intervals contained in $[0, 1]$ $- \bigcup_1^n S_k$ have length less than 2^{-n}. Thus, B contains no intervals of nonzero length, so that all inner sums for B are zero. However, no outer sum for B is less than $\frac{1}{2}$. To show this, we shall use a proof by contradiction. We assume that there are intervals $J_1, \cdots, J_p$ such that

$$B \subset \bigcup_{k=1}^n J_k \quad \text{and} \quad \sum_{k=1}^p |J_k| < \tfrac{1}{2} - \varepsilon,$$

where $\varepsilon > 0$. By stretching the intervals slightly and then discarding the end points if any, we see that the intervals $J_1, \cdots, J_p$ can be chosen to be open. Then the set that contains these intervals and all intervals used in forming the sets $\{S_k\}$ is a cover of $[0, 1]$ by open intervals. From the Heine-Borel theorem, it follows that there is a finite subset $\{I_1, \cdots, I_n\}$ of these intervals that covers $[0, 1]$. However,

$$|I_1| + \cdots + |I_n| < (\tfrac{1}{2} - \varepsilon) + \sum_{k=1}^{+\infty} \frac{1}{2^{k+1}} = 1 - \varepsilon.$$

This contradicts the fact that no outer sum for $[0, 1]$ is less than 1.

The set B itself is closed, since it is the complement in $[0, 1]$ of the open set $\bigcup_1^{+\infty} S_k$. Also, for any particular integer n, the complement in $[0, 1]$ of $\bigcup_1^n S_k$ contains B and is the union of a finite number of closed intervals. For any positive number ε, we can stretch these intervals slightly and discard the end points so that the total increase in length is less than ε. The union then is an open set G for which $G - B$ is contained in the union of intervals, the sum of whose lengths is not greater than

$$\varepsilon + \sum_{k=n+1}^{+\infty} (\text{length of } S_k) = \varepsilon + \sum_{k=n+1}^{+\infty} \frac{1}{2^{k+1}} = \varepsilon + \frac{1}{2^{n+1}}.$$

This shows that B is measurable in the sense of Definition 11-5.6, to be given after we introduce the useful concept of outer measure.

DEFINITION 11-5.5. The *outer measure* of a subset A of R^n is the number

$$\mu^*(A) = \inf \left\{ \sum_{n=1}^{+\infty} c(I_n) : A \subset \bigcup_{n=1}^{+\infty} I_n \right\},$$

where each I_n is an open n-D interval and $c(I_n)$ is its content.†

Every subset of R^n has outer measure, possibly equal to $+\infty$, but outer measure is not additive on the algebra of all subsets of R^n [see Section 11-8]. As we shall see later [Theorem 11-5.3 and 11-6.2], the next definition describes a σ-algebra of subsets of R^n on which μ^* is countably additive.

There are two simple properties of outer measure that will be very useful:

$$\mu^*(A) \leq \mu^*(B) \quad \text{if} \quad A \subset B; \tag{11-22}$$

$$\mu^* \left(\bigcup_{n=1}^{+\infty} A_n \right) \leq \sum_{n=1}^{+\infty} \mu^*(A_n). \tag{11-23}$$

If $A \subset B$, then any cover of B by intervals also is a cover of A. This establishes (11-22). To prove (11-23), we suppose ε is a positive number and that, for each p,

$$A_p \subset \bigcup_{n=1}^{+\infty} I_n^p, \quad \sum_{n=1}^{+\infty} c(I_n^p) < \frac{\varepsilon}{2^{p+1}} + \mu^*(A_p).$$

---

† It is immaterial whether we require every interval to be open or allow the intervals to be arbitrary [see problem 3]. However, there will be occasions when it will be convenient to use open intervals.

Then the union of the sets I_n^p contains $\bigcup_1^{+\infty} A_n$. Also, the sum of the lengths of all of these intervals is less than $\varepsilon + \sum_1^{+\infty} \mu^*(A_n)$. Thus,

$$\mu^*\left(\bigcup_{n=1}^{+\infty} A_n\right) < \varepsilon + \sum_{n=1}^{+\infty} \mu^*(A_n) \quad \text{if} \quad \varepsilon > 0.$$

This implies (11-23).

DEFINITION 11-5.6. A *Lebesgue measurable set* in R^n is a subset B of R^n with the property that, for any positive number ε, there is a closed set F and an open set G such that

$$F \subset B \subset G \quad \text{and} \quad \mu^*(G-F) < \varepsilon.$$

It will be useful to have available other characterizations of Lebesgue measurable sets. Some of these are given by the next theorem, whose proof uses the next lemma.

LEMMA. Let G be an open subset of R^n. For any interval I with nonzero content, G is the union of a countable set of nonoverlapping closed intervals with edges parallel to and not longer than the edges of I.

PROOF. First, we represent the entire space R^n as the union of non-overlapping intervals congruent to I. Explicitly, if I has edges $\mathbf{v}_1, \cdots, \mathbf{v}_n$, then we can use intervals of type

$$\{(k_1\mathbf{v}_1 + \cdots + k_n\mathbf{v}_n) + \alpha_1\mathbf{v}_1 + \alpha_2\mathbf{v}_2 + \cdots + \alpha_n\mathbf{v}_n : 0 \leqq \alpha_i \leqq 1\},$$

where $k_1, \cdots, k_n$ are integers. We let all of these intervals that are contained in G be members of a collection $\mathscr{I}$ of intervals. Then we subdivide each interval not in this collection into 2^n congruent intervals and let all of these intervals that are contained in G be members of $\mathscr{I}$. Continuing this, we obtain our collection $\mathscr{I}$ of intervals The union of these intervals is G, since if $\mathbf{x} \in G$, then $\mathbf{x}$ has a neighborhood U in G that contains all intervals containing $\mathbf{x}$ whose edges are sufficiently short. It remains to show that $\mathscr{I}$ is a countable collection of intervals. Each of the intervals has interior points with all coordinates rational. Let S be a set that contains exactly one such point from the interior of each member of $\mathscr{I}$. For each $k \geqq n$, let S_k be the set of all members $(r_{i_1}, r_{i_2}, \ldots, r_{i_n})$ of S with $i_1 + i_2 + \cdots + i_n = k$. We then order S as a sequence by ordering each of the finite sets S_k and then using the rule that $\mathbf{x}$ precedes $\mathbf{y}$ means either $\mathbf{x} \in S_i$ and $\mathbf{y} \in S_j$ with $i < j$, or both $\mathbf{x}$ and $\mathbf{y}$ belong to some S_k and $\mathbf{x}$ precedes $\mathbf{y}$ in S_k. Now we order $\mathscr{I}$ as a sequence by replacing each member of S by the corresponding member of $\mathscr{I}$.

THEOREM 11-5.2.   Each of the following is a necessary and sufficient condition for a subset B of R^n to be Lebesgue measurable.

   (i) For any positive number ε, there is a set S which has the following properties: S is the union of a countable collection S of closed intervals; $\mu^*(B \nabla S) < \varepsilon$; and every bounded set contains points of at most a finite number of members of S.†

   (ii) For any positive number ε, there is an open set G such that

$$B \subset G \quad \text{and} \quad \mu^*(G - B) < \varepsilon.$$

   (iii) For any positive number ε, there is a closed set F such that

$$F \subset B \quad \text{and} \quad \mu^*(B - F) < \varepsilon.$$

PROOF.   We shall show first that every measurable set satisfies (ii) and (iii), that every set which satisfies (ii) also satisfies (i), and that every set which satisfies (i) is measurable.   Then we shall complete the proof by showing that a set is measurable if it satisfies (iii).

If B is measurable and $\varepsilon > 0$, then there is a closed set F and an open set G such that $F \subset B \subset G$ and $\mu^*(G - F) < \varepsilon$.   It then follows from (11-22) that

$$\mu^*(G - B) \leqq \mu^*(G - F) < \varepsilon \quad \text{and} \quad \mu^*(B - F) \leqq \mu^*(G - F) < \varepsilon.$$

Thus, every measurable set satisfies (ii) and (iii).

Now suppose that B satisfies (ii), so that there is an open set G with $B \subset G$ and $\mu^*(G - B) < \frac{1}{2}\varepsilon$.   From the lemma, we know that there is a sequence $\{I_n\}$ of nonoverlapping intervals whose union is G and whose edges all have length not greater than 1.   For each integer n, let U_n be the ball consisting of all vectors with length not greater than n. Then the sum of the contents of those intervals that are members of the sequence $\{I_n\}$ and are contained in U_n is finite, since this sum is not larger than the content of U_n.   Let S_n be the union of a finite subset of the intervals that are contained in U_n and not contained in U_{n-1}, chosen so that the sum of the contents of all other intervals of this type is less than $\varepsilon/2^{n+1}$.   If $S = \bigcup_1^{+\infty} S_n$, then $S \subset G$ and

$$B \nabla S = (S - B) \cup (B - S) \subset (G - B) \cup (G - S).$$

Since $\mu^*(G - B) < \frac{1}{2}\varepsilon$ and $\mu^*(G - S) < \sum_1^{+\infty} \varepsilon/2^{n+1} = \frac{1}{2}\varepsilon$, we have

$$\mu^*(B \nabla S) < \varepsilon.$$

---

† $B \nabla S$ is the *symmetric difference* of B and S [see problem 10, page 6].

We shall now prove that every set which satisfies (i) is measurable. If B satisfies (i), then for any $\varepsilon > 0$ there is a set S that has the properties described in (i). Since the faces of an interval have zero outer measure, we have $\mu^*(S \triangledown B) < \varepsilon$ and $\mu^*(S' \triangledown B) < \varepsilon$, where S' is the union of the interiors of the closed intervals whose union is S. This implies that

$$\mu^*(S-B) < \varepsilon, \quad \mu^*(B-S) < \varepsilon, \quad \mu^*(S'-B) < \varepsilon, \quad \mu^*(B-S') < \varepsilon.$$

Since $\mu^*(S-B) < \varepsilon$, there is a sequence of open intervals $\{I_n\}$ such that

$$S-B \subset \bigcup_{n=1}^{+\infty} I_n \quad \text{and} \quad \sum_{n=1}^{+\infty} c(I_n) < \varepsilon. \tag{11-24}$$

Now we define F by

$$F = S - \bigcup_{n=1}^{+\infty} I_n.$$

Then $F \subset B$ follows from (11-24). The set S is closed, since a bounded neighborhood of any point in R^n contains points of only a finite number of the closed intervals whose union is S. Therefore, since $\bigcup_1^{+\infty} I_n$ is open, the set F is closed. Similarly, for the open set S' there are open intervals $\{J_n\}$ such that

$$B-S' \subset \bigcup_{n=1}^{+\infty} J_n \quad \text{and} \quad \sum_{n=1}^{+\infty} c(J_n) < \varepsilon.$$

We let

$$G = S' \cup \left(\bigcup_{n=1}^{+\infty} J_n \right).$$

Then G is open and $B \subset G$. Since

$$G - F = (G-B) \cup (B-F)$$

$$= \left\{ \left[S' \cup \left(\bigcup_{n=1}^{+\infty} J_n \right) \right] - B \right\} \cup \left\{ B - \left[S - \left(\bigcup_{n=1}^{+\infty} I_n \right) \right] \right\}$$

$$\subset (S'-B) \cup \left(\bigcup_{n=1}^{+\infty} J_n \right) \cup (B-S) \cup \left(\bigcup_{n=1}^{+\infty} I_n \right),$$

we have $\mu^*(G-F) < 4\varepsilon$. This completes the proof that B is measurable if B satisfies (i).

To complete the proof of Theorem 11-5.2, we must show that B is measurable if B satisfies (iii). If B satisfies (iii), then for any $\varepsilon > 0$ there is a closed set F such that $F \subset B$ and $\mu^*(B-F) < \varepsilon$. Then $\sim F$ is open, $\sim B \subset \sim F$ and,

$$\mu^*[(\sim F) - (\sim B)] = \mu^*(B-F) < \varepsilon.$$

Thus, $\sim B$ satisfies (ii) and therefore $\sim B$ is measurable. This means that for any $\varepsilon > 0$ there is a closed set F_1 and an open set G_1 such that

$$F_1 \subset \, \sim B \subset G_1 \quad \text{and} \quad \mu^*(G_1 - F_1) < \varepsilon.$$

Then $\sim G_1 \subset B \subset \, \sim F_1$, $\sim G_1$ is closed, $\sim F_1$ is open, and

$$\mu^*[(\sim F_1) - (\sim G_1)] = \mu^*(G_1 - F_1) < \varepsilon.$$

Thus, B is measurable.

THEOREM 11-5.3. The collection of all Lebesgue measurable subsets of R^n is a σ-algebra.

PROOF. From Definition 11-5.6, a set A is measurable if and only if there is a closed set F and an open set G such that

$$F \subset A \subset G \quad \text{and} \quad \mu^*(G - F) < \varepsilon.$$

Then $\sim G \subset \, \sim A \subset \, \sim F$ and

$$\mu^*[(\sim F) - (\sim G)] = \mu^*(G - F) < \varepsilon.$$

This implies $\sim A$ is measurable. To complete the proof, we must show that $\bigcup_1^{+\infty} A_n$ is measurable if each A_n is measurable. If each A_n is measurable, then it follows from (ii) of Theorem 11-5.2 that, for any positive number ε and any n, there is an open set G_n such that

$$A_n \subset G_n \quad \text{and} \quad \mu^*(G_n - A_n) < \frac{\varepsilon}{2^n}.$$

Then $\bigcup_1^{+\infty} G_n = G$ is open and $\bigcup_1^{+\infty} A_n \subset G$. Also,

$$G - \bigcup_{n=1}^{+\infty} A_n = \bigcup_{n=1}^{+\infty} G_n - \bigcup_{n=1}^{+\infty} A_n \subset \bigcup_{n=1}^{+\infty} (G_n - A_n),$$

so that it follows from (11-22) and (11-23) that

$$\mu^*\left(G - \bigcup_{n=1}^{+\infty} A_n\right) \leqq \sum_{n=1}^{+\infty} \frac{\varepsilon}{2^n} = \varepsilon.$$

Therefore, $\bigcup_1^{+\infty} A_n$ is measurable.

It is a trivial consequence of Theorem 11-5.2 that all sets with content, all open sets, and all closed sets are measurable, and that a set is measurable if its outer measure is zero. Since the collection of measurable sets is a σ-algebra and contains all open sets, it also contains the smallest σ-algebra that contains all open sets. The members of this smallest σ-algebra containing all open sets are called *Borel sets*. Of course, it is the same as the smallest σ-algebra that contains all closed sets. In particular, all intersections of open sets and all unions of closed sets are Borel sets. Not all measurable sets are Borel sets, but all measurable sets differ from a Borel set by a set of measure zero [see problem 4].

PROBLEMS

1. Prove that if $\mu^*(A) = 0$, then $\mu^*(A \cup B) = \mu^*(B)$.

2. Prove that a bounded subset A of R^n is measurable if and only if, for any positive number ε, there is a set S which is the union of a finite number of closed intervals and which has the property that $\mu^*(A \bigtriangledown S) < \varepsilon$.

3.* Prove that, for any set A, $\mu^*(A) = \inf\{\sum_1^{+\infty} c(I_n) : A \subset \bigcup_1^{+\infty} I_n\}$, where each I_n is a *closed n-D* interval.

4. Prove that each of the following is a necessary and sufficient condition for a set B to be Lebesgue measurable.

   (a) There is a set G such that $B \subset G$, $\mu^*(G - B) = 0$, and G is the intersection of a countable set of open sets.

   (b) There is a set F such that $F \subset B$, $\mu^*(B - F) = 0$, and F is the union of a countable set of closed sets.

   (c) There is a measurable set A such that $A \subset B$ and $\mu^*(B - A) = 0$.

   (d) There is a measurable set C such that $B \subset C$ and $\mu^*(C - B) = 0$.

   (e*) There are measurable sets A and C such that $A \subset B \subset C$ and $\mu^*(C - A) = 0$.

5. Explain why a set A is measurable if and only if $A \cap I$ is measurable for all bounded intervals I.

6. Prove that the Cantor set of problem 6, page 126, is a closed set that is not the union of a countable number of intervals.

7.* Prove that any open set on the real line can be represented as the union of disjoint open intervals in exactly one way. [*Hint:* For each x in the set, let I_x be the union of all intervals that contain x.]

8. Prove each of the following.

   (a) Every closed set in R^n is the intersection of a suitable sequence of open sets.

(b) Every open set in R^n is the union of a suitable sequence of closed sets.

(c) The set of rational numbers in the interval $[0, 1]$ is not the intersection of a sequence of open sets. [*Hint:* Show that if $\{r_n\}$ $\subset \bigcap_1^{+\infty} G_n$, then there is a nested sequence $\{I_n\}$ of closed bounded intervals such that, for each n, $r_n \notin I_n$ and $I_n \subset G_n$.]

11-6. LEBESGUE MEASURE

In the preceding section, we described the collection of Lebesgue measurable sets and proved it to be a σ-algebra. Also, we established several other basic facts about measurable sets. This will make it easy to define Lebesgue measure and to prove that Lebesgue measure is a countably additive measure.

DEFINITION 11-6.1. The *Lebesgue measure* $\mu(A)$ of a Lebesgue measurable set A is the outer measure of A. That is, $\mu(A) = \mu^*(A)$ if and only if A is measurable.

In order to prove that Lebesgue measure is countably additive [Theorem 11-6.2], it is helpful first to establish the characterizations of measure of an open set as described in the next theorem.

THEOREM 11-6.1. If G is an open set, then the Lebesgue measure of A is equal to each of the following expressions:

(i) $\sum_1^{+\infty} c(I_n)$, where $\{I_n\}$ is any sequence of nonoverlapping closed intervals whose union is G;

(ii) sup {inner sums for G}.

PROOF. We shall let the reader prove that $\mu(G) \leq \sum_1^{+\infty} c(I_n)$ if $G = \bigcup_1^{+\infty} I_n$ and each I_n is closed. The proof only involves embedding each I_n in a slightly larger open interval so that Definition 11-5.5 can be used [see problem 3, page 612]. A proof by contradiction will be used to show that $\mu(G) = \sum_1^{+\infty} c(I_n)$, starting with the assumption that $\mu(G) < \sum_1^{+\infty} c(I_n)$. Then $\mu(G) \neq +\infty$ and there is a positive number δ and an n such that

$$\mu(G) < \sum_{j=1}^{n} c(I_j) - \delta. \tag{11-25}$$

Now let $\{K_n\}$ be a sequence of open intervals for which

$$G \subset \bigcup_{n=1}^{+\infty} K_n \quad \text{and} \quad \mu(G) + \delta > \sum_{n=1}^{+\infty} c(K_n). \tag{11-26}$$

Since $\bigcup_1^n I_j$ is a compact set, it follows from the Heine-Borel theorem that there is an integer p such that

$$\bigcup_{j=1}^n I_j \subset \bigcup_{j=1}^p K_j. \tag{11-27}$$

If $A \subset B$ and A and B have content, then $c(A) \leqq c(B)$ [see III, page 605]. Thus, from (11-25), (11-26), and (11-27), we have

$$\mu(G)+\delta < \sum_{j=1}^n c(I_j) = c\left(\bigcup_{j=1}^n I_j\right) \leqq c\left(\bigcup_{j=1}^p K_j\right) \leqq \sum_{j=1}^p c(K_j) < \mu(G)+\delta,$$

and therefore $\mu(G)+\delta < \mu(G)+\delta$. This contradiction completes the proof of (a).

Since any inner sum for G is equal to the outer measure (and content) of a particular set contained in G, it follows from (11-22) that

$$\mu(G) \geqq \sup \{\text{inner sums for } G\}.$$

If $G = \bigcup_1^{+\infty} I_n$, then, for each n, $\sum_1^n c(I_j)$ is an inner sum for G. From (a), $\lim_{n \to +\infty} \sum_1^n c(I_j) = \mu(G)$. Thus,

$$\mu(G) = \sup \{\text{inner sums for } G\}.$$

THEOREM 11-6.2. Lebesgue measure is a countably additive measure.

PROOF. We shall prove first that μ is additive, i.e., that μ is a measure. It follows directly from Theorem 11-6.1 that $\mu(G_1 \cup G_2) = \mu(G_1) + \mu(G_2)$ if G_1 and G_2 are disjoint open sets. We shall prove next that $\mu(F_1 \cup F_2) = \mu(F_1) + \mu(F_2)$ if F_1 and F_2 are disjoint closed sets. For this, we use the fact that there are disjoint open sets G_1 and G_2 with $F_1 \subset G_1$ and $F_2 \subset G_2$.† Since $F_1 \cup F_2$ is measurable, it follows from (ii) of Theorem 11-5.2 that there is an open set G such that

$$F_1 \cup F_2 \subset G \quad \text{and} \quad \mu[G-(F_1 \cup F_2)] < \varepsilon.$$

With $G_1^* = G_1 \cap G$ and $G_2^* = G_2 \cap G$, we have

$$F_1 \subset G_1^*, \qquad F_2 \subset G_2^*, \qquad G_1^* \cap G_2^* = \Phi,$$

$$\mu[(G_1^* \cup G_2^*)-(F_1 \cup F_2)] < \varepsilon.$$

---

† For example, let G_1 be the set of all x with the property that there is a member ϕ of F_1 and a positive number ε such that $d(x, \phi) < \frac{1}{2}\varepsilon$ and the ε-neighborhood of ϕ contains no members of F_1; then G_2 can be defined similarly.

Using these facts and (11-22) and (11-23), we obtain

$$\mu(F_1 \cup F_2) + \varepsilon > \mu(F_1 \cup F_2) + \mu[(G_1^* \cup G_2^*) - (F_1 \cup F_2)]$$
$$\geqq \mu(G_1^* \cup G_2^*) = \mu(G_1^*) + \mu(G_2^*) \geqq \mu(F_1) + \mu(F_2).$$

This shows that $\mu(F_1 \cup F_2) + \varepsilon > \mu(F_1) + \mu(F_2)$ for every positive number ε. Since $\mu(F_1 \cup F_2) \leqq \mu(F_1) + \mu(F_2)$ follows from (11-23), we have $\mu(F_1 \cup F_2) = \mu(F_1) + \mu(F_2)$.

Now let A_1 and A_2 be any two disjoint measurable sets. From (iii) of Theorem 11-5.2, there are closed sets F_1 and F_2 such that

$$F_1 \subset A_1, \quad F_2 \subset A_2, \quad \mu(A_1 - F_1) < \tfrac{1}{2}\varepsilon, \quad \mu(A_2 - F_2) < \tfrac{1}{2}\varepsilon.$$

Then

$$\mu(A_1 \cup A_2) \geqq \mu(F_1 \cup F_2) = \mu(F_1) + \mu(F_2)$$
$$> \mu(F_1) + [\mu(A_1 - F_1) - \tfrac{1}{2}\varepsilon] + \mu(F_2) + [\mu(A_2 - F_2) - \tfrac{1}{2}\varepsilon]$$
$$\geqq \mu(A_1) + \mu(A_2) - \varepsilon.$$

Thus, $\mu(A_1 \cup A_2) > \mu(A_1) + \mu(A_2) - \varepsilon$ for every positive number ε. Since $\mu(A_1 \cup A_2) \leqq \mu(A_1) + \mu(A_2)$, it follows that

$$\mu(A_1 \cup A_2) = \mu(A_1) + \mu(A_2).$$

To show μ is countably additive, we suppose $A = \bigcup_1^{+\infty} A_n$, where each A_n is Lebesgue measurable and $A_i \cap A_j = \Phi$ if $i \neq j$. We must show that $\mu(A) = \sum_1^{+\infty} \mu(A_n)$. From (11-22), we have

$$\mu(A) \geqq \mu\left(\bigcup_{j=1}^{p} A_j\right) \quad \text{for all} \quad p.$$

Using additivity, we obtain from this that $\mu(A) \geqq \sum_1^p \mu(A_j)$ for all p. Thus, $\mu(A) \geqq \sum_1^{+\infty} \mu(A_j)$. Since $\mu(A) \leqq \sum_1^{+\infty} \mu(A_j)$ follows from (11-23), we conclude that $\mu(A) = \sum_1^{+\infty} \mu(A_j)$.

PROBLEMS

1. Prove that for any set A, $\mu^*(A) = \inf \{\mu(G) : A \subset G$ and G is open$\}$.

2. Give an example of an open set G for which $\mu(G) < \mu$ (closure of G).

3. Give an example of a closed set F such that $\mu(G) < \mu(F)$ if $G \subset F$ and G is an open set.

4. For a subset A of a bounded interval T, let the *inner measure* $\mu_*(A)$ be defined by $\mu_*(A) = c(T) - \mu^*(T - A)$. Prove each of the following.

(a) The inner measure of a bounded set A does not depend on the interval T.

(b) A bounded set A is measurable if and only if $\mu^*(A) = \mu_*(A)$.

5. Prove that a necessary and sufficient condition for a subset A of R^n to be Lebesgue measurable is that

$$c(I) = \mu^*(I \cap A) + \mu^*(I \cap \sim A) \quad \text{for all } n\text{-}D \text{ intervals } I.$$
(11-28)

Do this by completing the following steps.

(a) Show (11-28) is satisfied if A is measurable.

(b) Suppose A is a set for which (11-28) is satisfied. Choose open sets G_1 and G_2 such that $I \cap A \subset G_1$, $\mu(G_1) < \frac{1}{2}\varepsilon + \mu^*(I \cap A)$, $I \cap \sim A \subset G_2$, and $\mu(G_2) < \frac{1}{2}\varepsilon + \mu^*(I \cap \sim A)$. Prove and use the following continued inequality to show that $\mu(G_1 \cap G_2) < \varepsilon$ and that $A \cap I$ is measurable:

$$\begin{aligned}
c(I) &\leqq \mu(G_1 - G_2) + \mu(G_1 \cap G_2) + \mu(G_2 - G_1) \\
&\leqq \mu(G_1 - G_2) + 2\mu(G_1 \cap G_2) + \mu(G_2 - G_1) = \mu(G_1) + \mu(G_2) \\
&< \varepsilon + c(I).
\end{aligned}$$

(c) Use part (b) and show that A is measurable if (11-28) is satisfied.

6. By completing the following steps, prove that a necessary and sufficient condition for a subset A of R^n to be Lebesgue measurable is that

$$\mu^*(S) = \mu^*(S \cap A) + \mu^*(S \cap \sim A) \quad \text{for all subsets } S \text{ of } R^n.$$

(a) Use problem 5 and show that this is a sufficient condition for A to be measurable.

(b) Suppose A is a measurable subset of R^n and S is an arbitrary subset of R^n. Choose intervals $\{I_n\}$ such that

$$\mu^*(S) > \varepsilon + \sum_{n=1}^{+\infty} c(I_n) \quad \text{and} \quad S \subset \bigcup_{n=1}^{+\infty} I_n.$$

Then use problem 5 to show that $c(I_n) = \mu(I_n \cap A) + \mu(I_n \cap \sim A)$ for each n, and

$$\mu^*(S) > \varepsilon + \mu^*(S \cap A) + \mu^*(S \cap \sim A).$$

(c) Use part (b) and prove that the given condition is satisfied if A is Lebesgue measurable.

11-7. LEBESGUE INTEGRATION

Since the collection of Lebesgue measurable subsets of R^n is a σ-algebra and Lebesgue measure is countably additive, all of the theory of measurable functions and integration discussed in Sections 11-2, 11-3, and 11-4 can be used with Lebesgue measure. Of course, Lebesgue measure is a particular measure. Thus, there are many theorems about Lebesgue measure that are not applicable to general measures. We shall study some of these theorems in this section.

First, we shall obtain a preliminary result [Theorem 11-7.1] that will be used in the proof of Theorem 11-7.2 and later to represent Lebesgue integrals as iterated integrals [Theorem 11-7.5], as was done for Riemann integrals in Theorems 5-2.5 and 5-4.1. Then we shall generalize previous interpretations of Riemann integrals as areas and volumes [Theorems 3-4.1, 3-5.1, 5-2.1, and 5-2.2]. This generalization is given by Theorems 11-7.2 and 11-7.3. These theorems will enable us to prove easily that every Riemann integrable function has a Lebesgue integral and the two integrals are equal.

THEOREM 11-7.1. Suppose W is a Lebesgue measurable set in R^n. Also suppose L is a directed line, the symbol t denotes distances of points along this line from some fixed point on the line, and that W_t denotes the intersection of W and the hyperplane† orthogonal to L at t. Then W_t is $(n-1)$-D measurable for almost all t, $\mu_{n-1}(W_t)$ is a measurable function on L, and

$$\mu(W) = \int_L \mu_{n-1}(W_t)\,d\mu_1, \tag{11-29}$$

where μ_1 denotes Lebesgue measure on L and μ_{n-1} denotes Lebesgue measure on R^{n-1}.

PROOF. Let us prove the theorem first for W an open set. If W is open, then W is the union of a sequence $\{I_n\}$ of nonoverlapping closed intervals whose edges are either parallel to L or perpendicular to L [see the lemma on page 608]. Let $h_p(t)$ be the $(n-1)$-D measure of the intersection of $\bigcup_1^p I_n$ and the hyperplane perpendicular to L at t. Then clearly

$$\mu\left(\bigcup_{n=1}^p I_n\right) = \int_L h_p(t)\,d\mu_1.$$

From (a) of Theorem 11-6.1 and the monotone convergence theorem, we then have

$$\mu(W) = \lim_{p \to +\infty} \mu\left(\bigcup_{n=1}^p I_n\right) = \lim_{p \to +\infty} \int_L h_p\,d\mu_1$$

$$= \int_L [\lim_{p \to +\infty} h_p]\,d\mu_1 = \int_L W_t\,d\mu_1,$$

---

† A *hyperplane* in R^n is a translate of an $(n-1)$-dimensional subspace of R^n. See pages 397–398.

where W_t is the $(n-1)$-D measure of the intersection of W and the hyperplane perpendicular to L at t.

Now let W be an arbitrary Lebesgue measurable set in R^n. For an arbitrary positive number ε, let F be a closed set and G be an open set such that

$$F \subset W \subset G \quad \text{and} \quad \mu(G-F) < \varepsilon.$$

Since $G - F$ is open, we know that

$$\mu(G-F) = \int_L \mu_{n-1}[(G-F) \cap H_t] \, d\mu_1,$$

where H_t is the hyperplane perpendicular to L at t. Therefore, for any positive number η,

$$\mu_1\{t: \mu_{n-1}[(G-F) \cap H_t] > \eta\} < \frac{\varepsilon}{\eta}.$$

Since ε was an arbitrary positive number, but η did not depend on ε, we have

$$\mu_1\left\{ \begin{array}{l} t: \mu_{n-1}[(G-F) \cap H_t] > \eta \\ \text{for all closed } F \text{ and open } G \text{ with } F \subset W \subset G \end{array} \right\} = 0.$$

This implies that W_t is measurable for almost all t.

Now let $\{G_n\}$ be a sequence of open sets in R^n such that $W \subset G_n \subset G_{n-1}$ for each n, and $\lim_{n \to +\infty} \mu(G_n - W) = 0$. Define a sequence of functions $\{g_n\}$ by letting $g_n(t)$ be the $(n-1)$-D measure of the intersection of G_n and the hyperplane perpendicular to L at t. Then, from the methods of the preceding paragraph,

$$\lim_{n \to +\infty} g_n(t) = \mu_{n-1}(W_t) \quad \text{a.e.} \tag{11-30}$$

Since we have shown that Theorem 11-7.1 is valid when W is open, we have $\int_L g_n \, d\mu_1 = \mu(G_n)$ and

$$\lim_{n \to +\infty} \int_L g_n \, d\mu_1 = \lim_{n \to +\infty} \mu(G_n) = \mu(W).$$

If $\mu(G_1) < +\infty$, then $\int_L g_1 \, d\mu_1 < +\infty$ and it follows from (11-30) and the Lebesgue convergence theorem [Theorem 11-4.3] that

$$\lim_{n \to +\infty} \int_L g_n \, d\mu_1 = \int_L \mu_{n-1}(W_t) \, d\mu_1,$$

and our proof is completed.　It is possible to choose G_1 to have finite measure unless $\mu(W) = +\infty$.　If $\mu(W) = +\infty$, then for any positive number K there is an interval I such that

$$\mu(I \cap W) > K.$$

Then, working with $K \cap W$, our preceding argument establishes that

$$\int_L \mu_{n-1}(W_t) \, d\mu_1 > K.$$

Thus, (11-29) is valid, since both members are $+\infty$.

There is a simple consequence of Theorem 11-7.1 that will be useful in proving the next theorem.　It follows so easily from Theorem 11-7.1 that no formal proof will be given.　This result is stated as the next lemma.　In this lemma, we use the definition that a *cylinder* in R^n is any set that consists of all line segments which are parallel to a given line L and join points in two bases, where the bases are two sets contained in hyperplanes perpendicular to L and one base is a translate of the other parallel to L.

LEMMA.　An n-D cylinder with nonzero altitude and base B is n-D measurable if and only if B is $(n-1)$-D measurable.　If h is the altitude and $\mu_{n-1}(B)$ is the $(n-1)$-D measure of B, then the n-D measure of the cylinder is $h \cdot \mu_{n-1}(B)$ unless $h = +\infty$ and $\mu_{n-1}(B) = 0$.　If $\mu_{n-1}(B) = 0$, then the n-D measure of the cylinder is zero.

THEOREM 11-7.2.　Suppose f is a function whose domain is a measurable subset T of R^n and whose range is a set of ordinary nonnegative real numbers.　Then f is measurable if and only if the region W between T and the graph of f is $(n+1)$-D measurable.　If f is measurable, then $\int_T f \, d\mu$ is equal to the $(n+1)$-D measure of W.

PROOF.　Let us assume first that f is measurable.　For a positive number M, let f_M be defined by $f_M(x) = \min \{f(x), M\}$.　If I is an interval in R^n and $\varepsilon > 0$, then, for any integer p such that $p\varepsilon \geq M$, we have

$$\sum_{n=1}^{p} n\varepsilon \cdot \mu[I \cap \{x: n\varepsilon \leq f_M(x) < (n+1)\varepsilon\}] \leq \int_{T \cap I} f_M \, d\mu$$

$$\leq \sum_{n=1}^{p} (n+1)\varepsilon \cdot \mu[I \cap \{x: n\varepsilon \leq f_M(x) < (n+1)\varepsilon\}]. \quad (11\text{-}31)$$

The first member of this inequality is the measure of a measurable set contained in the region W_I^M between $I \cap T$ and the graph of f_M, and the last member is the measure of a measurable set that contains W_I^M. Since the difference between these sums is not larger than $\varepsilon \cdot \mu(I)$, it follows that W_I^M is measurable [see problem 4(e), page 612]. Since W is a countable union of such sets W_I^M, W itself is measurable. It follows from the lemma that the first and last terms in (11-31) are sums of $(n+1)$-D measures of cylinders. The union of the first set of cylinders is contained in W_I^M and the union of the second set contains W_I^M. Therefore, $\mu_{n+1}(W_I^M) = \int_{T \cap I} f_M \, d\mu$. It follows from problems 5 and 6, page 595, that $\int_{T \cap I} f_M \, d\mu$ approaches $\int_T f \, d\mu$ as $M \to +\infty$ and I expands. We could also make direct use of Definition 11-5.5 to show that $\mu_{n+1}(W_I^M)$ approaches $\mu_{n+1}(W)$ as $M \to +\infty$ and I expands [see problem 10]. Therefore,

$$\mu_{n+1}(W) = \int_T f \, d\mu.$$

Now suppose that W is measurable. Let t denote the $(n+1)$st coordinate in R^{n+1} and L denote the t-axis, with T contained in the hyperplane H consisting of those points with $t = 0$. Then $\{x: f(x) \geq a\}$ is the projection into T of the intersection W_a of W and the hyperplane orthogonal to L at a. It then follows from Theorem 11-7.1 that W_a and $\{x: f(x) \geq a\}$ are measurable for almost all positive numbers a. For a particular number a, choose a sequence of positive numbers $\{\varepsilon_n\}$ with limit zero such that $\{x: f(x) \geq a + \varepsilon_n\}$ is n-D measurable for each n. Then

$$\{x: f(x) > a\} = \bigcup_1^{+\infty} \{x: f(x) \geq a + \varepsilon_n\},$$

so that $\{x: f(x) > a\}$ is measurable. Therefore f is measurable [see (ii) of Theorem 11-2.1].

The next theorem is a direct consequence of Theorem 11-7.2 and Definition 11-3.3, so no formal proof will be given.

THEOREM 11-7.3. Suppose f is a function whose domain is a measurable subset T of R^n and whose range is a set of ordinary real numbers. Then $\int_T f \, d\mu$ exists if and only if the region in R^{n+1} between W and the graph of f is measurable and either the part of W on the positive side† of R^n has finite $(n+1)$-D measure, or the part of W on the

---

† The "positive side" of R^n is the set of all points in R^{n+1} whose $(n+1)$st coordinate is positive.

negative side of R^n has finite $(n+1)$-D measure. If f is integrable, then $\int_T f\, d\mu$ is equal to the measure of the region between T and the graph of f^+ *minus* the measure of the region between T and the graph of f^-.

Since any set with content has measure, the next theorem is a consequence of Theorem 11-7.3 and theorems such as Theorems 3-5.1 and 5-2.2 for Riemann integrals.

THEOREM 11-7.4. Suppose f is a function which is Riemann integrable over an interval I in R^n. Then f is measurable and the Lebesgue integral of f over T exists and is equal to the Riemann integral.

THEOREM 11-7.5 [FUBINI]. Suppose T is a Lebesgue measurable set in R^n and f is a Lebesgue measurable function with domain T for which $\int_T f\, d\mu$ exists. For a particular integer k with $1 \leq k \leq n$, let the symbol x denote the value of the kth coordinate for points in R^n, let L be the line of points with all coordinates zero except the kth, let T_x denote the set of all points of T whose kth coordinate is x, and let f_x denote the function with domain T_x which coincides with f on T_x. If μ_1 and μ_{n-1} denote 1-D and $(n-1)$-D Lebesgue measure, then

$$\int_T f\, d\mu = \int_L \left[\int_{T_x} f_x\, d\mu_{n-1} \right] d\mu_1. \tag{11-32}$$

PROOF. The theorem follows directly from Theorems 11-7.1 and 11-7.2 if f is nonnegative. In general, we can write $f = f^+ - f^-$. Then we have (11-32) for f^+ and for f^-. Since not both $\int_T f^+\, d\mu$ and $\int_T f^-\, d\mu$ are $+\infty$, we can subtract the results to complete the proof.

PROBLEMS

1. Let f be continuous on a Lebesgue measurable subset B of R^n. Prove that f is Lebesgue measurable on B. [*Hint:* Use Theorem 2-2.2.]

2. Suppose f is a Lebesgue measurable function on R^1 and $\mathscr{B}$ is the collection of all sets B for which $\{x : f(x) \in B\}$ is a measurable set. Prove that $\mathscr{B}$ is a σ-algebra.

3. Let f be a Lebesgue measurable function on R^1. Prove that $\{x : f(x) \in B\}$ is a measurable set if B is a Borel set. [*Hint:* Use problem 2.]

4. Prove that if f is a Lebesgue measurable function on R^1 and g is continuous, then $g \circ f$ is measurable. [*Note:* $g \circ f$ is not necessarily measurable if g is measurable and f is continuous.]

5. Let f be a nonnegative Lebesgue measurable function on R^1. Prove that $\int_{-\infty}^{+\infty} f \, d\mu = \lim_{r \to +\infty} \int_{-r}^{+r} f \, d\mu$.

6. Let f be a Lebesgue measurable function on R^1 for which $\int_{-\infty}^{+\infty} f \, d\mu$ exists and is not $+\infty$ or $-\infty$. Show that F is continuous if F is defined for ordinary real numbers x by

$$F(x) = \int_{-\infty}^{x} f \, d\mu.$$

7. Let f be a Lebesgue measurable function on R^1 and $[a, b]$ be an interval for which $|\int_{[a,b]} f \, d\mu| \neq +\infty$. Prove that if $a < x < b$ and f is continuous at x, then

$$\frac{d}{dx} \int_{[a,x]} f \, d\mu = f(x).$$

8. Suppose f is differentiable at almost all points of the closed interval $[a, b]$. Prove each of the following.

(a) f is measurable on $[a, b]$.

(b) g is measurable on $[a, b]$ if $g(x) = f'(x)$ when x is in the domain of f' and $g(x) = 0$ otherwise. [*Hint:* $f'(x) = \lim_{n \to +\infty} n[f(x+1/n) - f(x)]$ for almost all x.]

(c) $\lim_{n \to +\infty} \int_a^b n[f(x+1/n) - f(x)] \, d\mu = f(b) - f(a)$ if f is continuous at a and at b and we let $f(x) = f(b)$ if $x > b$.

9. Suppose f is differentiable at *all* points of the closed interval $[a, b]$ and that $|f'|$ is bounded on $[a, b]$. Use problem 8 and the bounded convergence theorem to prove that

$$\int_a^b f' \, d\mu = f(b) - f(a).$$

10. Let W be a measurable subset of R^n. If I_r is an n-D interval with center at the origin and all edges of length at least r, prove that $\lim_{r \to +\infty} \mu(I_r \cap W) = \mu(W)$.

11-8. NONMEASURABLE SETS

Although there are sets in R^n that are not Lebesgue measurable, such sets can not be exhibited explicitly, even in R^1. In fact, the axiom of choice must be used to construct such a set. This axiom is independent of the axioms customarily used in axiomatic set theory. In addition to being needed in the proof of the next theorem, it has other important consequences that we shall not discuss, such as the "well-ordering principle" and "Zorn's lemma."

AXIOM OF CHOICE. Suppose S is a collection of nonempty sets. Then there is a function f whose domain is S and which has the property that $f(A) \in A$ for every set A that is a member of S.

The function f is called a *choice function*. It can be thought of as specifying a choice of a member of A for each set A in S. If the sets in S are disjoint, the axiom of choice can be described as asserting the existence of a "congress" that contains exactly one representative from each of the sets in S.

As we shall see, the sets P and $\sim P$ described in the next theorem are nonmeasurable. In fact, Theorem 11-8.2 shows that much more than this is true, namely, that $P \cap A$ is nonmeasurable whenever A is a measurable set with $\mu(A) > 0$.

THEOREM 11-8.1. There exists a subset P of the set of real numbers which has the property that P contains no closed set with nonzero measure and P is congruent to $\sim P$.

PROOF. Let $\approx$ be the relation for which $x \approx y$ means that there is an integer p and a nonnegative integer n such that

$$x - y = \frac{p}{2 \cdot 3^n}.$$

Clearly, this relation is reflexive and symmetric. It is transitive, since if $x - y = p/(2 \cdot 3^m)$ and $y - z = q/(2 \cdot 3^n)$, then

$$x - z = (x - y) + (y - z) = \frac{p \cdot 3^n + q \cdot 3^m}{2 \cdot 3^{m+n}}.$$

Therefore, the relation $\approx$ is an equivalence relation and defines a division of the set of real numbers into disjoint classes of mutually equivalent numbers [see Theorem 1-2.1]. Now we use the axiom of choice and let W be a set that contains exactly one member of each of these equivalence classes. We define sets P and Q by letting p and n denote integers and

$$P = \left\{ w + \frac{p}{3^n} : w \in W \text{ and } n \geq 0 \right\};$$

$$Q = \left\{ w + \frac{p}{2 \cdot 3^n} : w \in W \text{ and } p \text{ is odd and } n \geq 0 \right\}.$$

To show that $P \cap Q = \Phi$, we suppose that $w_1 + p/3^m = w_2 + q/(2 \cdot 3^n)$ and q is odd. Then

$$w_1 - w_2 = \frac{q \cdot 3^m - 2p \cdot 3^n}{2 \cdot 3^{m+n}},$$

where the numerator is odd and therefore nonzero. This is impossible, since then w_1 and w_2 belong to the same equivalence class and could not both belong to W. Now let us show that $P \cup Q$ is the set of all real numbers. For an arbitrary number x, let ω be the member of W that belongs to the equivalence class containing x. Then there are integers p and n such that $x = \omega + p/(2 \cdot 3^n)$, and $x \in P$ or $x \in Q$ according to whether p is even or p is odd. This concludes the proof that $Q = \sim P$.

Now note that

$$w + \frac{p}{3^n} + \frac{1}{2 \cdot 3^m} = w + \frac{3^n + 2p \cdot 3^m}{2 \cdot 3^{m+n}} \in Q \quad \text{if} \quad w \in W,$$

and

$$w + \frac{p}{2 \cdot 3^n} = \left[w + \frac{p \cdot 3^m + 3^n}{2 \cdot 3^{m+n}} \right] - \frac{1}{2 \cdot 3^m},$$

where the expression in brackets belongs to P if p is odd. Thus, for any integer $m \geq 0$, Q is the translation $P + 1/(2 \cdot 3^m)$ of P.

We shall use a proof by contradiction to show that P contains no closed sets with nonzero measure. Suppose $F \subset P$ and F is a closed set with $\mu(F) > 0$. Since we can intersect F with a suitable closed interval if necessary, there is no loss of generality in assuming that F has finite measure. Then there is a sequence of disjoint open intervals $\{I_n\}$ with

$$F \subset \bigcup_{n=1}^{+\infty} I_n \quad \text{and} \quad \mu(F) > \tfrac{3}{4} \sum_{n=1}^{+\infty} c(I_n)$$

[see (ii) of Theorem 11-5.2 and problem 7, page 612]. At least one of these intervals, which we shall designate by I, has the property that

$$\mu(F \cap I) > \tfrac{3}{4} c(I).$$

For every $n > 0$, the translate $P + 1/(2 \cdot 3^n)$ of P is contained in $\sim P$. Thus, $F + 1/(2 \cdot 3^n) \subset \sim F$, so that

$$\mu(\sim F \cap I) \geq \mu\left[\left(F + \frac{1}{2 \cdot 3^n} \right) \cap I \right] \geq \mu(F \cap I) - \frac{1}{2 \cdot 3^n}.$$

Since this is true for all n, we have

$$\mu(\sim F \cap I) \geqq \mu(F \cap I) > \tfrac{3}{4}c(I),$$

and

$$c(I) = \mu(F \cap I) + \mu(\sim F \cap I) > \tfrac{3}{4}\mu(I) + \tfrac{3}{4}\mu(I) = \tfrac{3}{2}c(I).$$

This contradiction completes the proof of the theorem.

The set P of Theorem 11-8.1 is nonmeasurable. To show this, we merely note that (iii) of Theorem 11-5.2 and measurability of P imply $\mu(P) = \mu(\sim P) = 0$ and

$$\mu(A) = \mu(A \cap P) + \mu(A \cap \sim P) = 0,$$

for all measurable sets A.

THEOREM 11-8.2. The set P of Theorem 11-8.1 has the property that, for every measurable set A with nonzero measure, $A \cap P$ is nonmeasurable. In fact, for every measurable set A,

$$\mu(A) = \mu^*(A \cap P) = \mu^*(A \cap \sim P).$$

PROOF. Suppose that $\mu^*(A \cap P) < \mu(A)$, so that there is a positive number ε with

$$\mu(A) > \mu^*(A \cap P) + \varepsilon.$$

Then $\mu^*(A \cap P)$ is finite and there is a closed set F and an open set G such that

$$F \subset A \quad \text{and} \quad \mu(A - F) < \tfrac{1}{2}\varepsilon,$$

$$A \cap P \subset G \quad \text{and} \quad \mu(G) < \mu^*(A \cap P) + \tfrac{1}{2}\varepsilon$$

[see Theorem 11-5.2 and Definition 11-5.5]. The set $F - G$ is closed, since it is equal to the intersection of the closed sets F and $\sim G$. Also, $F - G \subset \sim P$ and

$$\mu(F - G) = \mu[(A - G) - (A - F)] > \mu(A - G) - \tfrac{1}{2}\varepsilon$$

$$\geqq \mu(A) - \mu(G) - \tfrac{1}{2}\varepsilon > \mu(A) - \mu^*(A \cap P) - \varepsilon > 0.$$

This is impossible, since $\sim P$ is congruent to P and therefore cannot contain the closed set $F - G$ if $F - G$ has nonzero measure.

PROBLEMS

1. Let $\cong$ be the relation for which $x \cong y$ means that $x - y$ is a rational number. Show that $\cong$ is an equivalence relation.

2. For the equivalence relation of problem 1, let E be a set that contains exactly one member of $A \cap [0, 1]$ for each equivalence class A. Prove that E has zero measure if E is measurable. Do this by each of the following methods:

(a) Show that, if F is a closed set and $F \subset E$, then $\mu(F) = 0$. [*Hint:* See the proof of Theorem 11-8.1.]

(b) For a set S and a number α, let $S + \alpha$ denote the translation $\{s + \alpha : s \in S\}$ of S. Also, let $\{r_n\}$ be the set of rational numbers in the interval $[0, 1]$. Prove that the sets $\{E + r_n\}$ have the properties that any two are congruent, any two are disjoint, all are contained in the interval $[0, 2]$, but the sum of their measures is $+\infty$ unless $\mu(E) = 0$.

3. Explain why the set E of problem 2 is not measurable.

4. Let A and B be nonmeasurable subsets of measurable sets R and S, respectively. Prove that $A \cup B$ is nonmeasurable if $R \cap S = \Phi$.

5. Let μ_* denote the inner measure defined in problem 4, page 616. Prove that there are bounded sets A and B such that $\mu_*(B) = 0$ and $\mu_*(A \cup B) \neq \mu_*(A)$.

6. Prove that it is not true that a sufficient condition for Lebesgue measurability of a function f is that $\{x : f(x) = a\}$ is measurable for every extended real number a. [*Hint:* Show that f can be chosen so that $\{x : f(x) = a\}$ has at most one member and the set $\{x : 0 \leq f(x) < 1\}$ is nonmeasurable.]

7. Prove that there is a nonmeasurable function with domain $[0, 1]$ and range consisting of exactly two numbers.

ANSWERS

CHAPTER 1

SECTION 1-1, page 5.

1. (a) True. (c) False. **2.** (c) False. **3.** (a) The set of all dogs that hate men and are wild or large. (b) The set of all dogs that are wild or that are both large and hateful of men.

SECTION 1-2, page 11.

1. (a) Symmetric. (b) Reflexive, symmetric, transitive. (c) Reflexive, symmetric. (d) Reflexive, transitive. **5.** (a) No. (b) No. (c) Yes. (d) No. **6.** (b) $yR^{-1}x$ means $x = 2y(1-y)^{-1}$, $\{y: y \neq 1\}$, $\{x: x \neq -2\}$.

SECTION 1-3, page 18.

1. (b) All numbers, $\{y: y \geq -1\}$. (c) All numbers except 1 and -1, $\{y: y > 0\} \cup \{y: y \leq -1\}$. **2.** (b) $\{y: -\frac{5}{2} \leq y \leq -\frac{3}{4}\}$. (c) $\{y: -1 \leq y \leq 9\}$. **7.** (a) -14, -10; 1, 5; 7, 11. (b) 12, 2; 7, 7; 9, 9. (c) -54, -49; -4, 3; 36, 43. **8.** (a) $f \circ g = \{(2, 1), (3, 1)\}$; $g \circ f = \{(0, 5), (1, 0), (7, 0)\}$. (c) $(f \circ g)(x)$ is the father of the oldest brother of x, with the domain of $f \circ g$ the set of all people who have at least one brother; $(g \circ f)(x)$ is the oldest brother of x's father, with the domain of $g \circ f$ the set of all people whose fathers have at least one brother. (e) $(f \circ g)(x) = \ln(e^x + 1)$ for all x; $(g \circ f)(x) = x + 1$ for $x > -1$. (g) $f \circ g = \Phi$; that is, $f \circ g$ is the relation that is the empty set of ordered pairs; $(g \circ f)[(A, B)] = \sim A \cap \sim B$. **9.** (b) $g(x) = (7 + 5x)/(2x - 1)$, for $x \neq \frac{1}{2}$. (d) $g(x) = (e^x - 1)^{1/2} + 1$, for $x \geq 0$. **10.** $(a = -d)$ or $(a = d$ and $b = c = 0)$.

SECTION 1-4, page 30.

3. (a) 4. (b) $\frac{1}{2}(7 + \sqrt{13})$. (d) 2. **4.** (a) $\frac{3}{2}$. (b) $\frac{2}{3}$. (c) No α. **7.** (a) $\frac{1}{2}(1 + \sqrt{5})$. (b) $1 + \sqrt{2}$.

SECTION 1-5, page 37.

2. (a) $\frac{1}{7}$.   (c) $77/270$.

SECTION 1-7, page 50.

1. (a) $x = -3$, $y = 2$.   (b) $x = y = \frac{1}{2}\sqrt{2}$, or $x = y = -\frac{1}{2}\sqrt{2}$.   **4.** $x^2 + y^2$ $+\frac{5}{2}y + 1 = 0$; the circle with radius $\frac{3}{4}$ and center at $(0, -\frac{5}{4})$.   **8.** (a) -1. (b) $1 - i$.   (c) -1.   (d) $\frac{1}{2} - \frac{1}{2}\sqrt{3}\,i$.   **9.** (b) $7e^{\frac{1}{2}\pi i}$.   (d) $4\sqrt{6}e^{i(-5\pi/12)}$. (f) $2\sqrt{2}e^{i(7\pi/12)}$.   **10.** (a) 1, $-\frac{1}{2} \pm \frac{1}{2}\sqrt{3}\,i$.   **11.** (a) $\pm(\cos \frac{3}{8}\pi + i \sin \frac{3}{8}\pi)$, $\pm(\cos \frac{1}{8}\pi - i \sin \frac{1}{8}\pi)$.   **12.** $\sqrt[6]{2}\,e^{ki}$, where k is $\frac{1}{4}\pi$, $\frac{5}{12}\pi$, $\frac{11}{12}\pi$, $\frac{13}{12}\pi$, $\frac{19}{12}\pi$, or $\frac{7}{4}\pi$.

CHAPTER 2

SECTION 2-1, page 60.

10. (a) The set $\{2, 7\}$.   **11.** (a) The x-axis.   **14.** (a) Connected. (c) Disconnected.   (e) Connected.

SECTION 2-2, page 68.

1. (a) $-1 + \sqrt{1.00625}$, $1/321$.   (b) $-10 + \sqrt{100.00625}$, $1/3201$.   (c) $-k$ $+(k^2 + \varepsilon/16)^{\frac{1}{2}}$, the smaller of $1/16$ and $\varepsilon/(32k+1)$.   **2.** (a) $|\Delta x| < 5$. (c) $|\Delta x| < 1/100{,}100$.   **8.** (a) Impossible.   (b) Discontinuous.   (c) Discontinuous.   **15.** $-(1.5-)$, $0.0-$, 1.5.   **16.** (a) $-(1.5+)$, $-(0.3+)$, $1.9-$.   (b) $1.5+$.

SECTION 2-3, page 75.

7. (a) $1/70$.   (c) 4.   **9.** (a) Yes.   (b) Yes.   (c) No.

SECTION 2-4, page 83.

9. (a) True.   (b) True.   (c) True.   (d) False.   (e) False.   **10.** (a) True. (b) False.   (c) True.   (d) False.   **11.** (a) 24.   (b) -24.   (c) -21. **12.** (b) 0.   (c) No l.   **13.** (b) 0.   (c) 12.   (d) 0.

SECTION 2-5, page 90.

1. (b) $16, 1, 1$.   **2.** (a) $+\infty$.   (c) 0.   (e) Does not exist.   **3.** (a) $6, 3, 18, 2$. (b) $3, 0, 0$, does not exist.

SECTION 2-6, page 97.

1. (a) -2.   (b) 48.   (c) $\frac{1}{2}$.   (d) $\frac{1}{3}$.   **3.** (b) No discontinuities.   **7.** Continuous on the left: (b), (e); continuous on the right: (d).   **8.** (b) No discontinuities. (d) Jump discontinuity at all integers except zero (discontinuous on the left, continuous on the right); infinite discontinuity at zero (continuous on the right). **11.** (a) 2. (b) 3. (c) 8. (d) $\frac{1}{8}$.

SECTION **2-7**, page 102.

2. (b) 3. (c) 1. **4.** (a) $g(x) = (5x+7)/(2x-1)$. (b) $g(x) = \ln(e^x - 1)$, $x > 0$. (c) $g(x) = (e^x - 1)^{\frac{1}{2}} + 1$, $x \geq 0$.

SECTION **2-8**, page 106.

1. (a) 1. (b) $\sqrt{\frac{3}{2}}$. (c) $-\sqrt{13/3}$. (d) $3 - \sqrt{13}$.

SECTION **2-9**, page 113.

3. (a) 3/10. (b) $\frac{1}{2}$. (c) $1/e$. **5.** (a) No. (b) Yes. (c) Yes. (d) Yes.
6. (a) $\frac{5}{2}$. (b) $-\frac{1}{8}$. (c) 0. (d) 0. (f) 2. **8.** (a) 1. (b) 0. **9.** (b) 0.
11. (a) $+\infty$. (b) $+\infty$.

CHAPTER 3

SECTION **3-3**, page 139.

1. $41\frac{2}{3}$. **2.** $20\frac{1}{4}$.

SECTION **3-4**, page 145.

1. (a) 12. (d) $\frac{5}{2}$.

SECTION **3-6**, page 157.

1. (a) $\ln x$. (c) $-(\sin x)/x$. (e) $2xe^{-x^4} - e^{-x^2}$. **3.** $(b-a)^{-1} \int_a^b f(x)\, dx$.
4. (a) $\frac{1}{3}$. (b) 2. (c) $\frac{2}{3}$. (d) $24\frac{1}{5}$.

CHAPTER 4

SECTION **4-1**, page 172.

1. (a) $1+1+1+\cdots+1+\cdots$; divergent. (b) $\displaystyle\sum_{n=1}^{+\infty} \frac{1}{n(n+1)}$, $l = 1$.

(c) $2 - \displaystyle\sum_{n=2}^{+\infty} \frac{1}{(n-1)n}$, $l = 1$. **2.** (a) $S_n = 3 - 3^{1-n}$, $S = 3$.

(b) $S_n = x^{n-1}/(n-1)!$, $S = 0$. (c) $S_n = n/(n+1)$, $S = 1$.

(d) $S_n = \frac{1}{4} - \dfrac{1}{2(n+1)} + \dfrac{1}{2(n+2)}$, $S = \frac{1}{4}$. (e) $S_n = 1 + (-1)^{n+1}/(n+1)$, $S = 1$.

3. (a) Divergent. (c) Divergent. (e) Convergent ($S = 1$).

SECTION **4-2**, page 181.

1. (a) Divergent. (b) Convergent. (d) Convergent. (e) Convergent if $p > 1$; divergent if $p \leq 1$. **2.** (a) Convergent. (c) Divergent. (e) Convergent. **4.** (a) Convergent. (d) Divergent. (f) Convergent. (k) Divergent. **7.** (b) Divergent. **8.** (a) $k > 3$. (b) $x > 0$.

SECTION **4-5**, page 205.

1. (a) Divergent. (c) Divergent. (e) Convergent. **2.** (a) Convergent. (b) Convergent.

SECTION **4-6**, page 213.

4. (a) $x^3 - x^5/3! + x^7/5! - x^9/7!$. (b) $x + x^2 + \frac{1}{3}x^3 - x^5/30$. **6.** $x + \frac{1}{3}x^3 + 2x^5/15$.

SECTION **4-7**, page 221.

5. (a) No. (b) Yes. **6.** (a) Yes. (c) No. (e) No. (f) Yes. **8.** (a) 1. (c) $\frac{1}{2}$.

SECTION **4-8**, page 229.

1. (a) $\displaystyle\sum_{0}^{+\infty} \frac{(-1)^n}{(2n+1)n!}$. (c) $\displaystyle\sum_{0}^{+\infty} \frac{(-1)^n}{(n+1)(2n)!}$. (f) $\frac{1}{2}\ln 3 = \displaystyle\sum_{1}^{+\infty} \frac{1}{(2n-1)2^{2n-1}}$.

6. (a) $\frac{1}{4}$. (b) $1/18$. (c) $\frac{1}{4}\pi$. (d) $\ln 4 - 1$. (e) $\frac{1}{4}\pi - \frac{1}{2}\ln 2$. (f) $\ln 2$. **7.** (a) $5e$. (b) $7e$. (c) 8. (d) 208.

SECTION **4-9**, page 235.

1. (a) Nonuniform. (b) Uniform. (c) Nonuniform. (d) Nonuniform.

CHAPTER 5

SECTION **5-1**, page 242.

2. (a) 24π. (b) $\frac{4}{5}\pi$. **3.** $9\pi/280$. **4.** $512\pi/15$. **5.** (a) $\frac{1}{2}\pi^2$. **7.** (a) 63π. (b) $100/81$.

SECTION **5-2**, page 250.

1. (a) $4/3$. (b) $64\sqrt{2}/3$. **2.** (a) $45/4$. (b) 16π. (c) πa^4. **3.** (a) 9. (b) 12π. (c) $256/5$. **5.** $27/4$.

SECTION **5-3,** page 258.

2. (a) 2.   (b) $\frac{1}{4}(1-1/e)$.   (c) -2.

SECTION **5-4,** page 264.

1. (a) 5. (b) 32/5. (c) $\frac{3}{4}$.   **2.** 4.   **3.** $8\pi a^2bc$.   **4.** $\frac{1}{2}\pi^2 r^4$.   **5.** $\int_0^4 \pi x \, dx = 8\pi$.
6. $27\sqrt{3}\,\pi$.   **9.** (a) 32/15.   (b) 12/5.   (c) $2^{14}/105$.

10. $\displaystyle\int_{-2}^{+2}\int_{-1-(4-x^2)^{1/2}}^{-1+(4-x^2)^{1/2}}\int_{x^2+z^2}^{3-2z} f(x,\,y,\,z)\,dy\,dz\,dx.$

SECTION **5-5,** page 270.

1. (a) $8\pi/3$. (b) $8\pi/3$. (c) $3\pi^2$. (d) $5\pi/6$. (e) $\frac{1}{3}\pi(2-5/e)$.   **2.** (a) $2\pi^2 r^2 d$.
(b) $\frac{1}{2}\pi^2 r^2(r^2+4d^2)$.   **3.** (a) $4\pi/3$.   (b) $\frac{1}{3}\pi$.   **4.** (a) $18\pi/5$.   (b) $27\pi/4$.
(c) $27\pi/5$.   **5.** $38.17+$.   **6.** $10r^4/3$.

CHAPTER 6

SECTION **6-1,** page 280.

2. (a) All points $(x,\,y)$ with $x=y$.   None of these can be made points of
continuity.   (c) No discontinuities.   **4.** (a) 0.   (b) $(s^2-r^2)/(4+2r+2s)$.
5. (a) $2x-3y+z=6$.   (c) $3x+4y-z=4$.

SECTION **6-2,** page 289.

1. (a) $x^{y-1}[y^2-x^2\ln x]$.   (b) $3e^{x+y}+10te^{x+y}$.   (d) $y^z[x^{(y^z)}][3/x+(4z\ln x)/y$
$+5(\ln x)(\ln y)]$.   **2.** (a) $0,0$.   (b) $-16,9$.   (d) $0,0$.   **7.** (a) $df=\frac{2}{3}\,dx=\frac{2}{3}\,ds$.
(b) $df=3\,dx+5\,dy=11(dr-ds)$.

SECTION **6-3,** page 296.

1. (a) $\frac{1}{2}$.   (c) $\frac{1}{2}\pi-1$.   **2.** (a) $(\cos 2x-\cos x)/x$.   (b) $-2x\ln(1+x^4)$.   (c) 0.
3. $2(k+1)^{-3}$.   **4.** (a) $\ln(x+1)$ if $x\geqq 0$.   (b) $x^{-1/2}(\frac{1}{2}\pi+\ln 2-2)$.   **7.** $\frac{1}{2}\pi|x|$.
11. (a) $4x^{3/2}/[3\Gamma(\frac{1}{2})]$.   (b) $\frac{1}{2}x^2$.

SECTION **6-5,** page 307.

1. (a) $1+2x+3y+2x^2+6xy+9y^2/2$.   (b) x.   (c) $-1+\frac{1}{2}(x-\pi)^2+(\pi\ln\pi)$
$\times(x-\pi)(y-1)+\frac{1}{2}\pi^2(\ln\pi)^2(y-1)^2$.   (e) $1+x+x^2+xy$.   **2.** $11+(z-3)$
$+(y+2)(z-3)+2(x-1)(y+2)+(x-1)^2(y+2)$.   **3.** (a) Saddlepoint at
$(0,0)$.   (b) Abs. max. at $(-1,2)$.   (c) Abs. min. at $(-2,\frac{1}{2})$.   (e) Abs. min. at
$(1,1)$.   (f) Saddlepoint at $(0,0)$; rel. min. at $(0,-1)$; abs. min. at $(0,2)$.
5. $\frac{1}{2}\sqrt{2}$.   **8.** (a) $2,3,5$.   (b) $8abc/(3\sqrt{3})$.   (c) $6,6,3$.

CHAPTER 7

SECTION 7-1, page 317.

4. (a) $x = -2-2t$, $y = 4+t$, $z = 1$, $(2, 2, 1)$.   (c) $x = -1+3t$, $y = 3+2t$, $z = 0$, $(2, 5, 0)$.   **5.** (a) $x = 4-3u+2v$, $y = 2u$, $z = 4u-v$.   (c) $x = 2u+3v$, $y = 0$, $z = 3u+2v$.   **6.** $x = 1+u+2v$, $y = 2-u-v$, $z = -1+3u+v$.   **8.** (a) $x = 1+u-v$, $y = 2u-v$, $z = u+2v$.   **9.** (a) $(1, 2, 3)$.   (c) Empty intersection. **10.** $\sqrt{6}$.

SECTION 7-2, page 325.

3. (a) $\frac{1}{3}\pi$.   (c) $2.031 +$ (or $\cos\theta = -4/9$).   **4.** (a) $c[\mathbf{i}+(\sqrt{2}-1)\mathbf{j}+(\sqrt{3}-\sqrt{2})\mathbf{k}]$. (b) $c[\mathbf{i}+\mathbf{j}+3(\sqrt{2}-1)\mathbf{k}]$.   **5.** (a) $x = 2t, y = -t, z = 2t$; $x = 2t, y = -t, z = -2t$; $x = t, y = 2t, z = t$; $x = t, y = 2t, z = -t$.   (b) $x = 1-3t, y = 1+t, z = -1+t$; $x = 1-13t, y = 1+6t, z = -1+11t$; $x = 1-5t, y = 1+4t, z = -1+5t$; $x = 1-5t, y = 1+t, z = -1+5t$.   (c) $11x-26y-23z+64 = 0, 41x-26y+49z = 38$. **6.** (a) $\frac{3}{2}\sqrt{2}$.   **10.** (a) $(\frac{1}{8}, -\frac{3}{8})$.   (b) $(-3, -1)$, $(15/8, \frac{5}{8})$, $(5, -15)$. **11.** (a) $4x-y-z = \pm 6\sqrt{2}$.   (b) $9x+9y-17z = 36$.   (c) $x+2y-z = 9$.   (d) $5x-3y+z = 4\pm 2\sqrt{35}$.   **12.** $(963/58, -237/58, -549/58)$, 8.

SECTION 7-3, page 333.

1. (a) $t(\mathbf{i}-\mathbf{j})$.   (b) $t(\mathbf{i}+\mathbf{j}-2\mathbf{k})$.   **2.** $x = 1+6t$, $y = -2+5t$, $z = 3+23t$. **3.** (a) $5x-y+z = 7$.   (c) $x+y+z = 3$.   **4.** (a) $\frac{1}{2}\sqrt{13}$.   (b) 2.   **6.** (a) $\sqrt{55/6}$.

SECTION 7-4, page 340.

1. (a) $151.4+$.   (b) $\frac{1}{2}(e^k-e^{-k})$.   (c) $(8/27)(10^{3/2}-1)$.   (d) $\ln(1+\sqrt{2})$.   (e) π. (f) 8.   (g) $\sqrt{2}$.   **2.** (a) $\sqrt{14}$.   (b) $5\ln(2+\sqrt{3})$.   **3.** (b) 5.870.

SECTION 7-5, page 346.

1. (a) $59/24$.   (b) $\ln(1+\sqrt{2})$.   (c) $10/3$.   **2.** (a) $(8/3)[(\pi^2+1)^{3/2}-1]$. (c) $\pi\sqrt{1+4\pi^2}+\frac{1}{2}\ln(2\pi+\sqrt{1+4\pi^2})$.   **3.** (a) $\pi[2\sqrt{2}+\ln(3+2\sqrt{2})]$. (b) $(1/12)(27-5^{3/2})$.   (c) $26/3$.   (d) $2\pi^2(a^2+b^2)^{1/2}$.

SECTION 7-6, page 353.

2. (a) $x = -5-t$, $y = 6+t$, $z = 2-3t$.   (c) $x = 1$, $y = t$, $z = 1$.   **7.** (a) $\cos^{-1}(-1/\sqrt{14})$.   (b) $\frac{1}{2}\pi$.

SECTION 7-7, page 360.

1. $22/\sqrt{21}$.   **3.** $2, -1, 5, 49/\sqrt{129}$.   **6.** (a) $x-4y = -4; x = 4+t, y = 2-4t,$
$z = 0$.   (b) $y = 0; x = 0, z = 2$.   **7.** $x = y = 3z/2, x = y = -3z/2, x = y = 0,$
$x-y = z = 0$.   **8.** The points on the two lines: $x = t, y = 2-t, z = t,$ and $x = t,$
$y = -2-t, z = t$.   **9.** (b) $x = 1-4t, y = 1+2t, z = 2+t$.   **15.** $\lambda = 52$ and
$3x = -2y; \lambda = 26$ and $2x = 3y$.   **16.** (a) $2, 3, 5$.   (b) $8abc/(3\sqrt{3})$.   (c) $6, 6, 3$.

CHAPTER 8

SECTION 8-2, page 370.

1. (a) 2.   (b) $a^2(\frac{1}{2}\pi-1)$.   (c) π.   (d) $\frac{1}{3}\pi$.   (e) $4\pi+12\sqrt{3}$.   **2.** (a) 4.
(b) $\pi^3/48$.   (c) $\frac{1}{4}\pi$.   (d) $\frac{1}{2}\pi$.   (e) 4π.   **3.** (a) 6π.   (c) $\frac{1}{2}$.   (d) $\frac{1}{2}$.   **5.** (a) $1/840$.
(b) $\frac{3}{8}\pi$.   (c) $8/315$.   (d) $8/21$.

SECTION 8-3, page 380.

1. (a) $(1, 2, -3)$.   (b) $(6, -2, 6)$.   (c) $(-3, -2, 8)$.   **3.** (a) Yes.   (b) No.
(d) Yes.   (f) No.   **5.** (a) $(y, 0, 0)$.   (b) $(y, 0, 0)$.   (c) $(0, x, 0)$.   (d) $(0, 0, 0)$.
7. $(2, 2, 6), (-5, 13, -8), (1, -4, 1)$.   **11.** (a) $\begin{pmatrix} 1 & -\frac{2}{3} \\ 0 & \frac{1}{3} \end{pmatrix}$.   (c) Not invertible.

(f) $\begin{pmatrix} 1 & -1 & -2 \\ 0 & 1 & 1 \\ -1 & 1 & 3 \end{pmatrix}$.   **12.** (b) $\begin{pmatrix} 1 & -1 & 2 & -6 \\ 0 & 1 & -2 & 6 \\ 0 & 0 & 1 & -3 \\ 0 & 0 & 0 & 1 \end{pmatrix}$, $D+1$.

SECTION 8-4, page 394.

1. (a) $\{(x, y): x \neq -y\}$.   (b) $\{(x, y): x = 0\}$.   (c) $\{(x, y, z): xyz = 0\}$.
(d) $\{(\rho, \theta, \phi): \rho = 0$ or $\phi = k\pi\}$.   **2.** (a) $T^{-1}(u, v) = (-7u+3v, 5u-2v);$
$\begin{pmatrix} 2 & 3 \\ 5 & 7 \end{pmatrix}, \begin{pmatrix} -7 & 3 \\ 5 & -2 \end{pmatrix}$.   (b) $T^{-1}(u, v) = (uv-1, 1+v-uv);$ $\begin{pmatrix} 0 & -\frac{1}{3} \\ 1 & 1 \end{pmatrix}, \begin{pmatrix} 3 & 1 \\ -3 & 0 \end{pmatrix}$.
3. $(2.02, 1.22)$.   **4.** $1.81, 2.91$.   **5.** (a) $-.31$.   (c) 1.37.   **6.** $(3y-7)$
$\times (3+6y-7x^2y^2)^{-1}$.

SECTION 8-5, page 402.

4. (a) $\begin{pmatrix} \frac{3}{5} & -\frac{4}{5} \\ \frac{4}{5} & \frac{3}{5} \end{pmatrix}$.   **8.** (a) $(\sqrt{2}, 0, 1)$.   (b) $(1, 0, \sqrt{2})$.

SECTION 8-6, page 406.

1. 1.   **2.** 6.   **3.** $\sqrt{2}$.   **4.** 10.   **5.** 13/3.   **7.** $4-2\sqrt{3}$.

SECTION 8-7, page 416.

1. (a) 1.   (b) 6.   (c) $|u|$.   **2.** (a) 6.   (b) $u^2|v|$.   **3.** (b) $\int_{-1}^{0} \int_{0}^{2v+2} 2\,du\,dv$
$= 2$.   **4.** 25/2.   **5.** $\frac{3}{2}$.   **6.** 9.   **7.** $\pi(1-e^{-a^2})$.   **8.** $\frac{1}{2}\pi(1-e^{-a^2})$.
9. $\frac{2}{3}\sqrt{2}$.   **10.** (c) 4.   **11.** $-1/27$.

SECTION 8-8, page 421.

2. On the axis $\frac{4}{5}$ of the distance from the vertex to the base.   **3.** (a)
$[0, 0, (.700-)h]$.   (b) $[0, 0, (.747-)h]$.   **4.** (a) $\frac{4}{3}\pi a^3(8-3\sqrt{3})$.   (b) $18.1-$.
5. $8\pi a^3/3$, $(0, 0, -\frac{4}{5}a)$.   **9.** $\rho^3 \sin^2 A \sin B$, $\frac{1}{2}\pi^2 r^4$.   **10.** $\rho^4 \sin^3 A \sin^2 B$
$\sin C$, $(8\pi^2 r^5)/15$.

CHAPTER 9

SECTION 9-1, page 430.

1. (a) 2.   (b) $1-2\cos 1$.   (c) $-6\frac{9}{10}$.   **2.** (a) $\frac{1}{2}$.   (b) $\sqrt{2}/10$.   **3.** (a)
$5\sqrt{2}/2$.   **4.** (a) 305/16.   (b) $(135/8)(1+\ln 4)$.   **5.** (a) 0.   (b) 12.
6. (a) 0.   (b) $\frac{3}{8}\pi$.   **7.** (a) $\frac{1}{2}$.   **8.** (a) $\frac{1}{3}$.   **9.** (a) -2π.   **10.** (a) $66\frac{19}{30}$.
(b) $\frac{1}{4}$.   (c) $2\pi + 316/3$.

SECTION 9-2, page 440.

1. $\sqrt{6}\,\pi$.   **3.** $a^2(\pi-2)$.   **6.** (a) $4\pi(2-\sqrt{3})$.   (b) $\frac{1}{6}\pi(5\sqrt{5}-1)$.

8. (a) $\begin{cases} x = -1 + 3r - s, \\ y = 2 + 16r + 9s, \\ z = 4 + 2s. \end{cases}$ (b) $\begin{cases} x = 1 + 2s + \sqrt{3}t, \\ y = \sqrt{3} + 3\sqrt{3}s - t, \\ z = 1 + \frac{1}{6}\pi s. \end{cases}$

9. (a) $(2\mathbf{i}+\mathbf{j})/\sqrt{5}$.   (b) $(-4\mathbf{i}+5\mathbf{j}+\mathbf{k})/\sqrt{42}$.   **11.** (b) $\frac{2}{3}\pi(2\sqrt{2}-1)$.
(d) $\pi a^2(2-\sqrt{3})$.   **12.** 57π.   **13.** (b) $34\pi - \frac{1}{2}\sqrt{2}\,\pi \ln(2\sqrt{2}+3)$.   **14.** 24π
$+2\sqrt{2}\,\pi \ln(2\sqrt{2}+3)$.

SECTION 9-3, page 446.

1. (a) -72.   (b) 8π.   **2.** (a) $\frac{1}{2}$.   (b) π.   **3.** 6π.   **4.** (a) $3\sqrt{14}/2$.
(b) $\frac{1}{4}\pi$.   **5.** 2π.   **6.** 0.

SECTION 9-4, page 454.

6. $\sin^{-1}(y/x)+z$.

SECTION 9-5, page 466.

3. $\frac{3}{10}$.　**4.** (a) 28π.　(b) 0.　**5.** π.

SECTION 9-6, page 475.

2. $\frac{3}{8}\pi a^2$.　**3.** (b) $\pi|AB\cos\alpha|$.　**4.** $\frac{1}{2}\int_{\theta_1}^{\theta_2} r^2\, d\theta$.　**5.** (a) $X^2Y-\frac{1}{3}Y^3$.
6. (a) 0.　(b) 0.　(c) $3\sinh 6$.　**7.** (a) 4π, 0.　(b) 0, $\frac{32}{4}5^4$.　**8.** (b) $7\pi/2$.
10. $7+5m+3n$, where m and n are integers.　**11.** (a) -3.

SECTION 9-7, page 486.

1. (a) $-16\pi/7$.　(b) 20π.　**2.** (a) -4π.　**3.** (a) 0.　(b) -12.　**4.** π.
5. (a) π.　**8.** (a) 6.　(b) -2.　**9.** (a) x^2yz.　(b) $\frac{1}{4}(x^2+y^2+z^2)^2$.
10. $\tan^{-1} y/x-\tan^{-1} z/x$.　**11.** (a) 4π.　(b) 0.　(c) -2π.

SECTION 9-8, page 494.

1. (a) 8.　(b) 36π.　**2.** (a) 3.　(b) $-4\sqrt{3}\pi$.　**13.** (a) $(\frac{1}{2}xyz)\mathbf{i}+(-\frac{1}{2}z-\frac{1}{4}x^2z)\mathbf{j}$
$+(\frac{1}{2}y-\frac{1}{4}x^2y)\mathbf{k}$.　**14.** (a) $xyz(\mathbf{i}+z\mathbf{j}+x^2\mathbf{k})$.　(b) $(xz+xy)\mathbf{i}+(yx+yz)\mathbf{j}+$
$(zy+zx)\mathbf{k}$.

CHAPTER 10

SECTION 10-1, page 504.

4. (a) Yes.　(b) Yes.　(c) No.　(d) No.　**5.** (a) No.　(b) Yes.　**6.** (a) $V_4(iv)$.
(b) $V_1(i)$,　V_3.　**10.** (a) $\{(2, -2, 0, 4), (1, 1, 4, 0), (4, 0, -1, -2)\}$.
11. (a) $\{5x, 1, x^2-\frac{1}{3}\}$.

SECTION 10-2, page 517.

1. (a) 2, 1, 4.　**2.** (a) $\frac{1}{2}(e-e^{-1})$, $3e^{-1}$, $\frac{5}{2}(e-7e^{-1})$.

SECTION 10-3, page 532.

1. (a) $\frac{1}{2}+\frac{1}{2}\cos 6x$.　(b) $(4/\pi)(\sin x+\frac{1}{3}\sin 3x+\frac{1}{5}\sin 5x+\cdots)$.　(c) $(4/\pi)$
$\times\sum_1^{+\infty} (2n-1)^{-2}\cos(2n-1)x$.　(d) $2(\sin x-\frac{1}{2}\sin 2x+\frac{1}{3}\sin 3x-\cdots)$.
(e) $\frac{1}{3}\pi^2-4(1^{-2}\cos x-2^{-2}\cos 2x+3^{-2}\cos 3x-\cdots)$.　(f) $12(1^{-3}\sin x$
$-2^{-3}\sin 2x+3^{-3}\sin 3x-\cdots)$.　**9.** (a) $1+\sin\pi x$.　(b) $32\pi^{-2}\sum_1^{+\infty} (-1)^{n-1}$
$\times(2n-1)^{-2}\sin\frac{1}{2}(2n-1)\pi x$.　**10.** (a) $\frac{1}{2}\sqrt{3}\cos\pi x+\frac{1}{2}\sin\pi x$.　(b) $3-(4/\pi)$
$\times\sum_1^{+\infty} (\sin n\pi x)/n$.　(c) $\frac{4}{3}+4\pi^{-2}\sum_1^{+\infty} n^{-2}\cos n\pi x-4\pi^{-1}\sum_1^{+\infty} n^{-1}\sin n\pi x$.
11. (a) $a_n = 0$.　(b) $a_{2n+1} = 0$, $b_{2n} = 0$.　(c) $b_n = 0$, $a_n = 0$ unless $n = 4k$.
(d) $a_{2n+1} = 0, b_{2n+1} = 0$.　(e) $a_n = b_n = 0$ unless $n = 4k$.　(f) $a_n = b_n = 0$ unless
$n = 3k$.　(g) $a_n = b_n = 0$ unless $n = 6k$.　(h) $a_0 = \phi(0)$, $a_n = b_n = 0$ if $n \geq 1$.

SECTION 10-4, page 548.

1. (a) 1. (b) $(4/\pi) \sum_1^{+\infty} [\sin (2n-1)x]/(2n-1)$. (c) $2 \sum_1^{+\infty} (-1)^{n-1} n^{-1} \sin nx$.
(d) $-5 + 6 \sum_1^{+\infty} (-1)^{n-1} n^{-1} \sin nx$.   (e) $\frac{1}{3}\pi^2 + 4 \sum_1^{+\infty} (-1)^n n^{-2} \cos nx$.
(f) $12 \sum_1^{+\infty} (-1)^n n^{-3} \sin nx$.   (g) $-7\pi^4/15 + 48 \sum_1^{+\infty} (-1)^{n-1} n^{-4} \cos nx$.
(h) $\frac{1}{5}\pi^4 + \sum_1^{+\infty} (-1)^{n-1}(48n^{-4} - 8\pi^2 n^{-2}) \cos nx$.

SECTION 10-5, page 557.

5. (a) $2 \sin 2x \cos 3t$.   (b) $\sin 2x \sin 3t$.   (c) $(2x+3t)^2 + 5x$.   **6.** $32\pi^{-3}$
$\times \sum_1^{+\infty} (2n-1)^{-3} \sin \frac{1}{2}(2n-1)\pi x \cos \frac{3}{2}(2n-1)\pi t$.   **7.** $\frac{1}{5} \sin x \sin 5t -$
$8\pi^{-1} \sum_1^{+\infty} (2n-1)^{-3} \sin (2n-1)x \cos 5(2n-1)t$.

SECTION 10-6, page 570.

1. $20 + \sum_1^{+\infty} (-1)^{n-1} 4n^{-1}\pi^{-1} e^{-3n^2\pi^2 t/4} \sin \frac{1}{2}n\pi x$.   **2.** (a) $100\pi^{-1}[x +$
$\frac{4}{5}\sum_1^{+\infty} (2n-1)^{-1} e^{-(2n-1)^2 t/5} \sin (2n-1)x - 2 \sum_1^{+\infty} (-1)^{n-1} n^{-1} e^{-n^2 t/5} \sin nx]$.
(b) $50 + 50x\pi^{-1} + 50\pi^{-1} \sum_1^{+\infty} (-1)^n n^{-1} e^{-4n^2 t/5} \sin 2nx$.
3. $80\pi^{-1} \sum_1^{+\infty} (-1)^{n-1}(2n-1)^{-2} e^{-4(2n-1)^2 t} \sin (2n-1)x$.   **4.** (a) $100 +$
$10x - 5xy$.   (b) $10x + e^{\pi x/5} \sin \frac{1}{5}\pi y$.   **5.** $50 + 100xy + e^{-2y} \sin 2x + e^{-17t/9}$
$\times \sin x \sin 4y$.   **6.** (a) $100 - (50 \ln \frac{1}{4}r)/\ln \frac{7}{4}$.   (b) $20 + (2r - 28/r) \cos \theta$.
7. (a) $200\pi^{-1} \sum_1^{+\infty} r^{2n-1}(2n-1)^{-1} \sin (2n-1)\theta$.   (c) $2 + 4 \sum_1^{+\infty} (-1)^{n-1}$
$\times (4n^2 - 1)^{-1} r^n \cos n\theta$.

SECTION 10-7, page 577.

5. (a) $f(x) = 2(1 - \cos ax)/(\pi x^2)$. (b) $f(x) = 4(\sin x - x \cos x)/(\pi x^3)$. (c) $f(x) =$
$4abx\pi^{-1}[(a^2 + b^2 + x^2)^2 - 4b^2 x^2]^{-1}$.   **7.** $\pi^{-1} \tan^{-1} [(1-x)/y] +$
$\pi^{-1} \tan^{-1} [(1+x)/y]$.   **8.** $\pi^{-1}[y \ln (x^2 + y^2) - \frac{1}{2}y \ln [(x^2 + y^2 + 1)^2 - 4x^2] -$
$2x \tan^{-1} (x/y) + (1+x) \tan^{-1} [(1+x)/y] + (1-x) \tan^{-1} [(1-x)/y]$.
11. $(1 + 4t)^{-1/2} e^{-c^2 x^2/(1 + 4t)}$.

CHAPTER 11

SECTION 11-1, page 581.

6. (b) Additive and countably additive. (d) Neither additive nor countably
additive.   **7.** (b) An algebra, with m additive.

SECTION 11-6, page 615.

2. There are many examples; e.g., G can be $\bigcup_1^{+\infty} I_k$ with $c(I_k) < 2^{-k-1}$
for each k, where I_k is an open interval with center at r_k and $\{r_k\}$ is the set of
rational members of $[0, 1]$.

INDEX